Readings in

Biomedical Ethics

A Canadian Focus

Second Edition

Edited by

Eike-Henner W. Kluge

University of Victoria

Prentice Hall Allyn and Bacon Canada
Scarborough, Ontario

Canadian Cataloguing in Publication Data

Main entry under title:

Readings in biomedical ethics

2nd ed.
ISBN 0-13-095094-7

1. Medical ethics — Canada. 2. Bioethics — Canada. I. Kluge, Eike-Henner W.

R724.R43   1999   174'.2'0971   C98-930917-7

 © 1999, 1993 Prentice-Hall Canada Inc., Scarborough, Ontario
A Division of Simon & Schuster/A Viacom Company

Prentice-Hall, Inc., Upper Saddle River, New Jersey
Prentice-Hall International (UK) Limited, London
Prentice-Hall of Australia, Pty. Limited, Sydney
Prentice-Hall Hispanoamericana, S.A., Mexico City
Prentice-Hall of India Private Limited, New Delhi
Prentice-Hall of Japan, Inc., Tokyo
Simon & Schuster Southeast Asia Private Limited, Singapore
Editora Prentice-Hall do Brasil, Ltda., Rio de Janeiro

ISBN 0-13-095094-7

Vice-President, Editorial Director: Laura Pearson
Acquisitions Editor: Dawn Lee
Associate Editor: Sharon Loeb
Copy Editor: Susan Ginsberg
Production Editor: Melanie M. Meharchand
Production Coordinator: Peggy Kakaflikas
Permissions/Photo Research: Susan Wallace-Cox
Cover Design: Michael Stokely
Page Layout: Janette Thompson (Jansom)

1 2 3 4 5 WEB 03 02 01 00 99

Printed and bound in Canada.

Visit the Prentice Hall Canada Web site! Send us your comments,
browse our catalogues, and more. **www.phcanada.com**
Or reach us through e-mail at **phabinfo_pubcanada@prenhall.com**

To Candace

Contents

REFERENCES 526

Preface

Over the past few years, the delivery of health care has moved increasingly into the forefront of Canadian public and professional concern. There are several reasons for this. First, the attitude that health care is a right has become firmly entrenched in the Canadian perspective. At the same time, Canadians have become more knowledgeable about the types of health services that are available in principle. Therefore, when some of these are not being delivered, Canadians feel that their right to health care is being violated. Since health care is resource-intensive and health care funding is increasingly being constrained, this has led to rising public examination of the structure of health care delivery itself.

Second, the ethical perspective of the Canadian public has shifted towards an emphasis on individual autonomy. This is reflected in changed expectations about such things as involvement in health care decision making, access to records, professional accountability, and so on. All of these are matters that affect how health care is viewed from the consumer's perspective.

Third, the last few decades have seen a profound re-assessment of the role of health care professionals, both as private individuals and as professionals. This is evidenced by changes in the nature of the professional/patient relationship as well as by a shift in the understanding of how health care professionals should behave towards third parties, towards society in general as well as towards government — and even towards each other. It is also evidenced by increasing concern about the interactions between health care professionals and the health care industry as a whole.

These developments are part of a dynamic that is reshaping the nature and structure of the Canadian health care system. Changing demographics, a reduction in the availability of resources, and international trade agreements also enter the mix — as do a myriad of other factors. The overall situation can only be described as one of tremendous flux, and it is unpredictable what turn the next development will take or what its nature will be.

The readings in this volume reflect the diversity of opinion over how the relevant issues and developments should be viewed. An attempt has been made to give a balanced presentation. This has not always been possible since, in many cases, the views that exist are virtually legion. The *Further Readings* at the end of each chapter are intended to remedy this lack by indicating resources that might usefully be consulted when studying the relevant issues.

Benchmark legal cases have also been included. The reason is simple: Although ethics is not law, the delivery of health care is embedded in a social context, and the latter cannot be divorced from the law. Therefore the ethical issues that are encountered in the delivery of health care inevitably assume a legal tinge. It is in the legally circumscribed setting of ordinary practice that the ethical problems of health care delivery manifest themselves in their most acute form.

Like the delivery of health care, the law is in a state of flux. Recent examples include the law of informed consent, the law of patient records, abortion, assisted suicide, cessation of treatment — to mention but a few. The interesting thing about these changes is that they appear to involve not only legal precedent and statute but also ethical reasoning — as will be apparent to anyone who reads the cases that are reproduced below. Hence an understanding of the ethics of health care delivery, in its various aspects and its various guises, seems to be necessary for understanding the developments of the law itself. An understanding of the ethics may also provide an indication of where the law is likely to go in its next evolution.

The people whom I would like to thank include, of course, everyone at Prentice Hall, as well as Daryl Pullman (University of Waterloo), Karen Shirley (Camosun College), and David Elliot (University of Regina), all of whom acted as reviewers. The students in my bioethics courses posed insightful questions and frequently prompted me to reexamine ideas and search out writings with new perspectives. In putting together this volume, I have benefited from the comments and suggestions of many ethicists and philosophers who provided insight about what is important in contemporary bioethics. I thank all of them. Special thanks go to Erich Loewy (University of California—Davis), Arthur Schaefer (University of Manitoba), Earl Winkler, Alister Browne (University of British Columbia), and Geritt Clements (British Columbia Ministry of Health). To Peter Singer (University of Toronto), in whose project on health care directives I was privileged to participate, I owe thanks for reminding me of the importance of advance directives. To Christine Overall, who visited Victoria as a Lansdowne Scholar in Bioethics, I owe thanks for impressing on me the importance of feminist approaches to reproductive technologies.

PART I: HEALTH CARE AND ETHICS

CHAPTER 1
ETHICAL THEORY

Some people think that there are no objective standards of right and wrong: that right and wrong depend on how they *feel* or that it is determined by the *views of the society* in which they are embedded. Others believe that there are absolute standards that are independent of what people think about them — or whether people are aware of them in the first place.

Whether they realize it or not, all these people are holding *meta-ethical* positions. They are saying something *about* ethics: that ethics is a matter of feelings (ethical non-cognitivism), that it is relative to a particular point of view (ethical relativism), or that it is objective in nature (ethical objectivism).

These differences in opinion have practical implications. If ethical objectivism is correct, then it makes sense to study ethics and to try to understand what makes an action ethically acceptable and what doesn't. If ethical non-cognitivism is correct, then studying ethics is a waste of time. Finally, if ethical relativism is correct, then ethical judgements are always relative to the speaker, and there is no one standard of ethical conduct that can legitimately be applied to all people.

META-ETHICAL POSITIONS

Ethical Non-cognitivism

The basis of ethical non-cognitivism is that ethical disagreements can be highly emotional affairs where no amount of reasoning is likely to convince the other party. Even when our logic is shown to be faulty, we tend to insist on our respective position because it just "feels" right. Statements like, "I just know I'm right," or "I can't argue with you — you just don't understand!" reflect this position.

However, while we may be expressing our feelings when we make moral claims, we are doing more than that: we are also making cognitively significant claims about the world. Furthermore, our feelings or emotions may be fundamentally at variance with what we take to be ethically correct. Thus, it is possible for a physician to reject abortions on an emotional level and yet agree that ethically speaking, women have a right to abortions. This stance would be impossible if ethical assertions were merely expressions of the emotions we felt.[1]

Ethical Relativism

Ethical relativism avoids these problems. It says that while ethical statements *are* cognitively meaningful, they do not hold in any objective sense because they depend on our point of view.[2]

Ethical relativism allows us to account for the fact that people differ in their ethical positions. This is very attractive in a multicultural country like Canada because it allows us to accord equal respect to distinct values.

However, such respect is bought at a price. If we accept ethical relativism, then ethical disagreement among people who do not share the same perspective becomes impossible. Since all our ethical judgements would be relative, the fact that we had different perspectives would mean that we were not really disagreeing at all. On this approach, all ethical claims would carry the implicit rider "from my (our) point of view." What at first glance looked like a disagreement would become crossed monologues. Therefore we could not really say that people who advocate sex-selection or who practise gender-based discrimination, are morally wrong — or, for that matter, that laws allowing such actions should be changed because they are immoral. They would only be wrong (or immoral) from our point of view, and we would have to reject as moral imperialism any attempt at changing the relevant laws. This approach is troublesome.

Further, as Socrates already pointed out over two thousand years ago, ethical relativism confuses what is believed, legislated, or otherwise promulgated by a group of individuals, with the question whether the people who accept this are *correct*. Believing that one is right does not necessarily make one right — in ethics any more than in mathematics or in embryology.

In addition, ethical relativism assumes that if people agree on something, then it must be true. A moment's reflection shows that this consensus approach is rather silly. Historically, all sorts of propositions were universally accepted: for instance, that witches could change into cats, that combustion is due to phlogiston, that the earth is flat and is the centre of the universe, and that melancholy is due to an imbalance of the four humours. However, the fact that people agreed on these propositions did not make them true.

Moreover, as a matter of logic, the lack of universal agreement on matters of ethics does not mean that there are no universally valid ethical propositions.

That would be like saying that because there is no agreement on how prions produce mad cow disease, prions are not involved in the transmission of the disease. There may be all sorts of reasons why people don't agree on these things — including the possibility that people are just not sufficiently sophisticated to appreciate and understand the nature of the relevant biochemical processes.

The same holds true with ethical statements. People may just not be sufficiently sophisticated to have found the correct answer. As Kohlberg[3] and Piaget[4] have shown, our level of moral understanding depends on our level of intellectual sophistication, which changes over time and with training.

On the other hand, even if there were general agreement on a particular ethical issue, this would not establish the validity of the relevant ethical claim. For instance, there used to be general agreement that people of different races do not merit the same treatment because they are different. However, racial discrimination cannot be ethically justified in this fashion. Nor can we claim that we ought to kill socially useless people, or that one sex is superior to the other. In all of these cases we can say that while we understand how people could have come to hold such views historically, the people were morally wrong, the fact of their agreement notwithstanding.

Finally, ethical relativism is also suspect for a more *pragmatic reason*: our social practice is fundamentally at variance with it. For instance, the people who are currently prosecuting Bosnian war criminals do not justify their judgements by saying, "We are the stronger, therefore we will judge according to our own ethical standards. Your actions are ethically above reproach when considered from your point of view." Instead, the prosecutors are prosecuting the alleged war criminals for crimes against humanity because they believe that no matter what was accepted or legitimate according to the standards of the accused, what the accused did was ethically wrong in some absolute sense that transcends individual ethical frameworks. Their argument is that the accused knew — or should have known — that what they were doing was morally wrong. The fact that the accused's societies accepted and possibly even encouraged their behaviour does not excuse them.

One can generalize the preceding. We frequently make ethical claims about practices in other societies and about the principles that supposedly motivate them. We condemn judicial torture and repression through the work of the United Nations (U.N.) and Amnesty International; we object to the deliberate killing or genital mutilation of female infants in certain countries through the work of the U.N. and of International Planned Parenthood; and we maintain that drug trafficking is ethically reprehensible no matter what. Our critique is not blunted by the realization that these practices may well be defensible within the framework of the other society or from the perspective of the other point of view. On the contrary: we decry the very fact of such ethical divergence as being fundamentally misguided.

Ethical Objectivism

By contrast, ethical objectivism holds that right and wrong are objective phenomena. In this view, if we say that euthanasia is morally wrong or that it is ethically appropriate to allow people to make their own health care decisions, we are
making claims about the moral nature of the world.

The differences among these meta-ethical theories have more than merely
theoretical significance. If ethical objectivism is wrong, there is little point to reasoned discussion about the ethics of health care. The solution to disagreements
about issues such as resource allocation, the right to health care, or the ethical
duties of nurses or physicians, lies not in discussion and understanding, but in
political manoeuvring — or even the use of power. This approach would be
extremely troublesome in the Canadian context, with its deliberate and conscious acceptance of cultural diversity.

What, then, is ethics?

As a discipline, it is a branch of philosophy. It deals with questions of right
and wrong conduct, and with what we ought to do and what we ought to refrain
from doing. It considers issues of rights and obligations and how these are related to the social setting.

Ethics is not the only discipline that deals with such issues. Law, psychology, sociology, and theology deal with them as well. However, unlike psychology and sociology, ethics is not centrally concerned with describing and analyzing
how people feel or why they have the attitudes they do. Instead, it is normative or *prescriptive* in nature.

Law is also prescriptive because it tells people how they ought to behave.
However, law is based on the rules that societies have promulgated to regulate
the behaviour of their members. In that sense, law is arbitrary and depends on
the will of the lawmakers. Moreover, laws may be unethical — like the laws
that gave second-rank status to native Americans, that declared women nonpersons, or that allowed the nonconsensual sterilization of the mentally severely handicapped. And finally, laws hold only in the jurisdictions in which they have
been passed. Ethics, on the other hand, deals with persons insofar as they are
persons. It is therefore jurisdiction-invariant, and its injunctions are binding
even if no law recognizes them.

There are two fundamental questions that ethical objectivism has to answer:
What are these so-called moral facts? And why do people differ in their moral
positions? These are very difficult questions. They are the subject of study of
theoretical ethics.

The authors of the articles in this anthology share the assumption that ethical objectivism is correct. It is on this basis that they examine the issues that
arise in the delivery of health care. This does not mean that they all share the
same ethical viewpoint. Just as there are different meta-ethical positions, so
there are different ethical theories. The readings in this volume exemplify how

a difference in ethical theory can lead to a difference in conclusion on a particular issue. To appreciate this fully, it may be useful to give a brief sketch of some of the ethical theories on which the articles are based.

ETHICAL THEORIES

There are several kinds of objectivist ethical theories. The most common ones are *teleological* or consequentialistic ethics, *deontological* or rights and duties-oriented ethics, *virtue* ethics, *religious* ethics, *feminist* ethics, and *agapistic* ethics.

Teleological or Consequentialistic Theories

The most common teleological or consequentialistic ethics in our society is utilitarianism.[5] It is frequently used by health care administrators. For instance, it underlies the cost/benefit and cost/effectiveness considerations used in deciding whether to expand the emergency department of a hospital or to add a new psychiatric wing; it plays a major role in decisions about whether to use a medical as opposed to a surgical approach for cardiac problems.

Utilitarianism takes as its basic principle the so-called *principle of utility*. It goes something like this:

> One should always act in such a way as to bring about the greatest good and the least harm for the greatest number of people.

Or, alternatively,

> One should always act in such a way as to maximize the balance of good over harm for the greatest number of people.

The principle of utility leaves undefined the nature of the good that one is supposed to aim at and the nature of the harm that is to be avoided. This opens the door to different versions of utilitarianism. One such version defines the good in terms of material well-being or pleasure. It is called *hedonistic utilitarianism*.[6] Another identifies it as happiness, and is called *eudaemonistic utilitarianism*.[7] A third says that the good consists in the attainment of certain ideals. This is *ideal utilitarianism*.[8] A fourth variation claims that the good is really a combination of several of these goods. Not surprisingly, it is called *mixed utilitarianism*.[9] There is no agreement on which notion of the good is really correct.

Just as there are differences within utilitarianism about what the good is, so there are differences about how we are supposed to identify this good. Some claim that a special sort of insight or *intuition* is involved,[10] which allows us to identify what has *intrinsic value*. Other utilitarians focus on the *nature of human beings* and maintain that the good can be derived from human nature itself.[11] Still others say that good can only be identified by looking at what society prefers. While the first two approaches would yield an absolute answer as to the nature of the good, a preference-based approach insists that what counts as the good may change over time, as social attitudes and preferences change.

Finally, utilitarian theories may differ on how the test of utility is to be *applied*. *Act utilitarianism* proceeds on a case-by-case basis. It evaluates each situation on its own terms, without reference to universal rules or guidelines.[12] Health care professionals who adopt this approach would not follow general rules or guidelines of ethical decision making. Instead, they would calculate the utility of each situation separately and on its own.

Rule utilitarianism, on the other hand, maintains that utility is not something that can be calculated for individual acts but only for general rules of conduct. The basic position of this approach could be expressed as follows:

> Those rules of conduct are morally obligatory that produce, or are likely to produce, the greatest amount of good and the least amount of harm for the greatest number of people.[13]

Therefore, when it comes to dealing with actual situations, the decision making would identify the rule that should be applied in a particular case or on a particular occasion.

At first glance it might seem that, practically speaking, the differences among the various types of teleological theories are really unimportant. However, this is not true. Consider the following case:

> A small-town hospital is deciding whether to perform induced abortions. Some physicians who have privileges at the hospital say they are personally opposed to abortions and will not perform them. On the other hand, two of the local physicians are willing to do them. The hospital board has to decide whether to brave the storm of protest that it thinks will come from the more outspoken and religious members of the community if abortions are permitted, or simply continue with its previous policy of not doing abortions.

For the sake of discussion, let us ignore the impact that criminal legislation and the Code of Ethics of the medical profession would have on this case and consider only what would happen under the various utilitarian approaches.

If we assume that the hospital board follows a *rule utilitarian* approach, then if the board was moved by *hedonistic* considerations it would try to balance the problems the community would face if the hospital did abortions against the problems that the community would face if it continued not to do them. Here it would take into account such factors as the social resources that would be necessary to raise unwanted children, the cost of taking care of failed abortion attempts by women who try to induce their own abortions or have had them induced by nonmedical persons, the cost of the abortions themselves, and the impact that they might have on health care within the community. On balance, the hospital would probably decide that the greatest amount of pleasure and/or material good for society would be achieved if it performed induced abortions. The storm of protest that might result would be more than outweighed by the long-term savings in health costs alone.

On the other hand, if the board decided to adopt an *ideal utilitarian* perspective it might well reason differently. It would consider that ideal values like compassion and respect for life are fundamental in our society. It would balance these values against the strong emphasis that our society places on autonomy and self-determination and try to arrive at a solution. On this basis, it might well decide to perform abortions, but only under certain conditions such as in cases of rape or incest, or when there are medical indications — and even then, only as long as the pregnancy was not so far advanced that the fetus could survive if removed from the mother's body.

If the board adopted a *mixed utilitarian* perspective, it would try to balance ideal and hedonistic considerations against each other. It would be impossible to say beforehand what the board might decide because its decision would depend on the relative weight that was attached to the various parameters.

Finally, if the board adopted a *eudaemonistic utilitarian* outlook, it would proceed still differently. It would look for statistical data about the psychological sequelae of abortions and compare these with the effect on the happiness of mother, child and other affected parties when abortions are denied. It would then compare these with data about society's mood when abortions are performed as opposed to when they are not. It would try to calculate the greatest amount of overall "good," and reach a decision on this basis. In the current social climate, this would probably mean that the board would opt for going ahead with allowing abortions.

Finally, if the board were to approach the issue from an *act utilitarian* perspective, all the preceding types of considerations that deal with the nature of the good would still apply. However, the board would not try to decide what sort of *policy* it should adopt. Instead, it would set up a committee to look at each case separately without reference to hard and fast guidelines. The only principle that would guide the committee's deliberations would be the principle of utility. However, it is probably fair to say that it is unlikely that any hospital board would operate for long in this fashion. The running of a health care institution requires policies: something that is ruled out by the very nature of act utilitarianism.

Deontological Ethics

Deontological theories are not concerned with outcomes but with duties and rights. There are two major types: *monistic* approaches, which say that there is only one basic principle from which all judgements and rules of right and wrong must ultimately be derived; and *pluralistic* approaches, which say that there are several basic principles.[14]

The position of Immanuel Kant is probably the best-known and most influential monistic deontological ethics. Kant called his basic principle the "categorical imperative." He gave several formulations of it.[15] However, he claimed that all of them were equivalent to one another.

Two of these formulations are of special interest in health care. The first he simply called "categorical imperative." It goes like this: "Act only according to that maxim by which you can at the same time will that it should become a universal law."[16] The second version, which he called the "practical imperative," he stated as follows: "Act so that you treat humanity, whether in your own person or in that of another, always as an end and never as a means only."[17]

Each of these formulations provides a test for ethical acceptability. An example might clarify how this is the case:

> A physician has a patient with metastasized cancer of the lungs. The cancer is inoperable; it is unresponsive to chemotherapy and radiation treatment, and most likely it will be fatal within a year. The physician knows that the patient is psychologically labile and that if she was told of her condition, she would react extremely emotionally and might even suffer psychological harm. The physician wants to spare her patient the psychological trauma that she is convinced will result if this information is disclosed to the patient before the disease has progressed to the point of seriously incapacitating her. The physician, therefore, lies about the diagnosis and prognosis so as to give the patient a little time before she has to face the truth.

While lying to the patient might be defensible from a humanitarian perspective, Kant would argue that it is unethical because it fails the first test. The *maxim* or general rule guiding the physician would be to "lie when motivated by humanitarian considerations." However, Kant would say that if this maxim were to become a universal law, it would mean that anyone, on any occasion involving humanitarian motives, should lie.

However, what counts as a humanitarian motive depends on the perspective and values of the individual whose motive it is. Consequently no one could ever be sure that he or she was not being lied to by other people. Not only would that completely erode our confidence in other people, it would also mean that for all practical purposes the distinction between lying and telling the truth would disappear.[18] The maxim would thus fail the *universalizability test*.

Kant would argue further that the actions of the physician would fail the *end-in-itself test*. To lie to the patient is to withhold the information the patient needs in order to make reasonable, rational, and appropriate decisions about how to conduct the rest of her life. Therefore, to lie is to treat her not as an autonomous rational being who is an end-in-herself, but as an object, something to be manipulated. It does not matter that she is being manipulated with the best of intentions and "for her own good"; she is being manipulated nonetheless.

Unlike the Kantian monistic approach, *pluralistic deontological* ethics maintains that there are several basic or fundamental principles that are irreducible to each other and that have to be balanced against each other in a given situation. Among pluralistic deontologists, the following principles have found general acceptance[19]:

1. *Principle of Autonomy and Respect for Persons:*
   Everyone has a fundamental right to self-determination. This right is limited only by unjust infringement on the rights of others. ("Your right to swing your fist stops where my face begins.")

2. *Principle of Impossibility:*
   A right that cannot be fulfilled is ineffective as a right, and an obligation that cannot be met under the circumstances ceases to be effective as an obligation (e.g., one cannot have a right to health care resources that are not available; and one cannot have a duty to save the life of an incurably dying patient).

3. *Principle of Fidelity or Best Action:*
   Whoever has an obligation also has the duty to discharge that obligation in the best manner possible (e.g., if there is a duty to perform an operation, then the duty is to use the greatest skill and care possible).

4. *Principle of Equality and Justice:*
   A right is effective to the degree that it preserves or promotes justice (e.g., the duty to provide preferential health-resource allocation for persons with disabilities is based on this).

5. *Principle of Beneficence:*
   Everyone has a duty to maximize the good.

6. *Principle of Non-Malfeasance:*
   Everyone has a duty to minimize harm.[20]

The last two principles aim at the production of a particular kind of outcome. Hence they are really teleological in nature. However, there is a way of interpreting these principles so that they lose this teleological veneer. If we interpret the Principle of Beneficence as follows:

> Everyone has a duty to maximize the good of others where the nature of this good is defined by the other persons themselves.[21,22]

and if we interpret the Principle of Non-Malfeasance like this:

> Everyone has a duty to minimize harm to others where the nature of this harm is defined by the other persons themselves.

then the two principles are acceptable within a deontological framework. They are unacceptable when interpreted in any other way. It is precisely the failure to interpret the principles in this derivative sense that gives rise to professional *paternalism*.

The multiplicity of principles raises the question of what happens when the different principles conflict. For instance, what happens when the Principle of Equality and Justice conflicts with that of Beneficence, or the Principle of Autonomy with that of Best Fidelity or of Non-Malfeasance?

To deal with this problem, some deontologists have suggested that ethical principles should be understood as holding only *prima facie*.[23] That is to say, they should be understood merely as approximations that serve as guides. When deciding which principle takes priority in a given case, one should consider not only the nature of the act in question but also the personal, social and material aspects of the situation in which the relevant individuals are embedded.[24] This approach has become widely accepted.

Feminist Ethics

An ethical approach that has acquired some prominence of late is *feminist ethics*. It has been described as the "ethics of caring and response."[25] Its focus is the moral experience of women in what it describes as a male-dominated and male-oriented world. It argues that the moral and social experiences of women differ from those of men, and that these differences must be taken into count when ethically evaluating a particular situation. Ethical issues and dilemmas should not be resolved by blindly balancing competing rights and duties, or by automatically turning to virtues or applying principles such as autonomy, equality, and impartiality. Instead, they should be resolved by looking at the particulars of each situation and by determining how the responsibilities of the various actors arise from the relationships in which they are embedded.[26] Disagreements and problems should be solved, not in the spirit of exclusionary decision making but in the spirit of cooperative resolution.

Further, feminist ethics seeks to ground the difference between itself and more traditional ethical orientations by looking at the difference in social experience between men and women. The writings of Nel Noddings[27] and Carol Gilligan[28] are particularly noteworthy in this regard. The point they make is that directly or indirectly, the overt social structure of most societies has been male dominated, and the female experience in most of these societies has traditionally involved a greater or lesser degree of discrimination, which has left women disproportionately powerless.[29]

In the health care sector, feminists can point to medical experimentation as an illustrative example of such discrimination. As has recently been argued very persuasively,[30] medical experimenters have not directed their attention to the health care needs of women in an appropriate fashion because traditional rules have excluded women from being experimental subjects. Traditionally the excuse has been that participating in such experiments might pose a special risk to women's ability to bear (healthy) children. By contrast, no such considerations have been raised against the inclusion of fertile men in medical experimentation even though their ability to father (healthy) children might also be impaired. Not only does this reflect an inherent sexist bias at the very heart of traditional experimental protocols, it is also discriminatory in a much more profound fashion: female health care needs have essentially remained under-serviced.

A feminist ethical approach, when applied to biomedical issues, would therefore argue that questions about issues such as informed consent to research or abortion should not be decided by appealing to a set of virtues, by applying a set of principles, or even by attempting to balance conflicting duties and rights. Instead, one should arrive at a conclusion based on the social situation of the women and the reality of their bodily and social experiences in a male-dominated and male-oriented society. And more generally, divorced from a purely female-oriented concern, such an approach should acknowledge the functional embedding of all persons in their social contexts and should attempt to reach a resolution on the basis of consensus and cooperation.

Nevertheless, most feminist writings focus on the experiences of women. It is therefore not surprising that a great deal of feminist biomedical ethics has been concerned with matters that centre on the reproductive capacities of women. Issues such as abortion, contraception, the right to have (or refrain from having) children, maternal-fetal conflict, and assisted reproduction constitute noteworthy examples. The readings included below reflect this concern.

Virtue Ethics

Virtue ethics, as its name indicates, is based on the concept of virtue. As one of the most noted modern proponents of the theory has put it, a morally upright person is one who performs the right kinds of acts because he or she has a certain kind of character: namely, a virtuous character. This virtuous character is one that allows the individual to realize those characteristics and qualities that are definitive of human beings.[31]

Virtue ethics shares several important traits with other ethical approaches. Like feminist ethics, it rejects the position that ethics is fundamentally concerned with duties and rights.[32] Instead, it argues that the fundamental concern of ethics is the development of a virtuous character.[33] It is similar to deontological ethics in that it rejects the thesis that the greatest good for the greatest number is the ultimate aim of ethical action. At the same time, it has a certain similarity to teleological ethics in its central insistence that we should foster the attainment of a virtuous character or disposition.[34]

So far as virtue ethics is concerned, the virtues that find their most obvious expression in health care are those of compassion and care. This is not surprising, since these *other-directed* virtues have been synonymous with health care since its very beginning. This is also what makes virtue ethics so attractive to hands-on care-givers like physicians and nurses. However, virtue ethics also maintains that health care provides the opportunity for *self-directed* virtues, such as courage and forbearance. Consequently, it also has something to recommend it from the patient's perspective. *Social* virtues, such as justice and beneficence, have also emerged as important in recent discussions. These are virtues that find ready acceptance from the perspective of society as a whole.[35]

Still, it is probably fair to say that the application of virtue ethics to health is not yet completely worked out. One of the problems of virtue ethics as it is currently structured is that it provides no readily apparent conflict resolution mechanism. However, health care professionals are increasingly faced with limited resources, which means that they are faced with conflicting demands for materials, personnel, and time. Conflict resolution mechanisms are particularly important for dealing with such situations in order to decide who shall have when not all can have, or who shall have when not all can have whatever is available. Further, since health care measures frequently have a threshold level of effectiveness, a shared or cooperative approach will not be effective for any of the parties concerned and, in fact, may harm all of them to some degree. In cases like these, it is unclear which virtue would provide an answer — or should prevail. Finally, in a multicultural society like Canada, it is difficult to see what set of virtues all parties to the social contract would agree on. To fall back on the claim that these virtues can be identified by looking at what is good for human nature is to assume that all parties would agree on what human nature really is. So far, there has been no agreement on that score.

Religiously Oriented Ethics

Religiously oriented ethics evaluate ethical situations by reference to the set of religiously grounded guidelines or principles that are characteristic of the religion in question.[36] These principles or guidelines differ from religion to religion, although there is considerable overlap among religions that belong to the same grouping, for instance Islam, Christianity and Judaism.[37]

Probably the best-known example of how a religiously based ethics can affect the delivery of health care comes from acute care. Jehovah's Witnesses will refrain from accepting transfusions and blood products as a matter of religiously based ethical principle. Hence Jehovah's Witnesses view the non-consensual provision of blood and blood products to their children as a fundamental violation of the role of parents as substitute decision makers for their children. Another example comes from members of the Church of Christ, Scientist. Adherents of this religion reject all scientifically based health care interventions because according to their belief, ill health is a consequence of inadequate belief in the workings of the divine being. Ill health should therefore be cured by appropriate counselling and religious observances, not by active medical care.

However, the impact of religiously based ethics on the delivery on health care is much more profound than these two examples would suggest. The controversy over the moral status of abortion has historically been defined by the conflicting positions of opposing sides, one of which has a religious basis. Likewise, the controversies surrounding issues such as assisted reproduction, euthanasia, and withholding or withdrawal of treatment are heavily coloured by ethical positions that are based on religious precepts.

Nevertheless, the influence of religiously based ethics on biomedical controversies notwithstanding, in Canada there is a definite limit to the applicability of religious ethics in the arena of health care: a limit which, unlike the case of any other ethical perspective, is set by Canadian law. The Canadian Charter of Rights and Freedoms guarantees freedom of religion.[38] This guarantee entails that any institution receiving public funds for its operations and any health care provider under public jurisdiction may not establish or follow policies that have a sectarian and religious basis. Consequently, the impact of religious ethics on the delivery of health care is limited to private decisions made by individual health care consumers and to personal decisions made by health care professionals.

This does not mean that religiously based ethics has no impact on the delivery of health care in general. As was already indicated, the ongoing debate over such things as abortion, euthanasia and assisted suicide, as well as over the development and use of the new reproductive technologies is very much coloured by religiously based positions. It is merely to say that while public policy decisions may *agree* with a particular religion on a specific issue, such policy may never be *based* on a religious precept or be defensible solely in terms of a religious belief.

Agapistic Ethics

Agapistic ethics is an ethics of love and respect for all living things. It evaluates ethical situations by asking what love and respect for life would dictate. The spectrum of approaches that fall under this heading is very wide. Some extreme agapistic ethics argue that all life — and in particular all animal life — has equal moral standing[39]; others maintain that only animal life capable of sensation and experiencing pain has moral worth.

Agapistic ethics does not deny the need for research and experimentation. What it objects to is the treatment of non-human animals as though they had no moral standing. Such a position, so it contends, amounts to "speciesism," which is to say, the adoption of a racist attitude at the level of species.[40]

As with all other ethical approaches, there are variations on this position. Some agapists recognize differences among types of living things, and also among types of animals. They accept that living things like bacteria, worms, and similar entities don't have the same moral status as animals with nervous systems that allow them to sense the world and experience pain.[41] Nevertheless, even these agapists demand that no matter what their status, animals be used only when absolutely necessary, and only when it can be shown that animal experimentation is essential for developing a particular health care modality, and only if the cost in animal terms is proportional to the advancement in health care that would result from such an undertaking.[42]

Agapistic ethical approaches are most commonly encountered in the context of animal experimentation. They contend that animals should not be used to develop and test such things as surgical procedures, pharmacological products, or medical devices. Computer simulations should be used whenever possible, the use of human cell lines should be extended, and other alternatives to animal experimentation should be sought.[43]

Interestingly enough, agapists usually focus solely on the rights of non-human animals. The treatment that human beings visit on each other tends to escape their concern. Thus, few agapists have objected to certain violent methods of abortion even though they would condemn these methods as cruel and immoral if used to kill non-human animals. Likewise, most agapists have not objected to destructive experimentation on human fetuses for the purpose of developing reproductive techniques, even when the fetuses are at a stage of development that would trigger animal rights concerns. The reason for this probably lies in the assumption that there are mechanisms to safeguard the rights of human animals; whereas non-human animals cannot speak for themselves, and therefore require special attention.

Clearly, it is impossible for health care professionals to use an extreme agapistic approach in their professional lives. If one cannot draw an ethically valid distinction among different types of living things — for instance, if one cannot say that one type of living thing (say a human being) is ethically more important than another (say, a bacterium, an insect or a rat) — then one cannot use antibiotics, institute public health measures to control disease vectors, or take appropriate steps to save the lives of human beings suffering from parasitic worms. However, that would leave precious little room for health care as the notion is ordinarily understood. Only dietary and life-style measures would be ethically allowed, and only therapeutic practices such as bone-setting, midwifery, or psychiatry would be permissible.

Of course, if agapism is interpreted in its more moderate form, the consequences would not be quite so severe. However, by allowing a distinction among different kinds of living things, this form of agapism prompts the question: On what basis is this distinction being drawn?[44] It also prompts a further question: Why should the line be drawn on the basis of one particular set of criteria rather than another? For instance, why should one accept that birds occupy a more privileged ethical niche than filarial worms or trypanosomes? Why should one be more concerned about groundhogs than, say, micro-phages or viruses?

The usual reply here is that these animals have nervous systems that allow them to sense the world and to experience pain. However, this invites the question of why the ability to sense and to experience pain should be considered special. Is it a matter of *definition* that beings that sense and experience pain have a special moral status, or is there a more fundamental reason?

Furthermore, in some cases even this modified version of agapism presents its proponents with a dilemma. For example, allowing abortions for reasons of personal choice involves accepting the thesis that some animals may be killed for private value reasons. After all, human fetuses are also a form of animal life. On the other hand, consistent application of the same modified agapistic approach would require rejecting all abortions once the nervous system of the human fetus has started to develop. The modified version would also present its proponents with the dilemma of what to do when trying to control rodent-borne disease vectors such as the plague.

This is not to say that the agapistic approach has no relevance to the Canadian health care scene. Canadian society accepts the principle of respect for life as an important value. It even enshrines it in certain laws and regulations. However, Canadian society does not commit the logical mistake of confusing love and respect with obligation. Life — all life — merits special consideration and must be treated with respect. It might even be an appropriate object of love. But the fact that we respect or love something does not mean that we have an obligation towards it. Of course, we may voluntarily accord certain rights to something because we love or respect it. But that is an entirely different matter.

Therefore, agapistic perspectives do have something valuable to say for bio-medical ethics. However, what they have to say can be accommodated by accepting the premise that consistent ethical behaviour is governed not only by respect for ethical rights and obligations, but also by respect for personal and subjective values; and that these values may — and appropriately should — include the value of respect for life.

CONCLUSION

People in real life rarely follow one ethical theory. They usually combine several of them together. This is not surprising. Most people are not trained in ethics and therefore have little practice in keeping their ethical reasoning theoretically consistent.

At the same time, this mixing of ethical approaches can lead to severe problems in planning and delivery. For example, the administrator of a hospital may use cost/benefit considerations when deciding how many dialysis machines to purchase, but turn to deontological considerations when evaluating the professional actions of the staff who take cost/benefit considerations into account when deciding which patient should be dialyzed. Or, at a more general level, proponents of emergency health care sometimes advance deontological arguments that focus on the needs of particular individuals, whereas proponents of preventive health care measures, who tend to use a utilitarian perspective, usually try to maximize the common good. The conflict that is built into the very nature of the problematic is irresolvable unless the difference in ethical perspectives is identified and settled.

NOTES

1. Someone might attempt to explain such a stance in terms of self-deception. However, it is not at all clear that this would be successful. It would have to deny the reality of the overt emotional stance. For an interesting recent discus-

sion of emotion, see Robert M. Gordon, *The Structure of Emotions: Investigations in Cognitive Philosophy* (New York: Cambridge University Press, 1987).

2. For a sympathetic approach to ethical relativism, see R.B. Perry, *Realms of Value* (Cambridge, Mass.: Harvard University Press, 1954) and E. Westermarck, *The Evolution and Development of the Moral Ideal* (New York: MacMillan, 1906) and E. Westermarck, *Ethical Relativity* (New York: Harcourt Brace, 1932). For a critique see G.E. Moore, *Ethics* (London: Cambridge University Press, 1912) and Brandt, *Ethical Theory* (ref. note 9). For a good presentation of different cultural values and their impact on the ethics of health care decision making, see the proceedings of the *Conference on Transcultural Dimensions* (Washington: Fidia Research Group, 1990). See also E. Pellegrino, P. Mazzarella and P. Corsi, eds., *Transcultural Dimensions in Medical Ethics* (Frederick, Maryland: University Publishing Group, 1992).

3. Lawrence Kohlberg, *The Philosophy of Moral Development* (Chicago: Harper and Row, 1971).

4. See *infra*.

5. Aside, that is, from religiously oriented ethical approaches. Some of these also contain consequentialistic reasoning.

6. Cf. Brandt, *op. cit.* for a discussion of this notion. Traditionally, the concept of pleasure as the ultimate good is associated with Epicurus and his school in ancient Greece. For a modern variant, distinguishing between various types of pleasures, see Jeremy Bentham, *An Introduction to the Principles of Morals and Legislation*, chapters iv ff.

7. Cf. Lennart Nordenfelt, *On the Nature of Health* (Dordrecht and Boston: D. Reidel Publishing Co., 1987), chapter 3.

8. See G.E. Moore, *Principia Ethica* (Cambridge: Cambridge University Press, 1903).

9. For some interesting discussion on this issue, see Henry Sidgewick, *The Methods of Ethics* II: 3; J. Bentham, *The Principles of Morals and Legislation* 1– 4; J.S. Mill, *Utilitarianism* 2, 4, etc. See also Brandt, *Ethical Theory,* and G.E. Moore, *Principia Ethica.*

10. See Moore, *op. cit.*

11. W.R. Ross, *The Right and the Good* (Oxford: Clarendon Press, 1938).

12. See Brandt, *Ethical Theory*, 380–391.

13. Strictly speaking, this is an oversimplification. A complete formulation would require qualifiers that allow for the resolution of conflict among rules, where that set of rules is correct which, when followed conscientiously by all members of society, would maximize the welfare or good for all. See Brandt, *Ethical Theory*, 253 ff.

14. See W.K. Frankena, "Morality and Moral Philosophy," in *Ethics* (Englewood Cliffs, N.J.: Prentice-Hall, 1973), and R.B. Brandt, *Ethical Theory* (Englewood Cliffs, N.J.: Prentice-Hall, 1959) for analogous discussions.

15. Compare A.J. Paton, *The Categorical Imperative* (London: Hutcheson, 1947).

16. Immanuel Kant, *Foundations of the Metaphysics of Morals*, 422 [Prussian Academy page numbering].

17. Kant, *Foundations*, 429.

18. For a similar point see S. Bok, *Lying* (New York: Random House, 1978), chapter 4.

19. What follows is based in part on J.E. Magnet and E.W. Kluge, *Withholding Treatment from Defective Newborn Children* (Cowansville: Brown Legal Publ.,1985).

20. Perhaps a more familiar way of expressing this principle in the health care setting is *primum non nocere:* above all, do not harm. It is also sometimes expressed as "Do not intentionally or knowingly injure the patient," or as "Do not intentionally or knowingly expose the patient to unjustified risk." *Cf.* Tom L. Beauchamp and James F. Childress, *Principles of Biomedical Ethics,* 2nd edition (New York and Oxford: Oxford University Press, 1983), 106–147, especially at 108 ff. Also T.M. Garrett, H.W. Baillie, and R.H. Garrett, *Health Care Ethics: Principles and Problems* (Englewood Cliffs, New Jersey: Prentice-Hall, 1989), 51–55.

21. Another formulation of this principle is that we have a "duty to help others further their important and legitimate interest" when we can do so with minimal risks to ourselves.

22. Tom L. Beauchamp and James F. Childress, *Principles of Biomedical Ethics* (New York and Oxford: Oxford University Press, 1979), 136.

23. W.R. Ross, *The Right and the Good* (Oxford: Clarendon Press, 1938).

24. Ibid., chapter 2.

25. Nel Noddings, "Feminist Fears in Ethics," *Journal of Social Philosophy* (Fall/Winter 1990), reprinted in D.T. Goldberg, *Ethical Theory and Social Issues,* 2nd ed. (Orlando, FLA: Holt Rhinehart and Winston, Inc., 1990), 215–225, at 223.

26. C.J. Gilligan, *In a Different Voice* (Cambridge: Harvard University Press, 1982); J. Grimshaw, *Philosophy and Feminist Thinking* (Minneapolis: University of Minnesota Press, 1989); N. Noddings, *Caring: A Feminist Approach to Ethics and Moral Education* (Berkeley: University of Californian Press, 1984); S. Sherwin, *No Longer Patient: Feminist Ethics and Health Care* (Philadelphia: Temple University Press, 1992); R. Tong, *Feminine and Feminist Ethics* (Belmont, CA: Wadsworth, 1993).

27. N. Noddings, *Caring: A Feminist Approach to Ethics and Moral Education* (Berkeley: University of Californian Press, 1984).

28. C.J. Gilligan, *In a Different Voice* (Cambridge: Harvard University Press, 1982).

29. See Sherwin, *op. cit.* at 13.

30. V. Merton, "The Exclusion of Pregnant, Pregnable, and Once-Pregnable People (A.K.A. Women) from Biomedical Research," *American Journal of Law and Medicine* XIX:4 (1993): 369–451.

31. Alasdair MacIntyre, *After Virtue: A Study in Moral Theory* (Notre Dame University Press, 1984).

32. G.E.M. Anscombe, "Modern Moral Philosophy," *Philosophy*, 33 (1958): 1–19.

33. MacIntyre, *After Virtue: A Study in Moral Theory*. For a classic statement, see Aristotle, *Nicomachean Ethics*. For an attempt to apply it in the health care setting, see R.J. Christie and C.B. Hoffmaster, *Ethical Issues in Family Medicine* (New York and London: Oxford University Press, 1986).

34. Alasdair MacIntyre, *After Virtue: A Study in Moral Theory* (London: Duckworth, 1985), 150 ff.

35. See Christie and Hoffmaster, *Ethical Issues in Family Medicine*.

36. R. McCormick, "Theology and Bioethics," *Hastings Center Report* 19:2 (1989): 5–10. For specific examples, see E.D. Pellegrino, J.P. Langan, J.C. Harvey, eds., *Catholic Perspectives on Medical Morals* (Dordrecht: Kluwer Academic, 1989).

37. For an overview of some of the possible differences, see E.D. Pellegrino, P. Mazzarella and P. Corsi, eds., *Transcultural Dimensions in Medical Ethics* (Frederick, MA: University Publishing Group, 1992).

38. Constitution Act, 1982, R.S.C. 1985, Appendix II, No. 44, Schedule B, Part I Canadian Charter of Rights and Freedoms s. 2(a).

39. Albert Schweitzer, *Civilization and Ethics*, 3rd ed. (London: Black, 1949). For a more recent position, see Tom Regan, *The Case for Animal Rights* (Berkeley: University of California Press, 1983) and Peter Singer, *Animal Liberation* (New York: Avon Books, 1975); P. Rodd, *Biology, Ethics and Animals* (Oxford: Clarendon Press, 1990).

40. Singer, *op. cit.*

41. B.E. Rollin, *The Unheard Cry: Animal Consciousness, Animal Pain and Science* (Oxford: Oxford University Press, 1990).

42. R.M. Baird and S.E. Rosenbaum, eds., *Animal Experimentation: Moral and Ethical Aspects* (Buffalo, N.Y.: Prometheus, 1991).

43. See Regan, *op. cit.*

44. Tom L. Beauchamp, "Problems in Justifying Research on Animals," in *National Symposium on Imperatives in Research Animal Use: Scientific Needs and Animal Welfare* (Washington, D.C.: NIH, Publication No. 85-2746, 1985), 80 ff. *et passim*.

FURTHER READINGS

Deontological and Utilitarian Ethics:
Beauchamp, Tom L., and James F. Childress. *Principles of Biomedical Ethics*, 4th ed. New York and Oxford: Oxford University Press, 1994.

This is a classic text in biomedical ethics written by a deontologist and a utilitarian for the U.S. setting. Its usefulness is somewhat marred by the internal conflict between competing ethical approaches, and the U.S. focus, in its social and legal considerations, limits its applicability to the Canadian setting.

Bowie, Norman E. ed. *Ethical Theory in the Last Quarter of the Twentieth Century*. Indianapolis: Hackett Publishing, 1983.

This is a collection of essays by Stevenson, Frankena, Brandt, and Melden on value judgements, moral-point-of-view theories, utilitarianism, and the rights-based approach. It can serve as a way to focus some of the perspectives in the other readings mentioned.

Engelhardt, Jr., H.T. *The Foundations of Bioethics*. New York and London: Oxford University Press, 1986.

A classic application of deontological ethics to health care. The focus tends to be on the U.S. setting, which limits its usefulness for the Canadian context.

Frankena, William K. "Deontological Theories." In *Ethics*. Englewood Cliffs, N.J.: Prentice-Hall, 1963.

This selection from Frankena's classic introductory text on ethical theory discusses various types of deontological theories and attempts to relate them to one another.

Haering, Bernard. "Ethos, Ethical Code and the Morality of the Physician. In *Medical Ethics*, chapter 4. Notre Dame, Ind.: Fides, 1973.

Bernard Haering is a Catholic theologian who writes on medical ethics. This excerpt is from his text, which for years has served as a standard and middle-of-the-road guide to Catholic physicians.

Pellegrino, E.D., and J.P. Langan, J.C. Harvey, eds. *Catholic Perspectives on Medical Morals*. Dordrecht: Kluwer Academic, 1989.

A good collection of essays on the relationship between Catholicism and ethics in the context of health care. It addresses foundational issues within the pluralistic perspective that characterizes contemporary Catholic thought. The points raised in these discussions can be applied to other religious perspectives.

Taylor, Paul. "Utilitarianism." In *Principles of Ethics: An Introduction*. Belmont, Calif.: Wadsworth, 1975.

A classic exposition of utilitarian theory for those who do not want to go to the full-length work of Richard Brandt and others.

Feminist Ethics:

Chinn, P.L., and C.E. Wheeler. "Feminism and Nursing." *Nurs Outlook* 33(2) (March–April 1985): 74–78.

This is a good introductory paper applying, as the title suggests, feminist ethical theory to nursing issues.

Crowley, M.A. "Feminist pedagogy: nurturing the ethical ideal." *ANS* 11(3) (April 1989): 53–61.

Gilligan, C. *In a Different Voice*. Cambridge, Mass.: Harvard U. Press, 1982.

This is the classical work in feminist ethical theory. It is more reflective and not quite as extreme as later feminist writings. In it, Gilligan lays the foundation for an ethics of caring by trying to tie it to the different experiences that women have in (Western) society.

Noddings, N. *Caring: A feminist approach to ethics and moral education*. Berkeley: University of California Press, 1986.

This is a companion work to Gilligan's seminal study. Noddings adopts a more "philosophical" approach and erects a theoretical framework on Gilligan's work. In some ways, it can be described as a feminist version of Kohlberg's work.

Raymond, J.G. "Medicine as patriarchal religion." *J Med Philos* 7(2) (May 1982): 197–216.

Sherwin, S. "Concluding remarks: a feminist perspective." *Health Care Women Int* 8(4) (1987): 293–304.

A classic but short statement by a Canadian feminist philosopher.

Sherwin, S. *No Longer Patient: feminist ethic and health care.* Philadelphia: Temple University Press, 1992.

> This is an extensive and in-depth development of the implications of feminist theory on the delivery of health care by a well-known Canadian feminist philosopher.

Virtue Ethics:

Aristotle. *Nicomachean Ethics* (any edition).

> The original classical statement of virtue ethics by one of the founders of ethics as a field of study.

Foot, P. *Virtues and Vices.* Oxford: Basil Blackwell, 1978.

> A relatively recent statement of virtue ethics by one of Britain's best-known ethicists.

Geach, P. *The Virtues.* Cambridge: Cambridge University Press, 1977.

Kruschwitz, R.B., and R.C. Roberts, eds. *The Virtues: Contemporary Essays on Moral Character.* Belmont, Calif: Wadsworth, 1987.

> A collection of essays on virtue theory, which spans the whole spectrum of possible positions in virtue theory. Somewhat dated, but still very good.

MacIntyre, A. *After Virtue: A Study in Moral Theory.* London: Duckworth, 1985.

> Somewhat dated, but still the best-known exposition of virtue ethics in the last 20 years.

CHAPTER 2
HEALTH AS AN ETHICAL ISSUE

INTRODUCTION

What is truth? The question has occupied philosophers, lawyers and theologians since ancient times. *What is health?* must surely rank a close second in terms of difficulty. Time and again, physicians and philosophers have tried to define the notion, only to find that as their knowledge advanced, the definitions they had just settled on seemed inadequate. And yet it is clear that if health care is to be assigned its proper place in the sphere of social endeavours and if the health care professions are to have a clearly defined role and mandate, the notion has to have an appropriate and acceptable definition.

The issue has become particularly pressing in the twentieth century, as society came to accept the position that it has an obligation to provide at least some level of health care services for its members. If the nature of health could not be satisfactorily defined, then the limits of this social obligation could not be drawn properly either. That, so it was felt, would have important implications in terms of social policy.

Furthermore, when people say that society has an obligation to provide at least some level of health care for its members, they are not only talking about health care services on an individual basis. They are also thinking of the sorts of services that usually fall under the rubric of public health measures. These are services that are designed to maintain, raise and promote the health of all of society, collectively. Here, too, the notion of health plays a central role. Therefore, without some common understanding of what exactly health is, these services could be identified only in a very haphazard way.

But there were also other reasons for seeking a definition. In most countries — Canada included — people may not legally consent to have grievous harm inflicted on them. Inflicting such harm constitutes grounds for bringing a charge of assault and battery. However, much of health care involves procedures that, *prima facie*, fall under this rubric. Surgical interventions, psychiatric therapy, dental work, and even the most basic of nursing functions would all be implicated if they were not placed into a special category that would exempt them from this charge. Of course there is such a category: namely, the category of health care. However, in order for this category to be properly defined and delimited, what is needed is a proper definition of "health."

In other words, there has to be some way in which the notion of what harm a patient can legitimately agree to can be identified, and some way in which consent to such procedures can be legitimated. The concept of health assumes a fundamental role in all this.

For these and similar reasons, there began some time ago what can only be described as a hunt for an appropriate definition of "health." The lead was taken by the World Health Organization, with its 1958 definition of "health." It is included below. The reaction to this definition, however, was less than enthusiastic in some quarters. As a whole series of authors pointed out, the definition is extremely vague. For instance, what does "well-being" mean, or "infirmity"? It is also circular: it defines "health" in terms of its correlative, "disease." The notion of disease, however, could itself only be defined in terms of health; so this gets us nowhere. Furthermore, the definition is far too inclusive. It would have us classify social and moral problems as health problems. The selection from Daniel Callahan captures the thrust of most of this criticism very well.

Other definitions attempted to overcome these problems. For instance, health has been defined as "a state of physiological normalcy" or a "proper working order of the human body"[1]; as "the general condition of the body with respect to efficient or inefficient discharge of functions"; as "spiritual, moral or mental soundness or well-being"[2]; the ability to function "in a given physical and social environment"[3]; the "well-working of the organism as a whole"; "an activity of the living body in accordance with its specific excellence"[4]; or simply as "a state of physical well-being."[5]

However, these definitions also ran into criticism. In fact, the very attempt to define health at all came to be criticized. On a general level, the criticism maintained that a proper definition is impossible because concepts like those of health and disease are inherently value-laden. They include not only descriptive components but also normative ones. Some people[6] have argued that this is inadequate. To say that something is a disease commits us to saying something about human nature and the nature of human well-being, and this involves choices among human goods. This, in turn, involves considerations of what counts as the proper human state, which of course involve value judgements in an integral fashion. Therefore, to call someone ill is to make a social judgement.

The selection by Caroline Whitbeck presents a version of this critique. Whitbeck maintains that the notion of health is necessarily value-laden, because it is used to categorize what we find good or appropriate in people's capacity to act or respond to a wide variety of situations. However, she sees nothing wrong with this. In fact, she sees this valuational approach to be a proper role played by the notion of health itself. Furthermore, by introducing the notion of capacity, she expands the discussion to include the notion of functional potential. She expands the discussion still further by proposing that the concept of wholeness should be involved as well, and by saying that the more encompassing a person's capacity to respond appropriately to a wide variety of situations is, and the greater a person's capacity to achieve her/his goals under the circumstances is, the healthier the individual. In that sense, for Whitbeck, there is no upper limit to health.

Of course, there are other positions on health. The biostatistical model proposed by Boorse is one of the best-known.[7] It attempts to define the notion of health in terms of what is statistically normal for the species. However, such an approach would ignore the fact that a species as a whole may suffer from a particular disease or condition, whether that may be environmentally induced or genetically conditioned. Ultimately we do have to come to grips with the question whether it is true that the notion of health is necessarily value-laden. The issue is important because it has been argued that if we cannot give a value-free definition of health, then we will always have to ask ourselves whether the health services that are provided by our society are so coloured by our values that they, in fact, amount to a cultural agenda. This would have to be of particular concern to Canadians because Canada, by choice and by Charter, is a multicultural society.

NOTES

1. Joel Feinberg, "Disease and Values," in *Doing and Deserving: Essays in the Theory of Responsibility,* Joel Feinberg (Princeton: Princeton University Press, 1974), 253–255.

2. *Oxford English Dictionary.*

3. Réné Dubos, "Health as Ability to Function," in T.L. Beauchamp and L. Walters, eds., *Contemporary Issues in Bioethics* (Belmont: Dickenson Publ. Co., 1978), 99.

4. Leon Kass, "Regarding the End of Medicine and the Pursuit of Health," in *Contemporary Issues in Bioethics*, ref. note 3, 108.

5. Daniel Callahan, "The WHO Definition of Health," included below. A somewhat more theoretical and developed analysis is offered by Ellen Idler, "Definition of Mental Health and Illness and Medical Sociology," *Society, Science and Medicine* 3A, 723–731. She claims that these and other definitions are based on a Parsonian model of illness and disease: one that defines it as "an abstract, biomedical conception of pathological abnormality in people's bodies, where this is indicated by certain abnormal signs and symptoms which can be measured, recorded, classified and analyzed." To be quite correct, so she argues, the concept should be modified so that "subjective reality plays a role in determining whether an individual becomes ill in the first place." For other attempts to define "health," see President's

Commission for the Study of Ethical Problems in Medicine and Biomedical and Behavioral Research, *Securing Access to Health Care: A Report on the Ethical Implications of Differences in the Availability of Health Services* (U.S. Government Printing Office: Washington D.C., 1983), 3 vols., vols. two and three.

6. Tristram Englehardt, Jr., "Human Well-Being and Medicine: Some Basic Value-Judgments in the Biomedical Science," in *Science, Ethics and Medicine,* H.T. Engelhardt and D. Callahan, eds. (Institute of Society, Ethics and the Life Sciences, 1976).

7. C. Boorse, "Health as a Theoretical Concept," *Philosophy of Science* 44(1977): 542–573.

Preamble: Constitution of the World Health Organization

World Health Organization

The States Parties to this Constitution declare, in conformity with the Charter of the United Nations, that the following principles are basic to the happiness, harmonious relations and security of all peoples:

Health is a state of complete physical, mental and social well-being and not merely the absence of disease or infirmity.

The enjoyment of the highest attainable standard of health is one of the fundamental rights of every human being without distinction of race, religion, political belief, economic or social condition.

The health of all peoples is fundamental to the attainment of peace and security and is dependent upon the fullest co-operation of individuals and States.

The achievement of any State in the promotion and protection of health is of value to all.

Unequal development in different countries in the promotion of health and control of disease, especially communicable disease, is a common danger.

Healthy development of the child is of basic importance; the ability to live harmoniously in a changing total environment is essential to such development.

The extension to all peoples of the benefits of medical, psychological and related knowledge is essential to the fullest attainment of health.

Informed opinion and active co-operation on the part of the public are of the utmost importance in the improvement of the health of the people.

Governments have a responsibility for the health of their peoples which can be fulfilled only by the provision of adequate health and social measures.

Accepting these principles, and for the purpose of co-operation among themselves and with others to promote and protect the health of all peoples, the Contracting Parties agree to the present Constitution and hereby establish the World Health Organization as a specialized agency within the terms of Article 57 of the Charter of the United Nations.

The WHO Definition of Health

Daniel Callahan

There is not much that can be called fun and games in medicine, perhaps because unlike other sports it is the only one in which everyone, participant and spectator, eventually gets killed playing. In the meantime, one of the grandest games is that version of king-of-the-hill where the aim of all players is to upset the World Health Organization (WHO) definition of "health." That definition, in case anyone could possibly forget it, is, "Health is a state of complete physical, mental, and social well-being and not merely the absence of disease or infirmity." Fair game, indeed. Yet somehow, defying all comers, the WHO definition endures, though literally every other aspirant to the crown has managed to knock it off the hill at least once. One possible reason for its presence is that it provides such an irresistible straw man; few there are who can resist attacking it in the opening paragraphs of papers designed to move on to more profound reflections.

But there is another possible reason which deserves some exploration, however unsettling the implications. It may just be that the WHO definition has more than a grain of truth in it, of a kind which is as profoundly frustrating as it is enticingly attractive. At the very least it is a definition which implies that there is some intrinsic relationship between the good of the body and the good of the self. The attractiveness of this relationship is obvious: it thwarts any movement toward a dualism of self and body, a dualism which in any event immediately breaks down when one drops a brick on one's toe; and

it impels the analyst to work toward a conception of health which in the end is resistant to clear and distinct categories, closer to the felt experience. All that, naturally, is very frustrating. It seems simply impossible to devise a concept of health which is rich enough to be nutritious and yet not so rich as to be indigestible.

One common objection to the WHO definition is, in effect, an assault upon any and all attempts to specify the meaning of very general concepts. Who can possibly define words as vague as "health," a venture as foolish as trying to define "peace," "justice," "happiness," and other systematically ambiguous notions? To this objection the "pragmatic" clinicians (as they often call themselves) add that, anyway, it is utterly unnecessary to know what "health" means in order to treat a patient running a high temperature. Not only that, it is also a harmful distraction to clutter medical judgment with philosophical puzzles.

Unfortunately for this line of argument, it is impossible to talk or think at all without employing general concepts; without them, cognition and language are impossible. More damagingly, it is rarely difficult to discover, with a bit of probing, that even the most "pragmatic" judgment (whatever *that* is) presupposes some general values and orientations, all of which can be translated into definitions of terms as general as "health" and "happiness." A failure to discern the operative underlying values, the conceptions of reality upon which they are based, and the definitions they entail, sets the stage for unexamined conduct and,

Daniel Callahan, "The WHO Definition of Health," *The Hastings Center Studies,* 1:3 (1973).

beyond that, positive harm both to patients and to medicine in general.

But if these objections to any and all attempts to specify the meaning of "health" are common enough, the most specific complaint about the WHO definition is that its very generality, and particularly its association of health and general well-being as a positive ideal, has given rise to a variety of evils. Among them are the cultural tendency to define all social problems, from war to crime in the streets, as "health" problems; the blurring of lines of responsibility between and among the professions, and between the medical profession and the political order; the implicit denial of human freedom which results when failures to achieve social well-being are defined as forms of "sickness," somehow to be treated by medical means; and the general debasement of language which ensues upon the casual habit of labeling everyone from Adolf Hitler to student radicals to the brat next door as "sick." In short, the problem with the WHO definition is not that it represents an attempt to propose a general definition, but it is simply a bad one.

That is a valid line of objection, provided one can spell out in some detail just how the definition can or does entail some harmful consequences. Two lines of attack are possible against putatively hazardous social definitions of significant general concepts. One is by pointing out that the definition does not encompass all that a concept has commonly been taken to mean, either historically or at present, that it is a partial definition only. The task then is to come up with a fuller definition, one less subject to misuse. But there is still another way of objecting to socially significant definitions, and that is by pointing out some baneful effects of definitions generally accepted as adequate. Many of the objec-

tions to the WHO definition fall in the latter category, building upon the important insight that definitions of crucially important terms with a wide public use have ethical, social, and political implications; defining general terms is not an abstract exercise but a way of shaping the world metaphysically and structuring the world politically.

Wittgenstein's aphorism, "Don't look for the meaning, look for the use," is pertinent here. The ethical problem in defining the concept of "health" is to determine what the implications are of the various uses to which a concept of "health" can be put. We might well agree that there are some uses of "health" which will produce socially harmful results. To carry Wittgenstein a step further, "Don't look for the uses, look for the abuses." We might, then, examine some of the real or possible abuses to which the WHO definition leads, recognizing all the while that what we may term an "abuse" will itself rest upon some perceived *positive* good or value.

HISTORICAL ORIGIN AND CONTEXT

Before that task is undertaken, however, it is helpful to understand the historical origin and social context of the WHO definition. If abuses of that definition have developed, their seeds may be looked for in its earliest manifestations.

The World Health Organization came into existence between 1946 and 1948 as one of the first major activities of the United Nations. As an outcome of earlier work, an Interim Commission to establish the WHO sponsored an International Health Conference in New York in June and July of 1946. At that Conference, representatives of 61 nations signed the Constitution of the WHO, the very first clause of which presented the now famous definition of "health." The animating spirit behind the formation of the WHO was the belief that the improvement of world health would make an important contribution to world peace; health and peace were seen as inseparable. Just why this belief gained ground is not clear from the historical record of the WHO. While there have been many historical explanations of the origin of World War II, a lack of world health has not been prominent among them; nor, for that matter, did the early supporters of the WHO claim that the Second World War or any other war might have been averted had there been better health. More to the point, perhaps, was the conviction that health was intimately related to economic and cultural welfare; in turn, that welfare, so it was assumed, had a direct bearing on future peace. No less important was a fervent faith in the possibilities of medical science to achieve world health, enhanced by the development of powerful antibiotics and pesticides during the war.

A number of memorandums submitted to a spring 1946 Technical Preparatory Committee meeting of the WHO capture the flavor of the period. The Yugoslavian memorandum noted that "health is a prerequisite to freedom from want, to social security and happiness." France stated that "there cannot be any material security, social security, or well-being for individuals or nations without health ... the full responsibility of a free man can only be assumed by healthy individuals ... the spread of proper notions of hygiene among populations tends to improve the level of health and hence to increase their working power and raise their standard of living...." The United States contended that "international cooperation and joint action in the furtherance of all matters pertaining to health will raise the standards of living, will promote the freedom, the dignity, and the happiness of all peoples of the world."

In addition to those themes, perhaps the most significant initiative taken by the organizers of the WHO was to include mental health as part of its working definition. In its memorandum, Great Britain stated that "it should be clear that health includes mental health," but it was Dr. Brock Chisholm, soon to become the first director of the WHO, who personified what Dr. Chisholm himself called the "visionary" view of health. During the meeting of the Technical Preparatory Committee he argued that: "The world is sick and the ills are due to the perversion of man; his inability to live with himself. The microbe is not the enemy; science is sufficiently advanced to cope with it were it not for the barriers of superstition, ignorance, religious intolerance, misery and poverty....These psychological evils must be understood in order that a remedy might be prescribed, and the scope of the task before the Committee therefore knows no bounds."

In Dr. Chisholm's statement, put very succinctly, are all of those elements of the WHO definition which led eventually to its criticism: defining all the problems of the world as "sickness," affirming that science would be sufficient to cope with the causes of physical disease, asserting that only anachronistic attitudes stood in the way of a cure of both physical and psychological ills, and declaring that the cause of health can tolerate no limitations. To say that Dr. Chisholm's "vision" was grandiose is to understate the matter. Even allowing for hyperbole, it is clear that the stage was being set for a conception of "health" which would encompass literally every element and item of human happiness. One can hardly be surprised, given such a vision, that our ways of talking about "health" have become all but meaningless. Even though I believe the definition is not without its important insights, it is well to observe why, in part, we are so muddled at present about "health."

HEALTH AND HAPPINESS

Let us examine some of the principal objections to the WHO definition in more detail. One of them is that, by including the notion of "social well-being" under its rubric, it turns the enduring problem of human happiness into one more medical problem, to be dealt with by scientific means. That is surely an objectionable feature, if only because there exists no evidence whatever that medicine has anything more than a partial grasp of the sources of human misery. Despite Dr. Chisholm's optimism, medicine has not even found ways of dealing with more than a fraction of the whole range of physical diseases; campaigns, after all, are still being mounted against cancer and heart disease. Nor is there any special reason to think that future forays against those and other common diseases will bear rapid fruits. People will continue to die of disease for a long time to come, probably forever.

But perhaps, then, in the psychological and psychiatric sciences some progress has been made against what Dr. Chisholm called the "psychological ills," which lead to wars, hostility, and aggression? To be sure, there are many interesting psychological theories to be found about these "ills," and a few techniques which can, with some individuals, reduce or eliminate antisocial behavior. But so far as I can see, despite the mental health movement and the rise of the psychological sciences, war and human hostility are as much with us as ever. Quite apart from philosophical objections to the WHO definition, there was no empirical basis for the unbounded optimism which lay behind it at the time of its inception, and little has happened since to lend its limitless aspiration any firm support.

Common sense alone makes evident the fact that the absence of "disease or infirmity" by no means guarantees "social well-being." In one sense, those who drafted the WHO definition seem well aware of that.

Isn't the whole point of their definition to show the inadequacy of negative definitions? But in another sense, it may be doubted that they really did grasp that point. For the third principle enunciated in the WHO Constitution says that "the health of all peoples is fundamental to the attainment of peace and security...." Why is it fundamental, at least to peace? The worst wars of the 20th century have been waged by countries with very high standards of health, by nations with superior life-expectancies for individuals and with comparatively low infant mortality rates. The greatest present threats to world peace come in great part (though not entirely) from developed countries, those which have combated disease and illness most effectively. There seems to be no historical correlation whatever between health and peace, and that is true even if one includes "mental health."

How are human beings to achieve happiness? That is the final and fundamental question. Obviously illness, whether mental or physical, makes happiness less possible in most cases. But that is only because they are only one symptom of a more basic restriction, that of human finitude, which sees infinite human desires constantly thwarted by the limitations of reality. "Complete" well-being might, conceivably, be attainable, but under one condition only: that people cease expecting much from life. That does not seem about to happen. On the contrary, medical and psychological progress have been more than outstripped by rising demands and expectations. What is so odd about that, if it is indeed true that human desires are infinite? Whatever the answer to the question of human happiness, there is no particular reason to believe that medicine can do anything more than make a modest, finite contribution.

Another objection to the WHO definition is that, by implication, it makes the medical profession the gatekeeper for happiness and social well-being. Or if not exactly the gatekeeper (since political and economic support will be needed from sources other than medical), then the final magic-healer of human misery. Pushed far enough, the whole idea is absurd, and it is not necessary to believe that the organizers of the WHO would, if pressed, have been willing to go quite that far. But even if one pushes the pretension a little way, considerable fantasy results. The mental health movement is the best example, casting the psychological professional in the role of high priest.

At its humble best, that movement can do considerable good; people do suffer from psychological disabilities and there are some effective ways of helping them. But it would be sheer folly to believe that all, or even the most important, social evils stem from bad mental health: political injustice, economic scarcity, food shortages, unfavorable physical environments, have a far greater historical claim as sources of a failure to achieve "social well-being." To retort that all or most of these troubles can, nonetheless, be seen finally as symptoms of bad mental health is, at best, self-serving and, at worst, just plain foolish.

A significant part of the objection that the WHO definition places, at least by implication, too much power and authority in the hands of the medical profession need not be based on a fear of that power as such. There is no reason to think that the world would be any worse off if health professionals made all decisions than if any other group did; and no reason to think it would be any better off. That is not a very important point. More significant is that cultural development which, in its skepticism about "traditional" ways of solving social problems, would seek a technological and specifically a medical solution for human ills of all kinds. There is at least a hint in early WHO discussions that, since

politicians and diplomats have failed in maintaining world peace, a more expert group should take over, armed with the scientific skills necessary to set things right; it is science which is best able to vanquish that old Enlightenment bogeyman, "superstition." More concretely, such an ideology has the practical effect of blurring the lines of appropriate authority and responsibility. If all problems — political, economic and social — reduce to matters of "health," then there ceases to be any ways to determine who should be responsible for what.

THE TYRANNY OF HEALTH

The problem of responsibility has at least two faces. One is that of a tendency to turn all problems of "social well-being" over to the medical professional, most pronounced in the instance of the incarceration of a large group of criminals in mental institutions rather than prisons. The abuses, both medical and legal, of that practice are, fortunately, now beginning to receive the attention they deserve, even if little corrective action has yet been taken. (Counterbalancing that development, however, are others, where some are seeking more "effective" ways of bringing science to bear on criminal behavior.)

The other face of the problem of responsibility is that of the way in which those who are sick, or purportedly sick, are to be evaluated in terms of their freedom and responsibility. Siegler and Osmond (*Hastings Center Studies,* Vol. 1, No. 3, 1973, pp. 41-58) discuss the "sick role," a leading feature of which is the ascription of blamelessness, of non-responsibility, to those who contract illness. There is no reason to object to this kind of ascription in many instances — one can hardly blame someone for contracting kidney disease — but, obviously enough, matters get out of hand when all physical, mental, and communal disorders are put under the heading of "sickness," and all sufferers (all of us, in the end) placed in the blameless "sick role." Not only are the concepts of "sickness" and "illness" drained of all content, it also becomes impossible to ascribe any freedom or responsibility to those caught up in the throes of sickness. The whole world is sick, and no one is responsible any longer for anything. That is determinism gone mad, a rather odd outcome of a development which began with attempts to bring unbenighted "reason" and free self-determination to bear for the release of the helpless captives of superstition and ignorance.

The final and most telling objection to the WHO definition has less to do with the definition itself than with one of its natural historical consequences. Thomas Szasz has been the most eloquent (and most single-minded) critic of that sleight-of-hand which has seen the concept of health moved from the medical to the moral arena. What can no longer be done in the name of "morality" can now be done in the name of "health": human beings labeled, incarcerated, and dismissed for their failure to toe the line of "normalcy" and "sanity."

At first glance, this analysis of the present situation might seem to be totally at odds with the tendency to put everyone in the blame-free "sick role." Actually, there is a fine, probably indistinguishable, line separating these two positions. For as soon as one treats all human disorders — war, crime, social unrest — as forms of illness, then one turns health into a normative concept, that which human beings must and ought to have if they are to live in peace with themselves and others. Health is no longer an optional matter, but the golden key to the relief of human misery. We *must* be well or we will all perish. "Health" can and must be imposed; there can be no room for the luxury of freedom when so much is at stake. Of course the matter is rarely put

so bluntly, but it is to Szasz's great credit that he has discerned what actually happens when "health" is allowed to gain the cultural clout which morality once had. (That he carries the whole business too far in his embracing of the most extreme moral individualism is another story, which cannot be dealt with here.) Something is seriously amiss when the "right" to have healthy children is turned into a further right for children not to be born defective, and from there into an obligation not to bring unhealthy children into the world as a way of respecting the right of those children to health! Nor is everything altogether lucid when abortion decisions are made a matter of "medical judgment" (see *Roe vs. Wade*); when decisions to provide psychoactive drugs for the relief of the ordinary stress of living are defined as no less "medical judgment"; when patients are not allowed to die with dignity because of medical indications that they can, come what may, be kept alive; when prisoners, without their consent, are subjected to aversive conditioning to improve their mental health.

ABUSES OF LANGUAGE

In running through the litany of criticisms which have been directed at the WHO definition of "health," and what seem to have been some of its long-term implications and consequences, I might well be accused of beating a dead horse. My only defense is to assert, first, that the spirit of the WHO definition is by no means dead either in medicine or society. In fact, because of the usual cultural lag which requires many years for new ideas to gain wide social currency, it is only now coming into its own on a broad scale. (Everyone now talks about everybody and everything, from Watergate to Billy Graham to trash in the streets, as "sick.") Second, I believe that we are now in the midst of a nascent (if not actual) crisis about how "health" ought properly to be understood, with much dependent upon what conception of health emerges in the near future.

If the ideology which underlies the WHO definition has proved to contain many muddled and hazardous ingredients, it is not at all evident what should take its place. The virtue of the WHO definition is that it tried to place health in the broadest human context. Yet the assumption behind the main criticisms of the WHO definition seem perfectly valid. Those assumptions can be characterized as follows: (1) health is only a part of life, and the achievement of health only a part of the achievement of happiness; (2) medicine's role, however important, is limited; it can neither solve nor even cope with the great majority of social, political, and cultural problems; (3) human freedom and responsibility must be recognized, and any tendency to place all deviant, devilish, or displeasing human beings into the blameless sick-role must be resisted; (4) while it is good for human beings to be healthy, medicine is not morality; except in very limited contexts (plagues and epidemics) "medical judgment" should not be allowed to become moral judgment; to be healthy is not to be righteous; (5) it is important to keep clear and distinct the different roles of different professions, with a clearly circumscribed role for medicine, limited to those domains of life where the contribution of medicine is appropriate. Medicine can save some lives; it cannot save the life of society.

These assumptions, and the criticisms of the WHO definition which spring from them, have some important implications for the use of the words "health," "illness," "sick," and the like. It will be counted an abuse of language if the word "sick" is applied to all individual and communal problems, if all unacceptable conduct is spoken of in the language of medical pathologies, if

moral issues and moral judgments are translated into the language of "health," if the lines of authority, responsibility, and expertise are so blurred that the health profession is allowed to pre-empt the rights and responsibilities of others by re-defining them in its own professional language.

Abuses of that kind have no possibility of being curbed in the absence of a definition of health which does not contain some intrinsic elements of limitation — that is, unless there is a definition which, when abused, is self-evidently *seen* as abused by those who know what health means. Unfortunately, it is in the nature of general definitions that they do not circumscribe their own meaning (or even explain it) and contain no built-in safeguards against misuse, e.g., our "peace with honor" in Southeast Asia — "peace," "honor"? Moreover, for a certain class of concepts — peace, honor, happiness, for example — it is difficult to keep them free in ordinary usage from a normative content. In our own usage, it would make no sense to talk of them in a way which implied they are not desirable or are merely neutral: by well-ingrained social custom (resting no doubt on some basic features of human nature) health, peace, and happiness are both desired and desirable — good. For those and other reasons, it is perfectly plausible to say the cultural task of defining terms, and settling on appropriate and inappropriate usages, is far more than a matter of getting our dictionary entries right. It is nothing less than a way of deciding what should be valued, how life should be understood, and what principles should guide individual and social conduct.

Health is not just a term to be defined. Intuitively, if we have lived at all, it is something we seek and value. We may not set the highest value on health — other goods may be valued as well — but it would strike me as incomprehensible should someone say that health was a matter of utter indifference to him; we would well doubt either his sanity or his maturity. The cultural problem, then, may be put this way. The acceptable range of uses of the term "health" should, at the minimum, capture the normative element in the concept as traditionally understood while, at the maximum, incorporate the insight (stemming from criticisms of the WHO definition) that the term "health" is abused if it becomes synonymous with virtue, social tranquillity, and ultimate happiness. Since there are no instruction manuals available on how one would go about reaching a goal of that sort, I will offer no advice on the subject. I have the horrible suspicion, as a matter of fact, that people either have a decent intuitive sense on such matters (reflected in the way they use language) or they do not; and if they do not, little can be done to instruct them. One is left with the pious hope that, somehow, over a long period of time, things will change.

IN DEFENSE OF WHO

Now that simply might be the end of the story, assuming some agreement can be reached that the WHO definition of "health" is plainly bad, full of snares, delusions, and false norms. But I am left uncomfortable with such a flat, simple conclusion. The nagging point about the definition is that, in badly put ways, it was probably on to something. It certainly recognized, however inchoately, that it is difficult to talk meaningfully of health solely in terms of "the absence of disease or infirmity." As a purely logical point, one must ask about what positive state of affairs disease and infirmity are an absence of — absent from what? One is left with the tautological proposition that health is the absence of non-health, a less than illuminating revelation. Could it not be said, though, that at least intuitively everyone knows what health is by means of the experiential con-

trast posed by states of illness and disease; that is, even if I cannot define health in any positive sense, I can surely know when I am sick (pain, high fever, etc.) and compare that condition with my previous states which contained no such conditions? Thus one could, in some recognizable sense, speak of illness as a deviation from a norm, even if it is not possible to specify that norm with any clarity.

But there are some problems with this approach, for all of its commonsense appeal. Sociologically, it is well known that what may be accounted sickness in one culture may not be so interpreted in another; one culture's (person's) deviation from the norm may not necessarily be another culture's (person's) deviation. In this as in other matters, commonsense intuition may be nothing but a reflection of different cultural and personal evaluations. In addition, there can be and usually are serious disputes about how great a deviation from the (unspecified) norm is necessary before the terms "sickness" and "illness" become appropriate. Am I to be put in the sick role because of my nagging case of itching athlete's foot, or must my toes start dropping off before I can so qualify? All general concepts have their borderline cases, and normally they need pose no real problems for the applicability of the concepts for the run of instances. But where "health" and "illness" are concerned, the number of borderline cases can be enormous, affected by age, attitudinal and cultural factors. Worse still, the fact that people can be afflicted by disease (even fatally afflicted) well before the manifestation of any overt symptoms is enough to discredit the adequacy of intuitions based on how one happens to feel at any given moment.

A number of these problems might be resolved by distinguishing between health as a norm and as an ideal. As a norm, it could be possible to speak in terms of deviation from some statistical standards, particularly if these standards were couched not only in terms of organic function but also in terms of behavioral functioning. Thus someone would be called "healthy" if his heart, lungs, kidneys (etc.) functioned at a certain level of efficiency and efficacy, if he was not suffering physical pain, and if his body was free of those pathological conditions which even if undetected or undetectable could impair organic function and eventually cause pain. There could still be dispute about what should count as a "pathological" condition, but at least it would be possible to draw up a large checklist of items subject to "scientific measurement"; then, having gone through that checklist in a physical exam, and passing all the tests, one could be pronounced "healthy." Neat, clean, simple.

All of this might be possible in a static culture, which ours is not. The problem is that any notion of a statistical norm will be superintended by some kind of ideal. Why, in the first place, should anyone care at all how his organs are functioning, much less how well they do so? There must be some reason for that, a reason which goes beyond theoretical interest in statistical distributions. Could it possibly be because certain departures from the norm carry with them unpleasant states, which few are likely to call "good": pain, discrimination, unhappiness? I would guess so. In the second place, why should society have any interest whatever in the way the organs of its citizens function? There must also be some reason for that, very possibly the insight that the organ functioning of individuals has some aggregate social implications. In our culture at least (and in every other culture I have ever heard of) it is simply impossible, finally, to draw any sharp distinction between conceptions of the human good and what are accounted significant and negatively evaluated deviations from statistical norms.

That is the whole point of saying, in defense of the WHO definition of health, that it discerned the intimate connection between the good of the body and the good of the self, not only the individual self but the social community of selves. No individual and no society would (save for speculative, scientific reasons only) have any interest whatever in the condition of human organs and bodies were it not for the obvious fact that those conditions can have an enormous impact on the whole of human life. People do, it has been noticed, die; and they die because something has gone wrong with their bodies. This can be annoying, especially if one would, at the moment of death, prefer to be busy doing other things. Consider two commonplace occurrences. The first I have alluded to already: dropping a heavy brick on one's foot. So far as I know, there is no culture where the pain which that event occasions is considered a good in itself. Why is that? Because (I presume) the pain which results can not only make it difficult or impossible to walk for a time but also because the pain, if intense enough, makes it impossible to think about anything else (or think at all) or to relate to anything or anyone other than the pain. For a time, I am "not myself" and that simply because my body is making such excessive demands on my attention that nothing is possible to me except to howl. I cannot, in sum, dissociate my "body" from my "self" in that situation; my self is my body and my body is my pain.

The other occurrence is no less commonplace. It is the assertion the old often make to the young, however great the psychological, economic, or other miseries of the latter: "at least you've got your health." They are saying in so many words that, if one is healthy, then there is some room for hope, some possibility of human recovery; and even more they are saying that, without good health, nothing is possible, however favorable the other conditions of life may be. Again, it is impossible to dissociate good of body and good of self. Put more formally, if health is not a sufficient condition for happiness, it is a necessary condition. At that very fundamental level, then, any sharp distinction between the good of bodies and the good of persons dissolves.

Are we not forced, therefore, to say that, if the complete absence of health (i.e., death) means the complete absence of self, then any diminishment of health must represent, correspondingly, a diminishment of self? That does not follow, for unless a disease or infirmity is severe, it may represent only a minor annoyance, diminishing our selfhood not a whit. And while it will not do to be overly sentimental about such things, it is probably the case that disease or infirmity can, in some cases, increase one's sense of selfhood (which is no reason to urge disease upon people for its possibly psychological benefits). The frequent reports of those who have recovered from a serious illness that it made them appreciate life in a far more intense way than they previously had are not to be dismissed (though one wishes an easier way could be found).

MODEST CONCLUSIONS

Two conclusions may be drawn. The first is that some minimal level of health is necessary if there is to be any possibility of human happiness. Only in exceptional circumstances can the good of self be long maintained in the absence of the good of the body. The second conclusion, however, is that one can be healthy without being in a state of "complete physical, mental, and social well-being." That conclusion can be justified in two ways: (a) because some degree of disease and infirmity is perfectly compatible with mental and social well-being; and (b) because it is doubtful that there ever was, or ever could be, more than a transient state of "complete physical, mental and social well-being," for individuals or societies; that's just not the way life is or could be. Its attractiveness as an ideal is vitiated by its practical impossibility of realization. Worse than that, it positively misleads, for health becomes a goal of such all-consuming importance that it simply begs to be thwarted in its realization. The demands which the word "complete" entail set the stage for the worst false consciousness of all: the demand that life deliver perfection. Practically speaking, this demand has led, in the field of health, to a constant escalation of expectation and requirement, never ending, never satisfied.

What, then, would be a good definition of "health"? I was afraid someone was going to ask me that question. I suggest we settle on the following: "Health is a state of physical well-being." That state need not be "complete," but it must be at least adequate, i.e., without significant impairment of function. It also need not encompass "mental" well-being; one can be healthy yet anxious, well yet depressed. And it surely ought not to encompass "social well-being," except insofar as that well-being will be impaired by the presence of large-scale, serious physical infirmities. Of course my definition is vague, but it would take some very fancy semantic footwork for it to be socially misused; that brat next door could not be called "sick" except when he is running a fever. This definition would not, though, preclude all social use of the language of "pathology" for other than physical disease. The image of a physically well body is a powerful one and, used carefully, it can be suggestive of the kind of wholeness and adequacy of function one might hope to see in other areas of life.

A Theory of Health

Caroline Whitbeck

I. THE INITIAL DEFINITION OF HEALTH

People generally recognize the value of having the psychophysiological capacity to act or respond appropriately in a wide variety of situations. By "appropriately," I mean in a way that is supportive of, or at least minimally destructive to, the agent's goals, projects, aspirations, and so forth.[1] This good, I claim, is the good of health. The absence of any restrictions on a person's goals, projects, and aspirations in this definition is intentional. Even if we consider such unusual goals as the wish to die, we would find that it, too, is more easily and surely attained by a person with a wide range of capabilities.

To understand *fully* the concept of health, we need more than a definition of the term, we need to understand how the concept of health relates to a host of others, including those of disease, injury, fitness, prevention, "health hazard," motivational disturbance, health promotion, and medical care.[2] In what follows, I develop such a philosophical theory of health, and argue that health is a concept of a different order from the concept of disease (and, *mutatis mutandis*, those of injury and impairment). Although medicine, in the broad sense, is the body of knowledge and practice concerned with the prevention of disease and the treatment of disease and injury (and, to some extent impairment), and diseases and

injuries frequently *do* compromise the health of those who bear them, nonetheless, health promotion goes *beyond* the scope of medical care.

II. THE CONCEPT OF HEALTH AND PROPOSALS TO REFORM MEDICINE

If we bear in mind the human interest in health as here defined, we will have a perspective on the institution of medicine, in terms of which its scope and limits may be properly assessed. One implication of the theory outlined here is that *expertise* in medicine, even in the broad sense of medicine as we have defined, will not be relevant to many health decisions. The term "medicine" is used in a number of narrower senses, for example, to mean a discipline distinct from nursing, clinical nutrition, or public health. I refer to this as the "narrow sense." This is the sense in which we speak of "a license to practice medicine." Of course, the term is used still more narrowly to mean the nonsurgical specialties, or just one among these, internal medicine. When I speak of "medicine" without giving further qualification, I mean medicine in the broad sense, that is, all of those disciplines concerned with the treatment and prevention of disease and injury.

A number of recent proposals to change the emphasis or practice of medi-

---

C. Whitbeck, "A Theory of Health," in A.L. Caplan, H.T. Engelhardt, Jr. and J.J. McCartney, eds., *Concepts of Health and Disease: Interdisciplinary Perspectives* (Reading, Mass.: Addison-Wesley Publishing Co., 1981) pp. 611-626.

cine in both the broad and narrow sense of "medicine," have been couched in terms of "health." Although many of these proposed changes have merit, overuse of the term "health" has created new confusions about what health is. Among these proposed changes has been one to integrate a concern for prevention back into medicine in the narrow sense. Thus physicians are encouraged to help people recognize behavior that increases their risk of future disease and injury, by using some instrument like the Health Hazard Appraisal List. Unfortunately the new emphasis on recognizing the way in which certain ways of living predispose a person to injury or disease is often phrased as though it concerned health per se, whereas, in fact, it often involves *only* the prevention of disease and injury. (There are additional problems posed by the way in which this valuable re-emphasis on prevention is discussed. For example, the relevant variables are often termed "lifestyle variables" which makes it seem that *most* people have a wide range of choices in these matters, whereas, in fact, only the privileged have such a range of choices.)

Another proposal is one designed to combat the fragmentation of patient care, which has been one of the untoward side effects of the growth of specialty medicine. First nursing and, more recently, other provider groups have explicitly addressed the issue of developing a more comprehensive approach to patient care, because they have recognized that at present medical care often harms in one way while helping in another. Unfortunately, this proposal to make patient care more comprehensive has been phrased in terms of providing "health care." At the same time, greater appreciation of the fact that in developed nations most major illnesses are chronic illnesses, and thus not susceptible to cure, has led to greater attention to finding ways to care

for people whose conditions can only be managed (as opposed to cured). Although such continuing care generally does enhance people's health, it does so only by coping with particular problems.

Until recently, the term "health" was hardly mentioned in medical circles — the term does not even appear in the index of many standard medical texts, such as Beeson and McDermott, *Textbook of Medicine*. Then, the only danger of conceptual confusion regarding health arose from the attempt to define health entirely in terms of medical concepts, such as those of disease and injury. This attempt generated the so-called "negative notion" of health, health as the absence of disease, injury, and impairment. The term "health," however, was only rarely used in this way. Even in such expressions as "restoring the patient to health," "health" often does not mean "the absence of disease." Instead, "restoring the patient to health" merely means restoring the patient to a *premorbid* level of functioning where "premorbid" refers only to *a particular episode* of illness, so that the "health" of the "restored" patient still includes all his or her chronic diseases as well as poor physical condition, neurotic malaise, and so forth.

If there are any clear assets for human beings, health (considered as the psychophysiological capacity to respond appropriately to a wide variety of situations) is one. This evaluation of health accords with the historical one. Those philosophers from Aristotle to Rawls who have believed that there are some "natural goods" for human beings have placed health among those goods. In contrast, it is easy to find conditions that are generally agreed to be cases of disease, injury, or impairment, which could hardly be counted as the loss of a natural good by those who use this category, but, indeed, which under plausible circumstances would *ben-*

efit their bearers. Sterility and cowpox are examples that come quickly to mind. Indeed, as will be argued presently, the concepts of disease and health are value-laden in different respects.

My general thesis is that not only is health something over and above the absence of disease, injury, and impairment, but also that a high degree of health is compatible with some degree of disease, injury, and impairment. Moreover, the relationship between concepts of health and disease is an intimate one: people's interest in health, together with their aversion to pain, is the *origin* of their interest in having the means to prevent and effectively treat disease, injury, and impairment.

In taking the position that the concepts of health and disease are *not* complementary concepts, I differ with Engelhardt, Margolis, Boorse, and most recent writers on this subject, but concur with the ancient writers, for whom medicine and hygiene (the science of health promotion) were different disciplines.[3] To understand the intimate and complex relation between the concepts of health and disease, it is necessary to clarify what is meant by the terms "disease," and "impairment" and to elaborate the respects in which they are value-laden.

III. WAYS IN WHICH CONCEPTS MAY BE VALUE-LADEN

It is sometimes argued that the distinctions drawn in the language of a human community are, largely, the distinctions needed to carry out the projects recognized by that community, and as such, reflect the value commitments of that community. I think that there is something to the view that the distinctions made in a language reflect what the community using that language take to

be important, and to the extent that it is correct, there is a sense in which all general terms are value-laden.[4] The assertion that the concept of health and the concept of disease are value-laden only in this particular sense, could not be an interesting claim about *these* two concepts.

Some terms, such as "discovery," (an act of) "kindness," "hideous," "vicious," "sacred," "blunder," and "worthwhile," are value-laden in a very strong sense: to use these terms is to say that that to which they are applied is good or bad, valuable or worthless, in some way — aesthetically, ethically, religiously, prudentially, epistemically, or hedonistically. Health considered as the psychophysiological ability to act or respond appropriately, is a concept that is value-laden in this very strong sense.

I claim that the concept of disease[5] is value-laden in a third sense, which is distinct both from the very strong sense and from the weak sense in which all general terms may be said to be value-laden. I shall call this intermediary sense "the capability sense" and define it as follows: a concept or term will be said to be value-laden in the capability sense if, and only if, the concept or the definition of the term warrants the conclusion that people have an interest in *being able* to influence things of that type. The failure to recognize this third sense has obscured the understanding of the ways in which terms may be value-laden; the implicit assumption of most examinations of the extent to which concepts are value-laden has been that *either* a term is no more value-laden than the other general terms of a language, *or* it is value-laden in the very strong sense that application of the term implies the judgment that the particular to which it was applied is valuable (or worthless) in some respect.

In particular, people's interest in *being able* to prevent and treat diseases may be inferred from the concept of disease. Indeed, the interest in prevention and treatment is the basis of the distinction between disease processes and other atypical psychophysiological processes.

All human societies have devoted some of their resources to the development of medicinal or healing arts. This allocation represented the society's attempt to acquire these desired capabilities. Yet notice that, according to what I have argued, to say that a *particular* psychophysiological process is a case of disease is to say only that it is an instance of a kind of psychophysiological process that one wishes *to be able* to prevent or to treat effectively, not that the particular *case* of a disease itself is necessarily a misfortune for the bearer and hence necessarily something that is in the bearer's interest to have treated. The impairment, sterility, is one which people frequently go to some trouble and expense to acquire through medical intervention. The same was true of cases of cowpox before the development of smallpox vaccine. These examples of disease and impairment, which are commonly of net benefit to their bearer, together with the desirability of *being able* to prevent or treat diseases, shows that the concept is value-laden in what I have called, "the capability sense," rather than being value-laden in the very strong sense. The concepts of food, shelter, flood, and infestation are all capability-valued. One generally wishes *to be able* to produce or maintain a supply of food or shelter and *to be able* to prevent or eliminate infestations and floods, but on a given occasion it may not be in anyone's interest to produce or possess more food or shelter or to prevent or eliminate every infestation or flood.

Consider two identical physiological processes, one of which is counted as the early stages of a disease, and the other of which is regarded as a normal reaction to a

vaccination. This disparity casts doubt on any attempt to define "disease" purely in terms of physiological functioning, and hence, on the claim that disease is value-laden only to the same extent as biological concepts.

The definition of *disease* that I have offered is that diseases are, first of all, psychophysiological processes; second, they compromise the ability to do what people commonly want and expect to be able to do; third, they are not necessary in order to do what people commonly want to be able to do; fourth, they are either statistically abnormal in those at risk or there is some other basis for a reasonable hope of finding means to effectively treat or prevent them.[6]

According to these criteria, what qualifies as a disease is relative to a societal context insofar as what people are understood as wanting to do is relative to societal context. Statistical abnormality in those at risk (worldwide), however, is *independent* of societal context. Therefore, a psychophysiological process may qualify as a disease even if a society fails to *recognize* its presence because of its near ubiquity in those at risk in that society. The last three characteristics provide the basis for the interest in *being able to do something about* processes of this sort. It is the desirability of *being able to do something about things* of this sort which is the valuational component of terms like "disease," "food," or "flood."

The value of having a capability with respect to things of some type does not presume *anything* about the worth of particular things of that type. It is therefore as misleading to say that calling something a case of disease is to assert a prima facie case for preventing or eliminating it, as it is to say that calling an item "food" is to make a prima facie case that we want to produce or provide it.

IV. THE AGENT AND THE PATIENT

Health is frequently pursued through a variety of intermediary goals. One is the prevention and termination of particular processes and states that compromise health. Sometimes the way diseases compromise health is taken to be so important that the person whose health is at stake is thought of as an actual or potential "patient," that is, one who bears, or is *afflicted* with, or *suffers* from the process or condition in question. The passivity that is central to the concept of a "patient" is the person's passivity vis-à-vis the disease. (Passivity of the patient in the treatment process or as the client of the health professionals may or may not also exist as part of the social role of being a patient.) Notice that in talking about people's health, and not just the actual or potential diseases that may compromise that health, it is misleading to start by viewing these persons as actual or potential patients or bearers of disease.

The notion of health as the capacity to act or respond appropriately explicates the positive conception of health, which has been particularly evident in the practice of the self-help and mutual aid movements of this century and the last. It is closely connected with the idea of wholeness, rather than with a high level of functioning in some isolated areas or in some limited respects. Deriving from "hale," which means whole, health, in the positive sense, connotes wholeness of a person. Wholeness of a person is more than the wholeness of an organism, although the wholeness of the organism contributes to the health or wholeness of the person. This sense of wholeness of a person implies the ability to engage in distinctively human activities. I will use the term "capabilities" hereafter to mean the ability to engage in activities that are characteristically intentional

actions. In contrast, the term "capacity" is used for biological functioning, whether of organisms (as respiratory capacity) or of parts of organisms such as organs or cells (as the heart's capacity to pump blood).

To assess people's health, one must take into account their capabilities and not merely their biological capacities. Therefore, the notion of health or wholeness is closely associated with the notions of autonomy, with the ability to act to achieve one's purposes, and with the ability to live as a member of a human community. Accordingly, health, rather than being something that happens or fails to happen to a person in the way that diseases and injuries do, is the ability to act or participate autonomously and effectively in a wide range of activities. The term "wholeness" should not, however, suggest that there exists an upper limit, a state of optimum health. Such a suggestion would be foreign to the account given here since, presumably, people can always increase their ability to act appropriately in *some* situations. The absence of an upper limit on health does not make that concept any more obscure than concepts such as wealth, which also have no upper limit.

I will not address here the question of just what are the components of human life, because the theory of health that I am advancing does not require specification of these components. The best method is to begin by accepting an account of human life that is as broad as possible, since if some human activity is a mistaken, or stupid, or sloppy, or naive way of undertaking some other, quite different, human activity, this will eventually become clear as the two enterprises are examined further. However, if one starts from an assumption that some activity is just a mistaken way of doing something else and it turns out not to be, there will never be an opportunity to discover the error.[7]

It may be objected that some goals are themselves irrational and thus that it is odd to include such goals among those that the actions of a healthy person would contribute to attaining. To the extent that we believe that some goal is itself peculiar, however, or even irrational, we are inclined to say that it is something else that the person "really wants." The peculiar goal is only a means to some other end, and that if the further end were attained, the person would be satisfied and abandon the peculiar one. Thus if someone asserted that he or she wished to become miserable, one would assume either that this was only a means to some end, such as being so tranquil or resigned as to be beyond repulsion or attraction, or that this was an attempt to expiate some guilt, and if the guilt were lifted in some other way, the person would be satisfied. Nothing in this argument turns on a specification of the goals that are thought to be irrational or peculiar. The point is only that if we are willing to apply the term "irrational" to a goal, we are also inclined to say that the goal is only a means to some further end which we may regard as rational. Therefore, it should not seem paradoxical to define health in terms of a person's ability to act or respond in a way that is supportive of the person's goals, projects, and aspirations.

The notion of health expounded here, while much broader than the notion of a mere absence of disease, is not as broad as the much criticized definition of the World Health Organization: "the state of complete physical, mental and social well-being and not merely the absence of disease or infirmity." By this definition, all elements of social well-being, including wealth, legal capacity, political power, and social prestige, are a *part* of health. Although there are important *causal* connections between the components of social well-being and health (for example, people with social advantages do tend to have less disease), people do not become healthier just by becoming wealthier or by gaining the right to vote. Thus,

wealth, legal capacity, political power, and social prestige should *not* be considered a part of health, even if possession of them increases the likelihood that people will be healthier or less subject to disease.

Health as the ability to act or respond appropriately in a variety of situations requires more than many individual human capabilities and functional capacities. This conception requires the integration of such capabilities and capacities so that each is exercised in ways that serve the interests of the person in question. In particular, the psychophysiological changes that constitute a stress response will serve a person's interests in some situations but, in others, will simply be painful and taxing. (Contrast the situation in which a stress response permits someone to lift a heavy object that has fallen on someone else, with another situation in which the person undergoes these changes but no physical action is required and the person experiences the changes as anxiety and disturbed sleep.) Much more could be said about the compatibility or incompatibility of a person's projects and goals, and thus about the ease or difficulty with which appropriateness can be assessed in a particular case. But we have at least some idea of what it is to function or act in an appropriate way. We may then understand the claim that health is the capacity for a high level of integrated psychophysiological functioning, which enables the agent to act or respond to situations in a way that promotes the agent's projects and goals (and that promotes the availability of a wide range of responses in the future).

The failure of some writers on the concept of health to recognize the integration of functioning that characterizes health has led them to assume that an increase in health, in any positive sense of health, would be identical with an increase in isolated abilities, specifically *athletic* abilities. Such an approach to positive health predictably runs afoul of the fact that the development of a physique to perform some particular athletic feat with unusual excellence generally interferes with developing the physique to perform some *other* feat. The lesson to be learned from this fact is not that health cannot be conceived positively, but rather that an increase in health should not be confused with an increase in isolated capabilities and capacities. Although an increase in health cannot be identified with an increase in *isolated* capabilities, it is nonetheless possible to specify some significant components of health.

V. SIGNIFICANT COMPONENTS OF HEALTH

Consider the notion of physical fitness. In addition to being a significant component of health (so that, other things being equal, a more physically fit person is healthier, that is, is more able to respond appropriately in a wide range of situations), physical fitness is a concept that resembles the concept of health. That is, it is best characterized in general terms, which make no mention of the excellence with which a person performs specific feats. This may come as a surprise to those who measure fitness in terms of, say, the ability to run laps, and who confuse the concept of fitness with the procedure for measuring it. A high level of physical fitness is usually characterized as a state in which there is good muscle tone and improved circulation, bones are less brittle, and the person has greater cardiac reserve. It may be evident that one result of these changes, in addition to an increase in a variety of athletic abilities, is an increase in the capacity to withstand a wide range of insults with a minimum of injury or to retard or forestall the development of a wide range of diseases. The consequence that

being healthy (or having a high level of fitness) makes a person less liable to disease and injury is not an accidental feature of the concept of health that I have proposed. Since acting or responding in a way that minimizes disease and injury (that prevents its occurrence *or* lessens its severity) is a way of responding that generally promotes people's goals and projects, *any psychophysiological state* that makes one better able to ward off a wide variety of diseases and injury would for that reason be considered a significant component of health.

It is important to highlight two points implicit in what has just been said. First, it is *not* suggested that a significant component of health, such as fitness, is itself health. Quite to the contrary, the conception of health as a wholeness of the agent entails the *integration* of capabilities and capacities. Knowing that one person is more fit than another person does not by itself tell us which is healthier. Second, a decreased susceptibility to a specific disease, or injury, or to a narrow subclass of either, is not a significant component of health. Specific immunity is just that. Although immunity to a disease (say, measles) is useful in diminishing one's chance of becoming a patient, the capacity to respond in a desirable way only when exposed to measles virus is too specific to be a significant component of health in my theory. People who have lower risk of some specific type of injury may well have a greater life expectancy, but it is misleading to call them healthier. Such persons are only more likely to be healthy in the future than persons with greater risks. One may have increased risks for many reasons other than that of not being very healthy. For example, one may have a dangerous job. It is, therefore, misleading to use the Health Hazard Appraisal List in a way that puts not wearing seat belts on a par with smoking as an indication of being "less healthy," since smoking compromises health by compromising lung capacity *in addition* to increasing the risk of other diseases. Primary prevention, which increases safety, should be distinguished from primary prevention through promotion of health, since only the latter entails a change in psychophysiological state.

The distinction between a significant component of health, like fitness, and health itself, is important in other respects. If other things are equal, an increase in one significant component of health may make one healthier. But other things are rarely equal, and one can readily imagine a case in which a physically fit person would be less healthy than one who was out of condition. Suppose that the first was so ridden by phobias and neuroses that, in many situations, the most appropriate responses would be blocked by an anxiety reaction. Compared to such a person, a less neurotic but out-of-condition individual would be better able to respond in most situations, regardless of whether we view neuroses as disease. Suppose, on the other hand, that a person with a high level of one or more significant components of health (that is, being physically fit, or being aware of her or his emotions, or having a realistic view of both and of him/herself and others, or being able to handle stressful situations well), has a sprained finger or acne. It seems clear that such a person would be healthier than another person who was out of condition, out of touch with feelings, had an unrealistic view of people, or stayed in a state of high anxiety long after a stressful situation, but had no detectable disease or injury.

These possibilities illustrate again the crucial point that not only is health something over and above the absence of disease, but a high level of health may be compatible with some degree of disease, injury, and impairment. One reason for choosing *not* to seek treatment or not following recommended treatment for some disease, injury, or impairment would be

that undergoing the treatment excessively undermined the person's exercise of his or her capacities and capabilities, that is, the treatment would be detrimental to the person's health. This might occur not only in cases in which the treatment carried risk of further disease and injury, but in cases in which the treatment caused disruption of health maintenance routines, or resulted in loss of social supports (for example, because of travel required) or in other ways undermined the person's ability to deal with stress. Notice that refusal of treatment for health reasons contrasts with the refusal of treatment for economic or social reasons, although refusal of recommended treatment (often unfortunately called "noncompliance") for reasons such as these may also be a sensible decision.

VI. THE RELATION BETWEEN THE CONCEPTS OF HEALTH AND HAPPINESS

To recapitulate, health is a person's psychophysiological capacity to act or respond appropriately (in a way that is supportive of the person's goals, projects, and aspirations) in a wide variety of situations. Health encompasses certain significant components: among them, maintaining physical fitness, having a generally realistic view of situations, and having the ability to discharge negative feelings. The *net* effect of having a disease is frequently, although not invariably, to undermine a person's health. The institution of medicine is society's collective attempt to develop the means of preventing and treating conditions that are likely to undermine health.

The foregoing survey of the scope of the concept of health invites further statement about its limits. (The demarcation of health from such aspects of social well-being as wealth, social status, and legal capacity has already been discussed.) The distinction between health and happiness is particularly apropos. I argue that, to be happy, a person needs to be able to act in ways that serve *many goals, aspirations, and projects simultaneously*. The opportunity to do this is a function of at least four things: the range and relative importance of a person's goals, aspirations, and projects; the person's health (as previously characterized); the person's creativity; and the person's access to resources of all types (social, economic, and so forth). To consider creativity (as opposed to originality) as a significant component of health is consistent, at least, with the account of health we have given, although it is not entailed by it. The range and relative importance of a person's goals, aspirations, and projects, as well as a person's access to resources, however, are excluded from health in the presented theory. This demarcation accords with the intuition that having a diversity of interests, say, promoting social justice, pursuing truth, building close friendships, and living close to nature, can make it difficult to pursue all one's goals simultaneously, and can create unhappiness, yet does not compromise health. This demarcation is also consistent with the distinction between health and other social goods.

VII. CONDITIONS OF SELF-ALIENATION OR ALIENATED-SELF CONDITIONS

Other sorts of conditions, in *addition* to those of disease, injury, and impairment, *compromise a person's* ability to act or respond appropriately, but yet are not diseases, injuries, or impairments. These I call conditions of self-alienation, which may be classified into three or four general types.

The first of them is what Thalberg has called "motivational disturbance," namely, a condition in which a person has thoughts, feelings, or attitudes, or expresses types of behavior that are experienced as being at odds with his or her beliefs, basic attitudes, and habits. The second is akrasia or "weakness of will," a situation in which the person fails to act as he or she has resolved to act. (Akrasia may or may not have motivational disturbance admixed in a given case.) The third is a self-deception, which has been most aptly characterized by Fingerette as the condition in which people systematically avoid avowing some aspect of their engagements in the world. (The cardinal sign of avowing is the act of spontaneously spelling out that aspect of the engagement to oneself or others.) Fourth is what I will call remorse/self-hatred, which encompasses everything from rejection and de-identification with an aspect of the self (remorse) to rejection of the self in its entirety or at least in its central aspects (self-hatred).

Although it is undoubtedly evident that many of the conditions that I have characterized here as conditions of self-alienation would be classified as neuroses from the point of view of psychoanalytically oriented psychotherapy, I wish to leave open the question of whether, and to what extent, psychoanalytic nosology is correct and, in particular, whether some of what are now termed neuroses may turn out to be diseases (like toxic psychoses[8]) or impairments (like mental retardation), whereas others will be self-alienation problems as defined here. Psychiatric nosology is fluid and is likely to remain so for the foreseeable future.

These conditions are not discussed in detail here, but several points about them should be noted. First, they are value-laden in the capability sense, that is, in the way that medical conditions (diseases, injuries, and impairments) are. Furthermore, alienated-self problems frequently, but not invariably, compromise health. In particular, self-deception might enable a person to behave appropriately under circumstances that were too painful to acknowledge immediately, and hence *contribute* to health in this instance. Remorse might be necessary for rapid change and growth, and hence could contribute to integrated development.

Second, in the many societies the institutions that address these problems most directly have been religious, even where medicine and religion have been separated. This latter point may be important to make since we may be so struck by the popularity in our own culture of psychoanalysis or other secular approaches, such as EST, which have dealt with these problems, that we may lose sight of other conceptions that historically have dealt with the same phenomena. Commonly, the adherents of one practice claim that alternative practices actually increase self-alienation problems in general, and self-deception in particular, but I will not examine those controversies here.

The third point about these conditions is that, although they may predispose a person to medical problems or may frequently be aggravated by medical problems, this is no reason to regard them as medical problems. In the absence of evidence that they ought to be considered diseases, injuries, or impairments, we have no reason to think that expertise in medicine will be relevant to preventing or treating these conditions. This is not to say that *the presence* of such conditions may be ignored by medical personnel in the course of treating medical problems. In view of their causal connections to medical problems, they need to be *taken into account* in devising any plan for *comprehensive* medical care, even if they cannot be eliminated by medical intervention. In this respect, having an alienated-self condition is like having low income, or undergoing a grief reaction.

The subject of alienated-self conditions raises the question of agent competence in deciding what actions will promote health. Although diseases, injuries, and impairment *can* make people incompetent (such as when a person is delirious due to fever, or acutely psychotic due to a brain tumor or due to the ingestion of toxic substances, or unconscious due to a concussion of the brain), these situations are relatively easy to recognize. Furthermore, the effects of disease are more often less severe, and make the person more vulnerable and more in need of support, rather than incompetent. Self-alienation, however, creates a different sort of problem in that, when severe, it does not make the person incapable of acting in any coherent way at all, but may distort a person's decisions so that they fail to reflect the person's (integrated) self-interest. The burden of proof must be on the side of those who say that a particular person is so self-alienated as to be unable to make decisions that promote her or his own health.

Suppose, however, that a person is so self-alienated as to choose against his or her own interests. Suppose, for example, that a person's self-hatred is so great that he or she elects to have a succession of mutilating surgical procedures that are not warranted by evidence of grave health risks. In such a case, both medical practitioners as well as those who care about the person, might have a moral duty to try to dissuade the person from the operations. Such cases, though, are relatively rare. Since numerous studies show that the various (lay and professional) forms of psychotherapy have about the same recovery rate, there is no reason to think that self-alienation is not at least as amenable to self-care and mutual aid approaches as it is to medically and nonmedically oriented professional psychotherapies (although this will depend on the exact nature of the self-alienation). Certainly, the practice of self-care and mutual aid is especially conducive to enhanced self-esteem and reduced self-hatred.

VIII. THE ROLE OF MEDICINE IN HEALTH PROMOTION

Expertise in medicine — skill in the prevention of disease and the treatment of disease and injury — is not sufficient to make many decisions concerning health. What then is the role of medicine in health promotion? Because diseases and injuries frequently do compromise health, the ability to prevent disease and injury is an important component in an individual's or a society's attempts to promote people's health. However, I submit that the paradigm instance in which one person appropriately makes decisions about the promotion of another's health is not the situation in which a medical practitioner (nurse, physician, physical therapist) makes decisions about care of patients, but rather is the situation in which a parent reaches a decision on the care of a young child. Typically the parent considers such possible consequences of a course of action, as how it will affect the child's self-esteem, body awareness, trust of adults, relation to peers, and general comfort, as well as whether it will prevent disease or facilitate recovery from it. Now I am not suggesting that it would be appropriate for a practitioner, or any one else, to make decisions for another in the way in which the parent does for a child. Indeed, as I have argued, the person whose health is in question is in the best position to be aware of all of the factors involved. When that person is unconscious or otherwise incompetent to do so, those closest to the person and who care about him or her are in the best position to be aware of all of the factors that bear on their overall health. Of course, the person may not have anyone who cares about him or her deeply, in which case, there will be no good proxy to make the decision.

In some respects, consulting a medical practitioner is like consulting an architect: both have information about what can be done to achieve the ends of the client, what future options will be foreclosed by taking a given course of action, and the likely time and expense required for each option. The analogy breaks down, however, when the patient is significantly affected by fear, pain, or confusion due to the threat of disease or death or due to disease itself or to diagnostic and treatment procedures. Furthermore, those who care about the sick person may also be distraught. People generally are not fully articulate about all of the important factors in their lives, and those who are sick and stressed are still less so. Thus patients who are distraught cannot be expected to transfer all of the necessary information to a practitioner. Practitioners, therefore, need the skills to provide clients with support and an opportunity to discharge their pain and distress, so that they can make the momentous and often painful decisions with which they are faced. It is only when practitioners are themselves able to do this, or see that it is adequately done by others, that medical knowledge will be correctly applied, that is, applied in a way that promotes and enhances people's health.

IX. SUMMARY OF THE ARGUMENT

I might have called this chapter "a theory of health as the context for an adequate understanding of medicine," were that title not so long and awkward, since it gives a more precise specification of the subject. I began by observing that people generally recognize the value of having the psychophysiological capacity to act or respond appropriately in a wide variety of situations and claimed that this good is the good of health. I examined the ways in which the term "health" has been used in recent years, in order to unravel some of the confusions concerning it. I argued that whereas the term "health" is properly understood to be value-laden in the very strong sense, that is, to say something is healthy or that it promotes health, is to give a reason for saying that it is good. In contrast, the term "disease" is value-laden in a distinct and hitherto unrecognized sense, that is, when we apply it to a psychophysiological process, we judge that the process is one that would be good (for people) to *be able* to prevent or treat effectively. The concepts of health and disease are not complementary concepts, therefore, but turn out to be concepts of different orders. This point is brought out further by the contrast between disease as something that befalls its bearer and health as the integrated ability to engage effectively in a wide range of activities.

Although it is important to understand the integrated character of a high state of health, significant components of health can be identified. Among these are physical fitness, having a realistic view of oneself and others, and having the ability to handle stressful situations. Although the concept of health is much more than the absence of disease, and indeed a high level of health is compatible with having some disease, health contrasts both with other aspects of social well-being and with happiness. In addition to medical conditions, there is another class of conditions that often compromise health, which I call "self-alienation conditions." Because of the importance of the consideration of these and other factors that bear on a person's health and lie outside of the scope of medical expertise, decisions about the appropriateness of some medical intervention, that is, decisions about whether that intervention is likely to produce a net increase or enhancement in a person's health, cannot be decided on the basis of medical expertise alone. I argue that usually these are best made by the person whose health is at stake.

NOTES

I am most grateful to the Committee on the Status of Women of the American Philosophical Association for the invitation to present an earlier version of this paper at the Eastern Division Meetings in December 1977, to the late Jane English and other attendees and participants at that session for their comments and criticisms, and to the many people who have given me suggestions since that time, especially James Speer, Marilyn Thompson, Maradee Davis, Arthur Caplan, Edmund Erde, Joseph Margolis, and Christopher Boorse.

1. If one is able to respond appropriately, of course, one is also *able* to respond inappropriately.

2. In my discussion of medicine and medical concepts, such as the concept of disease, I assume to some extent the perspective of Western allopathic medical science. Specifically, I assume that medical science is generally correct in believing that certain sorts of things exist in nature: disease entities, microbes, cells, malignant cells, DNA, and so on. I do not assume, however, that every customary application of those concepts is correct. Thus, if it were true that pregnancy is frequently construed as a disease in medical theory and practice, I would not take that empirical fact about the explicit and implicit ascription of disease status as sufficient warrant to decide that pregnancy is a disease. Furthermore, although I do not assume anything about the existence or nonexistence of nat-

ural entities answering to the description of the theoretical terms in nonallo-pathic medicine, theoretical notions such as "chi," I accept on its own merits any evidence for the efficacy of practices, like acupuncture, which are explained in terms of notions like "chi" in those nonallopathic traditions.

3. Today one scarcely hears "hygiene" used to mean the promotion of health except in such contexts as the "Natural Hygiene Movement." The term "hygienic" (and its cognate, "sanitary") have lost their connection with health and have come to mean merely clean (although modern usage dictionaries do not seem to have caught on to this fact). Sometimes, the cleanliness involved has at least a pro-phylactic function, as is the case with dental hygiene, but often "hygiene," and "san-itary" mean only clean, that is, free from matter that is regarded as ugly or taboo, but in no way is the meaning related to health or the prevention or treatment of disease. This is aptly illustrated by the application of the term "sanitary nap-kin" to a product which, like a table napkin, merely serves to keep clothes clean.

4. It is surprising how often people will speak as though value commitments are "subjective" in the pejorative sense of being preferences which may be based as easily on individual or collective whim as on considered judgment. Since one hears this from nonphilosophers as often as from philosophers, it is more than the legacy of the philosophical thesis of emotivism. However, since many, if not most, of the projects recognized in a human community are requisite for the survival of the community in its present form, the community's interest in these projects can hardly be viewed as capricious.

5. From here on when I speak of disease my remarks apply, *mutatis mutandis,* to injury and impairment as well. I take the latter concepts to be value-laden in the same way as those of disease. What is required to fulfill the *mutatis mutandis* clause is spelled out in my "Four Basic Concepts of Medical Science," *PSA 1978,* vol. 1, pp. 210–222. There I also delineate the confusions that may arise if the dif-ferences between disease, injuries, impairments, and symptoms are not recog-nized. The distinctions between these concepts, however, are not important for the present discussion.

6. I have explained and argued for this definition in "Four Basic Concepts of Medical Science" in *PSA 1978*, vol. 1, pp. 210–222.

7. This way of putting the matter assumes that any activity to which people have devoted a good deal of time and effort is, at worst, a mistaken way of doing something else, and not *just* a mistake.

8. I have argued elsewhere that it is unlikely that the separation of organic or somatic factors from psychosocial factors in the determination of the etiology of diseases, or the etiology of self-alienation, can be done so clearly and unequiv-ocally that there will be any generally useful distinction to be marked by calling some diseases "mental" and others "physical," or "somatic."

REFERENCE

Whitbeck, Caroline. "Four Basic Concepts of Medical Science." *PSA 1978,* 1 (1978):210–222.

CHAPTER 3
THE RIGHT TO HEALTH CARE

INTRODUCTION

When it comes to health care, the belief of most Canadians can be summed up in three words: *universality*, *equality* and *portability*. That is to say, most Canadians believe that *everyone* has a right to health care. Access to appropriate health care should not depend on the condition of the individual or on her or his ability to pay, but should be open to everyone on an equitable basis. This is sometimes also expressed by saying that the majority of Canadians believe that health care should be a socially insured service.

Furthermore, most Canadians also believe that everyone has the right to the *same level* of service, no matter what province they are in.

Finally, most Canadians believe that even though the insurance for these services is a provincial matter, it should be *portable*, so that no matter in what province the individual happens to find her- or himself, the services will be paid for.

Canadians have not always felt this way. Until the 1930s, they agreed with the citizens of most other countries that health care is a commodity like all others, and that those who could not afford to pay for it did not have a right to it. However, the experiences of the depression of the 1930s fostered a gradual change in this perspective, and by the 1940s, the outlook had changed fundamentally. First in Saskatchewan and then in other provinces, the now-prevailing attitude became politically dominant. It led to the establishment of universal health and hospital insurance in Saskatchewan in 1945[1] and successively in other provinces. It was reflected in the Hall Report of 1964 and in the Lalonde Report of 1974, and ultimately led to the Canada Health Act of 1984, which was proclaimed in 1985. Today, all Canadian provinces and territories have a universal health care system, where physicians and hospitals provide services according to province-wide schedules, and where only certain services have to be paid for by patients themselves.[2]

Furthermore, not all countries share the current Canadian perspective; and even those who accept the general principles do not all share the conviction to the same degree. For instance, although the U.K. accepts the general principle of social responsibility for health care, it also believes that society does not have an obligation to provide all medically possible, or even all medically indicated, services to all of its citizens. It therefore allows the growth of private clinics and private hospitals for those who are able to pay.

Closer to home, the U.S. has traditionally maintained that health care is a service like all other services, and that it should therefore be available only to those who can pay for it. While in recent years the U.S. government has moved towards a more socially responsible perspective by establishing Medicare and Medicaid programs, the fact remains that there are over 35 million uninsured people in the U.S. who have either inadequate access to health care, or none at all.[3]

John Iglehart provides a U.S. perspective of the Canada Health Act and the health care system based on it. He compares and contrasts it with the U.S. and the U.K. approaches. He argues that while Canada's commitment to universal health care is something of which Canada can be "justifiably proud," the system as a whole is threatened by rising costs. In the future — so he argues — Canada cannot continue to fund the system solely by tax dollars. Other sources of funding — and other methods of funding — may have to be explored. Further, he suggests that the attempts to deal with this problem have been made more difficult by the fact that while health care is a provincial responsibility, a lot of the funding comes from the federal government, which is steadily reducing its transfer payments to the provinces in that regard. He suggests that any attempt to retain the provincial health care plans, "which are admired throughout the world," may well be threatened unless a more meaningful dialogue is instituted between the two levels of government.

Benjamin Freedman and Françoise Baylis approach the Canadian health care system from the perspective of Canadians who are committed to the continued existence of socialized medicine as a matter of ethical conviction. Nevertheless, they point out that there are certain assumptions that underlie the establishment of a socialized health care system. In their minds, the most notable of these is that payment in government-funded health insurance programs should be limited only to those procedures that are medically necessary. They argue that such an approach results in serious inequities and in a dislocated service delivery.

NOTES

1. It was enacted in the Saskatchewan Hospitalization Act, 1946, which followed the Health Services Act of 1945. The program outlined in this legislation did not become fully operative until an agreement was reached with the College of Physicians and Surgeons of Saskatchewan, with the so-called Saskatoon

Agreement of 1962. See also Mr. Justice Emmett Hall, *Report of the Royal Commission on Health Services* (Ottawa: Queen's Printer, 1964) for a discussion of the evolution of health services in Canada.

2. The idea of equitable access, which underlies the Canada Health Act, is currently under threat because of the Government Expenditures Restraint Act (1990, effecitve 1991). It effectively removes federal transfer payments, and especially established program financing (EPF), of which health care is one of the most important. The effect of this Act is that it will become impossible for the poorer Canadian provinces to provide the same degree of health care services to their residents as the richer provinces.

3. President's Commission for the Study of Ethical Problems in Medicine and Biomedical and Behavioral Research, *Securing Access to Health Care: A Report on the Ethical Implications of Differences in the Availability of Health Services* (U.S. Government Printing Office: Washington D.C., 1983), 3 vols.

Canada Health Act

Program Criteria

Program criteria

7. In order that a province may qualify for a full cash contribution referred to in section 5 for a fiscal year, the health care insurance plan of the province must, throughout the fiscal year, satisfy the criteria described in sections 8 to 12 respecting the following matters:

    (a) public administration;

    (b) comprehensiveness;

    (c) universality;

    (d) portability; and

    (e) accessibility. 1984, c. 6, s. 7.

Public administration

8. (1) In order to satisfy the criterion respecting public administration,

    (a) the health care insurance plan of a province must be administered and operated on a non-profit basis by a public authority appointed or designated by the government of the province;

    (b) the public authority must be responsible to the provincial government for that administration and operation; and

    (c) the public authority must be subject to audit of its accounts and financial transactions by such authority as is charged by law with the audit of the accounts of the province.

Designation of agency permitted

(2) The criterion respecting public administration is not contravened by reason only that the public authority referred to in subsection (1) has the power to designate any agency

    (a) to receive on its behalf any amounts payable under the provincial health care insurance plan; or *(b)* to carry out on its behalf any responsibility in connection with the receipt or payment of accounts rendered for insured health services, if it is a condition of the designation that all those accounts are subject to assessment and approval by the public authority and that the public authority shall determine the amounts to be paid in respect thereof. 1984, c. 6, s. 8.

Comprehensiveness 9. In order to satisfy the criterion respecting comprehensiveness, the health care insurance plan of a province must insure all insured health services provided by hospitals, medical practitioners or dentists, and where the law of the province so permits, similar or additional services rendered by other health care practitioners. 1984, c. 6, s. 9.

Universality 10. In order to satisfy the criterion respecting universality, the health care insurance plan of a province must entitle one hundred per cent of the insured persons of the province to the insured health services provided for by the plan on uniform terms and conditions. 1984, c. 6, s. 10.

Portability 11. (1) In order to satisfy the criterion respecting portability, the health care insurance plan of a province

(a) must not impose any minimum period of residence in the province, or waiting period, in excess of three months before res-

idents of the province are eligible for or entitled to insured health services;

(b) must provide for and be administered and operated so as to provide for the payment of amounts for the cost of insured health services provided to insured persons while temporarily absent from the province on the basis that

(i) where the insured health services are provided in Canada, payment for health services is at the rate that is approved by the health care insurance plan of the province in which the services are provided, unless the provinces concerned agree to apportion the cost between them in a different manner, or

(ii) where the insured health services are provided out of Canada, payment is made on the basis of the amount that would have been paid by the province for similar services rendered in the province, with due regard, in the case of hospital services, to the size of the hospital, standards of service and other relevant factors; and

(c) must provide for and be administered and operated so as to provide for the payment, during any minimum period of residence, or any waiting period, imposed by

the health care insurance plan of another province, of the cost of insured health services provided to persons who have ceased to be insured persons by reason of having become residents of that other province, on the same basis as though they had not ceased to be residents of the province.

Requirement for consent for elective insured health services permitted

(2) The criterion respecting portability is not contravened by a requirement of a provincial health care insurance plan that the prior consent of the public authority that administers and operates the plan must be obtained for elective insured health services provided to a resident of the province while temporarily absent from the province if the services in question were available on a substantially similar basis in the province.

Definition of "elective insured health services"

(3) For the purpose of subsection (2), "elective insured health services" means insured health services other than services that are provided in an emergency or in any other circumstance in which medical care is required without delay. 1984, c. 6, s. 11.

Accessibility

12. (1) In order to satisfy the criterion respecting accessibility, the health care insurance plan of a province

(a) must provide for insured health services on uniform terms and conditions and on a basis that does not impede or preclude, either directly or indirectly whether by charges made to insured

persons or otherwise, reasonable access to those services by insured persons;

(b) must provide for payment for insured health services in accordance with a tariff or system of payment authorized by the law of the province;

(c) must provide for reasonable compensation for all insured health services rendered by medical practitioners or dentists; and

(d) must provide for the payment of amounts to hospitals, including hospitals owned or operated by Canada, in respect of the cost of insured health services.

Reasonable compensation

(2) In respect of any province in which extrabilling is not permitted, paragraph (1)(c) shall be deemed to be complied with if the province has chosen to enter into, and has entered into, an agreement with the medical practitioners and dentists of the province that provides

(a) for negotiations relating to compensation for insured health services between the province and provincial organizations that represent practising medical practitioners or dentists in the province;

(b) for the settlement of disputes relating to compensation through, at the option of the appropriate provincial organizations referred to in paragraph (a), conciliation or binding arbitration by a panel that is equally representative of the provincial organizations and the province and that has an independent chairman; and

(c) that a decision of a panel referred to in paragraph *(b)* may not be altered except by an Act of the legislature of the province. 1984, c. 6, s. 12.

Conditions for Cash Contributions or Payments

Conditions   13. In order that a province may qualify for a full cash contribution referred to in section 5 or payment of the full amount referred to in section 6 for a fiscal year, the government of the province

(a) shall, at the times and in the manner prescribed by the regulations, provide the Minister with such information, of a type prescribed by the regulations, as the Minister may reasonably require for the purposes of this Act; and

(b) shall give recognition to the contributions and payments by Canada under this Act in any public documents, or in any advertising or promotional material, relating to insured health services and extended health care services in the province. 1984, c. 6, s. 13.

Defaults

Referral to Governor in Council consultation process   14. (1) Subject to subsection (3), where the Minister, after consultation in accordance with subsection (2) with the minister responsible for health care in a province, is of the opinion that

(a) the health care insurance plan of the province does not or has ceased to satisfy any one of the criteria described in sections 8 to 12, or

(b) the province has failed to comply with any condition set out in section 13,

and the province has not given an undertaking satisfactory to the Minister to remedy the default within a period that the Minister considers reasonable, the Minister shall refer the matter to the Governor in Council.

(2) Before referring a matter to the Governor in Council under subsection (1) in respect of a province, the Minister shall

(a) send by registered mail to the minister responsible for health care in the province a notice of concern with respect to any problem foreseen;

(b) seek any additional information available from the province with respect to the problem through bilateral discussions, and make a report to the province within ninety days after sending the notice of concern; and

(c) if requested by the province, meet within a reasonable period of time to discuss the report.

Where no consultation can be achieved   (3) The Minister may act without consultation under subsection (1) if the Minister is of the opinion that a sufficient time has expired after reasonable efforts to achieve consultation and that consultation will not be achieved. 1984, c. 6, s. 14.

Order reducing or withholding contribution

15. (1) Where, on the referral of a matter under section 14, the Governor in Council is of the opinion that the health care insurance plan of a province does not or has ceased to satisfy any one of the criteria described in sections 8 to 12 or that a province has failed to comply with any condition set out in section 13, the Governor in Council may, by order,

(a) direct that any cash contribution or amount payable to that province for a fiscal year be reduced, in respect of each default, by an amount that the Governor in Council considers to be appropriate, having regard to the gravity of the default; or

(b) where the Governor in Council considers it appropriate, direct that the whole of any cash contribution or amount payable to that province for a fiscal year be withheld.

Amending orders

(2) The Governor in Council may, by order, repeal or amend any order made under subsection (1) where the Governor in Council is of the opinion that the repeal or amendment is warranted in the circumstances.

Notice of order

(3) A copy of each order made under this section together with a statement of any findings on which the order was based shall be sent forthwith by registered mail to the government of the province concerned and the Minister shall cause the order and statement to be laid before each House of Parliament on any of the first fifteen days on which that House is sitting after the order is made.

Commencement of order

(4) An order made under subsection (1) shall not come into force earlier than thirty days after a copy of the order has been sent to the government of the province concerned under subsection (3). 1984, c. 6, s. 15.

Reimposition of reductions or withholdings

16. In the case of a continuing failure to satisfy any of the criteria described in sections 8 to 12 or to comply with any condition set out in section 13, any reduction or withholding under section 15 of a cash contribution or an amount payable to a province for a fiscal year shall be reimposed for each succeeding fiscal year as long as the Minister is satisfied, after consultation with the minister responsible for health care in the province, that the default is continuing. 1984, c. 6, s. 16.

When reduction or withholding imposed

17. Any reduction or withholding under section 15 or 16 of a cash contribution or payment may be imposed in the fiscal year in which the default that gave rise to the reduction or withholding occurred or in the following fiscal year. 1984, c. 6, s. 17.

Extra-Billing and User Charges

Extra-billing

18. In order that a province may qualify for a full cash contribution referred to in section 5 for a fiscal year, no payments may be permitted by the province for that fiscal year under the health care insurance plan of the province in respect of insured health services that

have been subject to extra-billing by medical practitioners or dentists. 1984, c. 6, s. 18.

User charges 19. (1) In order that a province may qualify for a full cash contribution referred to in section 5 for a fiscal year, user charges must not be permitted by the province for that fiscal year under the health care insurance plan of the province.

Limitation (2) Subsection (1) does not apply in respect of user charges for accommodation or meals provided to an in-patient who, in the opinion of the attending physician, requires chronic care and is more or less permanently resident in a hospital or other institution. 1984, c. 6, s. 19.

Deduction for extra-billing 20. (1) Where a province fails to comply with the condition set out in section 18, there shall be deducted from the cash contribution to the province for a fiscal year an amount that the Minister, on the basis of information provided in accordance with the regulations, determines to have been charged through extra-billing by medical practitioners or dentists in the province in that fiscal year or, where information is not provided in accordance with the regulations, an amount that the Minister estimates to have been so charged.

Deduction for user charges (2) Where a province fails to comply with the condition set out in section 19, there shall be deducted from the cash contribution to the province for a fiscal year an amount that the Minister, on the basis of information provided in accordance with the regulations, determines to have been charged in the province in respect of user charges to which section 19 applies in that fiscal year or, where information is not provided in accordance with the regulations, an amount that the Minister estimates to have been so charged.

Consultation with province (3) The Minister shall not estimate an amount under subsection (1) or (2) without first undertaking to consult the minister responsible for health care in the province concerned.

Separate accounting in Public Accounts (4) Any amount deducted under subsection (1) or (2) from a cash contribution in any of the three consecutive fiscal years the first of which commences on April 1, 1984 shall be accounted for separately in respect of each province in the Public Accounts for each of those fiscal years in and after which the amount is deducted.

Refund to province (5) Where, in any of the three fiscal years referred to in subsection 4), extra-billing or user charges have, in the opinion of the Minister, been eliminated in a province, the total amount deducted in respect of extra-billing or user charges, as the case may be, shall be paid to the province.

Saving (6) Nothing in this section restricts the power of the Governor in Council to make any order under section 15. 1984, c. 6, s. 20.

Purpose and Function in Government-Funded Health Coverage

Benjamin Freedman and Françoise Baylis

ABSTRACT

Government-funded health insurance programs that claim to provide comprehensive funding of their clients' demands have commonly adopted a purposive (deductive) approach to the problem of health care funding. This involves determining the extent of covered benefits by seeking an "adequate" definition of health or health care. Payment is then limited to only those procedures medically required or indicated. In this paper we argue that the purposive approach is inadequate, and that attempted adherence to it results in a curious dislocation of service, serious inequities, and an unhealthy contemplation of the definition of health. These problems are the result of structural deficiencies in the approach, and so will not be rectified by tinkering with the definitions adopted. As an alternative, we present an outline of a functional (inductive) approach, which seeks to identify which of the expectations of its clients the government health insurance system may realistically satisfy.

Government-funded health insurance schemes are under increasing pressure to reconcile finite medical resources with seemingly infinite demands for medical services. Consequently, problems regarding the macroallocation of available resources must constantly be readdressed.

The substantive macroallocational questions are familiar: What proportions of health care funding should be directed toward acute, chronic, or preventive care, or toward research in these respective areas? What, if any, provision should be made for the funding of novel therapies? When more than one approach to a disorder is available (e.g., medical or surgical treatment of angina pectoris), should the insurance program reward the use of the cheapest option (one assumption underlying the DRG system; see Wasserman 1983), the option which the physician believes is clinically preferable, or that which the patient prefers, perhaps on grounds of compatibility with lifestyle?

Questions such as these underline the need for a demarcation principle which government-funded health insurance programs could use to determine what should and should not be funded. The usefulness of such a principle is obvious, particularly from the government's perspective, when one considers how quickly new approaches to health care are adopted by health care providers (creating a demand for insurance reimbursement on their behalf). Current examples would include transportation, advanced diagnostic and imaging equipment, and expensive techniques for the treatment of infertility (most notoriously, *in vitro* fertilization). A demarcation principle would serve to limit the constantly expanding claims for health insurance coverage which feed upon (and, when suc-

Benjamin Freedman and Françoise Baylis, "Purpose and Function In Government-Funded Health Coverage," *Journal of Health Policy, Politics and Law* 12:1 (Spring 1987): 97–112.

cessful, fuel) the unrealistic expectation that the government-funded health care system can guarantee everyone a long, happy, and productive life.

At present, the approach to funding adopted by government health care programs is eclectic. Aside from strictly medical concerns, attention is given to factors deriving from economics, politics, and public policy. Even within the mélange of compromise that constitutes health insurance, however, we may discern a basic theme of demarcation: absent special considerations, a purposive (deductive) approach is commonly used in deciding whether a specific service should be a covered benefit. The results of this theme may be reconstructed in almost syllogistic terms: the insurance scheme should fund that which yields, or leads to, health (major premise); the proposed service does (or does not) yield or lead to health (minor premise); therefore the proposed service should (should not) be reimbursed. Presented in this way, the deductive approach is, of course, an artificial reconstruction of a more complicated reality. In the cases that we will be presenting, however, it plausibly captures an important theme in insurance decision making as that is publicly presented.

The Preamble to the Ontario Health Insurance Plan's *Schedule of Benefits* (1983), for example, states at the outset that "Insured medical services are limited to the services which are medically necessary ..." (p. 1). This we understand to mean that only those services designed to restore health ("medically necessary") are to be funded. The purposive concept of medical necessity is therefore ostensibly an *exclusive* criterion of demarcation — that is, a necessary but not sufficient condition for coverage. However, medical necessity also serves as an *inclusive* criterion of demarcation. The fitting of contact lenses, for example, is not a covered benefit unless it is being done to correct aphakia, myopia

greater than nine diopters, irregular astigmatism, or keratoconus (p. 20). Similarly, other services commonly sought for reasons of vanity or convenience are not covered benefits unless they are called for by some substantial degree of medical necessity. A case in point is cosmetic surgery, which is not an insured benefit "except where medically required" (p. 19).

The deductive model, idealized as it is, is a plausible — sometimes, the *only* plausible — reconstruction of a number of specific decisions on insurance coverage. Although it is initially appealing, we shall argue that this form of reasoning results in some obvious inequities and distortions in government coverage practice. An alternative approach, which may be termed functional or inductive, will be suggested. The functional approach would have us resolve the problem of demarcation by asking whether the specific service in question represents a demand which the health care system may efficiently satisfy. The question of whether the funded service supplies "health" or "health care" is thereby intentionally finessed.

The examples we shall be using are drawn largely from Canadian (and predominantly Ontarian) experiences. They are intended to serve for purposes of illustration alone. If successful, they point to problems and approaches generally prevalent among any government-funded insurance scheme which claims to comprehensively fund the health demands of the serviced population.

THE PURPOSIVE APPROACH

In ordinary language, "purpose" broadly refers to the end one has in view in acting in a certain way (i.e., "purposively"). The use of the term implies the conscious choice of both a goal and an action designed to achieve the stated goal. By extension, we may think of objects as purposively designed. For example, a television receiver is built with the end of it serving as a decoder of electronic impulses. In designing it, a certain size and shape are chosen on the grounds of fitness toward that end (Turkel 1984); any components which prove unreliable in achieving that end are either discarded or redesigned. Social institutions, such as traffic regulation, can also be construed as purposive. A panoply of elements (road markings, rules, etc.) are chosen subordinate to the primary goal of the swift and accident-free motion of traffic.

Similarly, some view medical practice as a purposive enterprise. It is usual to distinguish medical from nonmedical interventions — to demarcate medical practice — by referring to current beliefs concerning what promotes or conserves health; in theory new forms of medical treatment are accepted into practice and old ones discarded primarily on the basis of their fitness to serve the purpose of health. It is on this basis alone that physicians, in the course of their daily practice, "may, unquestioned and with impunity, slice, puncture, bind, grind, inject, and extract various organic and inorganic substances into and from" their patients (Freedman 1984, 5).

As health is the organizing principle and rule of demarcation for medical practice, it is natural to assume that this concept should apply as well to that system which funds medical practice. That is, it seems natural to assume that problems of demarcation in health care funding cannot be decided unless prior agreement has been arrived at concerning the definition of health, so that the nature of "medically necessary" services may be ascertained. By extension, a government-funded health insurance program may be purposively understood as an institution designed to secure health, although it is constrained by economic and political factors.

If the purpose of the government-funded insurance system is to promote health, and if that purpose is to serve as its rule of demarcation, a definition of health must be presented. However, the definition of health and related concepts (such as illness and disease) has resisted numerous scholarly efforts. Those definitions which have gained favorable attention have succeeded by stipulating a definition which could then be explicated or operationalized (Boorse 1975). But this approach will not serve the purposes of a government-funded health insurance scheme, since these purposes require a definition or an understanding of health with a basis in social consensus and usage.

The most widely known and most frequently criticized definition of health is found in the Preamble to the Constitution of the World Health Organization: "Health is a state of complete physical, mental and social well-being and not merely the absence of disease or infirmity" (WHO 1976). Daniel Callahan, a relatively sympathetic commentator on the WHO definition, notes nonetheless that this definition fosters "the cultural tendency to define all social problems, from war to crime on the streets, as 'health' problems" (Callahan 1973, 78). It "makes the medical profession the gate-keeper for happiness and social well-being ... the final magic-healer of human misery" (p. 81).

These eloquent criticisms relate to the one point that makes the WHO definition of health inadequate for the purposes of our discussion: it provides a government-funded health insurance scheme with no rule of demarcation whatsoever. Because of the wide currency the WHO definition enjoys, this criticism has been voiced in the world of practice as well as in the dusty pages of journals. For example, in Canada abortions are not illegal, provided that (among other conditions) they have been approved by a committee of physicians that finds the abortion necessary to preserve the life or health of the applicant.[1] Some abortion committees have adopted the WHO understanding as their working definition of health. According to many critics, this indicates that the committees have abandoned the effort at demarcating therapeutic abortions from those sought for nontherapeutic reasons.

Mindful of the need for demarcation, Callahan offered the following definition of health as a counterproposal: "Health is a state of physical well-being," a state which need not be "complete" but must be "at least adequate, i.e., without significant impairment of function" (Callahan 1973, 87). With this narrow definition of health, mental illness would qualify as "ill health," if at all, only if it substantially interfered with functioning.

Would Callahan's definition, or one equally narrow, represent a satisfactory rule of demarcation for government-funded health insurance schemes? It is important to examine this question at some length, because the narrowness of the definition as well as its common-sense roots make it attractive to economically pressed governments. Therefore, even if Callahan would not use his definition of health as a rule of demarcation, governments faced with competing priorities might be tempted to do so.

In judging the adequacy of any proposed rule of demarcation, two different kinds of questions may be asked. First, *could* the rule serve (i.e., would it clearly distinguish between those services to be included and those to be excluded from the funding system)? Second, *should* the rule serve (i.e., if applied, would it yield satisfactory results)? The first question concerns the formal adequacy of the rule; the second, its substantive adequacy.

The notions of "well-being" and of "impairment of function" are two crucial elements of Callahan's definition which are unavoidably ambiguous; these ambiguities speak to the issue of formal adequacy. To revert to the example introduced earlier, consider a patient suffering from exercise-onset angina pectoris. Two types of treatment are available. One option is medical management, which requires of the patient a commitment to control of diet, a modification of activity, and the tolerance of some degree of continued pain. The alternative is surgical intervention, which avoids the above problems at the expense of discrete surgical risk and substantial surgical and hospitalization costs. An appeal to "well-being" and "functioning" fails to indicate which of these forms of treatment should appropriately be funded. The problem is further complicated when one considers that the judgments of the patient and of the physician may differ; and, whereas people tend to think of "health" or "therapy" as technical concepts whose application is in the hands of professionals, they tend to define other concepts like "well-being" and "functioning" for themselves. The formal adequacy of Callahan's definition is therefore in question.

What about the substantive adequacy of the definition as a demarcation rule? This may seem to beg the question. We need a demarcation rule because we don't know what should and what should not be funded; therefore, how can we question such a rule by saying that it includes or excludes the wrong items? But this point presumes a false dichotomy, as often occurs when applying deductive approaches to social questions. We may (we almost certainly do) have some idea of the results desired from a rule of demarcation. We likely wish to develop a demarcation rule to sharpen an initially hazy understanding, rather than to fill a total vacuum.

Substantively, a rule may be faulty because it is either overinclusive, underinclusive, or both. Callahan's definition of health, if used as a demarcation rule, would be both. It would be overinclusive because it fails to account for the quantity of resources expended in marginal improvements in well-being or functioning. It does not tell us when the game is no longer worth the candle; and, as was noted at the outset, it is because medicine continues to yield improvements in these parameters, albeit at ever-increasing expense, that the problem we are discussing arises.

Callahan's definition would be underinclusive as well, because if it were applied rigorously benign and worthwhile services would be excluded from coverage. In his concern to combat the view that medicine should be held responsible to deliver perfect happiness, Callahan eliminates any role medicine might legitimately satisfy in this direction. Sometimes medical expertise is necessary to provide a modicum of happiness; if the costs thereby incurred are trivial enough, and the benefits (even in mere happiness) great enough, why should the required service not be funded?

Consider the following. The removal of tattoos is not usually necessary to restore function; nor, strictly speaking, is it a necessary component of well-being. Yet, the safe eradication of tattoos may require medical expertise. In Ontario, in most cases the provincial health insurance scheme does not cover the cost of tattoo removal. However, an exception is made for the eradication of prisoner-of-war or concentration camp tattoos. In some isolated instances well-being or functioning might require the removal of such tattoos, and to these cases Callahan's principle would extend. But in the usual case physical well-being and functioning are not impaired by these offensive tattoos. Is it wrong to fund this service simply out of consideration for the victims' feelings, in a situation where practical concern for these feelings requires medical expertise?

Evidently a definition of health from either end of the continuum — the relatively inclusive WHO definition, and the rather exclusive definition proposed by Callahan — will not serve as a satisfactory demarcation principle. However, quite apart from the specific problems arising from any particular definition of health, a further obstacle confronts the definitional approach to health care funding in that no definition of health has garnered general agreement. This lack of consensus is no mere accident. While on the surface the debate concerning the definition of health is technical in nature, it is clear in the writings of Szasz (1961), Kass (1975), and others that this debate serves an ideological role as well. Often the definitions advocated reflect broad views concerning such disparate issues as technocracy, nature versus nurture, and the allowable limits of eccentricity in liberal societies. Unhappily, therefore, it may be the case that consensus regarding the definition of health will have to wait for prior consensus on political and social ideology.

Also, the economic facts of health care may be another source of dissent regarding the definition of health and disease. Consider a study by Campbell, Scadding, and Roberts (1979), in which subjects were presented with a number of conditions and asked whether these represented "disease." The conditions ranged from malaria and tuberculosis to drowning and starvation. Physicians, and especially general practitioners, were more likely to characterize a condition as "disease" than were lay respondents. The authors suggest that the operational equivalents of "disease" are different in the two groups. For the layman, "disease" means "Do I need a doctor?" For the physician, it means "Is it useful for me to use this label?" An alternative suggestion compatible with the observed differences is that physicians, especially family practitioners, have a vested economic interest in broadening the scope of the term "disease."

We have been arguing that reliance upon the definition of health for the purposive elucidation of a government-funded insurance program is unlikely to result in a consensual, usable, and fair system. To this one might object that the preceding argument has erred in identifying the purpose of a government-funded health insurance system as the provision of "health." A health insurance system cannot provide *health*, but at best can only provide *health care*.

This amended purposive description is not, however, immune from the criticisms noted above. The objection purports to take a realistic look at what the government-funded insurance system actually does: it funds "health care." This is presumed to be a less ambiguous concept than "health." However, the definition of health care itself is crucially dependent upon prior agreement on the definition of health, so the objection only succeeds in pushing the problems we have noted one step back.

Others will object that the health care system provides neither "health" nor "health care" but "medical care" *tout court*. This, however, is no more serious an objection, for although the term "medical care" is perhaps even less ambiguous than the term "health care," the problem remains in that "medical care" is commonly understood to require that a physician's expertise be applied on behalf of restoring or preserving the health of patients. Furthermore, if we were to be fully realistic, we would have to admit that government-funded health insurance systems do not fund medical care or health care any more than they fund health. Rather, they fund health care providers, as public monies are made available precisely to pay for medical services rendered.

STRUCTURAL DEFICIENCIES OF THE PURPOSIVE APPROACH

As noted above, the two definitions of health drawn from either end of the continuum fail to adequately demarcate insur-able services. It does not necessarily follow from this, however, that a definition in between these extremes would not serve.

Allowing for the remote possibility that a consensual definition of health were to be adopted, some important structural problems would remain to confront any purposive system of government-funded health insurance. These problems derive from the approach's top-down, deductive fashion of reasoning, and therefore would not be solved by any improvement in the formulation of the premises. In particular, they would persist despite changes in the definition of health or health care.

An inherent problem with the purposive-deductive approach is its rationalization of the issue of demarcation. In principle, once the premises have been adopted, all of the solutions are present; as logicians say, deductive reasoning produces no new knowledge not already embedded in the premises. Two difficulties follow from this. The purposive approach does not in principle allow for an incremental solution to the issues, within which some procedures might be funded on a trial basis while other relevantly similar procedures await the lessons of experience. Furthermore, this rationalized approach does not permit any wisdom of quantification, a problem noted earlier in reference to Callahan. It does not allow us by its premises to say that some procedure does not fall on the "fundable" side of the demarcation line, but that it is still worthy of funding (e.g., tattoo removal), or alternatively that some procedure might fall on the "fundable" side of the demarcation line, but that it is nonetheless too expensive a proposition to fund (e.g., heart transplants).

A further problem is who decides whether some service is fundable under the definition consensually adopted. He almost certainly will be some professional: possibly the individual health care provider, but more likely some government official. Thus, control of the health insurance system passes into the hands of the technocracy, and the patient is lost in the shuffle, as is indeed lay input in general (which currently may be provided through political representation and control). How is the technocracy to resolve these problems? In the deductive mode of reasoning, issues of application are reduced to a search for semantic clarity and consensus. Practical issues of whether it is useful, fair, or right to cover a given treatment for a given condition are converted into an obsessive contemplation of the definition of health.

PROBLEMS OF THE PURPOSIVE APPROACH IN PRACTICE

The purposive-deductive approach is necessarily obsessed with determining whether a condition is "really" an illness. Two representative cases illustrate this point, though many other examples could be cited if space permitted. Jane Smith (a real case, though not her real name) approached an endocrinologist with a presenting complaint of excessive growth of facial and body hair. After an extensive workup (covered, incidentally, by the provincial health plan) in which no endocrinological disorder was established, she was diagnosed as suffering from "essential hirsutism." Mrs. Smith then requested of the physician a referral to an electrolysist, in the belief that the health care plan would then cover the cost of treatment. This request was refused. She was told that if the condition was causing her acute discomfort or embarrassment, she could be referred to a psychiatrist, who could then make the referral for hair removal. The kinds of questions the psychiatrist would be likely to ask could equally well have been asked by the endocrinologist. However, he felt constrained by the purpo-

sive nature of the system to validate the electrolytic referral by means of special expertise (into mental illness) which he did not feel he possessed. Thus, inappropriate gate-keeping mechanisms which are both costly and inefficient were introduced. This case illustrates one way in which the technocratic and logomachistic tendencies of the purposive approach reinforce one another.

To further illustrate this point, consider the treatment of infertility, which might include hormonal therapy or surgery as well as counseling. These therapies ordinarily are thought to fall within the boundaries of medical care. But the purposive approach must question whether infertility itself is really a "disease." If we look to an American example, Great Southern Life of Houston, a private insurance company, is reported as having denied coverage for *in vitro* fertilization on the grounds that it is "not a treatment of an illness" *(Surrogate Parenting News 1983)*. Presumably a government-funded health care system similarly concerned with purposive considerations might apply the same reasoning.

Another distinction covertly used is that of the internal versus the external. There is a vague feeling that health care is a concept that relates to the individual rather than to the environment, and that fundable, fee-for-service health care interventions may be demarcated in part as those which represent internal adjustments to the human organism rather than modifications of the organism's environment. When a malnourished patient is nursed back to health through intravenous infusions, that is health care; when he or she is given money or remunerative employment supplying the wherewithal for self-nourishment, that is not health care.

The distinction makes less sense in other contexts. What of a patient suffering from a definable illness whose comprehensive treatment would include environmental modification? A major and growing current example are those patients suffering from pan-allergic syndromes. It is sometimes claimed that the alleviation of the symptoms from this disorder requires a total readjustment of the patient's living arrangements, such as moving into a cabin tiled with ceramics and discarding a wardrobe laced with allergens. Although this is asserted to be the treatment of choice, it is "external" and therefore not a covered benefit under the government health insurance scheme. Similarly, prosthetics that are implanted, like heart pacemakers, are covered benefits under Ontario's health insurance scheme, whereas externally attached prosthetics, like limbs, generally are not paid for by the Ontario Health Insurance Plan (OHIP).

THE FUNCTIONAL APPROACH: AN ALTERNATIVE

Most social institutions are established with a purpose in view. When a government-funded health insurance program is initiated, the purpose is vaguely understood to contribute to the provision of health or health care. This original purpose is in fact critical to the establishment of a government health insurance program, which is often given higher priority than comparable welfare schemes dealing in less critical services and commodities. But once an insurance scheme is in place, it would be foolish to freeze the system in its embryonic state. With the continuing development of a health insurance plan, as it confronts issues of macroallocation and demarcation, there is no need to restrict it to the a priori wisdom that went into its establishment. On these grounds we advocate a functional approach to government health care funding.

In accordance with common usage, we define a "function" as any output of a sys-

tem which is positively evaluated, whether that output was intentional or not.[2] Purposes are therefore a subset of functions, the latter including happy surprises in addition to anticipated outcomes. To revert to our earlier example, the purpose of a television set is to decode electronic signals. In most homes, however, it will also service a variety of additional functions: conversation piece, plant stand, and so on.

What would be distinctive about a functional approach to a government-funded health insurance plan? Three main differences stand between a purposive and a functional approach. These differences have to do with the characterization of those conditions which the government health insurance program should ameliorate, the demarcation of reimbursable from non-reimbursable services, and the relationship between the health plan and other government services.

With the purposive approach to the question of health care funding, funding decisions turn on whether a condition represents ill health, a disease, an illness. With a functional approach, in contrast, questions outside the realm of health are also considered. For example, has the condition resulted in impaired occupational performance? (In the infamous words of an anonymous Polish public health official, "Tuberculosis slows production.") Does the person afflicted with the condition experience disturbed functioning in other areas as a result? Is he severely distressed or depressed as a result of the condition? Is he experiencing pain? These types of considerations do sometimes appear in the purposive conception, but in a distorted, Procrustean way, as questions concerning "mental health" or "adjustment."

To illustrate this point, consider how the different approaches would deal with a difficult case of demarcation like sex-reassignment surgery. The purposive approach would need to discover whether the surgery represented the treatment of a genuine disease. In this context, the neologism "gender dysphoria" has been introduced, and psychiatrists continue to battle over its propriety and etiology. With a functional approach the questions considered in reaching a funding decision on a macro level (by bureaucrats) and in implementing the decision at the micro level (by physicians) are more straightforward. How seriously has the applicant's life been affected? How likely is it that he/she will improve with the treatment? Is the cost justified by these benefits? Admittedly, similar questions might be asked by psychiatrists in the gender dysphoria debate. We suggest, however, that such questions are both clearer and more realistic when not filtered through the prism of a definition of disease.

The second contrast between the purposive and the functional approach is evident when deciding about the funding of discrete services. Whereas with the purposive approach one asks whether some service represents health care, with the functional approach one would ask if the service or procedure is good, worthwhile, and desired.

Consider fertility interventions. For the vast majority of women, tubal ligation per se has almost no discrete medical justification (although it certainly will "cure" the "disorder" of fecundity). On these grounds, Kass (1975) has suggested that tubal ligation or vasectomy not be included within the medical orbit. But clearly, tubal ligation is a much-desired intervention; it has recently become the most popular form of female contraception in Canada. And clearly, medical expertise is necessary to provide ligations. Also, from the economic point of view of the insurance plan, sterilization is one of the most efficient interventions available, obviating both medical costs or parturition and costs of care of the (forever-to-remain) unborn. Whereas the purposive conception forces government health care officials to conceptualize health matters in futile and disingenuous ways, the functional conception allows one to examine the real underlying concerns. Does a requested procedure — for example, tubal ligation — represent a treatment whose cost is rationally proportionate to the need it serves?

When the issue is phrased in this way, we are required to confront questions which are never raised by the purposive approach. For example: Does the procedure in question address a human want or need, or perhaps something people *ought* to want or need? As difficult as these questions are, they seem to us to be the right ones to address. Among their advantages is the fact that their solution demands of us that we understand and respect the patient's perceptions of health care.

A recent study (Freedman 1983) yielded some suggestive data on this very point. The study included interviews of Canadian women applying for microsurgical attempts at reversing a prior ligation (tubal reanatomosis). During the interviews, the women were asked "Do you see the reversal of the sterilization as a health procedure (like an appendectomy) or as a social procedure requiring medical assistance (like cosmetic surgery)?" Most of these women, both in questionnaires and during the subsequent interviews, classified the procedure they requested as medical, but the interview responses of some of the women revealed ambivalence stemming from a variety of considerations. The following representative statements are worthy of careful consideration as they encapsulate a lay response to the issue of demarcation: "I think for my mental and emotional well-being it is necessary. It is not like cosmetic surgery, like something I could do. It is something that is inside of me. I never thought I'd feel as strongly about [it]." "No [it's not a social procedure] … I don't feel that having a tubal done is the same thing as having a reversal done. I'm having it [the reversal] done so that we can have children … So I really don't see it as being something that you do just to fit in. It's hard to explain but that's the way I feel about it."

How did these laypeople go about resolving this critical question of demarcation? What themes emerge from their responses? Hints are found of a variety of approaches, including the "internal/external" approach. However, their major point of consensus was the belief that because the procedure was so important to them personally, and because a doctor was needed to perform it, the procedure *must* be medical.

The population from which these responses were drawn would be expected to provide tendentious replies. It is in these women's interest to argue that the procedure they are requesting is medical in nature, and hence reimbursable. However, this fact only sharpens the point, because we would expect that they would be choosing the most persuasive demarcation principle available to support their claim.

The third divergence between the two approaches concerns the relationship between the health care system (and its public funding agent) and other elements of society. The purposive approach makes of the health care system a hermetically sealed enterprise, self-directed in terms of its original purpose and resistant to other legitimate social concerns and institutionalized values. On the other hand, with the functional approach, other social interests and resources are taken into account in deciding whether to supply a particular benefit when its request is justified in terms of health.

A functionalist perspective also allows one to consider whether the health care system is the best institution to respond to demands for particular needs. Needs (or wants) and the associated goods and services that have traditionally been seen as medical in nature may be better served by some other social institution. Alcoholism, obesity, and other diseases of lifestyle are notoriously resistant to treatment by the medical model. For the purposive approach, however, provided that these conditions are diseases and that a physician is prepared to "treat" them, such treatments would be insured. The fact that other social institutions could better deal with these conditions is irrelevant from a purposive perspective. With a functional approach one questions whether we might not be better served by "divestiture" of these conditions from medicine, at least at this point in time. Conversely, the health care system may be better suited to providing some needs which traditionally have been served outside the medical model. One such possibility might be the care of the families of dying patients by physicians, nurses, or medical social workers, a role traditionally relegated to pastors and family support systems. The funding of such a service should not wait upon the discovery of a new "disease" ("impending grief syndrome"), but should proceed immediately upon the recognition that these forms of care are valid, useful, and best accomplished within the institutions of the health care system.

QUESTIONS FOR THE FUNCTIONAL APPROACH

It might seem that the functional approach is necessarily heir to all of the criticisms presented above concerning the WHO definition of health. Under a functional approach, as under the WHO definition, the full range of human suffering and discontent become potential targets of a government-supported health care system. In fact, some might even argue that the functional approach is even more latitudinous than WHO, although it is hard to imagine what has been left out once "a complete state of physical, mental and social well-being" has been included.

This criticism, however, dissolves in the face of a critical distinction. The problem with the WHO definition, which is that it fails to exclude anything from coverage, arises in the context of a purposive system. In contrast, with a functional approach to health care funding, demarcation does not *end* with the recognition of a need or demand for services, but rather only *begins* at this point. It must then be determined whether the health care system, with its particular expertise and modalities of intervention, may redress that need efficiently; whether another social program or practice would better serve; or whether the need is so difficult to satisfy or so at odds with other values that it should not be served at all.

The whole point of the functional approach is the recognition that decisions regarding coverage involve more than semantics. In a purposive approach, once we know that a procedure serves health, we have an argument (which, to be sure, might need to be tempered by political or economic realities) that it should be funded. In a functional approach, when we know that a procedure satisfies a demand, we simply know that it is *potentially* fundable — not that it should be funded, let alone that it should be funded by the health care system.

A further point worth noting is that since functionalism contains no single decision rule for demarcation, it must address new problems which do not trouble a purposive system. However, the fact that a theory raises new questions does not necessarily count as a strike against it, provided that the questions are ones which are worth confronting. In fact, a theory might be deficient precisely because it fails to raise questions which should be answered, as at times the purposive approach slurs over the complications faced by the functional approach. In general the new problems which the functional approach must

address are actually complications which arise due to the fact that patient choice is allowed, and that services traditionally considered nonmedical may be included within the boundaries of health care; therefore, a greater range of alternatives must be considered. For example, a possible negative consequence of allowing patient choice is that the costs involved might be greater. This criticism, however, also applies to the purposive approach, as the following examples will serve to illustrate.

Under the Ontario Health Insurance Plan postmastectomy breast reconstruction surgery is a covered service. This type of procedure fits comfortably within the naïve notion of health services, since it involves a direct "internal" procedure on a patient's behalf. On the other hand, prosthetic devices, being "external," have not been a covered benefit for adults and have represented a repeated source of political contention. A system which proceeds under the strong purposive principle of demarcation does not recognize the need to fund environmental adjustments, since these would fall under the rubric of social welfare rather than health care. Ontario, therefore, has long refused to cover the costs of breast prostheses and surgical brassieres for victims of breast cancer, while still funding surgical breast reconstruction for those interested in pursuing that course.

A complicated situation arose in Ontario when a woman eligible for a breast reconstruction procedure offered to exchange this service for a Tucker valve set (a prosthetic device needed for "normal" speech after she had undergone a tracheotomy). The trade would have been cost-effective for the Ministry of Health, and might have saved $1000 or more. The insurance plan declined the offer as there was no apt bureaucratic means of accepting it, given that the health insurance plan funds "services" and not "goods" (*London Free Press 1982*).

Another Ontario woman suffering from a lung condition lived at home, using a mobile oxygen cart. Eventually her monthly oxygen bills — which the public health insurance program would not cover — rose to over $700. At this point, entering the hospital became, for her, the only practical economic move, because then the insurance plan would supply her with oxygen gratis. The average cost of inpatient hospital care was estimated at approximately ten times the cost of the oxygen alone *(London Free Press 1984)*. This situation similarly indicates the unreasoning prejudice a purposive system may have against environmental adjustment.

A functional approach would deal with such situations differently since patient choice would be independently relevant (if not necessarily decisive) in determining fundability. The implications of this are obviously quite serious, particularly as patients persist in expressing individual preferences on this issue, a fact which must be taken seriously by a system concerned with lay input. Honoring the choice of patients will at times be far more expensive than acceding to the choice dictated by a purposive demarcation rule. Patient autonomy in relation to funding decisions has not been an issue; but, without presuming any particular resolution, we suggest that it should be.

A functional conception would need to reexamine funding of the diverse forms of health care practice. In Ontario's quasi-purposive system, all reimbursements flow directly to, or indirectly from, physicians. Doctors may perform a service directly, or engage another professional (e.g., psychologist, physiotherapist) on a salaried basis to work under their direction, with the physician billing the government insurance program. Since physicians are certified specialists in "health," this arrangement is acceptable (although certainly not inevitable) under a purposive system.

Similarly, although a physician may bill for consultation with a patient, parent, or other physician, he or she may not bill for consultation with nonphysician providers of health care. If a child is experiencing behavioral problems in school which have concerned the school psychologist, the physician may charge the government insurance plan for consultation with the parents, who may serve as middlemen between the school psychologist and the physician; but if the physician wishes to discuss the matter with the psychologist directly, he must do so on his own account. A functional system would necessarily call such arrangements into question.

As a result, in implementing a functional approach, a comprehensive government health plan would face bureaucratic dislocation. How serious would this be? To this, three points can be made: some dislocation has already occurred; some dislocation is good; and remaining dislocations need not all be faced at once.

Some dislocation has already occurred In Ontario, a system of psychiatric hospitals is run by the Ministry of Health. A system of facilities for the developmentally disabled is run by the Ministry of Community and Social Services (COMSOC). This kind of division would be preserved if a consistently functional approach were adopted. The facilities for the developmentally handicapped require a high level of expertise in development and programming, but the specific forms required — training of various sorts, behavioral techniques, and custodial care — are not specifically medical or nursing in nature (although both of these disciplines perform an important ancillary function). Indeed, because developmental handicap constitutes an "illness" under almost any definition, the division that currently exists between psychiatric and COMSOC facilities is inexplicable under a purposive conception.

Some dislocation is good Many of the decisions noted above (e.g., concerning prostheses and oxygen) would be inappropriate given a functionalist perspective. Their reversal involves dislocation in itself; but in the cases noted, that seems to be all to the good. Also, some bureaucratic awkwardness, intrinsic to a purposive system, would be resolved under a functional approach. While a physician may recover from the Ontario Health Insurance Plan on behalf of the examination of a patient carried out for investigation, confirmation, or documentation of an alleged sexual assault, a portion of its outlays on this behalf are then recovered from the Ministries of the Attorney General and the Solicitor General. Similar cumbersome paper shuffling may be involved in other instances which require medical expertise, albeit outside of medical treatment (e.g., in assessments for insurance or for the purpose of establishing workmen's compensation). It would seem that the only reason the money needs to be shuffled at present is to keep the accounts clear on behalf of a system that is purposively designed to fund health care.

Not all dislocations need be funded at once The saving grace of the functional approach is that it may, consistent with its own logic, be activated in an incrementalist fashion. The facts of bureaucratic life are, as are the facts of economic, political and medical life, all to be included within the calculation that should precede a decision on inclusion of a service within coverage.

In general, then, new questions of the division between medical and social services and of the cost-effectiveness of different modes of health care would directly arise under a functional system. Quantitative concerns would also need to be directly confronted: How serious is the need or desire? What value should be assigned to the honoring of the preferences of the patient? These questions need not be raised at all in a purposive system, which deals instead with questions concerning the nuances of the definitions of "health" and "health care." We will leave to others the task of parsing the seriousness of these questions. In choosing between these two approaches, however, we ought to consider which kinds of questions we want to contemplate, as well as which results we wish to achieve.

NOTES

1. Criminal Code of Canada, R.S.C. 1970, c. C-34, §251. [This section of the Criminal Code was struck down in 1988 by the Supreme Court in *Morgentaler.* See *supra*, chapter 13. Ed.]

2. "… functional analysis seeks to understand a behavior pattern or a sociocultural institution by determining the role it plays in keeping the given system in proper working order or maintaining it as a going concern" (Hempel 1985). For a general discussion of the functional approach see the chapter "The Logic of Functional Analysis," in *Aspects of Scientific Explanation* (New York: The Free Press, 1985), 297–330.

REFERENCES

Boorse, C. 1975. "On The Distinction Between Disease and Illness." *Philosophy and Public Affairs* 5 (Fall): 49–68.

Callahan, D. 1973. "The WHO Definition of 'Health.'" *The Hastings Center Studies* 1: 77–87.

Campbell, E. J. M., J. G. Scadding, and R. S. Roberts. 1979. "The Concept of Disease." *British Medical Journal* 2 (September): 757-62.

Freedman, B. 1983–85. "Study of Ethical Issues In Infertility" (unpublished material).

1985. "Ethical Issues in Clinical Obstetrics and Gynecology." *Current Problems in Obstetrics, Gynecology and Fertility* 7 (March): 1–47.

Hempel, C. G. 1985. *Aspects of Scientific Explanation*. New York: The Free Press.

Kass, L. R. 1975. "Regarding the End of Medicine and the Pursuit of Health." *The Public Interest* 40 (Summer): 11–42.

London Free Press, 1982. "OHIP won't pay for vocal device it calls luxury." 5 June: 2.

1984. "Woman needing pure oxygen may be forced into hospital." 3 August: 12.

Ontario Health Insurance Plan. 1983. *Schedule of Benefits: Physician Services.* 1 January. Ministry of Health of the Province of Ontario.

Surrogate Parenting News. 1983. "Insurance Coverage of In Vitro." 1 (October/November): 71–72.

Szasz, T. 1961. *The Myth of Mental Illness.* New York: Dell Publishing Co.

Taylor, F. K. 1971. "A Logical Analysis of the Medico-Psychological Concepts of Disease." *Psychological Medicine* 1:356-64.

Turkel, Sherry. 1984. *The Second Self.* New York: Simon and Schuster.

Wasserman, J. 1983. "How DRGs Work." *The Hastings Center Report* 13 (October): 24.

World Health Organization. 1976. "Constitution of the World Health Organization." In *World Health Organization: Basic Documents,* ed. 26. Geneva: WHO.

Canada's Health Care System Faces Its Problems

John K. Iglehart

Canada's provincial health insurance plans have demonstrated an impressive capacity to operate successfully despite a basic policy conflict that says health care funding must be public and universal, physicians must retain their professional autonomy, consumers must have free choice of doctors and first-dollar coverage, and provincial governments must control their budgets. But now provinces are finding it increasingly difficult to maintain this equation because a variety of factors are perturbing its balance. In the face of a large deficit,* the national government continues to reduce its finan-

John K. Inglehart, "Canada's Health Care System Faces Its Problems," *New England Journal of Medicine* 1990; 322:8, 562–71.

*Since the time this was written, the deficit has turned into a surplus but the national debt remains. Consequently the federal government has made debt reduction a priority. The effect is the same: transfer funds to the provinces are continuing to be reduced or eroded. *The editor.*

cial commitment to the plans; patients and practitioners are demanding better access to the latest forms of medical technology; the supply of physicians continues to increase at a rate out-stripping the growth of the population; and doctors are restive as provinces work more aggressively to stem the rise in health expenditures.

Among industrialized nations, such conflicts are certainly not unique. Indeed, every major Western country grapples with similar issues to one degree or another. But when tax-financed programs in most nations are stretched to the limit, their stewards usually turn to private funding for relief. What is unique to Canada is the virtual absence of private-sector involvement in health insurance and the unwillingness of policy makers to encourage the development of such alternatives, which could ease the financial pressure on the provincial health plans. ...

Canada designed its provincial health insurance plans this way because of a strong belief that all citizens should have equal access to medical care, regardless of ability to pay. In essence, Canadian policy says that simply because people can afford to pay, they should not be able to purchase care that is better or more readily available than that available to the less well off. Canada has further discouraged private payment by requiring physicians who bill patients directly to leave the provincial health insurance plans altogether. As a result, such doctors are few....

This policy contrasts markedly with the method by which the bulk of care is financed in the pluralistic system of the United States and is contrary to the direction in which the socialized health schemes of Sweden and the United Kingdom are moving. Most U.S. policy makers and representatives of private-sector interests believe that except in the case of poor people, consumers should be directly responsible for a portion of the cost of care. ...

Whether Canada, faced with a budget deficit, general opposition to higher taxes, and real resistance to reducing the scope of covered medical benefits, can maintain a health care policy that relies on public expenditures and strongly discourages the infusion of private resources is a question asked more frequently there. At this point there is certainly no clamor for major change among private corporations; they seem well satisfied with letting government finance the bulk of medical care and limiting their involvement to pay for part of it through taxation.[1] ...Thus far, Canada has been able to finance its system of universal access to health care by constraining medical expenditures in various ways, as Evans outlined recently ... keeping its insurance overhead low through the administrative simplicity of its provincial plans, controlling payments to physicians and hospitals through negotiated fees and global budgets, and restraining the diffusion of forms of technology.[2]

THE PRINCIPLES OF CANADIAN HEALTH INSURANCE

...In sharp contrast to the United States, where the federal government holds far more authority over the financing of medical care than the states, Canadian health care is dominated by the provinces. The provincial medical associations are more influential than the Canadian Medical Association. In both domains, governmental and professional, the provincial entities strive to guard their prerogatives. The provinces have a broad constitutional authority to tax their citizens and private corporations. In consequence, they spend more in total tax revenues than the national government. Increasingly, the proportion (ranging from one fifth to one third) of tax revenues expended by the provinces is consumed by the provincial health insurance plans....

In most Canadian provinces, it is not prohibited for patients to pay privately for medical or hospital care. What is prohibited is for physicians or hospitals to treat both patients whose care is financed by the provincial plans and patients who pay directly, as is the case in Britain. Evans views this prohibition as a critically important constraint. He writes:

> The British private consultant can use his dual role to select and steer patients according to their resources and the nature of their problems. He can even use his position within the NHS to manipulate waiting lists and other aspects of access so as to ensure that private care will be preferable to those who can afford it. The Canadian physician who decides to "go private" must go all the way. He cannot use a strategic position within the public system to cream off only the profitable patients for his private services.[3]

Canada's capacity to protect all its citizens against the economic consequences of illness at a cost that is socially acceptable has been widely admired, but its resistance to private funding makes it an exception in the Western world. Even in Sweden, a generous welfare state and one of the world's most highly taxed nations, the governing Social Democrats are promoting health care alternatives in the private sector and lower taxes.[4]

CANADA'S STRUGGLE OVER CONFLICTING IMPERATIVES

As I suggested at the outset, Canada's provincial health insurance plans face an increasing financial struggle because of the conflicting imperatives built into them at their creation. One source of tension is the moderation of support for the plans from the national government. As medical costs escalated in the 1970s, Ottawa concluded that it would have to abandon its practice of making an open-ended financial contribution to the plans. The original formula by which the provinces were encouraged to create their plans was based on an agreement that no matter how rapidly medical expenditures grew, Ottawa and the provinces would share the costs equally. This formula was incorporated into the Hospital Insurance and Diagnostic Services Act of 1957 and again in the Medical Care Act of 1971 — the original federal laws on which the provincial plans were based.

Since 1977, through the enactment of the Federal/Provincial Fiscal Arrangements and Established Programs Act, the provincial governments have been placed at higher risk for increases in the cost of medical care. This change came about because the 1977 law linked the annual increase in the federal contribution to the provincial health insurance plans to the growth of the gross national product, leaving the provinces to absorb more of the health care costs when the aggregate outlays for health grew faster than the economy as a whole; health costs have increased more rapidly than the growth of Canada's economy in 8 of the past 13 years.

In 1986 and again in 1989, as Mulroney's government sought to reduce an annual budget deficit of $30.5 billion on federal tax revenues of $112.4 billion, the Progressive Conservatives ... altered the formula for the federal transfer of funds in ways that reduced the growth of Ottawa's contribution to the provincial plans (as well as to the costs of post-secondary education). Instead of a transfer formula based on the growth rate of a three-year running average of the gross national product, the formula is now based on this same prescription minus 3 percentage points of the gross national product. In the years 1987, 1988, and 1989, Canada's gross national product grew at rates of 9.4 percent, 9.2 percent, and 7.1 percent, respectively. The 3 percentage point reduction may seem small, but its cumulative effect on the provincial health budgets will amount to billions of dollars....**

In future years, officials in Ottawa anticipate that federal transfers, as a proportion of provincial health expenditures, will drop to percentages in the low 30s, although the precise projections are kept confidential. This trend, buried in the minutiae of federal-provincial transfer payments, has provoked little opposition from the provincial governments or the medical profession, although it is certain to intensify pressures on the health insurance plans.

One of the interesting aspects of Canadian health care is that the public is remarkably uninvolved in the ongoing struggles over resource allocation that pit the provincial governments against providers of care. An official of the Ontario Medical Association characterized this conflict as "tuxedo warfare," and with good reason. As political scientists would say, it engages the "elite" interest of government and medicine. Except for the occasional consumer who encounters an obstacle in obtaining access to care, the average citizen is not concerned about allocations of medical resources because government has insulated citizens time and again from worrying about the rising cost of care. ...One consequence of the overriding preference of policy makers to insulate consumers from paying for care directly is that the level of public support for the provincial plans remains very high....

CONSTRAINING THE DIFFUSION OF MEDICAL TECHNOLOGY

An important feature of Canada's approach to hospital budgeting is the separation of operating expenses and capital spending. Every year, Canada's 1243 hospitals (all but 9 of which are nonprofit institutions) must negotiate their annual operating budgets with the provincial government. They must apply separately for the approval and funding of new capital acquisitions. Thus, the provincial ministries have two major levers with which to control hospital growth. In some instances, hospitals raise private funds for new technological services through contributions from the community and philanthropic donors, but if an acquisition has not previously been approved by the government, the provincial plans often deny the necessary operating funds.

Through this process, the provincial plans have successfully contained the growth of hospital resources, including labor, supplies, and equipment.... A central feature of the strategy, used by all the provincial plans, is to distribute forms of medical technology according to region in a fashion that compels physicians to judge carefully which patients would profit from their use. Virtually all the most sophisticated forms of technology are diffused in teaching hospitals only. One consequence of this effort to restrain the use of modern techniques is that such techniques are far less available in Canada than in the United States. For example, a recent study by Rublee showed that in comparison with the Federal Republic of Germany and the United States, Canada has appreciably slowed the diffusion of six major forms of technology: open-heart surgery, cardiac

---

** This reduction in transfer payments is a major reason for the current provincial difficulties in funding health care. *The editor.*

catheterization, organ transplantation, radiation therapy, extracorporeal shock-wave lithotripsy, and magnetic resonance imaging (MRI).[5] Key comparisons between Canada and the United States reveal that there are nearly eight times more MRI and radiation-therapy units per capita in the United States, more than six times as many lithotripsy centers, roughly three times as many cardiac catheterization and open-heart surgery units, and slightly more organ transplantation units. Rublee, a researcher affiliated with the AMA, conceded that "the differences in levels of major technology, in themselves, indicate little about the overall effectiveness, achievements, and weaknesses of the health care systems of any of the three countries studied."[6]...

Because of the problems Canadians have had in gaining rapid access to some services (cardiac care, lithotripsy, radiotherapy, and renal dialysis), there has been an assumption, reinforced by news coverage, that patients in increasing numbers are turning for treatment to American medical facilities across the border. These reports were discussed ... by the Pepper Commission in a meeting partly devoted to a review of Canadian health care. Representative Willis D. Gradison, Jr. (R-Ohio), asked the committee's staff members to investigate the reports. They surveyed 10 institutions — Buffalo General Hospital, the Cleveland Clinic, the Detroit Medical Center, Henry Ford Hospital, Johns Hopkins Medical Center, Massachusetts General Hospital, the Mayo Clinic, the Memorial Sloan-Kettering Cancer Center, the University of Rochester Medical Center, and the University of Washington Medical Center. Only two of the institutions provided evidence that they had treated a substantial number of Canadians. Buffalo General reported that 3 percent of its patients were Canadian and that 50 of the 100 patients receiving monthly lithotripsy treatments were doing so under a formal

agreement with the province of Ontario. The University of Washington Medical Center reported that 125 of the 250 in vitro fertilization procedures it performed annually involved Canadians who paid about $5,000 out of pocket for each procedure. On the basis of these findings, the commission's staff reported to Gradison on August 10 that there was "no evidence that substantial numbers of Canadians are seeking care at American medical centers." In the vast number of cases, Canadians normally travel only to medical institutions adjacent to the border for treatment, so the survey was somewhat skewed because of the inclusion of hospitals located farther away. ...

There are various reasons that medicine remains, on balance, an attractive profession in Canada. One is that physicians are held in high esteem even though their public image has diminished a bit over the years.

Another reason is that because the 16 medical schools are public, university-based institutions, they are subsidized heavily by the federal and provincial governments. In 1988–1989, medical students paid school fees ranging from approximately $750 a year in Quebec to $3,000 a year in British Columbia. Thus, very few Canadian medical students begin their professional careers heavily in debt, in contrast to students in the United States.

Another important reason for the continued appeal of medicine as a career is that despite the growing number of practicing doctors, physicians remain Canada's highest-paid professionals, according to the reports of the Department of National Health and Welfare ... based on taxation data from Revenue Canada. Expressed in U.S. dollars, the average net income of physicians was $84,700 in 1987, as compared with $70,800 for dentists, $63,500 for lawyers and notaries, and $49,300 for accountants. A decade ago, the corresponding figures were $41,500 for physicians, $35,500 for dentists,

$34,200 for lawyers and notaries, and $29,400 for accountants. ....

On the other hand, physicians themselves are less concerned about the effect of their increasing numbers on the financial accounts of the provincial plans than about what they regard as governments' contradictory efforts to squeeze spending while promoting universal access. Concern over the current trends has been expressed by physicians in academic medicine and organized medicine, as well as by individual practitioners who do not participate in medical politics. ...

CONCLUSION

...Canada's health care system is buffeted by conflicting forces — its strong commitment to universal access, of which Canadians are justifiably proud; the accelerating efforts of the provinces to control costs while they continue to expand the scope of covered benefits; and the increasing frustration of practicing physicians and hospital stewards who are caught in the middle. Until recently, these tensions have remained within manageable bounds throughout Canada, but whether that will continue, without a new accommodation, particularly if the national economy slows, is an open question. Most of the provinces have created blue-ribbon working groups in the past several years to seek solutions to identified problems, and these exercises have eased some of the tension temporarily. But it seems inevitable that Canada will eventually reopen the question of how care is financed. The provinces will jeopardize their capacity to support other social priorities if they continue to rely on tax revenues to finance unlimited access to most health services and to produce more physicians than can be accommodated. At the same time, private investment could endanger the egalitarian nature of Canadian health care. Revising the current formulation of policy will require a more meaningful dialogue than exists at present among the federal and provincial governments, organized medicine, and other major stakeholders in the system. Without such dialogue, Canadians place at risk the future of their provincial health insurance plans, social enterprises that are admired throughout the Western world. The medical profession faces an additional challenge: to examine more rigorously the appropriateness and efficacy of the clinical care it renders.

NOTES

1. Doherty, K. "Is the Canadian system as good as it looks for employers?" *Bus Health* 1989; 7(7):31–4.

2. Evans, R.G., Lomas, J., Barer, M.L., et al. "Controlling health expenditures: the Canadian reality." *N Eng J Med* 1989; 320:571–7.

3. Evans, R.G. "We'll take care of it for you: health care in the Canadian community." *Daedalus* 1988; 117(4):155–89.

4. Greenhouse, S. "Sweden's social democrats veer toward free market and lower taxes." *New York Times*. October 27, 1989:A3.

5. Rublee, D.A. "Medical technology in Canada, Germany, and the United States." *Health Aff* (Millwood) 1989; 8(3):178–81.

6. See *supra*, note 5.

FURTHER READINGS

Bell, Nora K. "The Scarcity of Medical Resources: Are There Rights to Health Care?" *Journal of Medicine and Philosophy* 4: 2(1979) 158–169.

Daniels, Norman. *Just Health Care*. Cambridge and London: Cambridge University Press, 1985.

Deber, R.B. "Canadian Medicare: Can It Work in the United States? Will It Survive in Canada?" *American Journal of Law & Medicine* 19 (1993):75–93.

Drummond, M.F. *Principles of Economic Appraisal in Health Care*. Oxford: Oxford Medical Publications, 1980.

Feeny, David, Gordon Guyatt and Peter Tugwell, eds. *Health Care Technology: Effectiveness, Efficiency and Public Policy*. Montréal: Institute for Research on Public Policy, 1986.

Hall, Mr. Justice Emmett. *Report of the Royal Commission on Health Services*. Ottawa: Queen's Printer, 1964.

Health Care for the Elderly in the Year 2000: Symposium Proceedings. British Columbia Ministry of Health: Victoria, 1986.

Ingelfinger, Franz. "Haves and Have-Nots in the World of Disease." *The New England Journal of Medicine* 287 (Dec. 7, 1972) 1198–1199.

Iglehart, J.K. "The united States looks at Canadian Health Care." *The New England Journal of Medicine* 321(1989):1767–1772.

Kawachi, I. "QUALY's and Justice." *Health Policy* 13:2 (1989) 115-120.

Kilner, John. "The Ethical Legitimacy of Excluding the Elderly When Medical Resources Are Limited." In *Annual of the Society of Christian Ethics,* D. Yeagar, ed., Washington: Georgetown University Press, 1988.

Klarman, H.E., J.O. Francis and G.D. Rosenthal. "Cost-Effectiveness and Analysis Applied to the Treatment of Chronic Renal Disease." *Medical Care* 6 (1968) 48–54.

La Puma, John, and E. Lawlor. "Quality-Adjusted Life Years: Ethical Implications for Physicians and Policy Makers." *Journal of the American Medical Association* 263:21 (1990) 2917–1921.

McKeown, Thomas, and C.R. Lowe. *An Introduction to Social Medicine,* 2d ed. Oxford: Blackwell, 1974.

McKeown, Thomas. *The Role of Medicine: Dream, Mirage or Nemesis?* 2d ed. Oxford: Blackwell, 1979.

Millis, J.S. "Wisdom? Health? Can Society Guarantee Them?" *New England Journal of Medicine*, 283 (July 30, 1970), 260–61.

Mooney, Gavin, and Alistair McGuire, eds. *Medical Ethics and Economics in Health Care*. Oxford and New York: Oxford University Press, 1988.

Siegler, Mark. "A Right to Health Care: Ambiguity, Professional Responsibility and Patient Liberties." *Journal of Medicine and Philosophy* 4: 2 (1979), 148–57.

Veatch, Robert. "Just Social Institutions and the Right to Health Care." *Journal of Medicine and Philosophy*, 4: 2 (1979).

INTRODUCTION (a)

MACRO-ALLOCATION

No matter how technologically advanced a society may be, the amount of goods it can produce and the amount of resources that are available to it are finite. However, societies have an obligation to provide their members with certain services. Therefore, the finite resources that are available have to be divided among the various services that the society has to provide. Health care is only one of these services. Education, transportation, and defence are others. All have to be funded from the same limited resource pool. This means that sooner or later, the limits of the available resources will be reached and hard decisions will have to be made: What proportion of these resources should be assigned to health care? To education? To transportation? These are questions with which policy decision-makers have to wrestle on a constant basis. They are questions of macro-allocation.

However, the issue of macro-allocation goes further. Once a certain quantity of social resources has been assigned to health care, the question arises how these resources should now be allocated within health care itself. That is to say, how much should be apportioned to acute care, how much to continuing care, and how much to preventive medicine? Again, these are macro-allocation questions.

As though these questions were not difficult enough, there are other factors that complicate the issue. For instance, the average age of our population is rising. However, elderly people tend to consume more health care resources than younger persons and have conditions that are encountered only infrequently in young people. How many resources should be set aside specifically for seniors and age-related diseases? Then there is the cost factor associated with the increasing technological sophistication of medicine and health care delivery itself. Medical diagnostic tools and procedures like computer assisted tomography (CAT-scan), magnetic resonance imaging (MRI), positron emission tomography (PET-scans), amniocentesis, and phenylketonuria (PKU) testing, have improved the ability of physicians to detect diseases and conditions. However, the capital and operating costs associated with such developments are tremendous.

Furthermore, in many cases the hidden costs to the health care system arising from people who have been saved by these technologies are even greater. In other words, saving people's lives may be very expensive in terms of social and health care expenditure. Witness the hidden costs associated with saving severely disabled and premature newborn children or with saving elderly people who, in previous decades and with less sophisticated interventions, would have died.

Health care policy-makers, administrators, and health care providers are aware that no matter how beneficial a particular health care service may be, it has to be paid for and has down-stream costs associated with it. Many health care consumers do not have a similar awareness. They tend to look at health care delivery only from the perspective of people who would like to benefit from the service and who claim them as a matter of right, especially in light of the Canada Health Act. Are these claims legitimate? Health care administrators cannot lose sight of these questions because their job is to optimize the use of the resources that are available. By definition, therefore, they have to take a global perspective. In other words, their job is to find acceptable ways of solving the problem of macro-allocation.

There have been various attempts to deal with the problem. Some have suggested that cost/benefit analysis provides the answer[1]; others have focused on cost/effectiveness coefficients[2]; still others have claimed that quality adjusted life-years (QALYs) gained by types of interventions provide a solution; and so on. However, all these approaches have been economically driven. Oregon has recently departed from this approach. It has made an attempt to acknowledge that social values and preferences have a role to play in macro-allocation: since it is society itself that pays for the services, is it not reasonable to say that society should also have a say in which services are provided? The article by Robert Nelson and Theresa Drought presents the so-called Oregon Experiment and considers its ethical implications. It should be noted that the Oregon Experiment was intended only for those services that are funded by MEDICARE and MEDICAID, which is to say, for socially guaranteed services in the U.S. that are available only to people over 65 or under the poverty line. It would be interesting to ask, whether — and how — such an approach could be applied to the Canadian setting. Further, the Oregon approach did not truly consult all health care consumers in a democratic fashion: only selected individuals who are assumed to be representative of society as a whole. Is this appropriate?

Benjamin Freedman and the McGill/Boston Research Group focus on a different question: Under what circumstance should scarce resources be used to provide therapies for specific persons when the very same resources have not been shown to be effective — and when, moreover, the funding of these therapies will reduce the amount of money available to fund established therapies for whole groups of people? These are also questions at the policy level. They become particularly difficult when the persons who would be denied access to the relevant therapies because they are not funded are politically visible and active. Freedman *et al.* focus on HIV infected persons. There are many other examples.

NOTES

1. David Feeny, Gordon Guyatt and Peter Tugwell, eds., *Health Care Technology: Effectiveness, Efficiency and Public Policy* (Montreal: Institute for Research on Public Policy, 1986).

2. Eike-Henner W. Kluge, "Competition and Function: The Canada/US Free Trade Agreement and the Philosophy of Health Care," *Business and Professional Ethics Journal* 10:3 (Fall, 1991)29–52.

Justice and the Moral Acceptability of Rationing Health Care: The Oregon Experiment

Robert M. Nelson and Theresa Drought

In examining the Oregon plan, we will not question the assumption that society has an obligation to provide a "basic level" (Todd, 1989) or "decent minimum" (Buchanan, 1984) of medical care benefits, for such an obligation has achieved a certain level of consensus within our public debate. Rather, the issue is to determine of what this decent minimum consists.

It is unlikely that an agreed specification of a basic level of medical care will result from any particular theory of justice (Buchanan, 1984). Furthermore, the prevalent theories of justice fail to provide a firm basis for a guaranteed right to a decent minimum of medical care regardless of whether we could agree on the content of that right (Buchanan, 1984; Daniels, 1985). Whether the provision of medical care is an entitlement based on a claim against communal property (Engelhardt, 1986, pp. 360-365) or an enforceable duty of charity

R.M. Nelson and T. Drought, "Justice and the Moral Acceptability of Rationing Health Care: The Oregon Experiment," *Journal of Medicine and Philosophy* 1992; 17/1:97–117.

(Buchanan, 1984, pp. 66-72) appears to be of little practical significance in establishing a "basic" or "decent" level of benefits.

The Oregon plan assumes that the right to basic medical care is not an entitlement to a certain fixed level of benefits regardless of cost, for the communal resources that are committed to providing medical care may indeed be limited. A person's inability to obtain medical care because of a limit on available communal resources may be unfortunate, but not unfair (Engelhardt, 1986). In addition to whether available resources have been fairly distributed, the moral acceptability of any rationing scheme depends upon whether the resource scarcity is justified, that is, has an appropriate amount of resources been committed? An unwillingness to increase our contribution to communal resources in order to provide a certain "basic" level of medical care to those less fortunate may reflect a failure to act on a duty of charity (Buchanan, 1984).

THE PROBLEM OF COST-SHARING AND LIMITED FINANCIAL RESOURCES

The driving force for the Oregon legislation is clearly economic. The Oregon plan is predicated on a negative assessment of the ability of the state government to pay for all of the welfare programs, both social and medical, currently under its jurisdiction. The state's ability to pay for the non-federal share of the escalating cost of medical care provided through Medicaid is increasingly limited given decreasing tax revenues and a reluctance to increase taxes in the face of budget deficits.[1] Without an increase in tax revenue or a decrease in other social welfare programs, the state simply cannot afford to provide all necessary medical care[2] to residents who are otherwise uninsured

through employment or other mandated state and federal programs.

Given this limit on available resources, the government is faced with one of four choices for balancing the health care budget: (1) maintain (or decrease) the current level of spending and refuse to provide any medical care for a percentage of residents living below the federal poverty level (FPL); (2) maintain (or decrease) the current level of spending and refuse to provide certain forms of medical care for all residents living below the FPL; (3) maintain (or decrease) the current level of spending and cut reimbursement rates to providers in order to extend access to necessary medical care for most, it not all, residents living below the FPL[3]; and (4) increase the current level of spending in order to provide most, if not all, necessary medical care for all residents living below the FPL.

In order to control spending prior to the 1989 Basic Health Services Act, the Oregon legislature decreased eligibility requirements (first option) and cut reimbursement rates (third option — a standard method of cost control for public and private agencies nationally. Limiting access through decreased eligibility resulted in a subsequent increase in the number of uninsured individuals seeking medical care.[4] The increase in uncompensated care gave rise to mounting operating losses suffered by providers and promoted cost-shifting to the private sector. At the same time, private insurers were taking steps to protect themselves from cost-shifting and were attempting to maintain financial solvency through the increasing use of co-payments, deductibles and premium increases. In fact, the support that the business community has given the Oregon Basic Health Services Act is based on the conviction that private insurance premiums would level off due to the increased coverage ending cost-shifting (Lund, 1990)....[5]

Senate Bill 27, which is the centerpiece of the 1989 Oregon legislation, extends state provision of medical assistance to all eligible individuals whose family income is below the federal poverty level.[6] Any eligibility exclusions would be designed simply to eliminate duplicate coverage. The companion bill, SB 935, and the recently passed SB 1076, establish an employer mandate to provide "substantially similar" coverage for currently uninsured part- and full-time employees through the use of an employer payroll tax and tax credits. These two bills require full participation in providing minimum employee coverage by 1994. Finally, Senate Bill 534 creates a "high-risk" pool for the provision of medical insurance to individuals who have either been turned down for private insurance or who have one of a number of specified medical conditions. Taken together, the Oregon Basic Health Services Act would provide universal access to a basic minimum of medical services for all Oregon residents. The state would accept responsibility for all residents with incomes below the FPL; the business community would accept responsibility for all residents with incomes above the FPL and thus, presumably, employed.

Expanding access and increasing reimbursement can only lead to escalating medical care costs in the absence of restrictions on services to be provided. Accordingly, the mechanism proposed by SB 27 for holding down government spending on health care is the explicit rationing of medical procedures through the development of a "priority list." Once the priority list is generated, the legislature may decide to increase available revenue through taxes or by shifting resources from other programs in order to fund a certain level of medical care deemed "basic" (fourth option). Alternatively, the legislature may decide to decrease or maintain current levels of spending through restricting funded services according to the priority list (second option).[7]

The argument in support of this new approach is that instead of rationing health care based on people's ability to pay, the legislature will be rationing medical care based on the cost and effectiveness of the intervention. Supporters of the Oregon Basic Health Services Act believe that this rationing scheme is a fairer and more just approach to distributing medical care than the system currently employed (Kitzhaber, 1989).

The unusual feature of the Oregon legislation is the manner in which the basic level of medical care would vary according to the legislative commitment of the state's financial resources. Senate Bill 27 established the Health Services Commission and charged it with the task of developing a "list of health services ranked by priority, from the most important to the least important, representing the comparative benefits of each service to the entire population to be served" (SB 27, p. 2). Once this list is compiled, an independent actuary will determine the rates necessary to cover the costs of the services. The Oregon Legislature would then commit a certain level of funds, whereupon the Adult and Family Services Division would contract with health care providers to provide the covered services, reimbursing at cost to the provider.[8] As a result, the practical definition of "adequate care"[9] is simply what the legislature (and, by extension, the residents of Oregon) is willing to pay for in relation to other competing social welfare programs and the overall economic burden of taxation (Kitzhaber, 1989, p. 11). As a result, the basic level of medical care "floats" according to the available economic resources.[10]

The Oregon proposal explicitly endorses a three-tier approach to the delivery of medical care (Kitzhaber, 1989). The government would provide a basic minimum of medical care for those under the FPL; the business community would provide medical care for their employees at a level equal to or greater than the government sponsored tier, depending on such factors as collective bargaining and worker availability; finally, individuals would be free to use their available resources to purchase medical care on the open market (Thurow, 1985).

The extent to which controlling the escalating costs of medical care requires withholding necessary interventions from patients, that is, rationing, is a matter of much controversy. The dividing issue appears to be whether the current level of expenditure in the United States for medical care is excessive, or not; for without some mechanism for the control of spending, increasing access to medical care will simply increase costs as well. Suggested mechanisms of cost control range from increased consumer awareness and managed care plans (Enthoven and Kronick, 1989), through malpractice reform and streamlined administrative costs (American Medical Association, 1989), to a single payor plan and global budgeting (Himmelstein and Woolhandler *et al.,* 1989).

None of these proposals discuss whether access to necessary medical care will be restricted for certain populations. One proposal explicitly maintains that everyone will have access to all necessary medical care (Himmelstein and Woolhandler *et al.,* 1989).[11] The starting point for these proposals is that the proper criteria for the distribution of medical care is need (Todd, 1989, p. 46), as opposed to resource limitation or ability to pay. ...

Substantial differences arise, however, as to whether the level of medical care that all persons will have access to is necessarily uniform (Himmelstein and Woolhandler, 1989)[12] or non-uniform; and, if non-uniform, whether the basic level of medical care is set independent of economic constraints (American Medical Association, 1990; Enthoven and Kronick, 1989; Todd, 1989), or "floats" according to the level of available resources (Kitzhaber, 1990). Any policy that advocates universal access to non-uniform levels of medical care (that is,

a two or more tier system) involves rationing to the extent that the lowest level of available benefits excludes some medically necessary interventions, though this observation is often obscured by a veil of political rhetoric. Alternately, if all medically necessary interventions are included within the minimum level of "basic" benefits (Todd, 1989; Himmelstein and Woolhandler, 1989), it is doubtful that such a program could successfully control medical expenditures.

JUSTICE AND THE WITHHOLDING OF NECESSARY MEDICAL CARE

The fundamental issue is whether it is inequitable or unjust that certain individuals will be denied access to some medically necessary procedures.

A discussion of equity or fairness in the delivery of health care generally starts with the observation that "illness [that is, medical need] is the proper ground for the receipt of medical care" (Outka, 1974, p. 590). The appropriate level of care to be provided to each individual is thus based on medical necessity. Given the distinction between the provision and distribution of medical care, one can ask whether there can be an equitable or just distribution of care in the event that not all needs can be met. The formal principle of justice simply requires that the reasons for discrimination be relevant to the resource being distributed (Beauchamp and Childress, 1989, p. 259). Consequently, under conditions of scarcity, a policy that excluded certain medically necessary procedures "would not be unjust or unequal if done by definable sorts of cases," for example, according to the "category of illness" (Ramsey, 1978, pp. 262-63).

If, however, we allow some individuals to purchase the otherwise excluded medically necessary procedure, it would appear that we are restricting access based on ability to pay rather than on the category of illness. This line of reasoning brings us back to the position that we either restrict an individual's ability to purchase medical care on the open market (a generally unacceptable option) or extend the available "basic" minimum of medical care to include all medically necessary procedures (and thus fail to address the issue of resource scarcity entirely). The Oregon plan allows for the possibility that individuals who earn less than the FPL will be denied access to medically necessary procedures, while other more fortunate residents will either have broader coverage or be able to purchase the otherwise restricted care.

According to the above view of justice, this possibility is simply unjust.

Yet are we (society) obligated to provide all necessary medical care to those who are unable to afford it? Is it a necessary requirement of justice that the basic level of benefits available to members of society include all medically necessary procedures, that is, are all members of society entitled to this level of medical care?

The stipulation that the basic level of available benefits should include all medically necessary services is problematic. Clearly this should not imply that the services to be provided are those which physicians in fact choose to provide, as the wasteful spending habits of physicians are felt to be part of the cause (not the solution) of our current health care crisis. A system based on the "rationalization of care" according to "reasonable expectations of the benefits involved" (Todd, 1989) would not necessarily provide all that is currently understood as medically necessary. The setting of limits around the performance of technically feasible medical interventions based on assessments of burden and benefit involves judgments of both economic and moral value. Practice guidelines may

well improve the quality of delivered medical care and may reduce costs through the elimination of unnecessary tests and procedures. Guidelines, however, may not decrease the overall costs of medical care and would fail to address entirely the issue of the value of a particular intervention relative to other medical and social goods.

Egalitarian arguments in favor of a uniform level of medical care for all citizens would appear to curtail "individual rights to free association and the use of private property" (Engelhardt, 1986). There is no compelling reason why an individual should not be allowed to use his own private resources to purchase medical care above and beyond the established basic level of benefits.

Finally, the level of communal resources which are available for public welfare programs are limited by justified claims of private ownership that necessarily restrict the ability of government to tax individuals and businesses, and thus move property from private to public ownership. From this perspective, an individual's right to publicly sponsored medical care (as well as other welfare programs such as education and housing) is restricted by opposing rights of private property. It may be uncharitable, but not unjust, to fail to provide sufficient medical care to those less fortunate (Engelhardt, 1986, pp. 340-341). However, there is no *a priori* definition of communal property apart from those resources which are voluntarily (and charitably) committed to "communal undertakings" (Engelhardt, 1986, p. 133). Consequently, both the concept of adequate medical care and the level of communal resources to be committed to providing that care are matters of public discussion and negotiation (Engelhardt, 1986, p. 362) — a process (discussed below) which Oregon has indeed begun. There would thus appear to be no practical difference as to whether an entitlement to basic medical care is understood as a claim against communal property (Engelhardt, 1986, p. 361) or as an enforceable duty of charity (Buchanan, 1984, pp. 66-72). ....

THE PHYSICIAN'S OBLIGATION TO THE PATIENT

Senate Bill 27 requires a physician to inform a "patient of any service, treatment or test that is medically necessary but not covered ... if an ordinarily careful practitioner in the same or similar community would do so under the same or similar circumstances" (SB 27, Section 6, paragraph 7). Whereas ordinarily a physician would be liable for failing to provide a medically necessary service to a patient under his or her care, the Act provides immunity from "criminal prosecution, civil liability or professional disciplinary action" if the physician refuses to provide an unfunded service (SB 27, Section 10).

The requirement to inform a patient of medically necessary care that cannot be provided due to lack of funding maintains the role of the physician as "patient advocate," for it allows the patient the option of seeking the care in whatever way possible. Yet this advocacy role is purely as an advisor, for the physician is unable to act in a way consistent with the patient's need for medical care. The role of the physician as patient advocate is maintained at the expense of the physician's clinical autonomy. Yet the physician will also be under pressure to withhold marginally beneficial care that indeed would be covered under the Act in the interest of saving money. In the event of a budget deficit, Section 8 of SB 27 stipulates that the Oregon legislature should reduce medical care for those residents under the FPL by eliminating services according to the priority list. If physicians are not prudent in the use of the state's fiscal resources, otherwise covered services could be eliminated in order to balance the budget.

The granting of immunity from criminal and civil liability is appropriate as physicians in Oregon would have no control over the resources necessary to provide the otherwise indicated medical care. Furthermore, the requirement to provide information to the patient upholds an equal standard of care as far as a physician's professional advice and personal involvement is concerned (Morreim, 1989). Finally, the granting of institutional civil and criminal immunity limits the obligations of health care providers to those established by contract (Morreim, 1989). The contract is by definition the basic minimum standard of medical care, for there is no standard apart from that established by the contract.

Whatever moral obligation a physician may feel towards providing medically necessary care to all patients will prevent an easy accommodation to a "business as usual" approach to the care of patients covered under the Act. The Oregon legislation reveals that under conditions of economic scarcity it is false to assume that physicians can maintain a pure patient advocacy role within the framework of external societal restrictions on resource use (Veatch, 1986; Morreim, 1988).

ESTABLISHING THE BASIC LEVEL OF MEDICAL CARE

Once having agreed that we may design a delivery system that provides more than one tier of medical care, the important issue remains, that is, at what level is the basic minimum of medical care to be established? Should the basic level of care include all medically necessary procedures? If not, how are we to determine which medically nec-essary procedures are to be included? As discussed above, the specification of the content of a general right to a basic level of medical care will be the result, not of the popular acceptance of a general theory of justice, but of a process of "open discussion and fair negotiation" (Engelhardt, 1986, p. 362) based on our own individual and com-munal moral values. The amount of resources to be committed to providing a given level of medical benefits is a "matter of collective choice" (Buchanan, 1984, p. 78) reflecting the complexity of our individual and communal "moral vision" (Engelhardt, 1986, p. 362); that is, both the resources available and the benefits provided are matters for public discussion.

The Oregon legislature, in passing the Basic Health Services Act, recognized that: (1) all residents should have access to a basic level of medical care; (2) available funds for providing medical care are limited; and thus (3) some otherwise medically necessary care may not be provided as part of this basic package. The Oregon Health Services Commission (HSC) was given the task of establishing a priority list which could be used to provide efficacious and cost effective medical care in a manner consistent with the expressed values of Oregon residents.

Open forums for public discussion of societal values related to health care have been held in Oregon since the early 1980s. The Oregon Health Decisions (OHD) pro-gram was formed in 1982 to look at issues posed by the increasing numbers of med-ically indigent Oregon residents following the economic recession at the start of the decade. Their mission was to increase pub-lic awareness and build consensus on bioeth-ical issues, particularly: (1) what value is to be placed on more expensive curative med-ical care relative to the preventive services which are being increasingly curtailed by budget cutbacks; and (2) can the implicit rationing of medical care through restrict-ed access and decreased funding be made explicit and congruent with community val-ues (Crawshaw *et al.,* 1985).

The OHD program was the seed for the 1989 Oregon Basic Health Services Act. Thousands of Oregon residents were involved in these discussions, and three "Citizens Health Care Parliaments" were held between 1984 and 1988 to develop rec-ommendations based on a consensus of val-ues expressed by the participants[13] (Crawshaw, 1986; Garland and Kitzhaber, 1988; Crawshaw *et al.,* 1990). The 1989 Act is intended to embody the recommendations put forth by these community conferences.

The Health Services Commission sought to develop a means of ranking med-ical services using ostensibly objective and quantifiable measures of quality of well-being, quality adjusted life-years (QALYs), actuarial costs, outcomes with and without treatment, and community values. A pre-vious attempt at developing a priority list (Golenski and Blum, 1989) was discarded as vague and ill-defined, with too many medical procedures being given a high pri-ority. The HSC developed a formula that compared various disease categories with and without treatment according to the quality and quantity of expected outcome. In addition, the formula included an estimate of the cost of specific treatments (Oregon Health Services Commission, 1990).

This formula has proven difficult to apply for a number of reasons. First, the list of "condition-treatment pairs"[14] is enor-mous; second, the data for many of the variables is either unreliable or simply unavailable; third, many important ser-vices, such as disease prevention and screening, are excluded; fourth, comorbid-ity is not addressed; and, fifth, the formu-la relies on the controversial concept of Quality Adjusted Life-Years (QALYs). Though the formula has not been dis-carded and continues to be modified in hopes of producing a list based on objective data, the Commission developed an alternative method whereby broader categories were defined under which the "condition-treatment pairs" may be ranked according to the formula (Oregon Health Services Commission, 1991).[15]

The use of QALYs in establishing allocation schemes for medical care is appealing for it combines the elements of cost, quality and benefit in a single scale that then allows for comparison among otherwise incommensurable treatments and health states (Menzel, 1990, pp. 79-80). However, questions have been raised as to whether one can meaningfully measure quality-of-life, and whether accurate data is currently available for determining the burden and benefit of most medical interventions (LaPuma and Lawlor, 1990). The Oregon HSC used provider panels to generate prognostic data concerning condition-treatment pairs — a method that can be criticized as simply relying on collective anecdotes. Additional criticisms have included: (1) the moral validity of comparing the quality of life with the risk of death (Carr-Hill, 1989); (2) the change in an individual's evaluation of risk over time (Rawles, 1989); (3) the use of community values as an indication of individual preference (Carr-Hill, 1989; LaPuma and Lawlor, 1990); and (4) the concern that utility and efficiency will take precedence over patient autonomy and welfare (LaPuma and Lawlor, 1990).

THE PRIOR CONSENT OF THE RATIONED

Apart from the practical concern that there is currently insufficient data to allow for the rational use of a QALY-based formula, the ethical criticisms raised may be adequately addressed provided that those affected by the rationing scheme have given their "prior consent" (Menzel, 1990, pp. 79-96). The moral force of this or any other rationing scheme would thus be based, not on "aggregate welfare," but on respecting the autonomy and personal values of those who have designed and are affected by the policy (Menzel, 1990, pp. 10-19, 22-34).

An appeal to the "prior consent of a rational poor person" (Menzel, 1990, pp. 126-127) as a justification for rationing medical care fails to specify the mechanisms by which such consent would be obtained. Is a simple majority on a health care referendum sufficient, or would a more extensive consensus be required? Can we rely on an elected representative government to speak for the people, or on the deliberations of an appointed commission? Can a voucher system be designed by which the poor select their own mix of medical benefits up to a certain predetermined cost? Given that the level of communal resources available for medical care is also a matter for public discussion, what role do those funding the program, that is, residents with incomes above the FPL, have in consenting to the rationing scheme? Regardless of the mechanism, it is clear that prior consent, whether actual or presumed, "carries the burden of accurately discerning what people would in fact have agreed to" (Menzel, 1990, p. 34).

The Oregon attempt to establish a policy that would ration acute medical care presently fails to satisfy this moral requirement of "prior consent." Participation in the Oregon Health Decisions health care parliaments did not include adequate representation of minorities, the poor, and the medically indigent (Hasnain and Garland, 1990; Oregon Health Services Commission, 1990). The Quality of Well Being scale was developed through a telephone survey of only one thousand randomly selected residents, with no attempt to select adequate samples of individuals with different diseases and disabilities (Oregon Health Services Commission, 1990; Menzel, 1990, p. 84). It is unclear whether individuals were questioned about specific trade-offs between the potential risk of death versus the quality of life given treatment for various conditions. Further, there was no explicit link between initial questions of the value of various medical interventions and health states, and the subsequent use of those values by the Health Services Commission in determining allocations. The point is simple. Prior consent requires that the individuals whose medical care is being rationed should make the decisions over how to allocate the scarce resources.[16]

CONCLUDING REMARKS: THE MORAL ACCEPTABILITY OF RATIONING

The reality of the Oregon plan, and of any program that excludes necessary medical treatments from the basic level of care, is that some patients will die for lack of more extensive insurance coverage. Whether this outcome is morally acceptable or not will depend on a number of factors, the primary one being what the basic level of coverage *in fact* includes. The death of an elderly nursing home patient who is denied dialysis; the death of a child with leukemia who is unable to obtain a bone marrow transplant; the death of a young mother who is unable to obtain appropriate obstetrical services; the death of several children for lack of necessary immunizations — all would be judged differently depending on

our own understanding of what a decent minimum of medical care ought to include. As long as this minimum excludes what would otherwise be medically necessary care, we need to abandon as myth the goal of providing medical care solely according to need.

In sum, the moral acceptability of any rationing scheme depends upon two related questions: (1) Is the resource scarcity justified, that is, has an appropriate amount of resources been committed? and (2) Have these resources been fairly distributed, that is, what is the minimum share that each individual will receive? The Oregon Basic Health Services Act of 1989 fails to give us any indication of the overall amount of available resources or the level of medical benefits that will be provided to residents with incomes below the Federal Poverty Level. As such, no judgment of moral acceptability can be made until the Oregon Legislature has established the level of funding that will be provided.

This is not to say that the Health Services Commission and the legislature of Oregon will necessarily fail to design a just rationing program even if such a program does not provide all medically necessary care. There can indeed be a just distribution of medical care that excludes certain medically necessary procedures, whether based on QALYs or any other value-based determination. However, such a system has as its moral justification the "prior consent" of the residents of Oregon and, in particular, of those residents most affected by the excluded medical care.

NOTES

Supported in part by a National Research Service Award in Bioethics (RMN), National Center for Nursing Research, National Institutes of Health.

1. Oregon residents share with the rest of the country an unwillingness to increase taxes to pay for social programs, in spite of the fact that many people support an increase in government spending for health care (Blendon, 1988; Navarro, 1987).

In the fall of 1990, Oregon residents approved Measure 5 which restricts the state's ability to increase revenue through the raising of property taxes.

2. The description of medical interventions as either necessary or unnecessary is ambiguous. On the one hand, it may imply real urgency, for example, that someone will die or suffer serious harm without the intervention. On the other hand, physicians use the term "necessary" to indicate what's ordinary and routine, so that "necessary" comes to mean standard interventions regardless of the urgency of need. As argued below, without a specification of the relative necessity of various medical interventions, it is impossible to judge the merits or demerits of any rationing scheme. The Oregon plan to prioritize medical care can be described as a ranking of medical interventions according to relative necessity. We choose to leave our use of the term "medically necessary" ambiguous (as does the "rationing" literature), for to remove all ambiguity would require an established set of rankings.

3. Cutting reimbursement rates, however, tends to decrease the number of providers willing to care for this population. The result is that access is actually decreased while services are only apparently maintained.

4. As of June 1989, Medicaid eligibility included families under 58% of the Federal Poverty Level (FPL), pregnant women or women with young children up to 100% FPL, medically needy, and aged, blind or disabled. This left some 140,000 Oregon residents uninsured, or 47% of the population living below the FPL (Zermer, 1989).

5. To affirm the value of universal access to medical care does not necessarily imply that a certain level of medical care benefits is a basic human right. Universal access may be proposed as a solution to the problem of uncompensated care and cost-shifting (Kitzhaber, 1989), rather than on the basis of an entitlement (Todd, 1989). Universal coverage may also be viewed as the only way to decrease the burden of administrative expenses and allow for an effective mechanism of global budgeting (Himmelstein and Woolhandler, 1989).

6. Eligibility will be extended to all residents whose income is below 100% of the Federal Poverty Level, including single adults and childless couples (who are excluded under current rules). Pregnant women and children under the age of six years will be covered up to 135% of the FPL, consistent with changes in federal Medicaid legislation effective April 1, 1990.

7. The fact that SB 27 does not stipulate a "basic" level of medical care independent of available funding has led to the concern that the level of funding provided may be so low as to exclude many otherwise "basic" procedures. If we could agree on a specification of what a "basic" level of medical care included, the available funding could be adjusted accordingly. The Health Services Commission struggled with the task of defining a minimum benefit level independent of the funding provided. The desire to define the basic minimum of medical care to be made available may arise out of a discomfort with the level being set purely on economic grounds, as well as in response to special interests who press for a definition that would include medical care directed at their own needs. The Commission was caught between two opposing problems. On the one hand, it is clear that a def-

inition of basic minimum benefits potentially would undercut the intent of SB 27, given that Oregon residents to date have been unwilling to increase tax revenues to pay for medical care. On the other hand, if the level of funded benefits is so low as to be unacceptable, the state may fail to obtain the necessary federal waivers in order to allow the program to proceed, and may also lose the support of local citizen, labor and business groups. The success of SB 27 may then lie in having demonstrated that the "basic" level of medical care that society deems acceptable comes at a price which necessitates the raising of additional tax revenue or the severe curtailing of other social welfare programs.

8. The latest version of the priority list defined 709 line items containing at least one condition/treatment pair, grouped under 17 categories of care ranked in order of importance. The Health Services Commission recommended a Standard Benefits Package to the Legislature, indicating that the first nine categories should be considered "essential services," the next four categories "very important," and the last four categories "valuable to certain individuals" (Oregon Health Services Commission, 1991). The Oregon Legislature has referred to line 585 as a "critical level" of funding. This would cover nearly all of the items under "essential" services, the majority of items under "very important" services, and little of the services deemed only "valuable to certain individuals" (Thome, 1991).

9. Kitzhaber's use of the term "adequate" to describe the level of medical care that the state chooses to provide appears to exclude the possibility that the state may choose to provide inadequate medical care. The moral acceptability of Oregon's rationing scheme not only rests on the method of distributing funded benefits, but also on the total level of benefits provided. Kitzhaber appears to exclude the possibility that the State of Oregon may fairly distribute an unacceptably low level of medical benefits.

10. The moral acceptability of the level of medical care provided may hinge on the reasons why the state's financial resources are limited. It is one thing to claim that the money just doesn't exist (that is, that further taxes would hurt the economy or that further expenditures are prohibited by law, as in a constitutional requirement for a balanced budget); another thing, to claim that the money exists but that taxes cannot be raised (for example, that increased taxes would be unpopular even if it wouldn't hurt the economy or break the law); and still another thing, to say that we are unwilling to reallocate from other areas such as education in order to increase health care spending.

11. It seems unlikely that all medically necessary services could be provided on an equal basis to the entire population simply on the savings achieved by a central administrative and financial control. Inevitably, the central budgeting committee would either need to establish explicit criteria for the rationing of medical care (as Oregon is attempting to do) or ration through planned scarcity and subsequent "queuing" (as in Canada).

12. The proposal by the Physicians for a National Health Program calls for a single comprehensive program that would provide equal access to all medically necessary services, that is, universal access to equal medical care. The authors appear a bit too sanguine about the possibility of a medical board capping expen-

ditures through the determination of necessary versus unnecessary medical interventions. At the point that a necessary medical intervention must be eliminated in favor of balancing the budget, the restriction on the use of private financial resources and insurance in obtaining the benefit loses credibility. The point here is that their arguments in favor of universal access to equal medical care under a single national program are largely pragmatic, involving administrative savings, ease of application of benefits and the use of global budgeting. To the extent that an individual's liberty to purchase necessary though unfunded medical care through the use of personal resources is curtailed in the interest of an egalitarian system, such a program can be characterized as unjust (Engelhardt, 1986, p. 360).

13. While many residents were involved in these conferences, they were not truly representative of the overall population. In general, middle class, well-educated whites as well as health care professionals were over-represented, while minorities, the poor, and those with little education were under-represented. In particular, Medicaid recipients and the uninsured who will bear the burden of current rationing procedures were notable in their absence (Hasnain and Garland, 1990).

14. The formula is based on pairing ICD-9 diagnostic codes and the corresponding CPT procedural codes.

15. The line items based on condition-treatment pairs were ranked within the 17 categories according to the formula based on cost and QALYs. The categories were developed and ranked by the Health Services Commission taking into account the values and priorities expressed in the state-wide community meetings (Hasnain and Garland, 1990). The HSC then adjusted individual items in the overall priority list to more accurately reflect their collective judgments of the importance of the item in the overall ranking scheme (Thorne, 1991).

16. The Health Services Commission struggled with the definition of a basic level of medical care below which no resident of Oregon should fall. This task is outside of their mandate from the legislature and places the overall rationing scheme in jeopardy if the eventual level of resources committed to medical care falls below that necessary to fund the stipulated minimum level (see notes 7 and 8). Perhaps the Commission's desire to set a basic level of medical care is out of a recognition that they themselves should be willing to live under such a standard. If so, setting a decent minimum would serve as an affirmation of the moral principle of "prior consent." In addition, the desire to set a basic minimum level of medical care may acknowledge that the moral acceptability of any rationing scheme (and of the Commission's work) depends upon the balance between resources used and benefits provided.

REFERENCES

American Medical Association: 1990, *Health Access America: The AMA Proposal to Improve Access to Affordable, Quality Health Care,* Chicago, Illinois.

Baker, T., 1990: "Medicaid," personal communication, 18 September, 1990 Portland, OR.

Beauchamp, T. and Childress, J.: 1989, *Principles of Biomedical Ethics,* third edition, Oxford University Press, New York.

Blendon, R.J.: 1988, "What should be done about the uninsured poor?" *Journal of the American Medical Association* 260, 3176-3177.

Buchanan, A.: 1984, "The right to a decent minimum of health care," *Philosophy & Public Affairs* 13, 55-78.

Carr-Hill, R.: 1989, "Background material for the workshop on QALYS: Assumptions of the QALY procedure," *Social Science & Medicine* 29, 469-477.

Crawshaw, R.: 1986, "Society must decide — Oregon health decisions: Bioevaluation beyond bioethics," *The Western Journal of Medicine* 144, 246-248.

Crawshaw, R.: 1989, "Organ transplants — A search for health policy at the state level," *The Western Journal of Medicine* 150, 361-363.

Crawshaw, R., Carland, M., Hines, B., and Anderson, B.: 1990, "Developing principles for prudent health care allocation: The continuing Oregon experiment," *The Western Journal of Medicine* 152, 441-446.

Crawshaw, R., Garland, M., Hines, B., and Lobitz, C.: 1985, "Oregon health decisions," *Journal of the American Medical Association* 254, 3213-3216.

Daniels, N.: 1985, "Fair equality of opportunity and decent minimums: A reply to Buchanan," *Philosophy & Public Affairs 14, 106-110.*

Daniels, N.: 1988, *Am I My Parents' Keeper?* Oxford University Press, New York.

Engelhardt, H.T., Jr.: 1986, *The Foundations of Bioethics,* Oxford University Press, New York.

Enthoven, A. and Kronick, R.: 1989, "A consumer-choice health plan for the 1990s: Universal health insurance in a system designed to promote quality and economy" (two parts), The *New England Journal of Medicine* 320, 29-37, 94-101.

Garland, M. and Kitzhaber, J.: *1988, Principles for Health Care Resource Allocation,* adopted by the 1988 Citizens Health Care Parliament, Portland, OR.

Golenski, J. and Blum, S.: 1989, *The Oregon Medicaid Priority Setting Project,* The Fred Myers Charitable Trust, Bioethics Consultation Group, Berkeley, CA.

Hasnain, R. and Garland, M.: 1990, *Health Care in Common: Report of the Oregon Health Decisions Community Meetings Process,* Oregon Health Decisions, Salem, OR.

Himmelstein, D., Woolhandler, S., *et al.*: 1989, "A national health program for the United States: A physicians' proposal," *The New England Journal of Medicine* 320, 102-108.

Kitzhaber, J.: 1988, "Uncompensated care — The threat and the challenge," *The Western Journal of Medicine* 148, 711-716.

Kitzhaber, J.: *1989, Discussion Paper (August 1, 1989): Senate Bill 27,* Oregon State Senate, State Capitol, Salem, OR.

Kitzhaber, J.: 1990, "The Oregon basic health services act," Oregon State Senate, State Capitol, Salem, OR.

LaPuma, J. and Lawlor, E.: 1990, "Quality-adjusted life-years: Ethical implications for physicians and policymakers," *Journal of the American Medical Association* 263, 2917-2921.

Lund, D.: 1990, "Oregon faces new tax hurdle in Medicaid access plan," *American Medical News,* July 27, 1990, 11-12.

Menzel, P.: 1990, *Strong Medicine: The Ethical Rationing of Health Care,* Oxford University Press, New York.

Morreim, E.: 1988, "Cost containment: Challenging fidelity and justice," *Hastings Center Report* 18, 20-25.

Morreim, E.: 1989, "Stratified scarcity: Redefining the standard of care," *Law, Medicine & Health Care* 17, 356-367.

Navarro, V.: 1987, "Federal health policies in the United States: An alternative explanation," *The Milbank Quarterly* 65, 81-111.

Oregon Health Services Commission: 1990, *Preliminary Report: March 1, 1990,* Health Services Commission, Salem, OR.

————. 1991, *Prioritization of Health Services: A Report to the Governor and the Legislature,* Health Services Commission, Salem, OR.

Outka, G.: 1974, "Social justice and equal access to health care," *The Journal of Religious Ethics* 2, 11-32, as reprinted in S.J. Reiser, A.J. Dyck, and W.J. Curran *(eds.), Ethics in Medicine,* The MIT Press, Cambridge, Massachusetts, pp. 584-593.

Ramsey, P.: 1978, *Ethics at the Edges of Life,* Yale University Press, New Haven.

Rawles, J.: 1989, "Castigating QALYs," *Journal of Medical Ethics* 15, 143-147.

Thorne, J.: 1991, "Oregon's plan," presentation to *Rationing America's Medical Care: Opening Pandora's Box?* Center for Public Policy Education, The Brookings Institution, Washington, D.C.

Thurow, L.: 1985, "Medicine versus economics," *The New England Journal of Medicine* 313, 611-614.

Todd, J.: 1989, "It is time for universal access, not universal insurance," *The New England Journal of Medicine* 321, 46-47.

Veatch, R.: 1986, "DRGs and the ethical allocation of resources," *Hastings Center Report* 16, 32-40.

Welch, H. and Larson, E.: 1988, "Dealing with limited resources: The Oregon decision to curtail funding for organ transplantation," *The New England Journal of Medicine* 319, 171-173.

Zermer, M.: 1989, "Staff measure summary — SB 27," Oregon House of Representatives, prepared 16 June 1989.

Nonvalidated Therapies and HIV Disease

Benjamin Freedman and the McGill / Boston Research Group

The introduction of potential treatments for HIV disease has, in almost every instance, engendered controversy. The speedy approval of AZT (Zidovudine) has led to charges that FDA was inappropriately influenced by political considerations, and the current extensive studies on AZT are pointed out as evidence that the drug was granted approval before adequate testing had been completed.[1] The initial tests of ribavirin were criticized by some for their supposed inappropriate and unethical use

Benjamin Freedman and the McGill/Boston Research Group, "Nonvalidated Therapies and HIV Disease," *Hastings Center Report* 19:3 (June 1989)14-20.

of a placebo control group. Organized demonstrations have been held and legal action taken to rectify perceived delays in providing aerosolized pentamidine as prophylaxis against *pneumocystis carinii* pneumonia (PCP).[2]

The controversies that have swirled about nonvalidated treatments (NTs) for HIV disease touch upon crucial questions of ethics and public policy. These questions are unresolved within the communities professionally concerned — physicians, researchers, and government officials — as they are unresolved among patients and in society at large.

SCOPE AND CONTEXT OF THE PROBLEM

The definition of nonvalidated therapies has been itself a matter of some controversy in the literature.[3] In what follows, I shall mean by nonvalidated therapies those drugs, medical and surgical interventions, and regimens that are offered to and accepted by a patient on the basis of potential benefit, and that have neither been accepted nor discredited by the expert clinical community. Nonvalidated therapies are distinct from, on the one hand, customary and accepted treatments; and, on the other, quack remedies. Because of the uncertainty surrounding them, the ethics of practice in providing nonvalidated therapies cannot be subsumed under the general ethics of clinical practice; nor are such therapies uniformly provided pursuant to an approved protocol, and in those instances are not subjected to the moral canons of clinical research. What treatments currently fall within this rubric? And what are the characteristics of the population seeking NTs?

Discussions of policy and ethics regarding NTs tend to focus on investigational new drugs (INDs), which are novel pharmacologically active substances under testing for anti-viral, immunomodulating, or other beneficial effect.[4] AZT stands as the paradigm case, a drug whose only previous presumed use, as an anti-cancer agent, had been discredited in early trials.

Investigational new drugs are under the close control of regulatory bodies, such as FDA (in the United States) or Health Protection Branch (in Canada). The view that equates nonvalidated treatments with INDs, therefore, leads naturally to the presumption that reform of the policy and rules governing NTs must focus upon the conduct of such regulatory bodies. The scope of NTs is, however, much broader than that; and the power of regulatory agencies correspondingly limited.

Nonvalidated therapies without IND status fall into several categories; each shares the qualities of uncertainty, therapeutic intention, and immunity from regulatory control:

Licensed drugs offered for an unapproved use

Whereas a drug receives marketing approval after demonstrated safety and effectiveness under defined conditions of use, once approved, a licensed drug may be prescribed by a physician, exercising his or her clinical discretion, for other conditions.[5] U.S. regulations, for example, state that "the physician may, as part of the practice of medicine, lawfully prescribe a different dosage for his patient or may otherwise vary the conditions of use from those approved in the package insert without informing or obtaining the approval of the Food and Drug Administration."[6] Antabuse is an example of a drug licensed for one condition that is currently taken by many persons infected with HIV. Regulatory agencies have taken the stance that enforcing the restriction of licensed drugs to approved uses is beyond their jurisdiction. The point is not always appreciated. The expert panel FDA assembled on AZT, for example, had recommended that the drug be approved only as a treatment for AIDS patients who had had an episode of PCP.[7] In licensing the drug for marketing, however, FDA cannot enforce such a restriction.

Non-drugs and not-necessarily-drugs

Among the treatments touted for HIV are dietary and life-style changes, which are obviously beyond regulatory control. One interesting case is AL–721. This substance, with suspected anti-viral properties, is a special preparation of common foodstuffs. It is being marketed as a prescription drug in Great Britain, but because of the cost and delay involved in receiving U.S. regulatory approval, and under pressure from generic competitors, its manufacturer now plans to market it as a "food supplement" in the United States.[8] Other possible inclusions within this category would be substances such as dextran sulfate or DTC (Imuthiol), which are under clinical investigation but may be obtained by the public from nonpharmaceutical sources such as chemical supply houses and which the patient may then self-administer.

New combinations of treatments

As with the first category of unapproved use of licensed substances, attempting new combinations of treatments reproduces the combination of therapeutic intent and scientific uncertainty. Current AIDS research is largely preoccupied with testing new combinations of drugs and other treatments (for example, AZT in combination with interferon or acyclovir), and this category will necessarily grow as new drugs are included within the validated AIDS pharmacopoeia.

Smuggled substances

The growing use of drugs smuggled from Europe and Mexico by AIDS patients or their doctors has been widely noted; FDA has in fact recently informed its agents in writing to ignore the importation of unapproved drugs by patients for their own use.[9]

In the light of these categories of non-validated therapies, it is clear that the role of regulators, though crucial, is limited. By the same token, the central importance of the doctor-patient relationship in confronting these issues is brought to the fore. Only in the clinical setting can much use of NTs in HIV be monitored (if indeed it can be done there); only in that setting can such use be influenced by informed judgment. At the same time, it must be acknowledged that the controversies to date have largely swirled about IND treatments, and that IND policy is the element most given to rapid reform.

Previous experience with treatments for other conditions, notably tuberculosis, indicates that unproven therapy remains popular until such point as an effective therapy is developed; thus, the issue in HIV treatment is likely to persist for some time to come. Current research on those being treated for cancer by unorthodox means also has some lessons to teach us. Among cancer patients, there is a strong direct relationship between experienced toxicity from standard treatment and the subsequent use of unorthodox treatments. In addition, contrary to the stereotype of the uneducated, credulous patient victimized by the unscrupulous practitioner, "[t]he evidence seems overwhelming that socioeconomic status is either independent of the use of such therapies or that higher status and better educated individuals are over-represented among the patients of unorthodox practitioners."[10]

These characteristics have expressed themselves in our context of HIV disease in a way that raises an urgent ethical problem of equity.[11] In the United States, the bulk of the infected population is increasingly bifurcated, being composed of gay men on the one hand, and, on the other, intravenous drug users and their sexual partners. The latter group has little in the way of education, information, or resources to deploy toward novel therapies. Gay infected men, on the other hand — particularly as their illness progresses — have voted with their feet, vigorously gathering information about potential therapies and aggressively pursuing access to them. Within this group, motivated by desperation, the use of nonvalidated therapies with or without a physician's assistance may yet become the rule rather than the exception. At one meeting of Body Positive in 1987, for example, more than three quarters of the audience of 400 raised their hands when asked how many were taking experimental or alternative drug treatment.[12]

In part their efforts are expressed in unprecedented activity providing information about current clinical trials directly to infected persons. The American Foundation for AIDS Research publishes a pamphlet with regular updates listing the protocols of clinical trials currently underway, together with their operative criteria of inclusion and exclusion.[13] This publication is distributed gratis upon request to persons who have tested positive for HIV antibodies. Groups such as Project Inform in San Francisco and Treatment AIDS in Toronto gather information about the clinical use of NTs and distribute it to persons with AIDS via newsletters. Some sources will inform persons about means of preparation and self-administration of experimental substances, and how they may be smuggled into the country.

These facts raise some clear challenges to any proposal for reform of the process regarding NTs. Overall, the number of persons prepared to take the risks involved in receiving nonvalidated treatment far outnumber those who may be admitted to controlled scientific trials. The regulatory authorities are increasingly in danger of becoming irrelevant; as I will suggest below, the response to this adopted by FDA — strategic retreat in the form of the treatment IND exemption — only hastens this mounting irrelevancy, with added unfortunate precedential value for other conditions. In turn, the gay male community is left to self-help resources; without a counterbalance, this leaves it potential prey to rumor fostered by hope and nourished by companies who see a profit opportunity in the manufacture of nonvalidated therapies. Finally, the other major group of infected persons — inner-city IV drug users and their sexual partners — has no entrée to the system. Often excluded from trials because of supposed unreliability, or dropping out because of actual unreliability, and lacking the knowledge or resources to pursue NTs on an off-protocol basis, they are denied any potential benefits that may accrue to those receiving drugs prior to conclusion of the validating process.

SOME POLICY OPTIONS

Proposals for reforming the process for dealing with NTs fall along a continuum of change. The least radical changes involve reform of the manner in which the drug agencies operate under current regulations and statutory authority. Much remains to be done along these lines. "Compassionate use" exemptions, for example, could be interpreted broadly rather than narrowly; queuing and consequent delays in reviewing could be managed better than in noncrisis times; traditional cautious practices, such as requiring the replication of well-designed double blind randomized trials, could be amended. However, most attention has been focused upon radical proposed changes to the process altering the underlying philosophy of drug regulation.

An early proposal by Mathilde Krim may be the most familiar.[14] She had proposed maintaining the bureaucratic *status quo* with respect to asymptomatic infected persons, or those in the early stages of HIV disease (AIDS-Related Complex), but eliminating all restrictions to free access, via their physician, to any substance proposed for treatment of a person with full-blown AIDS. In exempting an entire class of patients from regulatory restraints on the basis of the severity of their illness, Krim's proposal represents a radical departure from traditional drug regulation philosophy, which held the critically ill to be in at least as great need of protection through regulation as any other patient.

Were Krim's proposal to be implemented, it might become impossible to conduct controlled trials on AIDS patients since they would all have unrestricted access to experimental substances. This consequence does not concern her, for in her view "[t]he most valuable proof of the efficacy of the drugs will be studies conducted on patients in the earlier stages of illness." The ravages involved in the progression to AIDS make it unlikely in her view that treatment would help, but nevertheless she believes that offering such treatment is ethically imperative:

> Permitting physicians to use experimental drugs to treat patients whose lives are in immediate jeopardy should not be done out of a wishful belief that the treatment would work. It should be done out of respect for the patient's right to fight for life with whatever tools we can offer.

AZT itself demonstrates several problems with her proposal. As AZT shows, AIDS patients can receive significant therapeutic benefit; meaningful controlled results can be obtained in tests upon a population with full-blown AIDS; and, the harm-benefit ratio associated with a drug changes over the course of disease, rendering drug toxicity that may be excessive early on acceptable as the patient's options shrink. Moreover, persons with AIDS die of opportunistic infections, not HIV, and treatments specific to these infections cannot be tested before they occur, whether early or late in the progressive breakdown of the immune system. In general, our growing knowledge of the erratic continuum of HIV disease makes a hard division between AIDS itself and everything up to it medically inappropriate.

One final point is most troubling. Even were it the case that an AIDS patient is beyond help, it does not follow that he or she is beyond being hurt as well — and both must be true if drugs are to be made available that have satisfied neither norms of safety or of efficacy. For example, the early experimental treatment suramin proved in tests to be both toxic and, in some instances, to contribute itself to worsening immune disorders. The death of an AIDS patient is not so imminent that it cannot be hastened by misguided treatment, nor is the disease so dreadful that the quality of life of its sufferers cannot be worsened by inappropriate treatment. As Oliver Wendell Holmes, Sr., once said, if all of the unproven remedies doctors carry in their saddle bags were to be dumped into the ocean, it would be so much the better for their patients and so much the worse for the fish.

A second radical proposal that has been implemented by FDA, the introduction of the category of the treatment IND, responds to some of these points.[15] The new category was adopted under the obvious impetus and avowed influence of the AIDS crisis, although since its recent adoption its most frequent use has been for non-AIDS drugs. The treatment IND category is intended to weaken substantially, without abandoning altogether, the requirement that a drug be demonstrably effective before being allowed into clinical practice. In brief, it requires that a drug for an immediately life-threatening condition be approved provided FDA is satisfied that it "may be effective" and the risk of its use is not "unreasonable and significant"; if a drug is intended for use on a serious but not immediately life-threatening condition, it shall be approved for clinical use upon demonstration of safety and preliminary evidence of effectiveness.[16]

It is still uncertain how this amended regulation will be interpreted and work out in practice. For example, a broad reading of the regulation would include asymptomatic HIV infection under the "immediately life-threatening" rubric, defined as "a stage of a disease in which there is a reasonable likelihood that death will occur within a matter of months *or in which premature death is likely without early treatment*" (emphasis added). The financial implications for drug companies are also unclear at this point. It appears that while the preparation of applications for treatment IND status will be fairly expensive, they will nonetheless still be much cheaper than the ordinary cost of drug development is currently[17]; and treatment IND status is granted prior to completion of Phase III trials, which represent by far the most expensive phase of drug testing for companies. Until the treatment IND category was introduced, drug companies were not permitted to charge for drugs in clinical trials without special approval. Supplying drugs for trials was considered part of the normal costs of doing business. Drug companies by contrast are automatically permitted to charge for the use of drugs with treatment IND status, at a rate that permits them "to recover costs of manufacture, research, development, and handling" of the drug. The companies are nonetheless forbidden to "commercialize" treatment INDs, a prohibition whose force and meaning remains uncertain.

The Pharmaceutical Manufacturers Association has warned that a company that can charge for its drug will have no incentive to complete the expensive testing necessary to achieve regular marketing approval.[18] In response, the regulations require that the companies whose product has been granted this status be vigorously engaged concurrently in completing testing and the approval process. As a matter of structural public policy, however, this seems an inadequate response. Heretofore, the drug companies' vigorous pursuit of testing was motivated by the pull toward potential drug profits, which could not be realized without FDA approval. Henceforward, rather than being pulled by natural market forces, testing will be pushed by FDA pressure. It is economically wasteful to substitute artificial regulatory pressure for natural market forces, and it is particularly doubtful that in the current context of scarce regulatory resources the money needed will be found — money that must be carved out of the same budget that is already failing to keep up with IND and other new drug (NDA) applications.

Other practical concerns stated by university researchers and the American Medical Association express fear that controlled clinical trials of drugs granted this status will become impossible due to a failure of enrollment of subjects. Patients may not agree to be randomized into treatment or placebo control groups if they have guaranteed access to the treatment by clinical prescription. Clamor to receive the "new treatment" may prove to be intensified by a now-unjustified reliance by patients upon regulators, for patients have become accustomed to the idea that a drug cannot be legally sold unless it is safe and effective. But the failure to complete these trials will serve neither those patients themselves — who serve as guinea pigs for treatments of unproved efficacy, and pay for the privilege — nor future patients, who are denied the advantage of prior validation of treatments.

One final conceptual difficulty of the regulations should be noted. It treats safety and efficacy as two separate categories. As long as a drug is shown to be safe (more precisely, not unreasonably risky) its treatment use may be authorized pending a finding of efficacy. But safety and efficacy must nearly always be judged in relative rather than absolute terms, and nearly always as a balance rather than as independent factors — a function rather than a conjunction. The bottom line — Is this drug worth prescribing or not? — is affected by knowledge concerning systemic or symptomatic benefit, side effects, and other factors, and safety and efficacy may only be understood as elements within this function. To make the same point in other words, a drug's pharmacologic activity is the basis of both positive and negative effects (that is, "efficacy" as well as "risk"). The only perfectly safe drug is a perfectly inert — hence, perfectly useless — drug. A regulation presuming the contrary will yield either limited or distorted application.

Libertarians have seen in AIDS an opportunity to further their anti-regulationist agenda. Dale Gieringer, on behalf of the Cato Institute, has suggested that the informed consent of the patient, rather than regulation, be the determinant of access to investigational drugs.[19] Any patient who, being fully informed about any new substance, chooses to risk his life and health by taking it, should be granted that option.

Confidence in consent is misplaced in this instance. By definition of nonvalidated therapies, the consent would be minimally informed at best. It would be consent granted under desperation, and consent that is likely fostered by drug company promotion. Adherence to such a consent in the form of administering such a drug also professionally impugns the responsible physician, who is trained to use his or her own edu-cated judgment rather than simply complying with patients' requests. The testing and medical research upon which this professional judgment relies would be entirely undercut by Gieringer's proposal.

WHAT CONSTITUTES A DESIRABLE POLICY?

The elements of desirable changes in policy toward nonvalidated treatments used for HIV disease have emerged from the above critique. The central points of the current philosophy of drug regulation should be conserved. In particular, drugs should not be licensed for marketing until they have been proved safe and effective under proposed conditions of use, a judgment that should be arrived at by a panel with comprehensive expertise rather than by private practitioners and their patients alone. (It may, however, be argued that "comprehensive expertise" requires representation from the points of view of patients and private physicians.) Finally, it is critically important that drug companies should not be permitted to reap any economic benefit from a drug until this process has been completed.

One additional desideratum is implicit in the above discussion: Any change in the process must be at least consistent with, if not positively enhancing of, the ability to speedily conclude sound scientific evaluations of any new treatments. Because of the ever-growing numbers of infected persons, practices and procedures within the context of the regulations should be streamlined to the maximum extent. Equally, however, the growing number of cases argues for the early resolution of the question of safety and effectiveness.

This double-edged character of the epidemic factor in AIDS may be illustrated by a simple analogy. A large boulder is rolling down a cliff, toward a populated area. An early nudge will achieve the largest alteration of its path with the minimum effort. But you want to be sure that you're nudging it in the right direction: because you don't want to waste your effort; because there may not be time to mount a second effort; because a misguided nudge might endanger a still-more-populated region. For AIDS, as for the boulder, the message is: Hurry up — carefully. More lives will be saved, in the end, by aiming accurately than by aiming early. Applied to the specific issue of drug licensure, the metaphor cautions us not to jeopardize the conclusion of needed clinical trials in the interest of satisfying patient demands for access to an NT.

This point requires some further discussion. It entails that, when conflict between a patient or treating physician's desire for access to a nonvalidated treatment and the pursuit and early conclusion of a sound, ethical trial is unavoidable, the latter may be allowed to take precedence. If, for example, it is only possible to recruit sufficient subjects by restricting access to the drug to those eligible persons who agree to enroll, we would be expressing such a preference. Yet seemingly, to do this would grant the progress of science priority over patient rights.

The justification depends upon establishing that the patient's right to medical treatment is unimpaired by denying the patient access to an unvalidated intervention. The ethics of a controlled clinical trial require that throughout its conduct a state of clinical equipoise exist between the experimental and control arm(s) (including placebo control, if any); in other words, that the relative therapeutic merit of the proposed innovation remains a genuinely undecided question amongst the community of expert practitioners.[20] It is this state of equipoise, of clinical uncertainty, that serves to justify the withholding of the innovation from the control population, because as long as this state of uncertainty persists,

the innovation cannot be classified for normative purposes as a medical treatment. Once the uncertainty has been resolved, however, the trial must ethically be terminated, and the now-validated treatment offered to all eligible patients.

The same ethical analysis concerning the right to treatment that applies to the control population applies to the patient population outside of the trial as well. A patient, within a trial as without, is unconditionally entitled to receive medical treatment. "Medical treatment" as a normative concept, however, must be defined and delimited by medical expertise rather than by a patient's beliefs. The right to medical treatment does not encompass every drug or intervention that a patient considers therapeutically worthwhile, on whatever evidence he or she has found convincing. Until the therapeutic advantage of an innovation has been demonstrated to the satisfaction of the community of expert practitioners, an innovation is no medical treatment, and so is not covered by a patient's right to access to medical treatments. Consistent with the above, however, we may add that to the extent that a patient's desire to receive an innovation may be satisfied without jeopardizing the conduct of a clinical trial, then, consistent with good clinical judgment, the desire of the patient should be allowed to prevail.

A reform that might satisfy these various desiderata would focus upon the factor missing from other proposals, the physician-researcher treating persons with HIV infection. The proposal builds upon the growing development of specialized research and treatment units for AIDS — for example, AIDS Clinical Trial Units (ACTUs) — which combine substantial expertise in AIDS diagnosis, treatment, and research, together with sophisticated laboratory support. Clinicians in these units are active collaborators in treatment protocols granted high priority by the AIDS Clinical Drug

Development Committee, and play an important role in developing treatment protocols and in their accelerated evaluation.[21] They have not yet been assigned any formal role, however, in expediting the evaluation of NTs, nor have other similarly designated expert units.[22]

The proposal is to institute similar units (or specified investigators), in the United States and Canada, which are formally granted the authority to utilize restricted investigational drugs on a compassionate use basis.[23] The regulatory authorities would be notified about such use, and would be able to monitor these Authorized Investigational Units (AIUs) and provide retrospective control, but their prior approval for individual use would not be needed. In effect, any drug having IND status would be available for the testing and clinical use of the designated AIDS facilities; something resembling "treatment IND" status would be granted at the (monitored) discretion of the expert practitioners of these units. Consistent with previous practice, drug companies would not be permitted to charge for drugs employed within protocols. For those drugs used on an "off-protocol" basis, they would be permitted to recover the direct marginal cost of production and handling only. Charges allowing amortization of other costs of research and development would not be permitted until the drug had completed the approval process, so that the natural incentives for completion of testing would be retained.

How would this improve upon the current system, and over the U.S. treatment IND modification? A number of points can be noted:

Regulatory expense and delay is minimized — or moved to after-the-fact review, when delay is not bought at the patient's expense.

Current practice on compassionate and other exemptions to access to investigational drugs would be formalized and regularized. Currently, such exemptions are said to rely upon the regulator's judgment that the practitioner in question possesses the needed expertise; under this proposal, a formal determination to this effect would be made of the unit as a whole, in advance of a request commonly made when a patient is *in extremis*.

The conflict of interest of drug companies in concluding trials would be eliminated. The personnel of the authorized unit, active researchers as well as clinicians, already possess and would retain a natural incentive vigorously to pursue to conclusion scientifically sound protocols. Even while ostensibly seeking the same goal — for example, approval of the drug regulatory authority — the incentive system governing the clinical investigator radically differs from that of a drug company. The researcher's incentives (publication, recognition, etc.) are themselves contingent upon satisfying norms of value and validity of clinical research. For the investigator, FDA approval is the by-product of sound, cautious research into a drug's safety and efficacy, and at most, from that point of view, serves to ratify the choices and findings of the investigator. FDA approval plays a different role in the rational economic calculations of a drug company; rather than a by-product, it is significant in itself as the major necessary step to licensure and marketing of a drug. Neither undue naïveté about the motivations of researchers nor excessive cynicism about the intentions of drug companies is required to conclude that it is safer to relax the regulatory harness upon the former than the latter.

Authorized units could be set up in such a way as to enhance the possibility of pooling uncontrolled data as well. For those receiving a drug outside of an approved protocol, there has always been difficulty in monitoring and assessing the significance of drug incidents and misadventures, which can be important clues, especially to low-probability adverse side effects. The uniformity of laboratory support and expertise of authorized centres that are the only ones accumulating experience with these substances would go some way toward satisfying the need for pooled uncontrolled data.

Optimal information could be provided to patients seeking access to nonvalidated treatments. At present, the local practitioner without an AIDS specialty is likely to be confronted with demands by the patient for some experimental treatment spoken of on the AIDS grapevine but of which the practitioner knows nothing. He faces an impossible dilemma in deciding whether to accede to or resist the request. Under the AIU system, for those nonvalidated treatments only available at authorized units or by practitioners under their aegis and guidance the dilemma would not occur. In addition, the formal role held by AIUs in the provision of NTs would foster a tendency for these units to act as clearing houses for the entire range of novel therapies, and as magnets for that segment of the patient population interested in access to NTs.

The proposal could ameliorate the relative lack of access to nonvalidated therapies on the part of intravenous drug users (IVDUs) and their sexual partners. First, by formalizing and extending the provision of nonvalidated therapies within specialized units, all patients treated within these units would have easier access to NTs. Second, the provision of NTs in these settings would not depend, as is often now the case, upon the informed and determined efforts of patients themselves, calling for resources beyond those possessed by IVDUs. Third and most importantly, nonvalidated treatments could be made available to IVDUs who are ineligible for participation within a protocol. (The major inequity suffered by this population in the U.S. — access to health care itself — would of course remain. However, it would not be compounded at the level of NTs.)

This proposal may be administered in a manner fully compatible with the need to complete testing on new agents, a concern that many other proposals to enhance access to NTs do not satisfy. One suggestion would be that the Authorized Investigational Unit only offer a nonvalidated therapy off-protocol to those persons ineligible for participation in the study. When a patient is ineligible for participation in research, or when enrollment in the protocol is complete (or closed), for example, the conduct of the trial is not affected by allowing a patient access to an investigational agent; and, as was argued above, until that point it is not unethical to so restrict access. These factors are better determined at a local level (the AIU) than by an outside agency.

Consideration of a final set of advantages afforded by this proposal requires some more fundamental consideration of the effect drug regulation has on medical research.[24] The process of regulatory review itself creates a large gulf between mandated clinical trials and clinical practice. For example, the regulatory focus upon new molecular entities artificially dichotomizes medical research which is, of its nature, a continuous phenomenon. The spectrum of nonvalidated therapies described above — unapproved uses for licensed drugs, new drug combinations, drugs illegally imported, and non-drug substances (foodstuffs, chemicals, and lifestyle alterations) — implicate uncertainties equivalent to those associated with investigational new drugs, but remain "research orphans," beyond the reach and concern of regulated investigations.

The clinical trials conducted on an investigational new drug are a powerful focusing lens, providing the most rapid reliable assessment of the agent in question. However, a medical analogue of Heisenberg's Uncertainty Principle obtains: a trial's power and precision are bought at some expense to our capacity to generalize its conclusions to common clinical practice. Studies are designed with rigorous criteria of inclusion and exclusion that define an atypical patient population (one that is, for example, homogeneous in age and gender and free from common intercurrent diseases) being treated in an atypical way (to exclude confounding synergistic and antagonistic effects of other common treatments). Yet upon approval for marketing, the practitioner is permitted (and perhaps required) to extrapolate these results toward a treatment recommendation in his or her variegated clinical practice. This extrapolation is difficult when the conduct of the trial has rigidly adhered to the focused protocol; regulation has provided no bridge between the world of the trial and that of the clinic.

In the real world, further complicating factors intrude. One such is the problem of relying upon the integrity and compliance of the enrolled patient/subject, who might be motivated to conceal facts that would threaten his continued participation in the trial. Nor is the problem one of patients alone: when a patient falls outside the trial's scope, physician and patient alike may chafe under this constraint; and when the nonvalidated therapy is only available within the protocol, sometimes, perhaps often, the inclusion criteria are fudged.[25] This clandestine practice, when discovered, renders results uninterpretable; and even when merely suspected, dubious.

Some of these differences between mandated clinical trials and clinical practice are necessary, and reflect diverse contexts and purposes. Yet the need to narrow these gaps has become increasingly apparent, and the present proposed AIUs could help. Their exemption from the need for prospective regulatory approval would enable the units to do coordinated research across the spectrum of nonvalidated therapies. Experience with patients on and off protocol will provide an important comparative perspective within the unit, and a firmer basis for the extrapolation of results to diverse patient populations. The ability to provide NTs to ineligible patients off protocol will take some pressure off physicians to evade rigid criteria of inclusion. The knowledge that the nonvalidated treatment is not confined to those satisfying criteria of inclusion will remove one motivation of patient deception. We might expect that in general, the natural trust existing between patient and physician will be bolstered by the patient's knowledge that his or her physician's clinical and ethical judgment is not subject to being countermanded by some distant bureaucracy. And finally, this renewed focus upon the role of the treating unit in providing nonvalidated treatments would allow a reevaluation of the process for non-IND innovations.

To recapitulate: The reform of designated units for investigational drugs would combine maximum flexibility with minimum delay, expense, and intrusion in the conduct of clinical trials. By giving AIDS researcher-practitioners more authority, it would undoubtedly add to their burden of moral responsibility (including the potential for an ethical conflict of interest between the roles of clinician and investigator). The reform should nonetheless be welcomed by them, for this increment of responsibility in effect amounts to granting them the ability to make effective decisions regarding the medical care of their patients without seeking prior bureaucratic permission. The combination of rapid access to new treatments consistent with sound evaluation and advancement of clinical practice should be welcomed by associations representing persons with AIDS as well. Finally, while regulators will have lost some prospective control over access to INDs, they would retain a monitoring retrospective function, as a check against eccentric enthusiasm that could develop at one or more designated centres. As such, they would be fulfilling their protective mandate vis-à-vis the public.

If the above is persuasive, it would seem that a compelling logical case could be made on behalf of utilizing the AIU model for other conditions, for example, cancer and its treatment. However, logic in advance of experience is unreliable. Indeed, prior to the recent AIDS challenge, the common response of FDA in the face of controversy was to yield in the individual case on an ad hoc basis, rather than modify the entire system to accommodate one exceptional circumstance. The more cautious approach is appropriate here: Try the AIU system out on AIDS on an experimental basis, and evaluate the results before considering whether the model merits broad application.

Numerous questions remain. For example, should the designated units approach be added to the current system of compassionate exemption, or substituted for it? (The former approach would avoid problems of access arising from the centralization of care embedded within this proposal.) Should units have authority limited to drugs currently being tested at those same units? Is coordination between on-protocol and off-protocol decisions of AIUs in a given geographical region required, to ensure satisfactory trial enrollment? What government controls or incentives might be needed to cause drug companies to supply drugs to those centres employing them off of protocol, on a pure cost-recovery basis?

Many more may be added. If the approach is promising, however, these questions should be pursued with the same appropriate urgency as attaches to scientific work on AIDS.

ACKNOWLEDGMENTS

The ideas in this paper were discussed at workshops of the McGill University/Boston University Cooperative Research Group on Ethics, Law and Policy on HIV. Major support for this work was provided by Grant #6605-2897, National Health Research and Development Program, Ministry of Health, Government of Canada. While it is not possible to acknowledge all who contributed, special thanks must be given to Margaret Sommerville, George J. Annas, Norbert Gilmore, and Julie Hamblin.

NOTES

1. "Are Experimental Drugs Moving Through System Too Slowly?" *AIDS Alert* 3:1 (1988), 1-6.

2. George J. Annas, "AIDS, Judges, and the Right to Medical Care," *Hastings Center Report* 18:4 (1988), 20-22.

3. Dale H. Cowan and Eva Bertch, "Innovative Therapy: The Responsibility of Hospitals," *Journal of Legal Medicine* 5:2 (1984), 219-51.

4. Mathilde Krim, "Making Experimental Drugs Available for AIDS Treatment," *AIDS and Public Policy Journal* 2:2 (1987), 1-5.

5. Lynn McMonagle, "Private Rights to Adulterated/Misbranded Articles," *AIDS and Public Policy Journal* 2:2 (1987), 33-49.

6. 37 *Fed. Reg.* 16,503 (1972).

7. David J. Rothman, "Ethical and Social Issues in the Development of New Drugs and Vaccines," *Bulletin of the New York Academy of Medicine* 63:6 (1987), 557-68.

8. "Makers of AL-721 to Market Compound as Food Supplement," *AIDS and Policy Law* 3:6 (1988), 6.

9. "In Brief: Unapproved Drugs," *Rx Ipsa Loquitur* 15:8 (1988), 3.

10. B.R. Cassileth and H. Brown, "Unorthodox Cancer Medicine," *CA-Cancer Journal for Clinicians* 38:3 (1988), 176-86.

11. I am grateful to Gary Freedman for raising this important point.

12. J.A. Revson, "HIV Positive: Living Under the Shadow," *Newsday,* 18 Feb. 1988, Part II, 4-5, 11.

13. American Foundation for AIDS Research, *AIDS / HIV Experimental Treatment Directory* (NY: AmFAR).

14. Mathilde Krim, "A Chance at Life for AIDS Sufferers," *New York Times,* 8 August 1986, A-27.

15. Frank E. Young *et al.,* "The FDA's New Procedures for the Use of Investigational Drugs in Treatment," *Journal of the American Medical Association* 259:15 (1988), 2267-70.

16. 52 *Fed. Reg.* no. 99, May 22, 1987, 19467-77.

17. Robert E. Wittes, "Noninvestigational Uses of Investigational Drugs: Some Implications of FDA's Revised Regulations," *Journal of the National Cancer Institute* 80:5 (1988), 301-304.

18. "Proposal to Make Investigational New Drugs Available Without Clinical Trial Participation in Certain Cases is Receiving Mixed Responses," *Journal of the American Medical Association* 257:22 (1987), 3020.

19. Dale Gieringer, "Twice Wrong on AIDS," *New York Times,* 12 January 1987, A-21.

20. Benjamin Freedman, "Equipoise and the Ethics of Clinical Research," *New England Journal of Medicine* 317 (1987), 141-45.

21. *Dateline: NIAID,* November 1987 (AIDS Research Issue), 7 ff.

22. I. Feldman *et al.,* "AIDS Center Designation/AIDS Intervention Management System," *AIDS and Public Policy Journal* 3:1 (1988), 29-31.

23. Currently, the open trial of long-term effects of AZT run by Burroughs-Wellcome in selected Canadian centres bears some resemblance to the system described herein, but differs in the degree of control granted to the drug company, in conformity with Canadian regulations on the control of investigational drugs. The designated centre approach has also been utilized in the introductory period of some medical devices and surgical procedures (for example, major organ transplants), but this has commonly been under the direction of insurers, governmental or private.

24. Dr. Norbert Gilmore cogently and forcefully presented these points.

25. Harold Vanderpool and Gary Weiss, "False Data and Last Hopes: Enrolling Ineligible Patients in Clinical Trials," *Hastings Center Report* 17:2 (1987), 16-19.

INTRODUCTION (b)

MICRO-ALLOCATION

The allocation of resources presents difficult problems when we are dealing with global budgets and groups of populations. The problems acquire a whole new dimension when we deal face to face with individual persons and are directly confronted with the consequences of the decisions we make. The "phenomenon of the identified victim" — the reluctance to deny resources to persons with whom we are in direct contact — tends to assert itself.

An example may bring the issue into focus. Consider the following case: Monica Urgele is an elderly person occupying an acute-care hospital bed. Her condition does not warrant her being there. However, she has been there for some time, and she does not want to move to the extended-care facility that would be more appropriate for her needs. It has been known for some time that in many cases, to move patients like Monica against their will is to run the risk of shortening their life span considerably. At the same time, to leave her in an acute-care bed is to deprive a whole series of patients (whose conditions warrant that they be in an acute-care facility) of appropriate care because they cannot be admitted since no bed is available. Does Monica Urgele take priority over the others? Should her physician discharge her to a more suitable facility and help the many at the (possible) cost of Monica Urgele's life expectancy? If we were Monica's physician, we would be less likely to relocate her than if we were an administrator who had to devise a policy about what to do with so-called "bed-blockers."

However, such individual allocation decisions have to be made all the time. They have to be made by the acute-care nurse who must decide how much time to spend with one patient at the expense of all the others who also need her/his care; by the physician who has to decide who shall have the only heart that is available for transplantation; the triage nurse in the emergency room who must decide who is to be taken care of first; or the long-term care nurse in the rural setting who has to make a service plan for seeing clients, where each client lives some distance away; and so on. All of them have to make micro-allocation decisions: decisions that deal with selective allocation at the individual level. These decisions are some of the most difficult issues facing health care professionals. And yet, sometimes these decisions have to made because the available resources simply cannot be shared. The article by Martin McKneally *et al.* considers the various ethical, legal, and medical parameters that go into making such decisions.

As McKneally *et al.* point out, in many cases there are standardized protocols that tell us how these decisions should be made.[1] Usually, they focus on the needs of the patients, the potential outcome of the interventions, and so on. However, in recent times another aspect of allocation has attracted much attention: an aspect that had previously been neglected and that is not incorporated into most current protocols. It centres on the issue of lifestyle and responsibility. When one of the patients has led an immoderate lifestyle — has drunk too much, smoked, was quite sedentary, followed an imprudent diet, etc. — whereas another patient has been the model of a responsible person, should both have equal access to the scarce resources?

Some commentators maintain that neither desert nor fault should enter into considerations of allocation because neither desert nor fault lie wholly within the control of the individual. Furthermore, society does not apply the criteria of desert and fault in other areas; therefore, with what justification would it apply them here?[2] Alvin Moss and Mark Siegler, on the other hand, argue that patients who develop a medical condition through no fault of their own should have higher priority for scarce health care than patients whose conditions are brought about by irresponsible behaviour. It would be interesting to consider how either stance accords with the underlying philosophy of the Canada Health Act.

Finally, given modern techniques and technologies, we can often resuscitate and keep alive someone who in previous years would have died. Sometimes these interventions prolong the life of the patient for only a short time and at a severely reduced quality of life — or more correctly, at a severely reduced quality of dying. Should intervention be attempted under such circumstances, especially since resources are scarce and medically the attempt will be futile? Or should we instead adopt the position that intervention is synonymous with care, and that not to intervene is to give up caring? This raises the question, What exactly is meant by futility? Should it be defined in medical terms alone? Should personal, social or other considerations enter the equation? Robert Truog, Allan Brett and Joel Frader address these issues in their article on futility. The issue is important because in the context of limited resources, what is given to the one is taken away from the other.

NOTES

1. See also P. Singer, "A Review of Public Policies to Produce and Dsitribute Kidneys for Transplantation," *Archives of Internal Medicine* 150:3 (March 1990):523–527.
2. Atterbury, "The Alcoholic in the Lifeboat: Should Drinkers Be Candidates for Liver Transplantation?" *Journal of Clinical Gastroenterology* 8(1986):1–4.

FURTHER READINGS

Feeny, David, Gordon Gyuatt, and Peter Tugwell, eds. *Health Care Technology: Effectiveness, Efficiency and Public Policy*. Montreal: Institute for Research on Public Policy, 1986.

Ingelfinger, Franz. "Haves and Have-Nots in the World of Disease." *The New England Journal of Medicine* 287 (Dec.7, 1972) 1198-1199.

Kluge, Eike-Henner W. "The Calculus of Discrimination: Discriminatory Resource Allocation for an Aging Population." From Thornton and Winkler, *op.cit*, 84-97.

President's Commission for the Study of Ethical Problems in Medicine and Biomedical and Behavioral Research. *Securing Access to Health Care* vols. 1-3. Washington, D.C.: U.S. Gov't. Printing Office, 1983.

Veatch, R.M. "Voluntary Risk to Health: The Ethical Issues." *Journal of the American Medical Association* 243 (Jan. 4, 1980) 50-55.

Should Alcoholics Compete Equally for Liver Transplantation?

Alvin H. Moss and Mark Siegler

The circumstances of liver transplantation are unique among organ transplantation because of the dire, absolute scarcity of donor livers and the predominance of one disease — alcohol-related end-stage liver disease — as the principal cause of liver failure. We propose that patients who develop end-stage liver disease through no fault of their own should have higher priority for receiving a liver transplant than those whose end-stage liver disease results from failure to obtain treatment for alcoholism. We base our proposal on considerations of fairness and on whether public support for liver transplantation can be maintained if, as a result of a first-come, first-served approach, patients with alcohol-related end-stage liver disease receive more than half the available donor livers. We conclude that since not all can live, priorities must be established for the use of scarce health care resources.

Until recently, liver transplantation for patients with alcohol-related end-stage liver disease (ARESLD) was not considered a treatment option. Most physicians in the transplant community did not recommend it because of initial poor results in this population[1] and because of a predicted high recidivism rate that would preclude long-term survival.[2] In 1988, however, Starzl and colleagues[3] reported 1-year survival rates for patients with ARESLD comparable to results in patients with other causes of end-stage liver disease (ESLD). Although the patients in the Pittsburgh series may represent a carefully selected population,[3,4] the question is no longer, Can we perform transplants in patients with alcoholic liver disease and obtain acceptable results? but Should we? This question is particularly timely since the Health Care Financing Administration (HCFA) has recommended that Medicare coverage for liver transplantation be offered to patients with alcoholic cirrhosis who are abstinent. The HCFA proposes that the same eligibility criteria be used for patients with ARESLD as are used for patients with other causes of ESLD, such as primary biliary cirrhosis and sclerosing cholangitis.[5]

Alvin H. Moss and Mark Siegler, "Should Alcoholics Compete Equally for Liver Transplantation? *JAMA 265*:(March 13, 1991) 1295-1298.

SHOULD PATIENTS WITH ARESLD RECEIVE TRANSPLANTS?

At first glance, this question seems simple to answer. Generally, in medicine, a therapy is used if it works and saves lives. But the circumstances of liver transplantation differ from those of most other lifesaving therapies, including long-term mechanical ventilation and dialysis, in three important respects:

Nonrenewable Resource

First, although most lifesaving therapies are expensive, liver transplantation uses a nonrenewable, absolutely scarce resource — a donor liver. In contrast to patients with end-stage renal disease, who may receive either a transplant or dialysis therapy, every patient with ESLD who does not receive a liver transplant will die. This dire, absolute scarcity of donor livers would be greatly exacerbated by including patients with ARESLD as potential candidates for liver transplantation. In 1985, 63 737 deaths due to hepatic disease occurred in the United States, at least 36 000 of which were related to alcoholism, but fewer than 1000 liver transplants were performed.[6] Although patients with ARESLD represent more than 50% of the patients with ESLD, patients with ARESLD account for less than 10% of those receiving transplants (*New York Times*. April 3, 1990: B6 [col 1]). If patients with ARESLD were accepted for liver transplantation on an equal basis, as suggested by the HCFA, there would potentially be more than 30 000 additional candidates each year. (No data exist to indicate how many patients in the late stages of ARESLD would meet transplantation eligibility criteria.) In 1987, only 1182 liver transplants were performed; in 1989, fewer than 2000 were done.[6] Even if all donor liv-

ers available were given to patients with ARESLD, it would not be feasible to provide transplants for even a small fraction of them. Thus, the dire, absolute nature of donor liver scarcity mandates that distribution be based on unusually rigorous standards — standards not required for the allocation of most other resources such as dialysis machines and ventilators, both of which are only *relatively* scarce.

Comparison with Cardiac Transplantation

Second, although a similar dire, absolute scarcity of donor hearts exists for cardiac transplantation, the allocational decisions for cardiac transplantation differ from those for liver transplantation. In liver transplantation, ARESLD causes more than 50% of the cases of ESLD; in cardiac transplantation, however, no one predominant disease or contributory factor is responsible. Even for patients with end-stage ischemic heart disease who smoked or who failed to adhere to dietary regimens, it is rarely clear that one particular behavior caused the disease. Also, unlike our proposed consideration for liver transplantation, a history of alcohol abuse is considered a contraindication and is a common reason for a patient with heart disease to be denied cardiac transplantation.[7,8] Thus, the allocational decisions for heart transplantation differ from those for liver transplantation in two ways: determining a cause for end-stage heart disease is less certain, and patients with a history of alcoholism are usually rejected from heart transplant programs.

Expensive Technology

Third, a unique aspect of liver transplantation is that it is an expensive technology that has become a target of cost containment in health care.[9] It is, therefore, essential to maintain the approbation and support of the public so that organs continue to be donated under appropriate clinical circumstances — even in spite of the high cost of transplantation.

General Guideline Proposed

In view of the distinctive circumstances surrounding liver transplantation, we propose as a general guideline that patients with ARESLD should not compete equally with other candidates for liver transplantation. We are *not* suggesting that patients with ARESLD should *never* receive liver transplants. Rather, we propose that a priority ranking be established for the use of this dire, absolutely scarce societal resource and that patients with ARESLD be lower on the list than others with ESLD.

OBJECTIONS TO PROPOSAL

We realize that our proposal may meet with two immediate objections: (1) Some may argue that since alcoholism is a disease, patients with ARESLD should be considered equally for liver transplantation.[10] (2) Some will question why patients with ARESLD should be singled out for discrimination, when the medical profession treats many patients who engage in behavior that causes their diseases.[11] We will discuss these objections in turn.

Alcoholism: How Is It Similar to and Different from Other Diseases?

We do not dispute the reclassification of alcoholism as a disease.[12] Both hereditary and environmental factors contribute to alcoholism, and physiological, biochemical,

and genetic markers have been associated with increased susceptibility.[13] Identifying alcoholism as a disease enables physicians to approach it as they do other medical problems and to differentiate it from bad habits, crimes, or moral weaknesses. More important, identifying alcoholism as a disease also legitimizes medical interventions to treat it.[14]

Alcoholism is a chronic disease,[12,15] for which treatment is available and effective. More than 1.43 million patients were treated in 5586 alcohol treatment units in the 12-month period ending October 30, 1987.[16] One comprehensive review concluded that more than two thirds of patients who accept therapy improve.[17] Another cited four studies in which at least 54% of patients were abstinent a minimum of 1 year after treatment.[18] A recent study of alcohol-impaired physicians reported a 100% abstinence rate an average of 33.4 months after therapy was initiated. In this study, physician-patients rated Alcoholics Anonymous, the largest organization of recovering alcoholics in the world, as the most important component of their therapy.[19]

Like other chronic diseases — such as type I diabetes mellitus, which requires the patient to administer insulin over a lifetime — alcoholism requires the patient to assume responsibility for participating in continuous treatment. Two key elements are required to successfully treat alcoholism: the patient must accept his or her diagnosis and must assume responsibility for treatment.[20,21] The high success rates of some alcoholism treatment programs indicate that many patients can accept responsibility for their treatment. ARESLD, one of the sequelae of alcoholism, results from 10 to 20 years of heavy alcohol consumption. The risk of ARESLD increases with the amount of alcohol consumed and with the duration of heavy consumption.[22] In view of the quantity of alcohol consumed, the years, even decades, required to develop ARESLD, and the availability of effective alcohol treatment, attributing personal responsibility for ARESLD to the patient seems all the more justified. We believe, therefore, that even though alcoholism is a chronic disease, alcoholics should be held responsible for seeking and obtaining treatment that could prevent the development of late-stage complications such as ARESLD. Our view is consistent with that of Alcoholics Anonymous: alcoholics are responsible for undertaking a program for recovery that will keep their disease of alcoholism in remission.[23]

Are We Discriminating Against Alcoholics?

Why should patients with ARESLD be singled out when a large number of patients have health problems that can be attributed to so-called voluntary health-risk behavior? Such patients include smokers with chronic lung disease; obese people who develop type II diabetes; some individuals who test positive for the human immunodeficiency virus; individuals with multiple behavioral risk factors (inattention to blood pressure, cholesterol, diet, and exercise) who develop coronary artery disease; and people such as skiers, motorcyclists, and football players who sustain activity-related injuries. We believe that the health care system should respond based on the actual medical needs of patients rather than on the factors (e.g., genetic, infectious, or behavioral) that cause the problem. We also believe that individuals should bear some responsibility — such as increased insurance premiums — for medical problems associated with voluntary choices. The critical distinguishing factor for treatment of ARESLD is the scarcity of the resource needed to treat it. The resources needed to treat most of these other conditions are only moderately or relatively scarce, and

patients with these diseases or injuries can receive a share of the resources (i.e., money, personnel, and medication) roughly equivalent to their need. In contrast, there are insufficient donor livers to sustain the lives of all with ESLD who are in need.[24] This difference permits us to make some discriminating choices — or to establish priorities — in selecting candidates for liver transplantation based on notions of fairness. In addition, this reasoning enables us to offer patients with alcohol-related medical and surgical problems their fair share of relatively scarce resources, such as blood products, surgical care, and intensive care beds, while still maintaining that their claim on donor livers is less compelling than the claims of others.

REASONS PATIENTS WITH ARESLD SHOULD HAVE A LOWER PRIORITY ON TRANSPLANT WAITING LISTS

Two arguments support our proposal. The first argument is a moral one based on considerations of fairness. The second one is based on policy considerations and examines whether public support of liver transplantation can be maintained if, as a result of a first-come, first-served approach, patients with ARESLD receive more than half the available donor livers. Finally, we will consider further research necessary to determine which patients with ARESLD should be candidates for transplantation, albeit with a lower priority.

Fairness

Given a tragic shortage of donor livers, what is the fair or just way to allocate them? We suggest that patients who develop ESLD through no fault of their own (e.g., those with congenital biliary atresia or primary biliary cirrhosis) should have a higher priority in receiving a liver transplant than those whose liver disease results from failure to obtain treatment for alcoholism. In view of the dire, absolute scarcity of donor livers, we believe it is fair to hold people responsible for their choices, including decisions to refuse alcoholism treatment, and to allocate organs on this basis.

It is unfortunate but not unfair to make this distinction.[25] When not enough donor livers are available for all who need one, choices have to be made, and they should be founded on one or more proposed principles of fairness for distributing scarce resources.[26,27] We shall consider four that are particularly relevant:

- To each, an equal share of treatment.
- To each, similar treatment for similar cases.
- To each, treatment according to personal effort.
- To each, treatment according to ability to pay.

It is not possible to give each patient with ESLD an *equal share*, or, in this case, a functioning liver. The problem created by the absolute scarcity of donor livers is that of inequality; some receive livers while others do not. But what is fair, need not be equal. Although a first-come, first-served approach has been suggested to provide each patient with an equal chance, we believe it is fairer to give a child dying of biliary atresia an opportunity for a *first* normal liver than it is to give a patient with ARESLD who was born with a normal liver a *second* one.

Because the goal of providing each person with an equal share of health care sometimes collides with the realities of finite medical resources, the principle of *similar treatment for similar cases* has been found to be helpful. Outka[26] stated it this way: "If

we accept the case for equal access, but if we simply cannot, physically cannot, treat all who are in need, it seems more just to discriminate by virtue of categories of illness, rather than between rich ill and poor ill." This principle is derived from the principle of formal justice, which, roughly stated, says that people who are equal in relevant respects should be treated equally and that people who are unequal in relevant respects should be treated differently.[27] We believe that patients with ARESLD are unequal in a relevant respect to others with ESLD, since their liver failure was preventable; therefore, it is acceptable to treat them differently.

Our view also relies on the principle of *To each, treatment according to personal effort*. Although alcoholics cannot be held responsible for their disease, once their condition has been diagnosed they can be held responsible for seeking treatment and for preventing the complication of ARESLD. The standard of personal effort and responsibility we propose for alcoholics is the same as that held by Alcoholics Anonymous. We are not suggesting that some lives and behaviors have greater value than others — an approach used and appropriately repudiated when dialysis machines were in short supply.[26-30] But we are holding people responsible for their personal effort.

Health policymakers have predicted that this principle will assume greater importance in the future. In the context of scarce health care resources, Blank[31] foresees a reevaluation of our health care priorities, with a shift toward individual responsibility and a renewed emphasis on the individual's obligation to society to maximize one's health. Similarly, more than a decade ago, Knowles[32] observed that prevention of disease requires effort. He envisioned that the next major advances in the health of the American people would be determined by what individuals are willing to do for themselves.

To each, treatment according to ability to pay has also been used as a principle of distributive justice. Since alcoholism is prevalent in all socioeconomic strata, it is not discrimination against the poor to deny liver transplantation to patients with alcoholic liver disease.[33] In fact, we believe that poor patients with ARESLD have a stronger claim for a donor liver than rich patients, precisely because many alcohol treatment programs are not available to patients lacking in substantial private resources or health insurance. Ironically, it is precisely this group of poor and uninsured patients who are most likely not to be eligible to receive a liver transplant because of their inability to pay. We agree with Outka's view of fairness that would discriminate according to categories of illness rather than according to wealth.

Policy Considerations Regarding Public Support for Liver Transplantation

Today, the main health policy concerns involve issues of financing, distributive justice, and rationing medical care.[34-37] Because of the many deficiencies in the U.S. health care system — in maternal and child health, in the unmet needs of the elderly, and in the millions of Americans without health insurance — an increasing number of commentators are drawing attention to the trade-offs between basic health care for the many and expensive, albeit lifesaving care for the few.[9,25,38,39]

Because of its high unit cost, liver transplantation is often at the center of these discussions, as it has been in Oregon, where the legislature voted to eliminate Medicaid reimbursement for all transplants except kidneys and corneas.[9] In this era of health care cost containment, a sense of limits is emerging and allocational choices are being made. Oregon has already shown

that elected officials and the public are prepared to face these issues.

In our democracy, it is appropriate that community mores and values be regarded seriously when deciding the most appropriate use of a scarce and nonrenewable organ symbolized as a "Gift of Life." As if to underscore this point, the report of the Task Force on Organ Transplantation recommended that each donated organ be considered a national resource for the public good and that the public must participate in decisions on how to use this resource to best serve the public's interests.[40]

Much of the initial success in securing public and political approval for liver transplantation was achieved by focusing media and political attention not on adults but on children dying of ESLD. The public may not support transplantation for patients with ARESLD in the same way that they have endorsed this procedure for babies born with biliary atresia. This assertion is bolstered not only by the events in Oregon but also by the results of a Louis Harris and Associates[41] national survey, which showed that lifesaving therapy for premature infants or for patients with cancer was given the highest health care priority by the public and that lifesaving therapy for patients with alcoholic liver disease was given the lowest. In this poll, the public's view of health care priorities was shared by leadership groups also polled: physicians, nurses, employers, and politicians.

Just because a majority of the public holds these views does not mean that they are right, but the moral intuition of the public, which is also shared by its leaders, reflects community values that must be seriously considered. Also indicative of community values are organizations such as Mothers Against Drunk Driving, Students Against Drunk Driving, corporate employee assistance programs, and school student assistance programs. Their existence signals that many believe that a person's behavior can be modified so that the consequences of behavior such as alcoholism can be prevented.[42] Thus, giving donor livers to patients with ARESLD on an equal basis with other patients who have ESLD might lead to a decline in public support for liver transplantation.

Should Any Alcoholics Be Considered for Transplantation? Need for Further Research

Our proposal for giving lower priority for liver transplantation to patients with ARESLD does not completely rule out transplantation for this group. Patients with ARESLD who had not previously been offered therapy and who are now abstinent could be acceptable candidates. In addition, patients lower on the waiting list, such as patients with ARESLD who have been treated and are now abstinent, might be eligible for a donor liver in some regions because of the increased availability of donor organs there. Even if only because of these possible conditions for transplantation, further research is needed to determine which patients with ARESLD would have the best outcomes after liver transplantation.

Transplant programs have been reluctant to provide transplants to alcoholics because of concern about one unfavorable outcome: a high recidivism rate. Although the overall recidivism rate for the Pittsburgh patients was only 11.5%, in the patients who had been abstinent less than 6 months it was 43%.[2] Also, compared with the entire group in which 1-year survival was 74%, the survival rate in this subgroup was lower, at 64%.[2]

In the recently proposed Medicare criteria for coverage of liver transplantation, the HCFA acknowledged that the decision to insure patients with alcoholic cirrhosis "may be considered controversial by some."[5]

As if to counter possible objections, the HCFA listed requirements for patients with alcoholic cirrhosis: patients must meet the transplant center's requirement for abstinence prior to liver transplantation and have documented evidence of sufficient social support to ensure both recovery from alcoholism and compliance with the regimen of immunosuppressive medication.

Further research should answer lingering questions about liver transplantation for ARESLD patients: Which characteristics of a patient with ARESLD can predict a successful outcome? How long is abstinence necessary to qualify for transplantation? What type of a social support system must a patient have to ensure good results? These questions are being addressed.[43] Until the answers are known, we propose that further transplantation for patients with ARESLD be limited to abstinent patients who had not previously been offered alcoholism treatment and to abstinent treated patients in regions of increased donor liver availability and that it be carried out as part of prospective research protocols at a few centers skilled in transplantation and alcohol research.

COMMENT

Should patients with ARESLD compete equally for liver transplants? In a setting in which there is a dire, absolute scarcity of donor livers, we believe the answer is no. Considerations of fairness suggest that a first-come, first-served approach for liver transplantation is not the most just approach. Although this decision is difficult, it is only fair that patients who have not assumed equal responsibility for maintaining their health or for accepting treatment for a chronic disease should be treated differently. Considerations of public values and mores suggest that the public may not support liver transplantation if patients with ARESLD routinely receive more than half of the available donor livers. We conclude that since not all can live, priorities must be established and that patients with ARESLD should be given a lower priority for liver transplantation than others with ESLD.

NOTES

The Center for Clinical Medical Ethics and Alvin H. Moss, MD, are supported by grants from the Henry J. Kaiser Family Foundation and the Pew Charitable Trusts. The opinions expressed are those of the authors and should not be taken to represent those of the foundation or trust.

The authors thank Abe Kaplan for assistance in literature review; Rolly Sullivan, MD, for information on alcoholism treatment programs; and Michael D. Swenson, MD, PhD, for review of an earlier draft of the manuscript.

1. Scharschmidt, B.F. "Human liver transplantation: analysis of data on 540 patients from four centers." *Hepatology.* 1984;4:95S-101S.

2. Kumar, S., Stauber, R.E., Gavaler, J.S., et al. "Orthotopic liver transplantation for alcoholic liver disease." *Hepatology.* 1990;11:159-164.

3. Starzl, T.E., Van Thiel, D., Tzakis, A.G., et al. "Orthotopic liver transplantation for alcoholic cirrhosis." *JAMA.* 1988;260:2542-2544.

4. Olbrisch, M.E., Levenson, J.L. "Liver transplantation for alcoholic cirrhosis." *JAMA.* 1989;261:2958.

5. Health Care Financing Administration. "Medicare program: criteria for Medicare coverage of adult liver transplants." *Federal Register.* 1990;55:3545-3553.

6. Office of Health Technology Assessment, Agency for Health Care Policy Research. *Assessment of Liver Transplantation.* Rockville, Md: U.S. Dept. of Health and Human Services; 1990:3,25.

7. Schroeder, J.S., Hunt, S. "Cardiac transplantation update 1987." *JAMA.* 1987;258:3142-3145.

8. Surman, O.S. "Psychiatric aspects of organ transplantation." *Am J Psychiatry.* 1989;146:972-982.

9. Welch, H.G., Larson, E.B. "Dealing with limited resources: the Oregon decision to curtail funding for organ transplantation." *N Engl J Med.* 1988;319:171-173.

10. Flavin, D.K., Niven, R.G., Kelsey, J.E. "Alcoholism and orthotopic liver transplantation." *JAMA.* 1988;259:1546-1547.

11. Atterbury, C.E. "The alcoholic in the lifeboat: should drinkers be candidates for liver transplantation?" *J Clin Gastroenterol.* 1986;8:1-4.

12. Mendelson, J.H., Mello, N.K. *The Diagnosis and Treatment of Alcoholism.* 2nd ed. New York, NY: McGraw-Hill International Book Co; 1985:1-20.

13. Blum, K., Noble, E.P., Sheridan, P.J., et al. "Allelic association of human dopamine D_2 receptor gene in alcoholism." *JAMA.* 1990;263:2055-2060.

14. Aronson, M.D. "Definition of alcoholism." In: Barnes, H.N., Aronson, M.D., Delbanco, T.L., eds. *Alcoholism: A Guide for the Primary Care Physician.* New York, NY: Springer-Verlag NY Inc; 1987:9-15.

15. Klerman, G.L. "Treatment of alcoholism." *N Engl J Med.* 1989;320:394-395.

16. *Seventh Special Report to the U.S. Congress on Alcohol and Health.* Washington, DC: U.S. Dept. of Health and Human Services; 1990. Publication 90-1656.

17. Saxe, L. *The Effectiveness and Costs of Alcoholism Treatment: Health Technology Case Study No. 22.* Washington, DC: Congress of the United States, Office of Technology Assessment;1983:3-6.

18. Nace, E.P. *The Treatment of Alcoholism.* New York, NY: Brunner/Mazel Publishers; 1987:43-46.

19. Galanter, M., Talbott, D., Gallegos, K., Rubenstone, E. "Combined Alcoholics Anonymous and professional care for addicted physicians." *Am J Psychiatry.* 1990;147:64-68.

20. Johnson, B., Clark, W. "Alcoholism: a challenging physician-patient encounter." *J Gen Intern Med.* 1989;4:445-452.

21. Bigby, J.A. "Negotiating treatment and monitoring recovery." In: Barnes, H.N., Aronson, M.D., Delbanco, T.L., eds. *Alcoholism: A Guide for the Primary Care Physician.* New York, NY: Springer-Verlag NY Inc; 1987:66-72.

22. Grant, B.F., Dufour, M.C., Harford, T.C. "Epidemiology of alcoholic liver disease." *Sem Liver Dis.* 1988;8:12-25.

23. Thoreson, R.W., Budd, F.C. "Self-help groups and other group procedures for treating alcohol problems." In: Cox, W.M., ed. *Treatment and Prevention of Alcohol Problems: A Resource Manual.* Orlando, Fla: Academic Press Inc; 1987:157-181.

24. Winslow, G.R. *Triage and Justice.* Berkeley: University of California Press; 1982:39-44, 133-150.

25. Engelhardt, H.T., Jr. "Shattuck Lecture: allocating scarce medical resources and the availability of organ transplantation." *N Engl J Med.* 1984;311:66-71.

26. Outka, G. "Social justice and equal access to health care." *J Religious Ethics.* 1974;2:11-32.

27. Beauchamp, T.L., Childress, J.F. *Principles of Biomedical Ethics.* 3rd ed. New York, NY: Oxford University Press; 1989:256-306.

28. Ramsey, P. *The Patient As Person.* New Haven, Conn: Yale University Press; 1970:242-252.

29. Fox, R.C., Swazey, J.P. *The Courage to Fail.* 2nd ed. Chicago, Ill: University of Chicago Press; 1978:226-265.

30. Annas, G.J. "The prostitute, the playboy, and the poet: rationing schemes for organ transplantation." *Am J Public Health.* 1985;75:187-189.

31. Blank, R.H. *Rationing Medicine.* New York, NY: Columbia University Press; 1988:1-37, 189-252.

32. Knowles, J.H. "Responsibility for health." *Science.* 1977;198:1103.

33. Moore, R.D., Bone, L.R., Geller, G., Marmon, J.A., Stokes, E.J., Levine, D.M. "Prevalence, detection, and treatment of alcoholism in hospitalized patients." *JAMA.* 1989;261:403-407.

34. Fuchs, V.R. "The 'rationing' of medical care." *N Engl J Med.* 1984;311:1572-1573.

35. Daniels, N. "Why saying no to patients in the United States is so hard: cost containment, justice, and provider autonomy." *N Engl J Med.* 1986;314:1380-1383.

36. Callahan, D. "Allocating health resources." *Hastings Cent Rep.* 1988;18:14-20.

37. Evans, R.W. "Health care technology and the inevitability of resource allocation and rationing decisions." *JAMA.* 1983;249:2047-2053, 2208-2219.

38. Thurow, L.C. "Learning to say no." *N Engl J Med.* 1984;311:1569-1572.

39. Caper, P. "Solving the medical care dilemma." *N Engl J Med.* 1988;318:1535-1536.

40. Task Force on Organ Transplantation. *Organ Transplantation: Issues and Recommendations.* Washington, DC: U.S. Dept. of Health and Human Services; 1986:9.

41. Louis Harris and Associates. *Making Difficult Health Care Decisions.* Boston, Mass: The Loran Commission; 1987:73-89.

42. Fishman, R. *Alcohol and Alcoholism.* New York, NY: Chelsea House Publishers; 1986:27-34.

43. Beresford, T.P., Turcotte, J.G., Merion, R., et al. "A rational approach to liver transplantation for the alcoholic patient." *Psychosomatics.* 1990;31:241-254.

Resource Allocation

Martin F. McKneally, Bernard M. Dickens, Eric M. Meslin, Peter A. Singer

Mr. C is a 21-year-old computer programmer with cystic fibrosis. Chronic rejection and poorly controlled fungal infections are destroying the lungs he received 15 months ago. He has intermittently required positive-pressure ventilation to maintain adequate oxygenation during flareups of infection or rejection. C has been listed as a candidate for a second transplantation. However, given the presence of infection and the risks associated with repeat transplantation, his predicted chance of survival is 65% at 1 month and 38% at 24 months.[1]

Mrs. D is a 42-year-old schoolteacher. She has been listed as a candidate for double lung transplantation because of rapidly progressing pulmonary hypertension associated with hemoptysis and hypoxemia. She is unable to manage at home because of decompensated right heart failure unresponsive to maximal therapy. As a first-time lung transplant candidate who is free of infection, D has a predicted chance of survival of 82% at 1 month and 62% at 2 years.[1]

The surgeon has 1 matching donor organ available for these 2 patients. He knows that the best outcome can be achieved by transplanting both lungs of the donor into the same patient.[2]

When 63-year-old Mr. E is brought to the emergency department with severe but potentially reversible brain injury after a motor vehicle accident, the attending physician considers going through the charts of

M.F. McKneally, B.M. Dickens, E.M. Meslin, P.A. Singer. "Bioethics for clinicans: 13. Resource allocation"—Reprinted from, by permission of the publisher, *CMAJ* 157:2 (1997)163–167.

each patient in the intensive care unit (ICU) in the hope of finding someone whose need for intensive care is less than that of Mr. E. She also considers sending Mr. E to the floor, but knows that this will overtax the capabilities of the floor staff, who are not prepared to manage the patient's elevated intracranial pressure and seizures. Because of recent hospital closures in the region, no other facility is available to share responsibility for the care of patients with neurosurgical problems of this magnitude.

WHAT IS RESOURCE ALLOCATION?

Resource allocation is the distribution of goods and services to programs and people. In the context of health care, macro-allocations of resources are made by governments at the national, provincial and municipal level. Meso-allocations are made at the level of institutions; for example, hospitals allocate their resources to programs such as cancer treatment, cardiology and dialysis. Micro-allocations are made at the level of the individual patient. Although these 3 levels are interrelated, in this article we focus on resource allocation from the perspective of the practising physician.

Commodity scarcity, illustrated by the lung-transplant case, is a shortage of a finite resource (such as an organ) because of natural limits to the availability of that resource. Fiscal scarcity, illustrated by the intensive care case, is a shortage of funds.[3]

WHY IS RESOURCE ALLOCATION IMPORTANT?

Rising public and professional expectations, an expanding pool of treatable patients and costly new technology must be balanced against tightly monitored health care budgets, competing government priorities and provincial deficits. Ethics, law, policy and empirical studies provide insights that can help clinicians as they try to distribute health care resources fairly.

ETHICS

The ethics of resource allocation may be considered in relation to the concept of justice and the physician's fiduciary duty toward the patient. According to Aristotle's principle of distributive justice, equals should be treated equally and those who are unequal should be treated unequally. Unequal treatment is justified when resources are allocated in light of morally relevant differences, such as those pertaining to need or likely benefit.[4] Characteristics such as sex, sexual orientation, religion, level of education or age alone are morally irrelevant criteria for resource allocation. Because there is no overarching theory of justice to balance competing claims between morally relevant criteria such as need and benefit, fair, open and publicly defensible resource allocation procedures are critical.

The lack of a comprehensive theory of justice gives rise to unresolved issues in rationing; these have been categorized by Daniels as follows[5]:

1. *The fair chances versus best outcomes problem.* To what degree should producing the best outcome be favoured over giving every patient an opportunity to compete for limited resources?

2. *The priorities problem.* How much priority should we give to treating the sickest or most disabled patients?

3. *The aggregation problem.* When should we allow an aggregation of modest benefits to larger numbers of people to outweigh more significant benefits to fewer people?

4. *The democracy problem.* When must we rely on a fair democratic process as the only way to determine what constitutes a fair rationing outcome?

These questions help to frame discussions of resource allocation issues and the development of policies and practices that balance the obligations of physicians as citizens in a just society with their obligations to individual patients. The power imbalance that exists between physician and patient creates a fiduciary duty on the physician's part to promote the patient's best interest. The extent of this ethical duty, which is fundamental to the physician's role in resource allocation, is a matter of controversy. For instance, Levinsky has argued that "physicians are required to do everything that they believe may benefit each patient without regard to costs or other societal considerations."[6] By contrast, Morreim has argued that "the physician's obligations to the patient can no longer be a single minded, unequivocal commitment but rather must reflect a balancing. Patients' interests must be weighed against the legitimate competing claims of other patients of payers, of society as a whole, and sometimes even of the physician himself."[7]

LAW

The Canadian Charter of Rights and Freedoms prohibits discrimination on various grounds, including physical or mental disability, but it applies only to governmental agencies, not to physicians or hospitals[8] unless they are under the day-to-day control of ministries of health or other branches of government.[9]

Human rights codes in several provinces prohibit discrimination on the basis of race, ethnicity, place of origin, religion, age, sex, sexual orientation and physical or mental disability. Evidence that resources were allocated purely on such grounds could lead to an inquiry and legal proceedings by a provincial human rights commission. However, if such factors were relevant to a medical prognosis, it is not clear how a human rights commission could challenge a physician's clinical assessment of a patient's eligibility for a particular treatment. Evidence might be needed of a systematic policy of discrimination or bias against a particular group on the part of the practitioner or institution.[10]

Because courts have been extremely reluctant to become involved in how physicians, hospitals and health authorities use their resources, the legal review of individual decisions involving resource allocation is improbable.[11] As a British judge has observed, "Difficult and agonizing judgments have to be made as to how a limited budget is best allocated to the maximum advantage of the maximum number of patients. That is not a judgment which the court can make."[12]

Nevertheless, the trial judge in a case heard in British Columbia criticized physicians for offering the explanation that they felt too constrained by the provincial medical insurance plan and their provincial medical association's standards to order a diagnostic CT scan. Although a finding of negligence was made on other grounds, the judge noted that while physicians may consider the financial impact of their decisions, financial considerations cannot be decisive. The physician's first duty is to the patient.[13]

It is understood in law that although there is no liability for making a decision that proves to be wrong,[14] there may be liability for making a decision *wrongly*. A decision is made wrongly if demands for economy distort the physician's judgement with respect to the care that is owed to the patient. An error in clinical judgement is not actionable, because the risk of being wrong is inherent in every exercise of judgement. However, to take decisive account of secondary concerns and subordinate the primary concern of care—the patient's well-being—to a budgetary issue is the wrong way for a physician to make a treatment decision.

POLICY

Clear, fair and widely accepted institutional or professional policies can provide guidance for physicians who are faced with difficult resource allocation decisions. Policies developed for the allocation of organs have reduced conflict between teams and helped prioritize recipients within organ transplantation programs, using generally accepted and publicly reviewed principles and guidelines.[15]

In Oregon, a priority list of treatments is being developed by citizens' committees with input from physicians. This evolving experiment in public policy ranks health care services on the basis of effectiveness and perceived value to the community. Public funds are assigned by the government to make services "above the funding line" available to citizens "below the poverty line."[16] Public funds assigned by the government to pay for health care are spent on treatments according to their priority on the list. Through multiple iterations and public debate, this experiment is producing a useful model for engaging stakeholders from government, the medical profession, and the public in the process of health policy development.[17,18]

In Canada, the CMA has provided a framework for decision making on core and comprehensive health care services that incorporates 3 major dimensions: quality, economics and ethics.[19] As well, Deber and colleagues have proposed a "four-screen" model based on effectiveness, appropriateness, informed choice and public provision.[20] Finally, the CMA's Code of Ethics states that physicians should recognize [their] responsibility "to promote fair access to health care resources" and should "use health care resources prudently."[21]

Empirical studies

Given the importance of resource allocation decisions in health care today, there is a surprising lack of empirical studies on this topic. In contrast to the hundreds of published studies on advance directives,[22] for example, fewer than 2 dozen empirical studies on resource allocation (excluding cost-effectiveness analyses of various diagnostic tests and treatments) came to light in our literature search. In this section we review some of these studies with reference to the primary questions they address.

Is resource allocation occurring now? In a study of dialysis referrals, Mendelssohn and associates found that 67% of Ontario physicians believed rationing of dialysis was occurring at the time of the survey, and 91% believed that such rationing would occur in the future.[23]

How do health care providers make resource allocation decisions? This question has been addressed by survey methods in the context of dialysis,[23] transplantation,[24-26] rural medicine,[27] and critical care.[28] For instance, a survey by the Society of Critical Care Medicine found that critical-care physicians considered quality of life as viewed by the patient, probability of survival, the reversibility of the acute disorder and the nature of any chronic disorder as important factors in deciding which patients to admit to the intensive care unit.[28]

Do people consider age a relevant variable in health care resource allocation? In a survey of public opinion in the United States, Zweibel and colleagues[29] found that most people accept the withholding of life-prolonging medical care from some critically ill older patients, but few would categorically withhold such care on the basis of age alone.

How do decision-makers balance concerns of efficiency and equity? Ubel and collaborators[30] surveyed prospective jurors, medical ethicists and experts in medical decision making to explore the trade-off between cost-effectiveness and equity in the setting of budget constraints. Many respondents said they would choose a less cost-effective test for the entire population over a more cost-effective test for half the population. Similarly, in a survey of public opinion in Australia, Nord and associates[31] found that a policy of maximizing cost-effectiveness received very limited support when the consequence was a loss of equity and access to services for elderly people and for people with limited potential for improving their health. In other words, equity was valued above cost-effectiveness in both of these surveys.

HOW SHOULD I APPROACH RESOURCE ALLOCATION IN PRACTICE?

The clinician's goal is to provide optimal care within the limits imposed by the allocation of resources to health care generally and to the institution, program, and specific situation in which an individual patient is treated. The following guidelines may prove helpful in practice:

- Choose interventions known to be beneficial on the basis of evidence of effectiveness.
- Minimize the use of marginally beneficial tests or marginally beneficial interventions.
- Seek the tests or treatments that will accomplish the diagnostic or therapeutic goal for the least cost.
- Advocate for one's own patients but avoid manipulating the system to gain unfair advantage to them.
- Resolve conflicting claims for scarce resources justly, on the basis of morally relevant criteria such as need (e.g., the patient's risk of death or serious harm could be reduced by the treatment) and benefit (e.g., published evidence of effectiveness),

using fair and publicly defensible procedures (ideally, incorporating public input).

- Inform patients of the impact of cost constraints on care, but do so in a sensitive way. Blaming administrative or governmental systems during discussions with the patient at the point of treatment should be avoided; it undermines care by reducing confidence and increasing anxiety at a time when the patient is most vulnerable.
- Seek resolution of unacceptable shortages at the level of hospital management (meso-allocation) or government (macro-allocation).

THE CASES

Mrs. D should receive the double lung. Although her need is approximately equal to that of Mr. C, her ability to benefit is substantially greater. The surgeon knows from sound empirical evidence that repeat lung transplantation has a poor prognosis, particularly when chronic infection exists.[1] He can minimize recriminations related to the team members' feelings of loyalty toward Mr. C if the transplantation program policy clearly spells out specific and fair procedures to follow when difficult allocation decisions must be made involving similarly deserving patients.

The attending physician should provide appropriate care for Mr. E in the emergency department, as this is the only facility available. She should involve the administrator on call to bring in additional skilled personnel to provide interim care in the emergency department and to help her arrange for the patient's transfer to a facility prepared to care for him. In this way, she clarifies the responsibility of the hospital to resolve the meso-allocation problem at an administrative level. The hospital may in

turn address the macro-allocation of
resources at the provincial or regional level
through its representatives to the government. The physician should not attempt to
resolve problems of this magnitude on her
own and should not compromise the care

of Mr. E. She may choose to contribute to
the resolution of similar problems in the
longer term by making suggestions about
system reform to the health ministry or by
helping with appeals for public support of
additional facilities.

NOTES

1. Novick R.J., Kaye M.P., Patterson G.A., Andreassian B., Klepetko W., Menkis A.H., et al. Redo lung transplantation: a North American-European experience. *J Heart Lung Transplant* 1993;12:5-16.

2. DeHoyos A.L., Patterson G.A., Maurer J.R., Ramirez J.C., Miller J.D., Winton T.L. Pulmonary transplantation: early and late results of the Toronto Lung Transplant Group. *J Thorac Cardiovasc Surg* 1992;103:295-306.

3. Morreim E.H. *Balancing act: the new medical ethics of medicine's new economics.* Washington: Georgetown University Press; 1995:47-51.

4. Doyal L. Needs, rights, and the moral duties of clinicians. In Gillon R., Lloyd A., editors. *Principles of health care ethics.* Chichester: John Wiley; 1994:217-30.

5. Daniels N. Four unsolved rationing problems: a challenge. *Hastings Cent Rep* 1994;24:27-9.

6. Levinsky N.G. The doctor's master. *N Engl J Med* 1984;311:1573-5.

7. Morreim E.H. *Balancing act:* 2.

8. *Stoffman v. Vancouver General Hospital* (1990), 76 DLR (4th) 700 (SCC).

9. *Fleming v. Reid* (1991), 82 DLR (4th) 298 (Ont CA) 8.

10. *Korn v. Potter* (1996), 134 DLR (4th) 43 7 (BCSC).

11. *Ethridge v. British Columbia Attorney-General* (1995), 125 DLR (4th) 323 (BCCA).

12. *R.v. Cambridge Health Authority* ex parte B (1995) 2 All ER 129 (CA) at 137, Sir Thomas Bingham, M.R.

13. *Law Estate v. Simice* (1994), 21 CCLT (2d) 228 (BCSC).

14. *Whitebone v. Jordan* (1981), 1 All ER 2 67 (HL).

15. Hauptman P.J., O'Connor K.J. Medical progress procurement and allocation of solid organs for transplantation. *N Eng J Med* 1997;3 36:422-31.

16. Hadorn D.C. Setting health care priorities in Oregon: cost-effectiveness meets the rule of rescue. *JAMA* 1991;265:2218-25.

17. Garland M.J. Oregon's contribution to defining adequate health care. In Chapman A.R., editor. *Health care reform: a human rights approach.* Washington: Georgetown University Press; 1994:211-32.

18. Kitzhaber J., Kemmy A.M. On the Oregon trail [review]. *Br Med Bull* 1995; 51:808-18.

19. Canadian Medical Association. *Core and comprehensive health care services—a framework for decision-making.* Ottawa: The Association, 1994.

20. Deber R., Lutchmie N., Baranek P., Hilfer N., Duvalko K.M., Zlotnik-Shaul R.,

et al. *The public/private mix in health care* [commissioned by the National Forum on Health]. In press;1429-37.

21. Canadian Medical Association. Code of ethics. *Can Med Assoc 1* 1996;155: 1176A-B.

22. Tengs T.O., Adams M.E., Pliskin J.S., Safran D.G., Siegel J.E., Weinstein M.C., et al. Five hundred life-saving interventions and their cost-effectiveness. *Risk Anal* 1995;15:369-90.

23. Mendelssohn D.C., Kua B.T., Singer P.A. Referral for dialysis in Ontario. *Arch Intern Med* 1995; 1 55:2473-8.

24. Olbrisch M.E., Levenson J.L. Psychosocial evaluation of heart transplant candidates: an international survey of process, criteria and outcomes. *J Heart Lung Transplant* 1991;10:948-55.

25. Levenson J.L., Olbrisch M.E. Psychosocial evaluation of organ transplant candidates: a comparative survey of process, criteria, and outcome in heart, liver and kidney transplantation. *Psychosomatics* 1993;34:314-23.

26. Mullen M.A., Kohut N., Sam M., Blendis L., Singer P.A. Access to adult liver transplantation in Canada: a survey and ethical analysis. *Can Med Assoc J* 1996;154:337-42.

27. Jecker N.S., Berg A.O. Allocating medical resources in rural America: alternative perceptions of justice. *Soc Sci Med* 1992;34:467-74.

28. The Society of Critical Care Medicine Ethics Committee. Attitudes of critical care medicine professionals concerning distribution of intensive care resources. *Crit Care Med* 1994;22:358-62.

29. Zweibel N.R., Cassel C.K., Karrison T. Public attitudes about the use of chronological age as a criterion for allocating health care resources. *Gerontologist* 1993;33:74-80.

30. Ubel P.A., DeKay M.L.,Baron J., Asch D.A. Cost-effectiveness analysis in a setting of budget constraints: Is it equitable? *N Eng J Med* 1996;3 34:1174-7.

31. Nord E., Richardson J., Kuhse H., Singer P. Maximizing health benefits vs. egalitarianism: an Australian survey of health issues. *Soc Sci Med* 1995;41:1429-37.

The Problem with Futility

Robert D. Truog, Allan S. Brett, and Joel Frader

"Futility" is one of the newest additions to the lexicon of bioethics. Physicians, ethicists, and members of the media are increasingly concerned about patients and families who insist on receiving life-sustaining treatment that others judge to be futile. A clear understanding of futility has proved to be elusive, however. Many clinicians view futil-

Robert D. Truog, Allan S. Brett and Joel Frader, "The Problem with Futility," *New England Journal of Medicine* 326:23 (1992)1560-1564.

ity the way one judge viewed pornography: they may not be able to define it, but they know it when they see it.[1]

The notion of futile medical treatment may go back to the time of Hippocrates, who allegedly advised physicians "to refuse to treat those who are overmastered by their diseases, realizing that in such cases medicine is powerless."[2] More recently, the concept has appeared frequently in court decisions and policy statements.[3-6] The so-called Baby Doe law exempts physicians from providing treatment that would be virtually futile.[7] The Council on Ethical and Judicial Affairs of the American Medical Association (AMA) recently concluded that physicians have no obligation to obtain consent for a do-not-resuscitate (DNR) order when cardiopulmonary resuscitation (CPR) is deemed futile.[8] The fact that this concept has appeared in law and policy may seem to indicate that it is clearly understood and widely accepted. In reality, however, the notion of futility hides many deep and serious ambiguities that threaten its legitimacy as a rationale for limiting treatment.

PARADIGMS OF FUTILITY

Contemporary discussions of futility have centered primarily on cases involving patients in a persistent vegetative state and those involving the use of CPR. A third type of case, involving organ-replacement technology, has received little attention but is helpful to our understanding of futility.

FUTILITY AND THE PERSISTENT VEGETATIVE STATE

The first type of scenario involving the question of futility is represented by the recent Minnesota case of Helga Wanglie.[9] Mrs. Wanglie was an 86-year-old woman who had been dependent on mechanical ventilation and in a persistent vegetative state for more than a year. Her husband insisted that she believed in maintaining life at all cost, and that when she was ready to go . . . the good Lord would call her."[10] Her physicians, on the other hand, believed that the continued use of mechanical ventilation and intensive care was futile. When attempts to transfer her elsewhere failed, they sought to have a court appoint an independent conservator with responsibility for making medical decisions on her behalf. The judge denied this petition and reaffirmed the authority of her husband as legal surrogate. Three days later, Mrs. Wanglie died.

Cases like that of Mrs. Wanglie seldom reach the courts, but they are probably not rare. A similar call involving a child with severe brain damage was concluded with a settlement favorable to the family before a judicial decision.[11]

FUTILITY IN CASES INVOLVING CPR

The second prototypical scenario involves the use of DNR orders. Although the techniques of CPR were originally intended only for use after acute, reversible cardiac arrests, the current practice is to use CPR in all situations unless there is a direct order to the contrary. Since cardiac arrest is the final event in all terminal illness, everyone is eventually a candidate for this medical procedure. DNR orders were developed to spare patients from aggressive attempts at revival when imminent death is anticipated and inevitable. Nevertheless, patients or families sometimes request CPR even when care givers believe such attempts would be futile. Some have argued that in these circumstances a physician should be able to enact a DNR order without the consent of the patient or family.[12-14]

FUTILITY AND ORGAN-REPLACEMENT TECHNOLOGY

Although the bioethical debate over the question of futility has been most concerned with cases involving CPR and the treatment of patients in a persistent vegetative state, a third type of futility-related judgment has gone essentially unchallenged. It involves the increasingly large number of interventions that could possibly prolong the life of virtually any dying patient. For example, extracorporeal membrane oxygenation can replace heart and lung function for up to several weeks. Physicians now use this intervention when they expect organ systems eventually to recover or while they await organs for transplantation. However, it could prolong the life of almost anyone with cardiorespiratory failure, reversible or not. Patients thus kept alive may remain conscious and capable of communicating. Care givers do not now offer this therapy to terminally ill patients, presumably because it would be futile. This judgment has gone largely unchallenged, yet it is not obvious why a clinician's unilateral decision not to use "futile" extracorporeal membrane oxygenation is inherently different from a decision not to use "futile" CPR or "futile" intensive care. If all three treatments can be characterized as objectively futile, then unilateral decisions not to offer them should be equally justified.

As it is used in these three cases, the concept of futility obscures many ambiguities and assumptions. These can be usefully grouped into two categories: problems of value and problems of probability.

FUTILITY AND VALUES

It is meaningless simply to say that an intervention is futile; one must always ask, "Futile in relation to what?" The medical literature provides many examples in which the importance of identifying the goals of treatment has not been fully appreciated. The effectiveness of CPR, for example, is often discussed in terms of whether patients who require the procedure can survive long enough to be discharged from the hospital.[15] This definition of success usually implies that short-term survival is a goal not worth pursuing. Patients or family members may value the additional hours of life differently, however. Indeed, physicians and other care givers have repeatedly been shown to be poor judges of patients' preferences with regard to intensive care.[16-18]

Schneiderman and colleagues have argued that treatments that merely preserve permanent unconsciousness or that cannot end dependence on intensive medical care should be considered futile.[19] Although society may eventually endorse decisions to override the previously expressed wishes of patients or the desires of surrogates who demand such treatments, it does not follow that the treatments are futile. Mr. Wanglie would have rejected this conclusion, and there is no reason to dismiss his view out of hand. The decision that certain goals are not worth pursuing is best seen as involving a conflict of values rather than a question of futility.

Certainly in this context, the plurality of values in our society makes agreement on the concept of futility difficult, if not impossible. Several groups have therefore attempted to arrive at a value-free understanding of the concept.[20,21] The most promising candidate thus far is the notion of "physiologic futility." As the guidelines on the termination of life-sustaining treatment prepared by the Hastings Center state, if a treatment is "clearly futile in achieving its physiological objective and so offer[s] no physiological benefit to the patient, the professional has no obligation to provide it."[20] For example, the physiologic objective of mechanical ventilation is to maintain adequate ventilation and oxygenation in the presence of respiratory failure, and the physiologic objective of CPR is to maintain adequate cardiac output and respiration in the presence of cardiorespiratory failure. The New York State Task Force on Life and the Law mistakenly concludes that CPR is physiologically futile when it will "be unsuccessful in restoring cardiac and respiratory function or [when] the patient will experience repeated arrest in a short time period before death occurs."[21] CPR is physiologically futile only when it is impossible to perform effective cardiac massage and ventilation (such as in the presence of cardiac rupture or severe outflow obstruction). Saying that CPR is physiologically futile when it will be unsuccessful in restoring cardiac function is like saying that mechanical ventilation is physiologically futile if it cannot restore respiratory function. The immediate physiologic effect of the intervention differs from the broader and more uncertain question of prognosis.

Physiologic futility, understood in narrow terms, comes close to providing a value-free understanding of futility. Unfortunately, it applies to a very small number of real cases involving CPR. Similarly, since in the case of Mrs. Wanglie mechanical ventilation could maintain adequate oxygenation and ventilation, her treatment could not be considered futile in the physiologic sense. Even the use of extracorporeal membrane oxygenation in terminally ill patients cannot be considered physiologically futile, since it can maintain circulation and ventilation. The concept of physiologic futility, therefore, falls short of providing guidance in most cases resembling those described above.

FUTILITY AND STATISTICAL UNCERTAINTY

In most medical situations, there is no such thing as never. Futility is almost always a matter of probability. But what statistical cutoff point should be chosen as the threshold for determining futility? The statement from the Council on Ethical and Judicial Affairs of the AMA concludes that physicians have no obligation to provide futile CPR, but it fails to specify any level of statistical certainty at which the judgment is warranted.[8] The AMA statement fails to acknowledge that this is even an issue. Should each physician decide independently what probability of success should be considered to indicate futility?

Even if we could agree on a statistical cutoff point for determining futility, physicians are often highly unreliable in estimating the likelihood of success of a therapeutic intervention. Psychological research [22,23] has shown that estimates of probability are susceptible to "severe and systematic errors."[22] Empirical studies have corroborated the limitations of clinical assessment in estimating both prognosis[24] and diagnosis.[25] Even in theory, statistical inferences about what might happen to groups of patients do not permit accurate predictions of what will happen to the next such patient. In addition, the tendency to remember cases that are unusual or bizarre predisposes physicians to make decisions on the basis of their experiences with "miraculous" cures or unexpected tragedies.

Schneiderman and colleagues recently argued that a treatment should be considered futile when 100 consecutive patients do not respond to it.[19] But how similar must the patients be? In assessing the efficacy of mechanical ventilation to treat pneumonia, for example, is it sufficient simply to recall the 100 most recent patients who received artificial ventilation for pneumonia? Or must this group be stratified according to age, etiologic organism, or coexisting illness? Clearly, many of these factors will make an important difference.

FUTILITY AND RESOURCE ALLOCATION

Although medical practice has increasingly emphasized patients' autonomy, there is growing pressure on physicians to slow the increase in health care costs by foreclosing some options. Thus, we have a tension between the value of autonomy, exercised in the form of consent to use or omit various interventions, and the desirability of a more Spartan approach to the consumption of medical resources. We promote patients' freedom to request whatever the medical menu has to offer, but we also require that interventions be guided by considerations of cost and the likelihood of benefit.[26] Unfortunately, there is no consensus about what constitutes a just method of balancing the preferences of individual patients against the diverse needs of society.

To some, the concept of futility provides at least a partial solution to this dilemma: it offers a reason to limit therapy without the need to define a fair procedure for allocating resources. This approach allows treatments to be denied on the grounds that they are simply not indicated, apart from the matter of cost. Despite its attractions, there are good reasons why we should not use this concept to solve problems of allocation.

First, arguments based on the futility concept conceal many statistical and value-laden assumptions, whereas strategies based on resource allocation force these assumptions to be stated explicitly. Societies may choose to limit the use of therapies that may be of value and have a reasonable likelihood of success in some cases. For example, the much discussed Oregon plan for allocating Medicaid funds[27] seeks to reflect community values in ranking various health care goals (placing preventive care ahead of cosmetic surgery, for example). Since rationing policies make explicit the values and probabilities that

futility-based arguments leave implicit, it is clearly preferable to develop and adopt them rather than use futility arguments as a cover for limiting the availability of scarce and expensive resources.

Another problem with invoking the idea of futility in the debate over allocation is that we have no reason to believe that it is applicable in enough cases to make a difference in the scarcity of medical resources. Although it may be true that beds in the intensive care unit (especially those used for extracorporeal membrane oxygenation) are relatively scarce, it seems unlikely that patients similar to Helga Wanglie occupy an important fraction of those beds, let alone account for a major proportion of the cost of medical care in the United States. From a macro-economic perspective at least, we must remain skeptical that an appeal to the idea of futility will get us very far.

MOVING BEYOND FUTILITY

Our rejection of futility as a useful concept does not imply that we endorse patients' unrestricted demands for interventions such as those described in our prototypical scenarios. On the contrary, when providers oppose such demands they are usually acting from a profound sense that further treatment would be fundamentally wrong. Our task is to take account of that sense of wrongness without resorting to unilateral, provider-initiated declarations of futility.

In many of the situations in which questions of futility arise, providers believe that the treatment in question would not be in the patient's interests, even from the patient's perspective, and that any insistence by the patient (or surrogate) on further interventions is based on faulty reasoning, unrealistic expectations, or psychological factors, such as denial or guilt. In these circumstances, providers are obligated to make every effort to clarify precisely what the patient intends to achieve with continued treatment. If the patient's goals appear to reflect unrealistic expectations about the probable course of the underlying illness or the probable effect of medical interventions, providers should attempt to correct those impressions. Because inadequate or insensitive communication by providers probably accounts for a substantial proportion of unrealistic requests, such discussions will successfully resolve many conflicts.[14,28] Empirical studies of ethics consultations have demonstrated precisely this point.[29,30]

Although this appeal to the patient's interests may seem to contain some of the same ambiguities as arguments using the concept of futility, there is a subtle but important distinction between the two. Judgments about what is in the patient's interest are properly grounded in the patient's perspective, whereas judgments cast in the language of futility falsely assume that there is an objective and dispassionate standard for determining benefits and burdens. Nevertheless, even after providers make sustained attempts to clarify patients' preferences, some patients or surrogates will continue to demand life-sustaining interventions when the care givers feel deeply troubled about providing them. In many such cases, unrestrained deference to the wishes of the patient or surrogate conflicts with two other values that do not require a unilateral judgment of the futility of treatment: professional ideals and social consensus.

The ideals of medical professionals include respect for patients' wishes, to be sure, but they also include other values, such as compassionate action and the minimization of suffering. Consider, for example, a bedridden victim of multiple strokes who has contractures and bedsores and who "communicates" only by moaning or grimacing when she is touched. Physicians

asked to perform chest compressions, institute mechanical ventilation, or use other life-sustaining interventions in such a patient may regard these actions as cruel and inhumane.[31] Moreover, physicians and other care givers have a legitimate interest in seeing that their knowledge and skills are used wisely and effectively. For example, if surgeons were repeatedly pressured to perform operations that they believed to be inappropriate, they would certainly suffer a loss of dignity and sense of purpose. Although appealing to professional ideals can serve as a convenient means of protecting the interests of physicians at the expense of patients' values, these ideals are legitimate factors to weigh against other values. To dismiss this perspective as irrelevant in decision making is to deny an essential part of what it means to practice medicine.

Although we believe that health care professionals should not be required to take part in care that violates their own morals, the law in this area remains uncertain. On the one hand, courts have upheld a state interest in protecting the ethical integrity of the medical profession. This may provide some basis for protecting doctors who wish to refrain from cruel or inhumane treatment, despite the wishes of the patient or surrogate.[32] On the other hand, in the two cases that have led to court decisions (those of Helga Wanglie[3] and of Jane Doe in Atlanta[33]), the judges upheld the surrogates' decision-making authority. Clearly, this area of the law remains to be defined.

Finally, social consensus is yet another expression of the values at stake in some medical decisions. In a pluralistic society, differences in personal values and interests occasionally run so deep that they cannot be resolved by the introduction of additional facts or by further private debate. At certain critical junctures, the resolution of these conflicts may require an explicit public process of social decision making.[34] Social consensus has been sought, for example, to address the issue of fair allocation of resources.[27] The involvement of society is also essential when the most highly charged questions of morality are at stake, as in the increasingly heated debate over euthanasia.[35]

In the prototypical scenarios described at the outset of this article, an ongoing attempt to achieve social consensus is perhaps most conspicuous with regard to the prolongation of life for patients in a persistent vegetative state. From a legal perspective, the relevant decisions began with the case of Karen Quinlan [36] and have extended through that of Nancy Cruzan.[37] These cases have increased awareness of the ethical issues raised by the situation of patients in a persistent vegetative state and have helped to consolidate the view that it is acceptable to withdraw life-sustaining treatment from patients in such a state. Controversy does remain about who has the ultimate authority to make these decisions. Some hold that the choice must remain with the patient or surrogate, whereas others believe that under some circumstances this prerogative may be overridden. For example, the Hastings Center[38] and the Society of Critical Care Medicine[39] have concluded that providing intensive care to patients in a persistent vegetative state is generally a misuse of resources, and the President's Commission stated that such patients should be removed from life support if such action is necessary to benefit another patient who is not in a persistent vegetative state.[40] It is unclear how this debate will conclude, but the confluence of medical, legal, and ethical thinking about the persistent vegetative state is an example of how social consensus may evolve.

In summary, the Wanglie case demonstrates how the resolution of these conflicts must proceed on many levels. Most such cases will benefit from sustained attempts to clarify the patient's values and the likelihood of the various relevant outcomes, and to improve communication with patients or their surrogates. When this approach fails, physicians and other care givers should ask themselves whether the care requested is consistent with their professional ethics and ideals. When these ideals appear to be violated, either alternative venues for such care should be found or the conflict should be addressed in a public forum. This broader review could be provided through institutional mechanisms, such as the hospital's ethics committee, or by the courts. The public scrutiny that attends such cases will further the debate over the appropriate use of medical resources and foster the development of consensus through legislation and public policy.

CONCLUSION

In outlining the perspectives of the principal stakeholders — patients and their surrogates, physicians, and society — we have avoided the construction of a rigid formula for resolving conflicts over interventions frequently regarded as futile. Because of clinical heterogeneity, pluralistic values, and the evolutionary nature of social consensus, most clinical decision making on behalf of critically ill patients defies reduction to universally applicable principles.

The notion of futility generally fails to provide an ethically coherent ground for limiting life-sustaining treatment, except in circumstances in which narrowly defined physiologic futility can be plausibly invoked. Futility has been conceptualized as an objective entity independent of the patient's or surrogate's perspective, but differences in values and the variable probabilities of clinical outcomes undermine its basis. Furthermore, assertions of futility may camouflage judgments of comparative worth that are implicit in debates about the allocation of resources. In short, the problem with futility is that its promise of objectivity can rarely be fulfilled. The rapid advance of the language of futility into the jargon of bioethics should be followed by an equally rapid retreat.

NOTES

1. *Jacobellis v. State of Ohio*, 84 S Ct 1676 (1964).
2. Hippocrates. The art. In Reiser S.J., Dyck A.J., Curran W.J., eds. *Ethics in medicine: historical perspectives and contemporary concerns.* Cambridge, Mass.: MIT Press, 1977:6-7.
3. Capron A.M. In re Help Wanglie. *Hastings Cent Rep* 1991;21(5):26-8.
4. Lantos J.D., Singer P.A., Walker R.M., et al. The illusion of futility in clinical practice. *Am J Med* 1989;87:81-4.
5. Standards for cardiopulmonary resuscitation (CPR) and emergency cardiac care (ECC). V. Medicolegal considerations and recommendations. *JAMA* 1974;227:Suppl:864-6.
6. Appendix A: the proposed legislation. In *Do not resuscitate orders: the proposed legislation and report of the New York State Task Force on Life and the Law.* 2nd ed. New York: The Task Force, 1986:83.
7. 1994 Amendments to the Child Abuse Prevention and Treatment Act. *Pub Law* 98-457, 1984.
8. Council on Ethical and Judicial Affairs, American Medical Association. Guidelines for the appropriate use of do-not-resuscitate orders. *JAMA* 1991;265:1868-71.
9. Miles S.H. Informed demand for "non-beneficial" medical treatment. *N Eng J Med* 1991;325:512-5.
10. Brain-damaged woman at center of lawsuit over life-support dies. *New York Times.* July 5, 1991:A8.
11. Paris J.J., Crone R.K., Reardon F. Physicians' refusal of requested treatment: the case of Baby L. *N Engl J Med* 1990;322:1012-5.
12. Blackball U. Must we always use CPR? *N Eng J Med* 1987;317:1281-5.
13. Hackler J.C., Hiller F.C. Family consent to orders not to resuscitate: reconsidering hospital policy. *JAMA* 1990;264:1281-3.
14. Murphy D.J. Do-not-resuscitate orders: time for reappraisal in long-term care institutions. *JAMA* 1988;260:2098-101.
15. Bedell S.E., Detbanco T.L., Cook E.F., Epstein F.H. Survival after cardiopulmonary resuscitation in the hospital. *N Engl J Med* 1983;309:569-76.
16. Danis M., Gerrity M.S., Southerland L.I., Patrick D.L. A comparison of patient, family, and physician assessments of the value of medical intensive care. *Crit Care Med* 1988;16:594-600.
17. Danis M., Jarr S.L., Southerland L.I., Nocella R.S., Patrick D.L. A comparison of patient, family, and nurse evaluations of the usefulness of intensive care. *Crit Care Med* 1987;15:138-43.

18. Danis M., Patrick D.L., Southerland L.I., Green M.L. Patients' and families' preferences for medical intensive care. *JAMA* 1988;260:797-802.

19. Schneiderman L.J., Jecker N.S., Jonsen A.R. Medical futility: its meaning and ethical implications. *Ann Intern Med* 1990;112:949-54.

20. The Hastings Center. *Guidelines on the termination of life-sustaining treatment and the care of the dying.* Bloomington: Indiana University Press, 1987:32.

21. Appendix C: New York Public Health Law Article 29-B — orders not to resuscitate. In *Do not resuscitate orders: the proposed legislation and report of the New York State Task Force on Life and the Law.* 2nd ed. New York: The Task Force, 1986:96.

22. Tversky A., Kahneman D. Judgment under uncertainty: heuristics and biases. *Science* 1974;185:1124-31.

23. Elstein A.S. Clinical judgment: psychological research and medical practice. *Science* 1976;194:696-700.

24. Poses R.M., Bekes C., Copare F.J., Scott W.E. "The answer to "What are my chances, doctor?" depends on whom is asked: prognostic disagreement and inaccuracy for critically ill patients. *Crit Care Med* 1989;17:827-33.

25. Poses R.M., Cebul R.D., Collins M., Fager S.S. The accuracy of experienced physicians' probability estimates for patients with sore throats: implications for decision making. *JAMA* 1985;254:925-9.

26. Aaron H., Schwartz W.B. Rationing health care: the choice before us. *Science* 1990;247:419-22.

27. Eddy D.M. What's going on in Oregon? *JAMA* 1991;266:417-20.

28. Younger S.J. Who defines futility? *JAMA* 1988;260:2094-5.

29. Brennan T.A. Ethics committees and decisions to limit care: the experience at the Massachusetts General Hospital. *JAMA* 1988;260:803-7.

30. La Puma J. Consultations in clinical ethics — issues and questions in 27 cases. *West J Med* 1987;146:633-7.

31. Braithwaite S., Thomasma D.C. New guidelines on foregoing life-sustaining treatment in incompetent patients: an anti-cruelty policy. *Ann Intem Med* 1986;104:711-5.

32. Meisel A. *The right to die.* New York: John Wiley & Sons, 1989:104.

33. *In re: Doe,* Civil Action No. D93064 (Fulton County, GA, October 17, 1991).

34. Callahan D. Medical futility, medical necessity: the-problem-without-a-name. *Hastings Cent Rep* 1991;21(4):30-5.

35. Misbin P.I. Physicians' aid in dying. *N Engl J Med* 1991;325:1307-11.

36. *In the Matter of Karen Ann Quinlan, an alleged incompetent.* 355 A.2d 647; or 70 NJ 10. March 31, 1976.

37. Annas G.J. Nancy Cruzan and the right to die. *N Engl J Med* 1990;323:670-3.

38. The Hastings Center. *Guidelines on the termination of life-sustaining treatment and the care of the dying.* Bloomington: Indiana University Press, 1987:112.

39. Task Force on Ethics of the Society of Critical Care Medicine. Consensus report on the ethics of foregoing life-sustaining treatments in the critically ill. *Crit Care Med* 1990;18:1435-9.

40. President's Commission for the Study of Ethical Problems in Medicine and Biomedical and Behavioral Research. *Deciding to forego life-sustaining ethical, medical, and legal issues in treatment decisions*. Washington, D.C.: Government Printing Office, 1983:188-9.

FURTHER READINGS

Anscombe, Elizabeth. "Who Is Wronged?" *The Oxford Review* 5 (1967) 16–17.

Atterbury, C.E. "The Alcoholic in the Lifeboat: Should Drinkers Be Candidates for Liver Transplantation?" *Journal of Clinical Gastroenterology*. 1986; 8:1-4.

Cassel, Christine et al, eds. *Geriatric Medicine*. New York: Springer Verlag, 1990.

Kluge, E.-H.W. "Designated Organ Donation: Private Choice in Social Context." *Hastings Center Report* September/October 1989, 10–15.

Kluge, E.-H.W. "Health Policy and the Allocation of Resources: The Ethics of Discrimination" in J.E. Thornton and E.R.Winkler, *Ethics and Aging: The Right to Live and the Right to Die*. Vancouver: The University of British Columbia Press, 1988.

Magnet, J.E. and E.-H.W. Kluge. *Withholding Treatment from Defective Newborn Children*. Cowansville: Brown Legal Publ., 1985, chapters 1 and 2.

Rachels, James F. "Who Shall Live When Not All Can Live?" *Soundings: An Interdisciplinary Journal* 53 (Winter, 1970) 339–355.

Report of the Council on Scientific Affairs of the American Medical Association. "Societal Effects and Other Factors Affecting Health Care for the Elderly." *Archives of Internal Medicine* 150: 6 (June 1990) 1184–1189.

Report of the Council on Ethical and Judicial Affairs of the American Medical Association. *Ethical Implications of Age-Based Rationing of Health Care*. Chicago, Ill.: American Medical Association, 1988, I–88.

Rescher, Nicholas. "The Allocation of Exotic Medical Lifesaving Therapy." *Ethics* 79 (1969) 173–180.

Singer, P. "A Review of Public Policies to Procure and Distribute Kidneys for Transplantation." *Archives of Internal Medicine* 150: 3 (March 1990) 523–527, 525–6.

Storch, Janet. *Patients' Rights, Ethical and Legal Issues in Health Care and Nursing*. Toronto: McGraw-Hill, 1984, 122.

Sugden, R. and A. Williams. *The Principles of Practical Cost-Benefit Analysis*. Oxford: Oxford University Press, 1978.

Thornton, James E. and Earl R. Winkler, eds. *Ethics and Aging: The Right to Live, the Right to Die*. Vancouver: The University of British Columbia Press, 1988.

Veatch, Robert. "Who Should Pay for Smokers' Medical Care?" *Hastings Center Report*, 4 (Nov. 1974), 8–9.

Veatch, R.M. "Voluntary Risk to Health: The Ethical Issues." *Journal of the American Medical Association* 243 (Jan. 4, 1980) 50–55.

Young, Robert. "Some Criteria for Making Decisions Concerning the Distribution of Scarce Medical Resources." *Theory and Decision* 6 (1975) 439–455.

CHAPTER 5
THE HEALTH CARE PROFESSIONAL-PATIENT RELATIONSHIP

INTRODUCTION

In human terms, the most important thing in the delivery of health care is the relationship between the health care professional and the patient. This is not to say that no other factors have to be taken into account, or that no other relationships are important. For instance, the availability of health care resources plays a crucial role because it defines the limits within which the delivery of care can take place. Likewise the relationship between the professional and the patient's next-of-kin, or with other health care professionals and society are also important, because they define the extended setting in which the delivery of care actually takes place.

However, the relationship between the professional and the patient is central because it is the basis of the health care professional's interaction with all the other parties. It is also the *raison d'être* of health care itself. Therefore it is logically primary. How this relationship is structured sets the tone for everything else.

It could be argued that the relationship between a public health professional and society as a whole is different. But even here similar ethical problems arise and similar ethical considerations apply. Issues such as those of authority, compliance, informed consent and, above all, trust are also implicated. The only difference is that in the case of public health, society itself has taken the place of the individual patient.

Of course the fact that society is composed of many individuals does introduce issues that do not exist in the usual health care professional-patient relationship. The question of aggregate as opposed to individual rights constitutes a particular thorny — and distinctive — issue. However, even here the relationship between the health care professional and the individual patient remains important; because in the end, activities that are directed towards the public good must be translated into actions that affect individual patients. With this, the professional-patient relationship once again comes to the fore.

The traditional view held by *physicians themselves* was that the physician is the captain of the ship, and that the patient has to follow orders. We find this view expressed in the writings of Hippocrates — himself a physician — and those of later medical writers like Galen, Razes, Maimonides and so on. For the English-speaking world, this view found its classic statement in Thomas Percival's *Medical Ethics*. (Incidentally, Percival also had a similar view of nurses and other health care workers.)

While for centuries this was the outlook of physicians themselves, for a long time society did not entirely share this perspective. Until well into the nineteenth century, the physician was seen as a figure of last resort — and even then, as someone who gave advice, but whose advice could be ignored by the patient. It was not until the nineteenth century, and even more in the twentieth when medicine became a legally recognized service-provider monopoly, that the physician came to be seen as the primary decision-maker: as the person who knew best, and who therefore had not only the right but also the duty to make the decision.

Nowadays, such a physician-centred perspective is no longer in vogue. In fact, this sort of approach to physician authority would be characterized as being extremely paternalistic in nature. The selections that follow present an examination of how the relationship between the health care professional and the patient should be structured from a contemporary perspective.

Robert Veatch identified four models of the physician-patient relationship. He distinguished between what he called the engineering model, the priestly model, the collegial, and the contractual model.[1]

According to the engineering model, the physician is nothing more than an "applied scientist," who simply presents the patient with diagnosis, prognosis and treatment options, but leaves the decision making completely up to the patient. Questions of ethics and values do not enter into the relationship so far as the physician is concerned. "The physician becomes a plumber without any moral integrity."

What Veatch called the priestly model is what is also often called the paternalistic model. This model is exactly the reverse of the engineering model. The physician here acts on the basis of the principle, "Benefit and do not harm the patient," but it is the physician who decides what constitutes benefit and harm. "The moral authority [of the physician] so dominates ... that the patient's freedom and dignity are extinguished."

According to the collegial model, both physician and patient are connected by common bonds of mutual loyalty, common interests and goals. It is also characterized by the assumption that physician and patient come together as independent equals.

Finally, the contractual model questions this assumption of equality. It recognizes the differences in knowledge and power between physician and patient, and tries to compensate for this in terms of an assumed — and sometimes even explicit — contractual perspective that leaves both parties their own dignity and moral authority.

There have been various reactions to and modifications of Veatch's analysis. The article by James Childress and Mark Siegler, included below, is one of the more noteworthy ones. Contrary to Veatch, Childress and Siegler argue that autonomy should not be the ideal that is aimed at in the physician-patient relationship, but rather a constraint that applies to both parties, and that the nature of the physician-patient relationship is more properly defined by the concept of autonomous negotiation. Further, they argue that societal constraints also enter the picture.

However, the patient interacts not only with physicians but also with nurses. In fact, in many instances more care is provided by nurses than by physicians — certainly on a continuing basis. It is not at all clear that an analysis that focuses on the physician-patient interaction is appropriate to, or captures the complexity of, the nurse-patient relationship. In an article especially for this volume, Janet Storch presents the perspective of the nurse.

NOTES

1. Robert M. Veatch, "Models for Ethical Medicine in a Revolutionary Age," Hastings Center Report 2 (June 1972):7.

Metaphors and Models of Doctor-Patient Relationships: Their Implications for Autonomy

James F. Childress and Mark Siegler

INTRODUCTION

Many metaphors and models have been applied to relationships between patients and physicians. One example is an interpretation of physician-patient relationships as paternalistic. In this case, the physician is regarded as a parent and the patient is regarded as a child. Opponents of such a paternalistic view of medicine rarely reject the use of metaphors to interpret medical relationships; rather, they simply offer alter-

Theoretical Medicine 5 (1984) 17-30.

native metaphors, for example, the physician as partner or the patient as rational contractor. Metaphors may operate even when patients and physicians are unaware of them. Physician-patient conflicts may arise if each party brings to their encounter a different image of medicine, as, for example, when the physician regards a paternalistic model of medicine as appropriate, but the patient prefers a contractual model.

As these examples suggest, metaphors involve seeing something as something else, for example, seeing a lover as a red rose, human beings as wolves, or medical therapy as warfare. Metaphors highlight some features and hide other features of their principal subject.[1] Thus, thinking about a physician as a parent highlights the physician's care for dependent others and his or her control over them, but it conceals the patient's payment of fees to the physician. Metaphors and models may be used to describe relationships as they exist, or to indicate what those relationships ought to be. In either the descriptive or the prescriptive use of metaphors, this highlighting and hiding occurs, and it must be considered in determining the adequacy of various metaphors. When metaphors are used to describe roles, they can be criticized if they distort more features than they illuminate. And when they are used to direct roles, they can be criticized if they highlight one moral consideration, such as care, while neglecting others, such as autonomy.

Since there is no single physician-patient relationship, it is probable that no single metaphor can adequately describe or direct the whole range of relationships in health care, such as open heart surgery, clinical research, and psychoanalysis. Some of the most important metaphors that have shaped health care in recent years include: parent-child, partners, rational contractors, friends, and technician-client. We want to determine the adequacy of these metaphors to describe and to direct doctor-patient rela-

tionships in the real world. In particular, we will assess them in relation to patient and physician autonomy.

METAPHORS AND MODELS OF RELATIONSHIPS IN HEALTH CARE

(1) The first metaphor is *paternal or parental,* and the model is paternalism. For this model, the locus of decision making is the health care professional, particularly the physician, who has "moral authority" within an asymmetrical and hierarchical relationship. (A variation on these themes appears in a model that was especially significant earlier — the priest-penitent relationship.) Following Thomas Szasz and Marc Hollender, we can distinguish two different versions of paternalism, based on two different prototypes.[2] If we take the *parent-infant relationship* as the prototype, the physician's role is active, while the patient's role is passive. The patient, like the infant, is primarily a dependent recipient of care. This model is applied easily to such clinical situations as anesthesia and to the care of patients with acute trauma, coma, or delirium. A second version takes the *parent-adolescent child* relationship as the prototype. Within this version, the physician guides the patient by telling him or her what to expect and what to do, and the patient co-operates to the extent of obeying. This model applies to such clinical situations as the outpatient treatment of acute infectious diseases. The physician instructs the patient on a course of treatment (such as antibiotics and rest), but the patient can either obey or refuse to comply.

The paternalist model assigns moral authority and discretion to the physician because good health is assumed to be a value shared by the patient and the physician and because the physician's competence, skills, and ability place him or her in a position to help the patient regain good health. Even if it was once the dominant model in health care and even if many patients and physicians still prefer it, the paternalist model is no longer adequate to describe or to direct all relationships in health care. Too many changes have occurred. In a pluralistic society such as ours, the assumption that the physician and patient have common values about health may be mistaken. They may disagree about the meaning of health and disease (for example, when the physician insists that cigarette smoking is a disease, but the patient claims that it is merely a nasty habit) or about the value of health relative to other values (for example, when the physician wants to administer a blood transfusion to save the life of a Jehovah's Witness, but the patient rejects the blood in order to have a chance of heavenly salvation).

As a normative model, paternalism tends to concentrate on care rather than respect, patients' needs rather than their rights, and physicians' discretion rather than patients' autonomy or self-determination. Even though paternalistic actions can sometimes be justified, for example, when a patient is not competent to make a decision and is at risk of harm, not all paternalistic actions can be justified.[3]

(2) A second model is one of *partnership*, which can be seen in Eric Cassell's statement: "Autonomy for the sick patient cannot exist outside of a good and properly functioning doctor-patient relation. And the relation between them is inherently a partnership."[4] The language of collegiality, collaboration, association, co-adventureship, and covenant is also used. This model stresses that health care professionals and their patients are partners or colleagues in the pursuit of the shared value of health. It is similar to the paternalist model in that it emphasizes the shared general values of the enterprise in which the participants

are involved. But what makes this model distinctive and significant is its emphasis on the equality of the participants' interpretations of shared values such as health, along with respect for the personal autonomy of all the participants.[5] The theme of equality does not, however, cancel a division of competence and responsibility along functional lines within the relationship.

Szasz and Hollender suggest that the prototype of the model of "mutual participation" or partnership is the adult-adult relationship. Within this model the physician helps the patient to help himself, while the patient uses expert help to realize his (and the physician's) ends. Some clinical applications of this model appear in the care of chronic diseases and psychoanalysis. It presupposes that "the participants (1) have approximately equal power, (2) be mutually interdependent (i.e., need each other), and (3) engage in activity that will be in some ways satisfying to both." Furthermore, "the physician does not know what is best for the patient. The search for this becomes the essence of the therapeutic interaction. The patient's own experiences furnish indispensable information for eventual agreement, under otherwise favorable circumstances, as to what 'health' might be for him."[6]

Although this model describes a few practices, it is most often offered as a normative model, indicating the morally desirable and even obligatory direction of practice and research.[7] As a normative model, it stresses the equality of value contributions and the autonomy of both professionals and other participants, whether sick persons or volunteers for research.

(3) A third model is that of *rational contractors*. Health care professionals and their patients are related or should be related to each other by a series of specific contracts. The prototype of this model is the specific contract by which individuals agree to exchange goods and services, and the

enforcement of such contracts by govern-mental sanctions. According to Robert Veatch, one of the strongest proponents of the contractual model in health care, this model is the best compromise between the *ideal of partnership,* with its emphasis on both equality and autonomy, and the *reality* of medical care, where mutual trust can-not be presupposed. If we could realize mutual trust, we could develop partner-ships. In the light of a realistic assessment of our situation, however, we can only hope for contracts. The model of rational con-tracts, according to Veatch, is the only real-istic way to share responsibility, to preserve both equality and autonomy under less than ideal circumstances, and to protect the integrity of various parties in health care (e.g., physicians are free not to enter contracts that would violate their con-sciences and to withdraw from them when they give proper notice).[8]

Such a model is valuable but problem-atic both descriptively and normatively. It neglects the fact that sick persons do not view health care needs as comparable to other wants and desires, that they do not have sufficient information to make rational contracts with the best providers of health services, and that the current structure of medicine obstructs the free operation of the marketplace and of contracts.[9] This model may also neglect the virtues of benevolence, care, and compassion that are stressed in other models such as paternalism and friendship.

(4) A fourth attempt to understand and direct the relationships between health care professionals and patients stresses *friendship*. According to P. Lain Entraglo,

> Insofar as man is a part of nature, and health an aspect of this nature and therefore a natural and objective good, the *medical relation* develops into comradeship, or association for the purpose of securing this good by

technical means. Insofar as man is an individual and his illness a state affecting his personality, the medical relation ought to be more than mere comradeship — in fact it should be a friendship. All dogma apart, a good doctor has always been a friend to his patient, to all his patients.[10]

For this version of "medical philia," the patient expresses trust and confidence in the physician while the doctor's "friend-ship for the patient should consist above all in a desire to give effective technical help — benevolence conceived and realised in technical terms."[11] Technical help and generalized benevolence are made "friendly" by explicit reference to the patient's personality.

Charles Fried's version of "medical philia" holds that physicians are *limited, special-purpose friends* in relation to their patients. In medicine, as in other profes-sional activities such as law, the client may have a relationship with the professional that is analogous to friendship. In friend-ship and in these relationships, one person assumes the interests of another. Claims in both sets of relationships are intense and demanding, but medical friendship is more limited in scope.[12]

Of course, this friendship analogy is somewhat strained, as Fried recognizes, because needs (real and felt) give rise to medical relationships, even if professionals are free not to meet them unless they are emergencies, because patients pay profes-sionals for their "personal care," and because patients do not have reciprocal loy-alties. Nevertheless, Fried's analysis of the medical relationship highlights the equali-ty, the autonomy, and the rights of both parties — the "friend" and the "befriend-ed." Because friendship, as Kant suggest-ed, is "the union of two persons through equal and mutual love and respect," the model of friendship has some ingredients of both paternalism (love or care) and anti-paternalism (equality and respect).[13] It applies especially well to the same medical relationships that fit partnership; indeed, medical friendship is very close to medical partnership, except that the former stresses the intensity of the relationship, while the latter stresses the emotional reserve as well as the limited scope of the relationship.

(5) A fifth and final model views the health care professional as a *technician.* Some commentators have referred to this model as plumber, others as engineer; for example, it has been suggested that with the rise of scientific medicine, the physician was viewed as "the expert engineer of the body as a machine."[14] Within this model, the physician "provides" or "delivers" technical service to patients who are "consumers." Exchange relations provide images for this interpretation of medical relations.

This model does not appear to be possible or even desirable. It is difficult to imagine that the health care professional as technician can simply present the "facts" unadorned by values, in part because major terms such as health and disease are not value-free and objective. Whether the "technician" is in an organization or in direct relation to clients, he or she serves some values. Thus, this model may collapse into the contractual model or a bureaucratic model (which will not be discussed in this essay). The professional may be thought to have only technical authority, not moral authority. But he or she remains a moral agent and thus should choose to participate or not in terms of his or her own commitments, loyalties, and integrity. One shortcoming of the paternalist and priestly models, as Robert Veatch notes, is the patient's "moral abdication," while one shortcoming of the technician model is the physician's "moral abdication."[15] The technician model offers autonomy to the patient, whose values dominate (at least in some settings) at the expense of the profession-

al's moral agency and integrity. In other models such as contract, partnership, and friendship, moral responsibility is shared by all the parties in part because they are recognized, in some sense, as equals.

RELATIONS BETWEEN INTIMATES AND BETWEEN STRANGERS

The above models of relationships between physicians and patients move between two poles: intimates and strangers.[16] In relations of intimacy, all the parties know each other very well and often share values, or at least know which values they do not share. In such relations, formal rules and procedures, backed by sanctions, may not be necessary; they may even be detrimental to the relationships. In relations of intimacy, trust rather than control is dominant. Examples include relationships between parents and children and between friends. Partnerships also share some features of such relationships, but their intimacy and shared values may be limited to a specific set of activities.

By contrast, in relations among strangers, rules and procedures become very important, and control rather than trust is dominant.[17] Of course, in most relations there are mixtures of trust and control. Each is present to some degree. Nevertheless, it is proper to speak about relations between strangers as structured by rules and procedures because the parties do not know each other well enough to have mutual trust. Trust means confidence in and reliance upon the other to act in accord with moral principles and rules or at least in accord with his or her publicly manifested principles and rules, whatever they might be. But if the other is a stranger, we do not know whether he or she accepts what we would count as moral principles and rules. We do not know whether he or she is worthy of trust. In the absence of intimate knowledge, or of shared values, strangers resort to rules and procedures in order to establish some control. Contracts between strangers, for example, to supply certain goods, represent instances of attempted control. But contractual relations do not only depend on legal sanctions; they also presuppose confidence in a shared structure of rules and procedures. As Talcott Parsons has noted, "transactions are actually entered into in accordance with a body of binding rules which are not part of the ad hoc agreement of the parties."[18]

Whether medicine is now only a series of encounters between strangers rather than intimates, medicine is increasingly regarded by patients and doctors and by analysts of the profession — such as philosophers, lawyers, and sociologists — as a practice that is best understood and regulated *as if it were* a practice among strangers rather than among intimates. Numerous causes can be identified: First, the pluralistic nature of our society; second, the decline of close, intimate contact over time among professionals and patients and their families; third, the decline of contact with the "whole person," who is now parcelled out to various specialists; fourth, the growth of large, impersonal, bureaucratically structured institutions of care, in which there is discontinuity of care (the patient may not see the same professionals on subsequent visits).[19]

In this situation, Alasdair MacIntyre contends, the modern patient "usually approaches the physician as stranger to stranger: and the very proper fear and suspicion that we have of strangers extends equally properly to our encounters with physicians. We do not and cannot know what to expect of them...."[20] He suggests that one possible response to this situation is to develop a rule-based bureaucracy in which "we can confront any individual who fills a given role with exactly the same expectation of exactly the same outcomes...." Our encounters with physicians and other health care professionals are encounters between strangers precisely because of our pluralistic society: several value systems are in operation, and we do not know whether the physicians we encounter share our value systems. In such a situation, patient autonomy is "a solution of last resort" rather than "a central moral good." Finally patients have to decide for themselves what will be done to them or simply delegate such decisions to others, such as physicians.

Just as MacIntyre recognizes the value of patient autonomy in our pluralistic society, so John Ladd recognizes the value of the concept of rights among strangers.[21] He notes that a legalistic, rights-based approach to medicine has several important advantages because rules and rights "serve to define our relationships with strangers as well as with people whom we know. ... In the medical context ... we may find ourselves in a hospital bed in a strange place, with strange company, and confronted by a strange physician and staff. The strangeness of the situation makes the concept of rights, both legal and moral, a very useful tool for defining our relationship to those with whom we have to deal."

Rules and rights that can be enforced obviously serve as ways to control the conduct of others when we do not know them well enough to be able to trust them. But all of the models of health care relationships identified above depend on some degree of trust. It is too simplistic to suppose that contracts, which can be legally enforced, do away with trust totally. Indeed, as we have argued, a society based on contracts depends to a very great extent on trust, precisely because not everything is enforceable at manageable cost. Thus, the issue is not simply whether trust or control is dominant, but, in part, the basis and extent of trust.

Trust, at least limited trust, may be possible even among strangers. There may be a presumption of trust, unless the society is in turmoil. And there may be an intermediate notion of "friendly strangers." People may be strangers because of differences regarding values or uncertainty regarding the other's values; they may be friendly because they accept certain rules and procedures, which may ensure that different values are respected. If consensus exists in a pluralistic society, it is primarily about rules and procedures, some of which protect the autonomy of agents, their freedom to negotiate their own relationships.

PHYSICIAN-PATIENT INTERACTIONS AS NEGOTIATIONS

It is illuminating, both descriptively and prescriptively, to view some encounters and interactions between physicians and patients as negotiations. The metaphor of negotiation has its home in discussions to settle matters by mutual agreements of the concerned parties. While it frequently appears in disputes between management and labor and between nations, it does not necessarily presuppose a conflict of interests between the parties. The metaphor of negotiation may also illuminate processes of reaching agreement regarding the terms of continuing interaction even when the issue is mainly the determination of one party's interests and the means to realize those interests. This metaphor captures two important characteristics of medical relationships: (1) it accents the autonomy of both patient and physician, and (2) it suggests a process that occurs over time rather than an event which occurs at a particular moment.

The model of negotiation can both explain what frequently occurs and identify what ought to occur in physician-patient interactions. An example can make this point: A twenty-eight-year-old ballet dancer suffered from moderately severe asthma. When she moved from New York to Chicago, she changed physicians and placed herself in the hands of a famed asthma specialist. He initiated aggressive steroid therapy to control her asthma, and within several months he had managed to control her wheezing. But she was distressed because her dancing had deteriorated. She suspected that she was experiencing muscle weakness and fluid accumulation because of the steroid treatment. When she attempted to discuss her concerns with the physician, he maintained that "bringing the disease under complete control — achieving a complete remission of wheezes — will be the best thing for you in the long run." After several months of unhappiness and failure to convince the physician of the importance of her personal goals as well as her medical goals, she sought another physician, insisting that she didn't live just to breathe, but breathed so that she could dance.[22]

As in this case — and despite the claims of several commentators — people with medical needs generally do not confront physicians as strangers and as adversaries in contemporary health care. As we suggested earlier, even if they can be viewed as strangers in that they often do not know each other prior to the encounter, both parties may well proceed with a presumption of trust. Patients may approach physicians with some trust and confidence in the medical profession, even though they do not know the physicians before them. Indeed, codes of medical ethics have been designed in part to foster this trust by indicating where the medical profession stands and by creating a climate of trust. Thus, even if patients approach individual physicians as strangers, they may have some confidence in these physicians as members of the profession as they negotiate the particular terms of their relationship. At the other extreme, some patients may approach physicians as adversaries or opponents. But for negotiation to proceed, some trust must be present, even if it is combined with some degree of control, for example, through legal requirements and the threat of legal sanctions.

The general public trust in the medical profession's values and skills provides the presumptive basis for trust in particular physicians and can facilitate the process of negotiation. But, as we noted earlier, in a pluralistic society, even people who are strangers, i.e., who share very few substantive values, may be "friendly" if they share procedural values. Certain procedural values may provide the most important basis for the trust that is necessary for negotiation; indeed, procedural principles and rules should structure the negotiation in order to ensure equal respect for the autonomy of all the parties.

First, the negotiation should involve adequate disclosure by both parties. In this process of communication — much broader and richer than most doctrines of informed consent recognize — both parties should indicate their values as well as other matters of relevance. Without this information, the negotiation cannot be open and fair. Second, the negotiation should be voluntary, i.e., uncoerced. Insofar as critical illness can be viewed as "coercing" individuals through the creation of fear, etc., it may be difficult to realize this condition for patients with certain problems. However, for the majority of patients this condition is achievable. Third, the accommodation reached through the negotiation should be mutually acceptable.[23]

What can we say about the case of the ballet dancer in the light of these procedural requirements for negotiation? It appears that the relationship foundered not because of inadequate disclosure at the outset, or along the way, but because of the patient's change in or clarification of her values and the physician's inability to accommodate these other values. The accommodation reached at the outset was mutually acceptable for a time. Initially their values and their metaphors for their relationship were the same. The physician regarded himself as a masterful scientist who was capable technically of controlling a patient's symptoms of wheezing. In fact, he remarked on several occasions: "I have never met a case of asthma I couldn't help." The patient, for her part, selected the physician initially for the same reasons. She was unhappy that her wheezing persisted, and she was becoming discouraged by her chronic health problem. Because she wanted a therapeutic success, she selected an expert who would help her achieve that goal. Both the patient and the physician made several voluntary choices. The patient chose to see *this* physician and to see him for several months, and the physician chose to treat asthma aggressively with steroids.

In a short time, the patient reconsidered or clarified her values, discovering that her dancing was even more important to her than the complete remission of wheezing, and she wanted to renegotiate her relationship so that it could be more mutual and participatory. But her new metaphor for the relationship was incompatible with the physician's nonnegotiable commitment to his metaphor which the patient had also accepted at the outset. Thus, the relationship collapsed. This case illustrates both the possibilities and the limitations of the model of negotiation. Even when the procedural requirements are met, the negotiation may not result in a satisfactory accommodation over time, and the negotiation itself may proceed in terms of the physician's and the patient's metaphors and models of the relationships, as well as the values they affirm.

Autonomy constrains and limits the negotiations and the activities of both parties: Neither party may violate the autonomy of the other or use the other merely as a means to an end. But respecting autonomy as a constraint and a limit does not imply seeking it as a *goal* or praising it as an ideal.[24] This point has several implications. It means, for example, that patients may exercise their autonomy to turn their medical affairs completely over to physicians. A patient may instruct the physician to do whatever he or she deems appropriate: "You're the doctor; whatever you decide is fine." This relationship has been characterized as "paternalism with permission,"[25] and it is not ruled out by autonomy as a constraint or a limit. It might, however, be ruled out by a commitment to autonomy as an ideal. Indeed, commitment to autonomy as an ideal can even be paternalistic in a negative sense; it can lead the health care professional to try to force the patient to be free and to live up to the ideal of autonomy. But our conception of autonomy as a constraint and a limit prevents such actions toward competent patients who are choosing and acting voluntarily. Likewise, maintenance, restoration, or promotion of the patient's autonomy may be, and usually is, one important goal of medical relationships. But its importance can only be determined by negotiation between the physician and the patient. The patient may even subordinate the goal of autonomy to various other goals, just as the ballet dancer subordinated freedom from wheezing to the power to dance.

This view of autonomy as a limit or a constraint, rather than an ideal or a goal, permits individuals to define the terms of their relationship. Just as it permits the patient to acquiesce in the physician's recommendations, it permits the physician to enter a contract as a mere technician to provide certain medical services, as requested by the patient. In such an arrangement, the physician does *not* become a mere means or a mere instrument to the patient's ends.

Rather, the physician exercises his or her autonomy to enter into the relationship to provide technical services. Such actions are an expression of autonomy, not a denial of autonomy. If, however, the physician believes that an action requested by the patient — for example, a specific mode of therapy for cancer or a sterilization procedure — is not medically indicated, or professionally acceptable, or in the patient's best interests, he or she is not obligated to sacrifice autonomy and comply. In such a case, the professional refuses to be an instrument of or to carry out the patient's wishes. When the physician cannot morally or professionally perform an action (not legally prohibited by the society) he or she may have a duty to inform the patient of other physicians who might be willing to carry out the patient's wishes. A refusal to be an instrument of another's wishes is very different from trying to prevent another from redefining his or her goals.

Negotiation is not always possible or desirable. It is impossible, or possible only to a limited extent, in certain clinical settings in which the conditions for a fair, informed, and voluntary negotiation are severely limited, often because one party lacks some of the conditions for autonomous choices. First, negotiation may be difficult if not impossible with some types of patients, such as the mentally incompetent. Sometimes paternalism may be morally legitimate or even morally obligatory when the patient is not competent to negotiate and is at risk. In such cases, parents, family members, or others may undertake negotiation with the physician, for example, regarding defective newborns or comatose adults. But health care professionals and the state may have to intervene in order to protect the interests of the patient who cannot negotiate directly. Second, the model of negotiation does not fit situations in which patients are forced by law to accept medical interventions such as compulsory vaccination, involuntary commitment, and involuntary psychiatric treatment. In such situations, the state authorizes or requires treatment against the wishes of the patient; the patient and the physician do not negotiate their relationship. Third, in some situations physicians have dual or multiple allegiances, some of which may take priority over loyalty to the patient. Examples include military medicine, industrial medicine, prison medicine, and university health service. The physician is not free in such settings to negotiate in good faith with the patient, and the patient's interests and rights may have to be protected by other substantive and procedural standards and by external control. Fourth, negotiation may not be possible in some emergencies in which people desperately need medical treatment because of the risk of death or serious bodily harm. In such cases, the physician may *presume* consent, apart from a process of negotiation, if the patient is unable to consent because of his/her condition or if the process of disclosing information and securing consent would consume too much time and thus endanger the patient. Finally, procedural standards are important for certain types of patients, such as the poor, the uneducated, or those with "unattractive medical problems" (e.g., drug addiction, obesity, and hypochondriasis). In such cases, there is a tendency — surely not a universal one — to limit the degree of negotiation with the patient because of social stigmatization. A patient advocate may even be appropriate.

In addition to the procedural requirements identified earlier, there are societal constraints and limits on negotiation. Some actions may not be negotiable. For example, the society may prohibit "mercy killing," even when the patient requests it and the physician is willing to carry it out.[26] Such societal rules clearly limit the autonomy of both physicians and patients, but some of these rules may be necessary in order to protect important societal values. However, despite such notable exceptions as "mercy killing," current societal rules provide physicians and patients with considerable latitude to negotiate their own relationship and actions within that relationship.

If negotiation is a process, its accommodations at various points can often be characterized in terms of the above models — parent-child, friends, partners, contractors, and technician-consumer. Whatever accommodation is reached through the process of negotiation is not final or irrevocable. Like other human interactions, medical relationships change over time. They are always developing or dissolving. For example, when a patient experiencing anginal chest pain negotiates a relationship with a cardiologist, he may not have given or even implied consent to undergo coronary angiography or cardiac surgery if the cardiologist subsequently believes that it is necessary. Medical conditions change, and people change, often clarifying or modifying their values over time. In medical relationships either the physician or the patient may reopen the negotiation as the relationship evolves over time and may even terminate the relationship. For example, the ballet dancer in the case discussed above elected to terminate the relationship with the specialist. That particular relationship had not been fully negotiated in the first place. But even if it had been fully negotiated, she could have changed her mind and terminated it. Such an option is essential if the autonomy of the patient is to be protected over time. Likewise, the physician should have the option to renegotiate or to withdraw from the relationship (except in emergencies), as long as he or she gives adequate notice so that the patient can find another physician.

NOTES

1. On metaphor, see George Lakoff and Mark Johnson, *Metaphors We Live By* (Chicago: University of Chicago Press, 1980).

2. See Thomas S. Szasz and Marc H. Hollender, "A contribution to the philosophy of medicine: The basic models of the doctor-patient relationship," *Archives of Internal Medicine* 97 (1956) 585-92; see also, Thomas S. Szasz, William F. Knoff, and Marc H. Hollender, "The doctor-patient relationship and its historical context," *American Journal of Psychiatry* 115 (1958) 522-28.

3. For a fuller analysis of paternalism and its justification, see James F. Childress, *Who Should Decide? Paternalism in Health Care* (New York: Oxford University Press, 1982).

4. Eric Cassell, "Autonomy and ethics in action," *New England Journal of Medicine* 297 (1977) 333-34. Italics added. Partnership is only one of several images and metaphors Cassell uses, and it may not be the best one to express his position, in part because he tends to view autonomy as a goal rather than as a constraint.

5. According to Robert Veatch, the main focus of this model is "an equality of dignity and respect, an equality of value contributions." Veatch, "Models for ethical medicine in a revolutionary age," *Hastings Center Report* 2 (June 1972) 7. Contrast Eric Cassell who disputes the relevance of notions of "equality" and "inequality." *The Healer's Art — A New Approach to the Doctor-Patient Relationship* (Philadelphia: J. B. Lippincott Company, 1976), 193-94.

6. Thomas S. Szasz and Marc H. Hollender, "A contribution to the philosophy of medicine," 586–587. (See Note 2.)

7. See, for example, Paul Ramsey, "The ethics of a cottage industry in an age of community and research medicine," *New England Journal of Medicine* 284 (1971) 700-706; *The Patient As Person: Explorations in Medical Ethics* (New Haven: Yale University Press, 1970), esp. Chap. 1; and Hans Jonas, "Philosophical reflections on experimenting with human subjects: Ethical Aspects of Experimentation with Human Subjects," *Daedalus* 98 (1969) 219-47.

8. Robert Veatch, "Models for ethical medicine in a revolutionary age," 7. (See Note 5.)

9. See Roger Masters, "Is contract an adequate basis for medical ethics?" *Hastings Center Report* 5 (December 1975) 24-28. See also May, "Code and covenant or philanthropy and contract?" in *Ethics in Medicine: Historical Perspectives and Contemporary Concerns,* ed. by Stanley Joel Reiser, Arthur J. Dyck, and William J. Curran (Cambridge, Mass.: The MIT Press, 1977), 65-76.

10. P. Lain Entralgo, *Doctor and Patient,* trans. from the Spanish by Frances Partridge (New York: McGraw-Hill Book Co., World University Library, 1969), 242.

11. Ibid., 197.

12. See Charles Fried, *Medical Experimentation: Personal Integrity and Social Policy* (New York: American Elsevier Publishing Co., Inc., 1974), 76. Our discussion of Fried's position is drawn from that work, *Right and Wrong* (Cambridge, Mass.: Harvard University Press, 1978), Chap. 7, and "The lawyer as friend:

The moral foundations of the lawyer-client relation," *The Yale Law Journal* 85 (1976) 1060-89.

13. Immanuel Kant, *The Doctrine of Virtue,* Part 11 of *The Metaphysic of Morals,* trans. by Mary J. Gregor (New York: Harper and Row, Harper Torchbook, 1964), 140.

14. Thomas S. Szasz, William F. Knoff, and Marc H. Hollender, "The doctor-patient relationship and its historical context," 525. See also Robert Veatch, "Models for ethical medicine in a revolutionary age," 5, and Leon Kass, "Ethical dilemmas in the care of the ill: What is the physician's service?" *Journal of the American Medical Association* 244 (1980) 1815 for criticisms of the technical model (from very different normative positions).

15. Veatch, "Models for ethical medicine in a revolutionary age," 7.

16. See Stephen Toulmin, "The tyranny of principles," *Hastings Center Report* 1 (December 1981) 31-39.

17. On trust and control, see James F. Childress, "Nonviolent resistance: Trust and risk-taking," *Journal of Religious Ethics* 1 (1973) 87-112.

18. Talcott Parsons, *The Structure of Social Action* (New York: The Free Press, 1949), 311.

19. On the factors in the decline of trust, see Michael Jellinek, "Erosion of patient trust in large medical centers," *Hastings Center Report* 6 (June 1976) 16-19.

20. Alasdair MacIntyre, "Patients as agents," in *Philosophical Medical Ethics: Its Nature and Significance,* ed. by Stuart F. Spicker and H. Tristram Engelhardt, Jr. (Boston: D. Reidel Publishing Co., 1977).

21. John Ladd, "Legalism and medical ethics," *The Journal of Medicine and Philosophy* 4 (March 1979) 73.

22. This case has been presented in Mark Siegler, "Searching for moral certainty in medicine: A proposal for a new model of the doctor-patient encounter," *Bulletin of the New York Academy of Medicine* 57 (1981) 56-69.

23. Ibid. for a discussion of negotiation. Other proponents of a model of negotiation include Robert A. Burt, *Taking Care of Strangers — The Rule of Law in Doctor-Patient Relations* (New York: Free Press, 1979) and Robert J. Levine, *Ethics and Regulation of Clinical Research* (Baltimore: Urban and Schwarzenberg, 1981).

24. See the discussion in Childress, *Who Should Decide?* Chap. 3.

25. Alan W. Cross and Larry R. Churchill, "Ethical and cultural dimensions of informed consent," *Annals of Internal Medicine* 96 (1982) 110-113.

26. See Oscar Thorup, Mark Siegler, James Childress, and Ruth Roettinger, "Voluntary exit: Is there a case of rational suicide?" *The Pharos* 45 (Fall 1982) 25-31.

Moral Relationships Between Nurse and Client: The Influence of Metaphors

Janet L. Storch, RN, PhD

Metaphors have been commonly used to characterize the nature of the health professional-client relationship, with particular attention to the moral dimensions of that relationship. Metaphors often highlight significant aspects of a relationship, providing us with concrete ways of thinking about the nature of the relationship. However, any metaphor must be used with caution, recognizing that it has the capacity to enlighten, to mislead, and to constrain our thinking. Given the power that metaphors can exert on our practice, critical reflection on how they can shape the moral dimensions of the client-professional relationship is essential.

In this essay, an overview of the types of nurse-client relationships described in the literature through the use of metaphors is provided. The ways in which various metaphors can assist us with or detract us from a clear understanding of our moral agency and our moral duties to our clients/patients are then examined by considering metaphors that are limiting, misguided, or helpful in clarifying the nature of that moral relationship. Finally, a synopsis of key aspects of this special relationship concludes the essay. In an era when health care delivery is beset by a variety of sociopolitical ideologies, it is timely for nursing to embrace metaphors that articulate the values inherent in its practice.

METAPHORS AND MODELS TO DEFINE RELATIONSHIPS

Before embarking on the discussion, a brief commentary on the use of metaphors is in order. A metaphor is defined as a figure of speech in which one thing is compared to another thing by being spoken of as if it were the other. Although metaphors are commonly used in poetry and in lyrics, as well as in ordinary conversation to embellish discourse, they can be most useful in helping us to see some aspects of life, such as interpersonal relationships, in a way that enhances our understanding. Thus, we are directed to see and to think about that relationship in a particular way. That is, metaphors lead us to emphasize certain aspects of the relationship and minimize others. At the same time, metaphors offer alternative views or ways of seeing a relationship. In this way, metaphors can have a powerful influence on our language, on how we think, and on how we come to understand that aspect of life. In many respects, this influence is positive and enlightening. At the same time, this emphasis can lead to a distortion in thinking because it can overemphasize one view at the expense of other equally valid views that become excluded from consideration.

Janet L. Storch, RN, PhD, Professor and Director, School of Nursing, University of Victoria, Victoria, B.C. This article was written in January 1998 especially for this volume.

That exclusion itself is significant because it allows us to "not see" the whole picture (Morgan, 1997).

Veatch (1972) and Callahan (1988) are two ethicists who have employed metaphors to facilitate understanding of health professional-patient relationships. Several models and metaphors have been identified in health care and health ethics literature. They are captured in the table on the following page (Table 5.1). Some of these metaphors focus on the comparison of physicians to engineers, to priests, or to contractors (see Veatch, 1972). These metaphors portray medicine as among the first of professions. A more recent discussion, by Emanuel and Emanuel (1992), is based on various approaches in one's relationships with clients rather than on strictly metaphorical comparisons. Consideration of these approaches seems to have been directed towards moving the medical profession forward to keep pace with the changed expectations of the public to be served.

In the discourse about nurse-client relationships that uses metaphorical thinking, there is clearly some "borrowing" of approaches from the literature describing other health professional-patient relationships through model and metaphor. There are also significant contrasts in the types of models and metaphors utilized to understand the nature of the relationship between physicians and patients when compared with those used to characterize nurse-client relationships. In general, nurse-client models and metaphors are more concrete and, therefore, more explicit in their characterization of nursing (e.g., mother, servant). This concreteness can create particular problems for the nursing profession. The nursing profession can be characterized so clearly that images are difficult for the public, other professions, and nurses themselves to shed with ease. It may even be difficult to recognize the distortions the metaphors convey.

METAPHORS AND NURSE-CLIENT RELATIONSHIPS

It seems unlikely that any other vocation or profession has experienced the diversity of imagery and metaphor that nursing has encountered in the Western world over the past century. Initially the depiction of nursing was through pictures (painted or sketched), often with metaphors as captions (e.g., Angels of Mercy). More recently, the use of written metaphors to describe and analyze nurses and nurse-client relationships has been common. One can only surmise that the penchant for "picturing" the nurse historically is related to a fascination with the female figure. Physicians have also experienced imagery of their roles and relationships with patients, but the images and metaphors of physicians have not been so varied, so gender related, nor so extensive. As noted earlier, the concrete nature of nursing metaphors, such as those depicted in Table 5.1, is also significant. Many of the conclusions about nursing embedded in the minds of readers or viewers have been based upon these metaphors and have been difficult for nursing to overcome. These metaphors are rooted in long-standing historical images.

Historical Images of Professional Nursing

In 1995, the International Council of Nurses, the International Red Cross, and the Red Crescent Museum in Geneva developed an exhibition to capture in images, text, and testimonials the first 30 years (1900-1930) of "...nursing's rise as an intellectual, socially responsible endeavor" (*Profession: Nurse* 1995, p. 11). This exhibition included a wide range of posters, postcards, drawings, paintings, and photographs that depicted nurses and conveyed a sense of the nurse's role and relationship to patients and to society.

Table 5.1
MODELS AND METAPHORS IDENTIFIED IN THE LITERATURE

Physician-Patient Relationships and Health Professional-Patient Relationships

VEATCH 1972
1. Engineering
2. Priestly
3. Collegial
4. Contractual

MAY 1975
1. Contract
2. Covenant

BAYLES 1981
1. Agency (Employer)
2. Contract
3. Friendship
4. Paternalistic
5. Fiduciary

CALLAHAN 1988
1. Contract
2. Covenant
3. Advocate
4. Fiduciary

EMANUEL & EMANUEL 1992
1. Paternalistic
2. Informative
3. Interpretive
4. Deliberative

Nurse-Client Relationships

SMITH 1980
1. Nurse as surrogate mother
2. Nurse as technician
3. Nurse as contracted clinician

WINSLOW 1984
1. Military metaphor
2. Legal metaphor (Advocacy)

FOWLER 1984
1. Mercantile
2. Indentured Servant
3. Engineering
4. Priestly
5. Collegial
6. Contractual
7. Friendship (Aristotelian)
8. Covenantal

BROCK 1980
1. Nurse as parent surrogate
2. Nurse as physician surrogate
3. Nurse as healer
4. Nurse as patient advocate or protector
5. Nurse as educator
6. Nurse as contracted clinician

MITCHELL 1990
1. Domestic (Servant)
2. Family (Mother Surrogate)
3. Medical (Physician Extender)
4. Business (Employee)
5. Advocacy (Patient Advocate)
6. Contractual (Contracted Clinician)
7. Friendship (Friend)

The pictures and other material provided images of nurse as mother, sister, friend, lover, guardian angel, or army sergeant. In the accompanying publication, produced by the International Red Cross and Red Crescent Museum, the authors note that these images of nursing (these metaphors of nursing) were widely used during the First World War for purposes of raising funds for the war effort, raising morale, and stimulating patriotic zeal. "A mother figure to all the wounded, the needy and children, a nurse — with or without the red cross or crescent on her uniform — was often perceived as a savior in the glow of fervent patriotism.... Nurses were viewed as moral figures above all suspicion and were therefore used for propaganda purposes..." (*Profession: Nurse*, 1995, p. 26).

Following World War I, as the image of the universal mother and guardian angel gave way to Post War realities, nurses began to be depicted as fighters or soldiers who fought the residual ills of the War and epidemics, and worked in communities with social welfare officers to fight social ills.

The World Wars, and wars of the previous century, had a profound influence on the development of nursing. Florence Nightingale's work in founding nursing as a profession was given impetus by the Crimean War. And the influence of military models of health care delivery and hospital organization directed the manner in which nursing unfolded as an independent entity. Only in the latter three decades of the twentieth century has the influence of some of these metaphors begun to fade from view. In fact, some of these historical images or metaphors of nursing continue to have a profound effect on the public's view of nurses, fellow health professionals' understanding of nurse-client relationships, and the views of nurses themselves. Some of these views or perceptions have served to limit the significance of professional nursing.

Limiting Metaphors: Nurse As Parent, Nurse As Servant, Nurse As Friend

Assuming the majority of people hold positive perceptions of parents, and of mothers in particular, the metaphor of *nurse as parent surrogate* or *nurse as mother surrogate* to describe the nurse-client relationship allows us to see some fundamental foundations of that relationship. It is a relationship based upon trust, integrity, promise-keeping, dedication, and nurturance. Taking that metaphor of mother or parent further, one can understand the nurse-client relationship to involve some degree of protection of the client in care, an attempt to help clients gain or regain independence, and a commitment to never abandon a client in need. Inasmuch as this metaphor serves to enlarge understanding about these moral features of the relationship, it is well used.

However, in highlighting some similar characteristics, there can be a tendency to overgeneralize. All features of the nurse-client relationship come to be seen as "parenting" or "mothering" relationships. The ways in which this might distort the nature of the relationship are many. Nursing comes to be seen as largely women's work and as a selfless endeavour. Like mothering, nursing then comes to be viewed as something that anyone can do. In making these assumptions, it becomes easy to discount nursing knowledge, skill, and expertise. The "tender loving care" provided by nurses may appear to be just like mother's care and concern, with little more knowledge required than what arises from trying to be caring and helpful to another.

Mitchell (1990) has labeled the mother/parent metaphor a *family metaphor*. She identifies a primary concern within the metaphor of surrogate mother to be found in "...the arrangement of health care services and relationships according to family roles, with the physician as father, nurse as mother, and patients as dependents..." (page 5). In this scenario the nurse is expected to work (likely harder than anyone else) to maintain harmony in the home, i.e., the hospital. Further, the nurse as helpmate, is not accorded power for decision making. This has significant implications for the nurse's ability to exercise his or her moral agency.

The *friendship metaphor* has positive parallels to the family metaphor, including expectations that clients can depend upon nurses and that nurses would value truth-telling and fidelity. It is misleading, however, in that the nurse-client relationship cannot be a relationship of equals, like friendship. Clients are often in a vulnerable state during their health care encounter and there is, by reason of that vulnerability and by reason of the different type and level of knowledge about the client's condition, an asymmetry of power in the healing relationship.

Finally, the *nurse as servant metaphor* adds one level of clarity to the nurse-client relationship, but at the price of potentially serious misconceptions about the relationship. From a positive view, the servant metaphor emphasizes service to others, and in this way captures the moral ideal of service critical to professional roles. In this case, nurses as professionals use their knowledge and skills in service to others. The misleading aspects of the metaphor include the implication that nurses will do anything that needs to be done at work, including domestic work (Mitchell, 1990). This has led to the serious exploitation of nurses in the past and to a significant extent in the present. Nurses' responses to such exploitation have been to establish unions for some protection from the arbitrariness of employers. Through unions they have set limits on the work they are required to do and the times in which they will do it. Nevertheless, in our current era of health care cost constraint, nurses are all too often expected to fill in the gaps when resources are cut.

A serious distortion of the metaphor of nurse as servant is the characterization of the nurse as an *indentured servant* who just "follows orders"(Fowler, 1984). This understanding of the nurse's role and relationship within the health care team led to obedience, in which the nurse cedes his or her moral agency to institutional directives, with the result that both nurse and client suffer. From this indentured servant metaphor, the long history of nurse as handmaiden to the physician has also been prominent. This places the client in a secondary position relative to the nurse-physician, then nurse-client relationship. Indeed, the Nightingale pledge that many nurses took at either capping ceremonies or graduations in times past included the phrase "...with loyalty will I endeavor to aide the physician in his work and devote myself to the welfare of the patient" (Storch, 1982, p. 202). In this sense, devotion to the patient was considered to be realized through loyally aiding the physician (Fowler, 1984). It was not until the middle of the twentieth century that those two commitments (to physician and to patient) were disentangled. By the early 1970s the International Council of Nurses Code of Ethics stated with unmistaken clarity that "The nurse's primary responsibility is to those people who require nursing care" (Storch, 1982, p. 201). Yet, amongst physicians, health administrators and the public, there are still many who wonder why nurses are not "doing nursing" anymore (e.g. Stein, 1990). Whether their puzzlement is written or stated, the source of concern often can be traced to the query about why nurses are not there to "aid" physicians any longer or to follow orders without question(s).

Misguided Metaphors

Use of the *metaphor of technician* or *nurse as engineer* to describe the nurse-patient relationship emphasizes the task aspect of nursing roles. The strength of this metaphor rests in its emphasis on technical competence. Competence is a highly valued dimension of the nurse-patient relationship since "...caring without knowledge remains simply a matter of good intentions..." (Falk Raphael, 1996). Unless the nurse meets the level of technical competence to carry out her tasks, "...the whole relationship begins with a lie" (Pellegrino, 1979, p. 48).

However, emphasizing the technical and task aspects of nursing captures only a fraction of nursing knowledge and skill, and the metaphor of technician limits understanding about the work that nurses do. As "re-engineering" of care-giver roles has become fashionable (Schweikhart and Smith-Daniels, 1996), this distortion of role has led to the devaluing of wholistic nursing practice and, alarmingly, to simplistic solutions to nursing replacement. Since many can see only the "tasks" nurses do, the rest of nursing work remains invisible. For example, in the giving of a medication, what is observed is a pill moving from the nurse's hand to the client's mouth. What is unobserved is the nurse's assessment of the client's condition while that simple act is in progress — respirations, pallor, comfort, degree of mobility, ease of swallowing, skin turgor, evidence of edema, etc. — the mental note taken of a plan of care on-course or one in need of modification (based on expert knowledge of the condition, the drug, and environmental stressors). Verbal and nonverbal communication occur in that simple but highly complex interaction. Opportunities arise to engage in client teaching, support, guidance, and reassurance. Perhaps, most important, is the sense of presence the expert nurse brings to the encounter — a way of being with the client that reflects the depth of care and concern, laced with competence to deliver, for that one individual. Thus, the concrete task observed is not the real work of nursing: the real work of nursing requires knowledge and skill that is all but invisible to the observer. The type of care expert nurses provide must begin with considerable

investment in the relationship, involves the use of self, and involves attention to the uniqueness of that client.

These same misguided task-oriented conclusions are operative in the *physician extender* and *physician surrogate* metaphors. While there are aspects of medical tasks and medical work that nurses are able to perform, even in performing those tasks nursing work is different. Taking on specific tasks of medicine does not equate to being either a physician extender or a physician surrogate, or a physician for that matter. Nursing roles and relationships are different, with different goals and different processes of care. For example, both physicians and nurses will monitor arterial blood gas results. The physician monitors those results to diagnose cardio-pulmonary dysfunction; the nurse monitors the same results to plan activity, rest, and comfort.

Nursing knowledge increasingly involves many ways of knowing, beyond empirical knowledge and technical skill. It includes knowledge gained through empirics, but also knowledge drawn from ethics, personal knowledge, aesthetics, and sociopolitical knowing (Carper, 1978; White, 1995). Different knowledge and skill lead to different ways of approaching care, and to a different form of nurse-client relationship, including greater attention to "ways of being" in relationship with the clients (Silva, Sorrell and Sorell, 1995).

Helpful Metaphors: Nurse As in a Covenantal Relationship, As Healer, As Advocate

Among the many metaphors applied to nurse-client relationships are several that stand out as characterizing more clearly than others the ideals of what these relationships should be. Use of the metaphor of a *covenantal relationship* emphasizes that nurse and client are "...bound to one another in many ways, not the least of which is morally" (Fowler, 1984, p. 338). As members of a community, and within that community a health care system, nurses are expected to be faithful and to keep their promise of profession, i.e., to use their knowledge and skills to minimize harm and to benefit others.

> A convenantal model calls attention to the reciprocal indebtedness of the public and the profession, suggesting that professional power is a gift from the public to the profession given in exchange for its expertise and orientation to the service of others (Bernal, 1992, p. 22).

In emphasizing concepts of relatedness and reciprocity, the covenantal model underscores nursing practice priorities of the 1990s.

The image of *nurse as healer* is a long standing metaphor utilized since the early 1900s to emphasize the healing powers of the nursing presence. Whether a nurse is fully present with a client through the painful journey of being a critically ill patient in ICU or CCU, through an outpatient experience of chemotherapy, or through a long period of rehabilitation at home recovering from a stroke, the professional nurse's ongoing presence can facilitate the individual to move towards restoration and healing. In this way the nurse has a different but complementary role to that of physician.

The *nurse as client advocate* was introduced in the early 1970s and was based on a clearer understanding of nurses' direct accountability (legal and ethical) to clients. Considerable attention in nursing literature (see for example, Donahue, 1978; Abrams, 1978; Curtin, 1979; Gadow, 1980; Kohnke, 1982; Fowler, 1989; Bernal, 1995) has been directed towards identifying the role of advocacy and types of advocacy (e.g., intervening, protecting, informing, supporting, speaking for, coordinating, empow-

ering, etc.) as well as problems for nurses in fulfilling a role as client advocate.

In 1984, Winslow analyzed the shift from a nursing practice based on a military model (characterized by hierarchy and obedience) to one based on a legal model that focused on advocacy for the client in health care. He identified several issues surrounding the nurse as patient or client advocate, including lack of clarity of the concept, the need to revise nursing practice acts to allow for this type of nursing role, the question as to whether clients and their families were prepared to accept advocacy as a nursing role, the potentially adversarial nature of advocacy, and the potential conflicting interests and loyalties inherent in advocacy. Advocacy has served as a powerful metaphor for nursing, although often with only superficial understanding of its real power.

As long as advocacy is confined to legal metaphor it is limiting. However, when it is viewed as "...not simply one more alternative to be added to the list of past and present concepts of nursing ...but as embracing all of them..." (Curtin, 1979, p. 2), its real meaning is understood. Benner (1994) characterized client advocacy as involving openness and engagement in moral and clinical reasoning. Drawing upon the work of Gadow (1980), who conceptualized "existential advocacy," Benner contrasts the "narrow legal sense of advocacy" (page 49) with a deeper and more meaningful form of advocacy. She describes this type of advocate as one who "stands alongside, who interprets, and understands..." (page 49) — language congruent with a covenantal relationship. She suggests that this enriched metaphor of client advocacy is manifest in the following way: managing and coordinating services to a client so that all services are directed toward an agreed upon intent to ensure client and family well-being, "...standing in for someone to give them voice... getting appropriate medical intervention for [clients]... and presencing and acknowledging loss and grief" with one who is dying (page 51).

These metaphors of nurse in a covenantal relationship, nurse as healer, and nurse as advocate, approach more closely than the previous metaphors the morally significant aspects of the nurse-client relationship. Their emphasis is on the moral commitment of the nurse to be a comforting presence to clients through difficult health situations; to be in relationship with clients; and to intervene, inform, support, and facilitate their empowerment. This emphasis provides insight into the "special" nature of the nurse-client relationship.

What Metaphors Enable Us to See and Learn

Metaphors used to describe the nurse-client relationship can be instructive and they can be limiting. Their limitations include their potential to further devalue nursing knowledge and skill, to perpetuate stereotypical notions of nurse-client and physician-client relationships, to mislead by suggesting equal partnership in that relationship, to perpetuate the task-oriented view of nurs-

ing, and to conflate nurse and physician roles. The strength of metaphors applied to nursing rests in the ability to understand more readily the historical shifts in nursing roles and nurse-client relationships and to appreciate both constancy and change in nurse-client relationships over time. Further, metaphors help to articulate the values in nursing practice in an era when roles are under threat from an economic imperative.

The constant themes of the nurse-client relationship accessed through metaphor are relationships based on the moral foundations of trust, integrity, respect, truthtelling, and promise-keeping. These themes are fundamental to nursing. The covenantal metaphor emphasis on reciprocity and connectedness makes more visible the foundation of the relationship. Metaphors have also served a useful purpose in drawing distinctions between medicine and nursing over time. When used with care, metaphors enable us to see and learn much about the nature of nursing and the nature of the nurse-patient relationship. Most importantly, the moral foundations of that relationship can become more visible and less difficult to articulate and defend.

REFERENCES

The author wishes to thank Dr. Gwen Hartrick, Dr. Patricia Rodney and Dr. Rita Schreiber for their critical review of this essay and for their helpful suggestions.

Abrams, Natalie (1978). "A contrary view of the nurse as patient advocate." *Nursing Forum* 17(3): 258-267.

Bayles, Michael D. (1981). *Professional Ethics*. Belmont: C.A. Wadsworth Publishing Co.

Baylis, Francoise, Downie, Jocelyn, Freedman, Benjamin, Hoffmaster, Barry, and Sherwin, Susan, eds. (1995). *Health Care Ethics in Canada*. Toronto: Harcourt Brace and Company.

Benner, Patricia (1994). "Caring as ways of knowing and not knowing." In *The Crisis of Care* (pp. 42-62). Edited by Susan Phillips and Patricia Benner. Washington D.C.: Georgetown University Press.

Bernal, Ellen W. (1992). "The nurse as patient advocate." *Hastings Center Report* 22(4): 18-23.

Brock, Dan W. (1980). "The nurse-patient relation: Some rights and duties." In *Nursing:*

Images and Ideals (pp. 102-124). Edited by Stuart F. Spicker and Sally Gadow. New York: Springer Publishing Co.

Callahan, Joan, ed. (1988). *Ethical Issues in Professional Life*. New York: Oxford University Press.

Carper, Barbara (1978). "Fundamental patterns of knowing in nursing." *Advances in Nursing Science* 1(1): 13-23.

Curtin, Leah (1979). "Nurse as advocate: A philosophical foundation for nursing." *Advances in Nursing Science* 1(3): 1-10.

Donahue, M. Patricia (1978). "The nurse: A patient advocate?" *Nursing Forum* 17(2): 143-151.

Emanuel, Ezekiel J. and Emanuel, Linda L. (1995). "Four models of the physician-patient relationship." In *Health Care Ethics in Canada* (pp. 163-179). Edited by Francoise Baylis et al. Toronto: Harcourt Brace and Company.

Fowler, Marsha (1984). Ethics and Nursing, 1893-1984: The Ideal of Service, the Reality of History. Doctoral Dissertation, University of Southern California.

_____ (1989). "Social advocacy." *Heart and Lung* 18(1): 97-99.

Gadow, Sally (1980). "Existential advocacy: Philosophical foundations of nursing." In *Nursing: Images and Ideals* (pp. 79-101). Edited by Stuart F. Smith and Sally Gadow. New York: Springer Publishing Company.

Kohnke, Mary (1982). *Advocacy: Risk or Reality*. Toronto: C.V. Mosby.

May, William F. (1975). "Code and covenant or philanthropy and contract." *Hastings Center Report* 5(6): 29-38.

Mitchell, Christine (1990). "The nurse-patient relationship: A source of some moral duties." In Humanities and the Health Professions, Occasional Papers of the Connecticut Humanities Council, No. 8, 3-16.

Morgan, Gareth (1997). *Images of Organizations*. Thousand Oaks: Sage Publications.

Profession: Nurse, Images 1900-1930 (1995). Geneva: Musée International de la Red Cross et du Red Crescent.

RNABC (1997). *The Role of the Nurse in Advocacy*. Vancouver: Registered Nurses Association of British Columbia.

Schweikhart, Sharon Bergman, and Smith-Daniels, Vicki (1996). "Reengineering the work of caregivers: Roles redefinition, team structures, and organizational redesign." *Hospital and Health Administration* 41(1): 19-35.

Silva, Mary, Sorrell, Jeanne, and Sorrell, Christine (1995). "From Carper's ways of knowing to ways of being: An ontological shift in nursing." *Advances in Nursing Science* 18(1): 1-13.

Smith, Sheri (1980). "Three models of the nurse-patient relationship." In *Nursing: Images and Ideals* (pp. 176-188). Edited by Stuart F. Spicker and Sally Gadow. New York: Springer Publishing Company.

Stein, Leonard, Watts, D.T., and Howell, T. (1990). "The doctor-nurse game revisited." *New England Journal of Medicine* 60(5): 812-816.

Storch, Janet L. (1982). *Patients' Rights: Ethical and Legal Issues in Health Care and in Nursing*. Toronto: McGraw Hill.

Veatch, Robert M. (1972). "Models for ethical medicine in a revolutionary age." *Hastings Center Report* 2(3): 5-7.

White, Jill (1995). "Patterns of knowing: Review, critique and update." *Advances in Nursing Science* 17(4): 73-86.

Winslow, Gerald R. (1984). "From loyalty to advocacy: A new metaphor for nursing." *Hastings Center Report* 14(3): 32-40.

FURTHER READINGS

Bayles, Michael D. "The Professional Client Relationship." From Michael D. Bayles, *Professional Ethics*. Belmont, Calif: Wadsworth, 1981.

Beauchamp, T.L. "The Promise of the Beneficence Model for Medical Ethics." *Journal of Contemporary Health Law and Policy* 6:(199) 145-155.

Becker, M. and L. Maiman. "Strategies for Enhancing Patient Compliance." *Journal of Community Health* 6 (1980) 113-132.

Buchanan, Allan. "Medical Paternalism." *Philosophy and Public Affairs* 7 (1978) 370-390.

Callahan, Joan C. "Paternalism and Voluntariness." *Canadian Journal of Philosophy* 16: 2 (1986) 199-220.

Childress, James I., and Mark S. Siegler. "Metaphors and Models of Doctor-Patient Relationships: Their Implication for Autonomy." *Theoretical Medicine* 5 (1984) 17-30.

Chinen, A. "Modes of Understanding and Mindfulness of Clinical Medicine." *Theoretical Medicine* 9: 1 (February 1988) 45-72.

Dworkin, Gerald. "Paternalism." *The Monist* 56 (Jan. 1972).

Gert, Bernard, and Charles M. Culver. "Paternalistic Behaviour." *Philosophy and Public Affairs* 6 (1976) 45-47.

Gordon, Harry H. "The Doctor-Patient Relationship: A Judaic Perspective." *The Journal of Medicine and Philosophy*, vol. 8 (1983) 243-255.

Graber, Glenn C. "On Paternalism in Health Care." In John W. Davis, Barry Hoffmaster and Sarah Shorten, eds., *Contemporary Issues in Biomedical Ethics* (Humana Press: Clifton, N.J., 1981).

Ingelfinger, Franz. "Arrogance." *New England Journal of Medicine* 303 (1980) 1509.

Katz, Jay. *The Silent World of Doctor and Patient*. Free Press: New York, 1984, I and II.

Masters, Roger. "Is Contract an Adequate Basis for Medical Ethics?" *Hastings Center Report* 5 (Dec. 1975) 24-28.

O'Hair, Dan. "Patient Preference for Persuasion." *Theoretical Medicine* 7 (1986) 147-164.

Percival, Thomas. *Medical Ethics*.

Roach, M.S. *The Human Act of Caring: A Blueprint for the Health Professions*. Ottawa: Canadian Hospital Association, 1987.

Smith, David H., and Lloyd S. Pettegrew. "Mutual Persuasion as a Model for Doctor-Patient Communication." *Theoretical Medicine* 7 (1986) 127-146.

Staum, Martin S., and Donald E. Larson, eds. *Doctors, Patients and Society: Power and Authority in Medical Care*. Wilfrid Laurier University Press: Waterloo 1981.

Storch, J. *Patients' Rights*. Toronto: McGraw Hill, 1982.

Szaz, Thomas, and Marc H. Hollender. "A Contribution to the Philosophy of Medicine: The Basic Models of the Doctor-Patient Relationship." *Archives of Internal Medicine* 97 (1956) 585-592.

Thomasma, D.C. "Beyond Medical Paternalism and Patient Autonomy: A Model of Physician Conscience for the Physician-Patient Relationship." *Annals of Internal Medicine* 98: 3 (February, 1983) 243-247.

Veatch, R. "Generalization of Expertise." *Hastings Center Studies* 1: 2 (1973), 29-40.

CHAPTER 6
INFORMED CONSENT AND THE COMPETENT PATIENT

INTRODUCTION

It is a fundamental principle of Canadian health care theory and law that, all other things being equal, competent patients have the right to accept or reject any treatment and any diagnostic or other intervention. The only limitation on this freedom is that the health of other people should not be threatened and that the rights of others should not be interfered with. As the old adage has it, "Your right to swing your fist stops where my face begins!"

However, someone who makes a decision without having appropriate or sufficient information is not in fact choosing freely. The very lack of information acts as a constraint on the choice of the decision-maker. Therefore, in order to be able to exercise their right of choice in a meaningful way, patients have to be informed. Canadian bioethics tries to capture this insight in the phrase "informed consent." Competent patients have the right to informed consent. Of course the phrase refers to more than just accepting a procedure, course of action or intervention. It also refers to refusal. The two are but different sides of the same coin.

The precise nature of informed decision making — and who should act as decision-maker when the patient is unable to do so — has been a matter of some controversy and uncertainty.

The focus of the readings in this chapter is the question of what informed consent really amounts to, and what must happen in order for a proper informed consent to exist.

The U.K. accepts what is called a professional standard of disclosure. A physician has to disclose to the patient all and only what another physician, similarly placed, would normally disclose. The U.S. accepts an objective reasonable-person standard. A physician need only disclose what the ordinary reasonable person would want to know before agreeing to or rejecting the procedure that is being offered.

The Canadian approach is different. *Reibl v. Hughes* is the classic Canadian legal case in this regard. It is a decision by the Supreme Court of Canada. It sets the standards that Canadian health care professionals must legally follow in order to have an informed consent from their patients.

The case puts more emphasis on patient autonomy than the U.S. cases.[1] It begins by recognizing that to be told something and to actually understand it are not necessarily the same thing. It therefore distinguishes between what the patient should be told — this has become known as the *standard of disclosure* — and the level at which the information must be pitched so that the patient can actually understand the information that is being provided. This has become known as the *standard of comprehension.*

It then says — and again this is somewhat different from the U.S. — that the appropriate standard of disclosure is not what the ordinary reasonable person would want to know, but what an objective reasonable person *in the patient's particular position* would want to know. As for the level at which the information must be pitched, it says that it must be geared to the level of the particular patient. It must not be assumed that just because people would normally understand the information the way it is being provided, therefore *this* patient actually understands it.

The two standards have become known as the *objective reasonable person standard of disclosure, geared to the particular patient*; and the *subjective standard of comprehension. Reibl v. Hughes* is important not only from a legal perspective. It also captures what would be expected from a deontologically oriented ethical perspective that places primary emphasis on the autonomy of persons.

The selection from the Royal College of Physicians and Surgeons gives some indication of how the medical profession has understood both the law and the ethics in this regard.

Benjamin Freedman's discussion is philosophical in orientation. It is conceptually much deeper than the other selections. Freedman raises questions such as: Where does the right to informed consent come from? How far does it extend? How much information — and what sort of information — should be revealed? Freedman maintains that there are two requirements for informed consent to be present: the consent must be voluntary and it must be informed. He also touches on the question of whether consent is invalidated by reward in the experimental setting.

Both selections make it very clear that informed consent is not something that takes place by having a patient sign a form. They agree that informed consent is a process that involves information transfer and agreement. The signed form is merely an indication that this process has taken place.

Further, the competent consent or refusal of the patient must be respected even if this means that the person may die. Ethically, this is clear. Legally, this has also found recognition in recent times: in the 1983 case of *Astaforoff*, [2] the 1990 case of *Malette v. Shulman*[3] and the 1992 case of *Nancy B.*[4] Finally, consent and refusal extend not only to what is done to the body of the patient but also to any part of the body, the fluids contained in it, etc.. The Supreme Court made this very clear in 1987 in *R. v. Pohoretsky*[5] and again in 1988 in *R. v. Dyment.* [6]

NOTES

1. See *Canterbury v. Spence* (1972), 464 F. 2d; *Cobbs v. Grant*, 502 P. 2d 1.

2. *Re Attorney General of British Columbia et al. And Astaforoff et al.* (1983) 6 C.C.C. (3d) 498 (B.C.C.A.). In this case, the court ruled that even though the prison authorities had a duty to provide the necessaries of life to a person in their charge, if that person competently refused such, this refusal had to be respected. It has since become well established that the duty to respect the person's wishes does not cease when the person becomes incompetent.

3. See *infra*, chapter 8.

4. *Nancy B v. Hotel-Dieu de Québec* [1992] R.J.Q. 361, 86 D.L.R. (4ᵗʰ) 385 S.C.C. Nancy B. was a young woman who was completely paralyzed as a result of Guillaine-Barrée Syndrome and hence was completely ventilator dependent. She requested that she be allowed to have her ventilator shut off even though that would lead to her death by suffocation. The court found in her favour; the ventilator was shut off and she died, sedated so that she would not experience the full effect of the suffocation.

5. *R. v. Pohoretsky* (1987), 58 C.R. (3d) 113, 33 C.C.C (3D) 398 (S.C.C). In this case the court ruled that taking blood samples without consent or judicial authority violates s. 8 of the Charter.

6. *R. v. Dyment* 1988), 66 C.R. (3d) 348, 45 C.C.C (3d) 244 (S.C.C.). The Supreme Court ruled that blood taken for medical purposes could not be used without the consent of the person or without due process of law.

Reibl v. Hughes

Supreme Court of Canada, Laskin, C.J.C., Martland, Dickson, Beetz, Estey, McIntyre and Chouinard J.J. October 7, 1980.

LASKIN, C.J.C.: — The plaintiff appellant, then 44 years of age, underwent serious surgery on March 18, 1970, for the removal of an occlusion in the left internal carotid artery, which had prevented more than a 15% flow of blood through the vessel. The operation was competently performed by the defendant respondent, a qualified neurosurgeon. However, during or imme-

Reibl v. Hughes, 16 O.R. (2d) 306, 78 D.L.R. (3d) 35, reversed 21 O.R. (2d) 14,6 C.C.L.T., 227, 89 D.L.R. (3d) 112; reverse [1980] 2 S.C.R. 880, 14 C.C.C.T.I., 114 D.L.R. (3d) 1, 33 N.R., 17.

diately following the surgery the plaintiff suffered a massive stroke which left him paralyzed on the right side of his body and also impotent. The plaintiff had, of course, formally consented to the operation. Alleging, however, that his was not an "informed consent," he sued for damages and recovered on this ground in both battery and negligence. The trial Judge, Haines J., awarded a global sum of $225,000 [78 D.L.R. (3d) 35, 16 O.R. (2d) 306].

A majority of the Ontario Court of Appeal ordered a new trial on both liability and damages [89 D.L.R. (3d) 112, 21 O.R. (2d) 14, 6 C.C.L.T. 227]. Speaking through Brooke J.A. (Blair J.A. concurring) the Court ruled out battery as a possible ground of liability on the facts of the case. Jessup J.A., dissenting in part, would have ordered a new trial on damages alone, accepting the judgment at trial on liability.

On the hearing of the appeal by this Court, leave to come here having been obtained by the plaintiff, counsel for the defendant respondent agreed to accept the award of damages and limited his contestation to liability, seeking not only to hold the judgment in appeal but a "variation" thereof by way of dismissal of the action. Although, strictly speaking, the claim for a variation should have been made the subject of a cross-appeal, counsel for the appellant took no objection and I see no reason why I should not regularize the claim for dismissal *nunc pro tunc*. Indeed, neither counsel wished to have a new trial, an understandable position when the physical damage suffered took place more than ten years ago. Unless, therefore, there are good reasons to support the order for a new trial on liability alone, the proper course is to determine whether to restore the judgment at trial on either or both grounds upon which it proceeded or whether the defendant should be relieved of liability.

It is now undoubted that the relationship between surgeon and patient gives rise to a duty of the surgeon to make disclosure to the patient of what I would call all material risks attending the surgery which is recommended. The scope of the duty of disclosure was considered in *Hopp v. Lepp*, a judgment of this Court, delivered on May 20, 1980, ... [112 D.L.R. (3d) 67, 22 A.R. 361, [1980] 4 W.W.R. 645], where it was generalized as follows [at p. 81]:

> In summary, the decided cases appear to indicate that, in obtaining the consent of a patient for the performance upon him of a surgical operation, a surgeon, generally, should answer any specific questions posed by the patient as to the risks involved and should, without being questioned, disclose to him the nature of the proposed operation, its gravity, any material risks and any special or unusual risks attendant upon the performance of the operation. However, having said that, it should be added that the scope of the duty of disclosure and whether or not it has been breached are matters which must be decided in relation to the circumstances of each particular case.

The Court in *Hopp v. Lepp* also pointed out that even if a certain risk is a mere possibility which ordinarily need not be disclosed, yet if its occurrence carries serious consequences, as for example, paralysis or even death, it should be regarded as a material risk requiring disclosure.

In the present case, the risk attending the surgery or its immediate aftermath was the risk of a stroke, of paralysis and, indeed, of death. This was, without question, a material risk. At the same time, the evidence made it clear that there was also a risk of a stroke and of resulting death if surgery for the removal of the occlusion was refused by the patient. The delicacy of the surgery is beyond question, and its execution is no longer in any way faulted. (I would note here that in this Court no issue was raised as to the adequacy of post-operative care.) How specific, therefore, must the information to the patient be, in a case such as this, to enable him to make an "informed" choice between surgery and no surgery? One of the considerations weighing upon the plaintiff was the fact that he was about a year and a half away from earning a lifetime retirement pension as a Ford Motor Company employee. The trial Judge noted (to use his words) ... that "Due to this tragedy befalling him at the time it did, he was not eligible for certain extended disability benefits available under the collective agreement between the Ford Motor Company of Canada Limited and its hourly employees of 10 years' standing." At the time of the operation, the plaintiff had 8.4 years' service with his employer. He stated in his evidence that if he had been properly informed of the magnitude of the risk involved in the surgery he would have elected to forego it, at least until his pension had vested and, further, he would have opted for a shorter normal life than a longer one as a cripple because of the surgery. Although elective surgery was indicated for the condition from which the plaintiff suffered, there was (as the trial Judge found) no emergency in the sense that immediate surgical treatment was imperative.

This brings me back to the question of the nature of the information provided by the respondent surgeon to the plaintiff and its adequacy in the circumstances. I will deal, in turn, with: (1) the findings and conclusion of the trial Judge on this issue; (2) whether, even on his findings, there was a basis for imposing liability for battery; (3) the assessment made by the Court of Appeal in ordering a new trial; (4) the evidence in the case, which consisted, in support of the plaintiff's case, mainly of the testimony of the plaintiff and of two neurosurgeons, Dr. Irving Schacter and Dr. Robert Elgie, and portions of the examination for discovery of the defendant and, in support of the defendant's case, the testimony of the defendant and of a neurosurgeon, Dr. William Lougheed, who were the only two witnesses called for the defendant; (5) the duty of disclosure and review of the findings below; and (6) whether causation was established.

...The well-known statement of Cardozo J. in *Schloendorff v. Society of New York Hospital* (1914), 211 N.Y. 125 at p. 129, 105 N.E. 92 at p. 93, that "every human being of adult years and sound mind has a right to determine what shall be done with his own body; and a surgeon who performs an operation without his patient's consent commits an assault, for which he is liable in damages" cannot be taken beyond the compass of its words to support an action of battery where there has been consent to the very surgical procedure carried out upon a patient but there has been a breach of the duty of disclosure of attendant risks. In my opinion, actions of battery in respect of surgical or other medical treatment should be confined to cases where surgery or treatment has been performed or given to which there has been no consent at all or where, emergency situations aside, surgery or treatment has been performed or given beyond that to which there was consent.

This standard would comprehend cases where there was misrepresentation of the surgery or treatment for which consent was elicited and a different surgical procedure or treatment was carried out. See, for example, *Marshall v. Curry,* [1933] 3 D.L.R. 260, 60 C.C.C. 136 (consent given to operation to cure hernia; doctor removes patient's testicle; action in battery); *Murray v. McMurchy,* [1949] 2 D.L.R. 442, [1949] 1 W.W.R. 989 (consent given to a caesarian operation; doctor goes on and sterilizes the patient; doctor liable for trespass to the person); *Mulloy v. Hop Sang,* [1935] 1 W.W.R. 714 (doctor told to repair hand and not to amputate; performs amputation; held liable in trespass); *Winn et al. v. Alexander et al.*, [1940] 3 D.L.R. 778, [1940] O.W.N. 238 (consent given to caesarian; doctor goes further and sterilizes the patient); *Schweizer v. Central Hospital et al.* (1974), 53 D.L.R. (3d) 494, 6 O.R. (2d) 606 (patient consented to operation on his toe; doctor operated on back instead [spinal fusion]; doctor liable for trespass to the person).

In situations where the allegation is that attendant risks which should have been disclosed were not communicated to the patient and yet the surgery or other medical treatment carried out was that to which the plaintiff consented (there being no negligence basis of liability for the recommended surgery or treatment to deal with the patient's condition), I do not understand how it can be said that the consent was vitiated by the failure of disclosure so as to make the surgery or other treatment an unprivileged, unconsented to and intentional invasion of the patient's bodily integrity. I can appreciate the temptation to say that the genuineness of consent to medical treatment depends on proper disclosure of the risks which it entails, but in my view, unless there has been misrepresentation or fraud to secure consent to the treatment, a failure to disclose the attendant risks, however serious, should go to negligence rather than to battery. Although such a failure relates to an informed choice of submitting to or refusing recommended and appropriate treatment, it arises as the breach of an anterior duty of due care, comparable in legal obligation to the duty of due care in carrying out the particular treatment to which the patient has consented. It is not a test of the validity of the consent.

3. THE ASSESSMENT OF THE COURT OF APPEAL

Brooke J.A., speaking for the majority of the Court of Appeal, noted, ...quite properly, that:

The duty [of disclosure] to the patient is determined by the Court and the evidence of the expert witnesses, if accepted, is relevant to determining whether or not the defendant has discharged that duty. To be actionable [in negligence] the defendant's failure in his duty of care must cause the plaintiff loss and damage.

He went on to examine the reasons of Haines J. and made the following observations upon that trial Judge's determination: ...

In finding that the plaintiff was left with the impression that the surgery carried no risk of consequence other than those in any surgical procedure I think it must be assumed that the learned trial Judge has rejected the defendant's explanation that the plaintiff was aware of the risk of a stroke as a risk of the surgery. Of some importance, the learned trial Judge makes no specific finding of credibility and indeed does not disbelieve the defendant's evidence that he thought the plaintiff understood the risk. However, the learned trial Judge did not put his judgment simply on the failure to warn, but also on the failure to take sufficient care to discuss the degree of risk. He relied upon the evidence of Dr. Elgie and Dr. Schacter and it is my respectful view that, having regard for the emphasis which the learned trial Judge places upon the statistical details, he has misunderstood the real significance of the evidence of these two doctors. Drs. Schacter and Elgie appear to have taken a similar approach to the question of explaining the risks of the surgery, but the emphasis is not on statistical detail. Dr. Elgie alone made reference to statistics in discussing the manner in which he would advise his patient when seeking a consent to perform this operation and in this respect his answer was different from that of Dr. Schacter.

Brooke J.A. was highly critical of the use of unexplained statistics which appeared to be directed to the degree of risk involved in the particular surgery. This is what he said in that respect: ...

One need only look at the contrast in the evidence of the statistics quoted by Dr. Hughes and Dr. Elgie to demonstrate the confusion that could arise from their use. When asked in cross-examination, Dr. Hughes' figure as to the incidence of death because of surgery was 4%, which was equal to Dr. Elgie's highest figure where he put the range between 2% and 4%, and with respect to the incidence of stroke causing paralysis or transient weakness, Dr. Hughes put the figure at 10% which was five times Dr. Elgie's lowest figure and almost two and one-half times his highest figure. Taken cumulatively, Dr. Hughes' figure at 14% is more than three times Dr. Elgie's lowest estimate and almost twice his highest. They were really very different. The reason for the difference went unexplained. No one asked the doctors. And yet the trial Judge referred principally in his reasons, and particularly in testing the defendant's conduct, to the statistics recounted by Dr. Hughes, which there was no suggestion the doctor attempted to use. If the difference is based solely or partly on the personal experience of the surgeons, and there is in the evidence some reason suggested that this may be so, then perhaps the explanation lies in the nature of the cases that each has dealt with and that the chance of

survivorship of those undertaken by one was less than the other. If this is so, there may have been good reason not to mention statistics to the patient, but rather to simply contrast his position if he undertakes the surgery with that of not undertaking it and urge him to proceed because of his youth and strength giving some assurance of survivorship. I do not think the evidence justifies the statement made by the learned trial Judge and I would hesitate to lay down any such requirements, for in my view, statistics can be very misleading. The manner in which the nature and degree of risk is explained to a particular patient is better left to the judgment of the doctor in dealing with the man before him. Its adequacy can be simply tested.

I think the Ontario Court of Appeal went too far, when dealing with the standard of disclosure of risks, in saying, as it did in the passage of its reasons just quoted, that "the manner in which the nature and degree of risk is explained to a particular patient is better left to the judgment of the doctor in dealing with the man before him." Of course, it can be tested by expert medical evidence but that too is not determinative. The patient may have expressed certain concerns to the doctor and the latter is obliged to meet them in a reasonable way. What the doctor knows or should know that the particular patient deems relevant to a decision whether to undergo prescribed treatment goes equally to his duty of disclosure as do the material risks recognized as a matter of required medical knowledge.

It is important to examine this issue in greater detail. The Ontario Court of Appeal appears to have adopted a professional medical standard, not only for determining what are the material risks that should be disclosed but also, and concurrently, for determining whether there has been a breach of the duty of disclosure. This was also the approach of the trial Judge, notwithstanding that on the facts he found against the defendant. (Indeed, the trial Judge seems also to have overstated the duty of disclosure. The Court of Appeal, in contrast, seems to have understated it. Generally, the failure to mention statistics should not affect the duty to inform nor be a factor in deciding whether the duty has been breached.) To allow expert medical evidence to determine what risks are material and, hence, should be disclosed and, correlatively, what risks are not material is to hand over to the medical profession the entire question of the scope of the duty of disclosure, including the question whether there has been a breach of that duty. Expert medical evidence is, of course, relevant to findings as to the risks that reside in or are a result of recommended surgery or other treatment. It will also have a bearing on their materiality but this is not a question that is to be concluded on the basis of the expert medical evidence alone. The issue under consideration is a different issue from that involved where the question is whether the doctor carried out his professional activities by applicable professional standards. What is under consideration here is the patient's right to know what risks are involved in undergoing or foregoing certain surgery or other treatment.

The materiality of non-disclosure of certain risks to an informed decision is a matter for the trier of fact, a matter on which there would, in all likelihood, be medical evidence but also other evidence, including evidence from the patient or from members of his family. It is, of course, possible that a particular patient may waive aside any question of risks and be quite prepared to submit to the surgery or treatment, whatever they be. Such a situation presents no difficulty. Again, it may be the case that a particular patient may, because

of emotional factors, be unable to cope with facts relevant to recommended surgery or treatment and the doctor may, in such a case, be justified in withholding or generalizing information as to which he would otherwise be required to be more specific.

...

If Canadian case law has so far proceeded on a subjective test of causation, it is in Courts other than this one that such an approach has been taken: see *Koehler v. Cook* (1975), 65 D.L.R. (3d) 766 at p. 767, [1976] W.W.D. 71, and *Kelly v. Hazlett* (1976), 75 D.L.R. (3d) 536 at pp. 565-6, 15 O.R. (2d) 290 at p. 320. The matter is *res integra* here. An alternative to the subjective test is an objective one, that is, what would a reasonable person in the patient's position have done if there had been proper disclosure of attendant risks. The case for the objective standard has been tersely put in the following passage from a comment in 48 N.Y.U.L. Rev. 548 (1973), at p. 550, entitled "Informed Consent — A Proposed Standard for Medical Disclosure":

> Since proximate causation exists only if disclosure would have resulted in the patient's foregoing the proposed treatment, a standard must be developed to determine whether the patient would have decided against the treatment had he been informed of its risks. Two possible standards exist: whether, if informed, the particular patient would have foregone treatment (subjective view); or whether the average prudent person in plaintiff's position, informed of all material risks, would have foregone treatment (objective view). The objective standard is preferable, since the subjective standard has a gross defect: it depends on the plaintiff's testimony as to his state of mind, thereby exposing the physician to the patient's hindsight and bitterness.

However, a vexing problem raised by the objective standard is whether causation could ever be established if the surgeon has recommended surgery which is warranted by the patient's condition. Can it be said that a reasonable person in the patient's position, to whom proper disclosure of attendant risks has been made, would decide against the surgery, that is, against the surgeon's recommendation that it be undergone? The objective standard of what a reasonable person in the patient's position would do would seem to put a premium on the surgeon's assessment of the relative need for the surgery and on supporting medical evidence of that need. Could it be reasonably refused? Brooke J.A. appeared to be sensitive to this problem by suggesting a combined objective-subjective test.

I doubt that this will solve the problem. It could hardly be expected that the patient who is suing would admit that he would have agreed to have the surgery, even knowing all the accompanying risks. His suit would indicate that, having suffered serious disablement because of the surgery, he is convinced that he would not have permitted it if there had been proper disclosure of the risks, balanced by the risks of refusing the surgery. Yet, to apply a subjective test to causation would, correlatively, put a premium on hindsight, even more of a premium than would be put on medical evidence in assessing causation by an objective standard.

I think it is the safer course on the issue of causation to consider objectively how far the balance in the risks of surgery or no surgery is in favour of undergoing surgery. The failure of proper disclosure pro and con becomes therefore very material. And so too are any special considerations affecting the particular patient. For example, the patient may have asked specific questions which were either brushed aside or were not fully answered or were answered wrongly. In the present case, the anticipation of a full pension would be a special consideration, and, while it would have to be viewed objectively, it emerges from the patient's particular circumstances. So too, other aspects of the objective standard would have to be geared to what the average prudent person, the reasonable person in the patient's particular position, would agree to or not agree to, if all material and special risks of going ahead with the surgery or foregoing it were made known to him. Far from making the patient's own testimony irrelevant, it is essential to his case that he put his own position forward.

The adoption of an objective standard does not mean that the issue of causation is completely in the hands of the surgeon. Merely because medical evidence establishes the reasonableness of a recommended operation does not mean that a reasonable person in the patient's position would necessarily agree to it, if proper disclosure had been made of the risks attendant upon it, balanced by those against it. The patient's particular situation and the degree to which the risks of surgery or no surgery are balanced would reduce the force, on an objective appraisal, of the surgeon's recommendation. Admittedly, if the risk of foregoing the surgery would be considerably graver to a patient than the risks attendant upon it, the objective standard would favour exoneration of the surgeon who has not made the required disclosure. Since liability rests only in negligence, in a failure to disclose material risks, the issue of causation would be in the patient's hands on a subjective test, and would, if his evidence was accepted, result inevitably in liability unless, of course, there was a finding that there was no breach of the duty of disclosure. In my view, therefore, the objective standard is the preferable one on the issue of causation.

In saying that the test is based on the decision that a reasonable person in the patient's position would have made, I should make it clear that the patient's particular concerns must also be reasonably based; otherwise, there would be more subjectivity than would be warranted under an objective test. Thus, for example, fears which are not related to the material risks which should have been but were not disclosed would not be causative factors. However, economic considerations could reasonably go to causation where, for example, the loss of an eye as a result of nondisclosure of a material risk brings about the loss of a job for which good eyesight is required. In short, although account must be taken of a patient's particular position, a position which will vary with the patient, it must be objectively assessed in terms of reasonableness.

...

5. BREACH OF DUTY OF DISCLOSURE: THE FINDINGS BELOW REVIEWED

In my opinion, the record of evidence amply justifies the trial Judge's findings that the plaintiff was told no more or understood no more than that he would be better off to have the operation than not to have it. This was not an adequate, not a sufficient disclosure of the risk attendant upon the operation itself, a risk well appreciated by the defendant in view of his own experience that of the 60 to 70 such operations that he had previously performed, 8 to 10 resulted in the death of the patients. Although the mortality rate was falling by 1970, the morbidity (the sickness or disease) rate, according to Dr. Hughes, was still about 10%. The trial Judge was also justified in finding that the plaintiff, who was concerned about his continuing headaches and

who was found to be suffering from hypertension, had the impression that the surgery would alleviate his headaches and hypertension so that he could carry on with his job. Dr. Hughes made it plain in his evidence that the surgery would not cure the headaches but did not, as the trial Judge found, make this plain to the plaintiff.

The foregoing findings have a basis in the evidence independent of any reliance on so-called statistics which was criticized by the majority of the Court of Appeal. Although Brooke J.A., speaking for the majority, appeared to discount the trial Judge's determinations because the latter made no specific finding on credibility, it is patent to me that the trial Judge's conclusions involved a weighing of the evidence and, hence, a measuring of its relative worth on the issues that he had to decide. There were inconsistencies in the defendant's evidence, as the trial Judge noted in his reasons, and it was for him to reconcile them in arriving at his findings. For example, the defendant said in-chief that he had told the plaintiff of the risk of a stroke during surgery and then said on cross-examination that the risks of the surgery were quite minimal. Again, on cross-examination, he said that he did not tell the patient that there was a risk of a stroke as a result of the surgery at any specific time thereafter, and he returned to an oft repeated statement that the chances of paralysis were greater without an operation than with it. (This was also the only reference by Dr. Lougheed, who testified for the defence, as to the risk involved in submitting to or foregoing the surgery. His evidence was almost exclusively related to post-operative care and whether a re-operation was feasible. He said it was not. However, as I noted earlier, post-operative care was not an issue in this Court.) Moreover, the defendant placed this risk as one within a few years and not within any immediate time. Indeed, when asked in cross-examination whether he told the patient that the surgery carried the risk of a stroke, he answered, "I didn't say that specifically." This was certainly a case in which a trial Judge, here an experienced Judge, was in a better position than an appellate Court or this Court to determine what evidence to accept and what conclusions to draw from it.

In the ... reasons of Brooke J.A., speaking for the majority of the Court of Appeal, there are two approaches on the crucial issue whether the defendant apprised the plaintiff of the risk of a stroke from the very operation. In the first ... passage, the learned Justice of Appeal appears to have viewed the trial Judge's finding on this question as a finding that the plaintiff was not made aware of that risk. This is clearly a correct assessment of the trial Judge's conclusion. However, Brooke J.A. went on to deal with the case and with the evidence as if there was a partial albeit not a sufficient disclosure of the particular risk, and he proceeded from there into an appraisal of the statistics to which the trial Judge referred and found fault in their use. In the second ... passage ... Brooke J.A. ... ignores the finding of the trial Judge that there was no disclosure of the risks inherent in the surgery itself. In my opinion, there was a failure by the Court of Appeal to address this point directly. In the light of the defendant's own evidence that there was a failure on his part to disclose the risk, even though the plaintiff himself raised the question of the risks he faced on the operating table, I do not see how there could be any doubt of a breach in this respect of the duty of disclosure.

Indeed, the reasons of the Court of Appeal ... appear to support the trial Judge's finding that there was no proper disclosure by the defendant of the risk of the surgery itself. Brooke J.A. said this on the question [at p. 119]:

He [the defendant] did not specifically discuss the questions of death or paralysis as risks of the surgery, his explanation being that he believed the patient was aware of the risk because of questions that he asked when the surgery was being discussed. It was his view that no further detail was necessary.

In this respect then, there would seem to be concurrent findings of fact against the defendant on a central point in case.

There were a number of relevant considerations informing the findings of the trial Judge, about which there was no dispute. First, there was no emergency making surgery imperative. There was no noticeable neurological deficit. The defendant himself placed the risk of a stroke as one off in the future, four to five years. Any immediate risk would be from the surgery and not from foregoing it. Moreover, it must have been obvious to the defendant that the plaintiff had some difficulty with the English language and that he should, therefore, have made certain that he was understood. Finally, there was no evidence that the plaintiff was emotionally taut or unable to accept disclosure of the grave risk to which he would be exposed by submitting to surgery. I do not see in the reasons of the majority of the Court of Appeal any evidentiary basis for challenging the findings of the trial Judge on the defendant's breach of the duty of disclosure. Of course, the medical evidence was relevant to what that duty entailed but, that said, it was for the trier of fact to determine the scope of the duty and to decide whether there had been a breach of the duty. As I have already said, the so-called statistical data used by the trial Judge did not affect the grounds upon which he made his critical findings. The Court of Appeal held, however, that the trial Judge did not examine the issue of causation with the necessary care that this issue required. He did not ignore it, even if he might have gone into it at greater length. The question that remains, therefore, is whether this was a sufficient basis upon which to direct a new trial.

6. CAUSATION

Relevant in this case to the issue whether a reasonable person in the plaintiff's position would have declined surgery at the particular time is the fact that he was within about one and one-half years of earning pension benefits if he continued at his job; that there was no neurological deficit then apparent; that there was no immediate emergency making the surgery imperative; that there was a grave risk of a stroke or worse during or as a result of the operation, while the risk of a stroke without it was in the future, with no precise time fixed or which could be fixed

except as a guess of three or more years ahead. Since, on the trial Judge's finding, the plaintiff was under the mistaken impression, as a result of the defendant's breach of the duty of disclosure, that the surgery would relieve his continuing headaches, this would in the opinion of a reasonable person in the plaintiff's position, also weigh against submitting to the surgery at the particular time.

In my opinion, a reasonable person in the plaintiff's position would, on a balance of probabilities, have opted against the surgery rather than undergoing it at the particular time.

CONCLUSION

I would, accordingly, allow the appeal, set aside the order of the Court of Appeal and restore the judgment at trial. The appellant is entitled to costs throughout.

Informed Consent:
Ethical Considerations for Physicians and Surgeons
The Royal College of Physicians and Surgeons of Canada

PREMISES

In the medical context, informed consent refers to the prerogative of patients to make decisions about their medical treatment. The nature of this prerogative is a matter of dispute in both law and ethics.

Physicians should learn about the legal requirements for informed consent (for

example, the 1980 Supreme Court of Canada judgement in the *Reibl versus Hughes* case). However, adherence to the law does not guarantee acceptable ethical behavior. Whether in the Code of Ethics of the Canadian Medical Association/Royal College or in specific physician-patient relationships, higher standards of informed consent than those required by law may be appropriate.

"Informed Consent: Ethical Considerations for Physicians and Surgeons," *Annals of the Royal College of Physicians and Surgeons of Canada*, 21:1 (1988).

There is a range of positions on decision-making authority in the physician-patient relationship. One extreme option, commonly called paternalism, would vest absolute authority in the physician. The other extreme would require the physician to do whatever the patient demands. Between these two poles are various forms of shared responsibility.

Medical paternalism has been found inappropriate for contemporary medical practice. It is considered to be at odds with the principle of individual autonomy, which has emerged as a paramount value in Western nations.

With the decline of paternalism there has arisen a great emphasis on patients' rights to decision-making authority in health care. Although this represents a necessary corrective to paternalism, there is a danger of exaggerating these rights at the expense of both the duties of patients to co-operate with physicians, and the rights of physicians and other health care professionals, which may conflict with those of patients.

Informed consent, however conceived, should not be an end, but a means of optimal medical care for all patients. Patients and physicians should strive for agreement about the treatment to be undertaken, but this is not always possible. Procedures need to be established to deal with situations in which the patient is not competent to participate in the decision-making process, or where physician and patient cannot agree on what should be done.

PRINCIPLES

An essential condition for the exercise of informed consent is good communication between physician and patients (or their surrogates). The physician has primary responsibility for ensuring that such communication occurs. Patients have an obligation to provide the physician with all relevant information about their conditions, to enable him or her to offer the best diagnosis and treatment.

Competent patients (those who can make rational decisions about their medical care), have the right to make such decisions. The physician is morally obliged to respect this right by providing patients with all reasonable data about diagnostic and therapeutic procedures, and possible alternatives and risks, and by allowing patients to make their decisions without coercion. Competent patients may waive this right to informed consent in full or in part, in which case the physician should provide whatever treatment he or she believes to be in the patients' best interests.

Incompetent patients should be treated in their best interests, as determined by the physician on the basis of the patients' expressed wishes while competent. For patients who have not indicated how they want to be treated, the physician should make the decision about treatment in consultation with the patients' families or guardians, other medical staff, and other persons he or she may wish to consult (for example, close friends, clergy) as time and circumstances permit.

PROCEDURES

The physician should encourage his or her patients to exercise their right to make their own decisions about their medical treatment. If he or she detects unusual hesitation on their part regarding their willingness or ability to make such decisions, he or she should ascertain whether they are competent and act accordingly.

If the patients are competent and wish to make their own decisions, the physician should provide all the information that they need to make adequately informed decisions. If the decisions involve treatment or refusal of treatment in which the physician cannot, in good conscience, participate, he or she should try to refer the patients to another physician or institution which can fulfill the patients' wishes.

If the patients are competent but cannot decide among treatment options, the physician might suggest that they seek a second opinion from another physician.

If the patients are competent but prefer to let the physician make the decisions, he or she should attempt to determine their reasons for so acting. If they seem reasonable (for example, uncertainty about treatment options or trust in the physician's judgement), he or she should act according to his or her estimation of the patients' best interests.

If the patients are obviously incompetent (infants, the unconscious, the severely retarded), the physician should consult, where possible, the families or guardians, and other medical staff before deciding on a course of treatment. Where parents or guardians request treatment that, in the physician's opinion, are contrary to the best interests of the patients, or refuse treatments that he or she believes are in their best interests, the physician should take whatever action is necessary to prevent harm to the patients; this may include recourse to the courts.

If the patients' competence is uncertain, the physician should attempt to minimize the uncertainty by seeking medical consultation before trying to secure informed consent. If the patients' decisions or refusal to decide seem unreasonable and are likely to result in serious harm to them, the physician should consult with the families, colleagues, and hospital authorities about the advisability of acting against, or in the absence of the patients' expressed wishes, at least until their competence is no longer in doubt.

In emergency situations where the patient is incompetent, the physician should provide whatever treatment he or she believes to be in the patient's best interests.

Where there is more than one physician dealing with a patient, each one should deal directly with the patient in securing informed consent for medical treatment. Physicians should not rely on medical students, nurses or other physicians to secure this consent.

Before undergoing exploratory surgery or other temporarily incapacitating treatment, patients should be adequately informed about the possible interventions which may be necessary while they are incompetent. They should be given the opportunity to indicate in advance which types of procedures they would be willing to undergo and which they would refuse.

MAXIMS

- Tell your patients all they want and need to know about their medical care.

- Know your own expertise as a physician and do not hesitate to refer patients to more qualified colleagues.

- Listen closely to your patients and, if necessary, their families and acquaintances in order to determine what is in their best interests.

- Aim for agreement with your patients as to the best medical treatment for them.

- Where agreement is absent, defer to your patients' judgement except where their competence is doubtful or lacking.

- In any circumstances involving apparently contentious issues of informed consent, record in the patient's clinical file all relevant information concerning the acquisition of such consent.

A Moral Theory of Consent

Benjamin Freedman

Most medical codes of ethics, and most physicians, agree that the physician ought to obtain the "free and informed consent" of his subject or patient before attempting any serious medical procedures, experimental or therapeutic in nature. They agree, moreover, that a proxy consent ought to be obtained on behalf of the incompetent subject. And informed consent is seen as not merely a legal requirement, and not merely a formality: it is a substantial requirement of morality.

Acceptance of this doctrine, however, requires the solution of a number of problems. How much information need be imparted? At what age is a person mature enough to consent on his own behalf? Can prisoners give a "free and informed consent" to be experimented upon? Lurking behind these and similar questions there are more fundamental difficulties. What are the functions of consent for the competent and the incompetent? What is the sense in which the patient/subject must be "free," "informed," and "competent?" It is by way of an approach to these latter questions that I shall attempt to respond to the more specific questions.[1]

I. CONSENT AND THE COMPETENT

The negative aspects of the doctrine of informed consent have ordinarily been the focus of attention; difficulties in obtaining the informed consent of the subject/patient render the ethics of experimentation and therapeutic measures questionable. Our common view of informed consent is that, when at all relevant, it represents a minimum condition which ethics imposes upon the physician. It is seen as a necessary condition for medical manipulation, but hardly as a sufficient condition.

The reasons why this is so — why it is not sufficient that an experimenter, for instance, have received informed consent from his subject before proceeding — are quite obvious. The scarcity of medical resources (which includes a scarcity of qualified physician-investigators) forbids us from wasting time upon poorly-designed experiments, or upon experiments which merely replicate well-established conclusions. There seems to be, as well, a limit to the dangers which we (ordinarily) allow subjects to face. We do not, as a matter of policy, think it wise to allow would-be suicides to accomplish their end with the aid of a scientific investigator. Many other reasons could be given for the proposition that a person does not have a right to be experimented upon, even when he has given valid consent to the procedure.

The Right to Consent

But there does seem to exist a positive right of informed consent, which exists in both therapeutic and experimental settings. A person who has the capacity to give valid

Benjamin Freedman, "A Moral Theory of Consent," *Hastings Center Report* 5:4 (August 1975); 32-39.

consent, and who has in fact consented to the procedure in question, has a right to have that fact recognized by us. We all have a duty to recognize a valid consent when confronted with it.

From whence derives this right? It arises from the right which each of us possesses to be treated as a person, and in the duty which all of us have, to have respect for persons, to treat a person as such, and not as an object. For this entails that our capacities for personhood ought to be recognized by all — these capacities including the capacity for rational decision, and for action consequent upon rational decision. Perhaps the worst which we may do to a man is to deny him his humanity, for example, by classifying him as mentally incompetent when he is, in fact, sane. It is a terrible thing to be hated or persecuted; it is far worse to be ignored, to be notified that you "don't count."

If an individual is capable of and has given valid consent, I would argue that he has a right, as against the world but more particularly as against his physician, to have it recognized that valid consent has been given. (The same applies, of course, with still greater force, with regard to *refusals* to consent to medical procedures.) The limited force of this claim must be emphasized: it does not entail a right to be treated, or to be experimented upon. It is a most innocuous right, one which most of us would have little hesitation about granting.

It is, therefore, curious that the literature on informed consent has failed to recognize this right — has, in fact, tacitly denied this right, at least as regards experimentation. In writings on informed consent it seems to have been assumed that if, under certain conditions, it is *doubtful* that valid consent to an experiment has been granted, it is best to "play it safe" ethically. In cases of doubt, we prefer not to take chances: in this case, we will not take a chance upon violating the canons of ethics

by experimenting without being certain that the subject has validly consented to the experiment. Since we do not at present know whether a prisoner can give a valid consent, let us not take chances: we call for a moratorium on prison experimentation. Since we do not know at what age a person has the capacity to give a valid consent, we avoid the problem by setting the age of majority at a point where it is beyond doubt that maturity has been attained. If we must err, we shall ensure that we err in being overly ethical.

The establishment of the innocuous right to have valid consent recognized as such eliminates this expedient. Other writers have conceptualized the conflict as one between a right and, at best, a mere liberty. From the patient's point of view, he has a right to have his health protected by the physician, and a mere liberty to be experimented upon. From the physician-investigator's point of view, he has a duty to protect the subject's health, and a mere liberty to experiment upon the subject (contingent, of course, upon obtaining the subject's consent). A recognition of the claims of personhood and autonomy, however, reveals this to be a conflict between rights and duties. The physician-investigator has a duty to recognize consent when validly offered. When the consent is of doubtful validity, therefore, the physician experiences a conflict between two duties. He will not be ethically well-protected by choosing not to experiment, for there exists the possibility — which, as cases are multiplied, becomes a probability — that he is violating a duty in so choosing. Problems in informed consent present us with a dilemma. It is no longer the case that the burden of proof devolves upon the would-be experimenter. The would-be abstainer-from-experiments may have to prove his case as well.

These considerations give us a new point of departure in investigating problems of informed consent. They show us that there is no "fail-safe" procedure which we can fall back upon in cases of doubt. Rather, what is required is an exhaustive examination of each case and issue, to see whether or not a valid consent has in fact been obtained.

When we fail to recognize a valid consent, of course, more is involved than a denial of personhood. Other benefits may be denied as well. Dr. Vernon Mark, for example, maintains that psychosurgery should not be done on prisoners with epilepsy because of the problem in obtaining a voluntary consent from prisoners.[2] But a resolution of this problem has not been shown to be impossible. Surely, the proper thing to do here would be to see whether prisoners can or cannot give valid consent to such a procedure. To remain satisfied with doubts, to fail to investigate this question, complex though it be, results in a denial of medical treatment for the prisoner, as well as representing a negation of the prisoner's human capacities. In depriving prisoners of the opportunity to serve as subjects in medical experiments, there are losses other than those of human respect.[3] Not the least of these is the loss of an opportunity to be of altruistic service to mankind.[4] Even a child feels at times a need to be useful; in promoting a moratorium on prison experimentation we deny prisoners the satisfaction of this psychic need. We should not need a reminder from John Stuart Mill that there are "higher" as well as "lower" pleasures and needs.

The right to have valid consent recognized as such does not indicate that we must experiment on prisoners. What it does indicate is that we have a moral responsibility to investigate in detail the question of whether prisoners can, under certain conditions, validly consent to experimentation. It also requires that we not prevent a researcher from experimenting on the basis of over-scrupulousness. If prisoners *can* give valid consent, we wrong not only the researcher but the prisoner as well by forbidding prison experimentation.

The Requirement of Information

The most common locution for the requirement which I am discussing is "informed consent" — we require "informed consent" to protect a doctor from legal liability resultant from his therapeutic endeavors, or to ensure the "ethicacy" of an experiment. But I believe "informed consent" to be a serious misnomer for what we do, in fact, want medical practice to conform to.

No lengthy rehearsal of the absurdities consequent upon taking the term "informed consent" at face value is necessary. The claim has been made, and repeated with approval, that "fully informed consent" is a goal which we can never achieve, but toward which we must strive. In order to ensure that fully informed consent has been given, it has seriously been suggested that only medical students or graduate students in the life sciences ought to be accepted as subjects for experimentation. *Reductio ad absurdum* examples of "fully informed consent" have been elaborated, in forms which list all the minutiae of the proposed medical procedure, together with all of its conceivable sequelae. With such a view of "informed consent" and its requirements, it is not surprising to find doctors who claim that since they cannot fully inform patients, they will tell them nothing, but instead will personally assume the responsibility for assuring the subject's safety.

In truth, a *reductio ad absurdum* of this view of "informed consent" need not be constructed; it serves as its own *reductio ad absurdum*. For there is no end to "fully informing" patients. When the doctor wishes to insert a catheter, must he commend to the subject's attention a textbook of anatomy? Although this, of course, would not suffice: he must ensure that the patient understands the text as well. Must he tell the patient the story of Dr. X, that bogey of first-year medical students, who, in a state of inebriation, inserted ("by mistake") his pen-refill instead of the catheter? With, of course, the assurance that *this* physician never gets drunk. ("Well, rarely, anyway.") Must the patient be informed of the chemical formula of the catheter? Its melting point?

The basic mistake which is committed by those who harp upon the difficulties in obtaining informed consent (and by critics of the doctrine) is in believing that we can talk about information in the abstract, without reference to any human purpose. It is very likely impossible to talk about "information" in this way; but impossible or not, when we do in fact talk about, or request, information, we do not mean "information in the abstract." If I ask someone to "tell me about those clouds" he will, ordinarily, know what I mean; and he will answer me, in the spirit in which he was asked, by virtue of his professional expertise as an artist, meteorologist, astronomer, sooth-sayer, or what-have-you. The meteorologist will not object that he cannot tell you the optical refraction index of the clouds, and therefore that he cannot "fully answer" your question. He knows that you are asking him with a given end in mind, and that much information about the cloud is irrelevant *relative to that purpose.*

That this "abstract information" requirement is not in question in obtaining valid consent is hardly an original point, but it is worth repeating. One of the leading court opinions on human experimentation puts it like this: "...the patient's interest in information does not extend to a lengthy polysyllabic discourse on all possible complications. A mini-course in medical science is not required...."[5]

The proper question to ask, then, is not "What information must be given?" That would be premature: we must first know for what purpose information is needed. *Why* must the patient be informed? Put that way, the answer is immediately forthcoming. The patient must be informed so that

he will know what he is getting into, what he may expect from the procedure, what his likely alternatives are — in short, what the procedure (and forbearance from it) will mean, so that a responsible decision on the matter may be made. This is the legal stance, as well as, I think, a "common-sensical" stance; as Alexander Capron writes, the information component in valid consent derives in law from the recognition that information is "necessary to make meaningful the power to decide."[6] The proper test of whether a given piece of information needs to be given is, then, whether the physician, knowing what he does about the patient/subject, feels that that patient/subject would want to know this before making up his mind. Outré, improbable consequences would not ordinarily, therefore, be relevant information. Exceptionally, they will be: for example, when there is a small risk of impotence consequent upon the procedure which the physician proposes to perform upon a man with a great stake in his sexual prowess. This is only sensible.

Our main conclusion, then, is that valid consent entails only the imparting of that information which the patient/subject requires in order to make a responsible decision. This entails, I think, the possibility of a valid yet ignorant consent.

Consider, first, the therapeutic context. It is, I believe, not unusual for a patient to give his doctor *carte blanche* to perform any medical procedure which the physician deems proper in order to effect a cure. He is telling the doctor to act as his agent in choosing which procedure to follow. This decision is neither unwise nor (in any serious sense) an abdication of responsibility and an unwarranted burden upon the physician. We each of us choose to delegate our power of choice in this way in dealing with our auto mechanic or stockbroker.

It may be harder to accept an ignorant consent as valid in the purely experimental context. I think, however, that much of this difficulty is due to our paucity of imagination, our failure to imagine circumstances in which a person might choose to proceed in this way. We might approach such a case, for example, by imagining a Quaker who chooses to serve society by acting as a research subject, but who has a morbid fear of knives and pointed instruments. The Quaker might say to the physician-investigator that he wants to serve science but is afraid that his phobia would overcome his better judgment. He might consequently request that any experiment which would involve use of scalpels, hypodermic needles, and such, be performed without informing him: while, say, he is asleep or unconscious. He might further ask the doctor not to proceed should the experiment involve considerable risk. In such a case, or one similar, we would find an instance of a valid yet ignorant consent to experimentation.

The ostensible differences between the therapeutic and experimental contexts may be resolved into two components: in the therapeutic context it is supposed that the physician knows what the sequelae to treatment will be, which information, by definition, is not available in the experimental situation; and in the therapeutic context the doctor may be said to be seeking his patient's good, in contrast to the experimental context where some other good is being sought. On the basis of these differences it may be claimed that a valid yet ignorant consent is enough permission for therapy, but not for experimentation.

Closer examination, however, reveals that these differences do not necessarily obtain. First, because I believe it would be granted that a valid yet ignorant consent can be given in the "therapeutic-experimental" situation, where a new drug or procedure is being attempted to aid the patient (in the absence of any traditional available therapy). In the therapeutic-experimental situation, as in the purely experimental situation, the sequelae are not known

(although of course in both cases some definite result is expected or anticipated). If a valid yet ignorant consent is acceptable in the one, therefore, it must be acceptable in the other.

Secondly, because it is patently not the case that we can expect there to be no good accruing to the subject of an experiment by reason of his participation. There are, commonly, financial and other "tangible" benefits forthcoming (laboratory training, and so on). And it must once again be said that the pleasures of altruism are not negligible. The proposed differences between experimentation and therapy do not stand up, and so we must say that if a valid yet ignorant consent is acceptable in the one it must be acceptable in the other. It must be remembered that this statement only concerns itself with one part of the consent doctrine, which is, itself, only one of the requirements which the ethical experiment must satisfy.

To mention — without claiming totally to resolve — two problems which may be raised at this point: First, it is said that a doctor often does not know what will happen as a consequence of a recommended procedure, and so cannot tell the patient what the patient wants to know. The obvious response to this seems to be right: the physician should, in that case, tell the patient/subject that he does not know what will happen (which does not exclude an explanation of what the doctor expects to happen, and on what he bases this expectation).

Second, it will be objected that the adoption of a requirement such as I propose would forbid the use of placebos and blind experiments. I am not sure that this is so; sometimes it must be the case that the subjects in an experiment may be asked (without introducing artifacts into the results) to consent to an experiment knowing that some will, and some will not, be receiving placebos. Another alternative would be to inform the subjects that the experiment may or may not involve some subjects receiving placebos.[7] I am aware, however, that these remarks are less than adequate responses to these problems.

Our conclusion, then, is that the informing of the patient/subject is not a fundamental requirement of valid consent. It is, rather, derivative from the requirement that the consent be the expression of a responsible choice. The two requirements which I do see as fundamental in this doctrine are that the choice be responsible and that it be voluntary.

The Requirement of Responsibility

What is meant by saying that the choice must be "responsible"? Does this entail that the physician may at any time override a patient's judgment on the basis that, in the physician's view, the patient has not chosen responsibly? Surely not; to adopt such a criterion would defeat the purpose embodied in the doctrine of consent. It would mean that a person's exercise of autonomy is always subject to review.

Still, some such requirement would appear to be necessary. A small child can certainly make choices.[8] Small children can also be intelligent enough to understand the necessary information. Yet surely we would not want to say that a small child can give valid consent to a serious medical procedure.[9] The reason for this is that the child cannot choose *responsibly*.

We are faced with a dilemma. On the one hand, it appears that we must require that the choice be responsible. To require only that the choice be free would yield counter-intuitive results. On the other hand, if we do require that the choice made be a responsible one, we seem to presuppose some body which shall judge the reasonableness of choices; this represents a paternalism which is antithetical to the doctrine of consent. An elderly patient chooses to forgo further life-saving measures. How are we to judge whether or not this choice is a responsible one?

The path between the horns of this dilemma involves saying that the "responsibility" which we require is to be predicated not on the nature of the particular choice, but on the nature of the patient/subject. What we need to know is whether *he* is a responsible man ("in general," so to speak), not whether the choice which has been made is responsible. In this way, we avoid the danger of upholding as "responsible" only those choices which we ourselves feel are good choices. We can and do admit into the community of responsible persons individuals who make choices with which we do not agree.

In this sense, responsibility is a dispositional characteristic. To say that someone is a responsible individual means that he makes choices, typically, on the basis of reasons, arguments, or beliefs — and that he remains open to the claims of reason, so that further rational argument might lead him to change his mind. It is to say that a person is capable of making and carrying through a life-plan — that he is prepared to act on the basis of his choices. It is to say that a person is capable of living with his life-plan; he can live with the consequences of his choices, he *takes responsibility* for his choices.[10] Of course, none of these are absolutes: all responsible people are at times pigheaded, at times short-sighted, at times flighty. That is to say, all responsible men at times act irresponsibly. Should the lack of responsibility persist, of course, to an extreme degree, we may say that the person has left the community of responsible folk.

Voluntarism and Reward

The other requirement of valid consent is that it be given voluntarily. The choice which the consent expresses must be freely made.

We all know some conditions which, if satisfied, make us say that a consent has been given involuntarily. The case which immediately springs to mind occurs when an individual succumbs under a threat: we call this duress or coercion. But the threat need not be overt; and perhaps there need not be a threat at all to render consent involuntary.

Hence, the major problem currently engendered by the requirement of voluntariness. It is typified by the prisoner who "volunteers" for an experiment in the hope or expectation of a reward: significantly higher wages, an opportunity for job training, better health care while involved in the experiment, a favorable report to his parole board. Is the consent which the prisoner offers a voluntary consent? The problem may be stated more generally thus: At what point does reward render consent involuntary?

The problem of reward is particularly difficult, since it involves questions of degree. Is a prisoner's consent involuntary if the reward for his participation in the experiment is a three-month reduction of sentence? Is it relevant here that the prisoner is serving a twenty-year sentence, rather than a one-to-five-year sentence? Does a possible increase in wages from twenty-five cents per hour to one dollar per hour constitute duress? Should we consider the percentage increase, or the increase in absolute value, or the increase in actual value which the seventy-five cent disparity represents in the prison environment?

To some, of course, questions like these have little meaning. They have little meaning to those who are indifferent to the demands of justice and autonomy which the consent doctrine represents, to those who are willing to buy guinea pigs, rather than to reward human beings. And they have little meaning for those who are convinced that prisoners are inherently unfree, and who thus would call for a total cessation of prison experimentation. Each of these positions denies, in an a *priori* fashion, freedom to prisoners; each must be rejected. A recognition of the fact that decisions about consent may be over- as well as under-protective forces us to deal with this sort of question, complex though it may be.

As is so often the case, posing the question in a different way may facilitate response. We have been considering the question of how much reward nullifies the validity of consent, how much reward renders the subject unfree. But is it in fact the case that *reward* is the disruptive factor here?

This problem may be clarified by the following examples. Imagine an upper-middle-class individual, who can provide for his family all of their needs and most of the amenities of civilized life. Let us say that this person is offered one hundred dollars to cross the street — if you like, make it one thousand or ten thousand dollars? He chooses to cross the street. Is his choice *involuntary?* Despite the substantial reward, I think most of us would agree that the consent was freely offered (and would that we should have such problems!).

Consider a person who deeply wants to be an astronaut. He is told that as part of the program he must participate in experiments to determine resistance to high-G conditions. Is his consent to this invalid, involuntary? I think not. We would say, this is part of his job; he should have expected it; and if he can't stand the heat, he should get out of the kitchen. In this vein, consider Evel Knievel, a financially prosperous man, who is offered millions of dollars to perform daredevil stunts. His choice may be bizarre, even crazy: but has his reward rendered it unfree?

Finally, consider a man who is informed by his doctor that he will most likely die unless he has open-heart surgery. His "reward" for consenting is his life; the penalty for not consenting is death. Does this mean this man cannot give the doctor valid consent — morally valid consent — to proceed?

There are two distinctions which, I think, go a long way towards dispelling these problems. First, I think it must be granted that natural contingencies ("acts of God," things which come to pass naturally, those contingencies which we cannot hold anyone responsible for) do not render a person unfree, nor do they render unfree the choices which a person makes in light of those contingencies.[11]

That natural contingencies do not render a man unfree is a point which is apt to be forgotten in the present context. I am not — in the morally relevant sense — lacking in freedom because I cannot, unaided, fly through the air, or live on grass. Nor am I unfree because my heart is about to give out. Nor am I unfree when, recognizing that my heart may give out, I choose to undergo surgery. I may, of course, be so crazed by knowing that I am near death's door that I am in a state of general impotence, and hence must have the choice made for me; but general incompetence is not in question here. The distinction between choices forced by man, and choices forced by nature, is, then, of importance.

The second distinction is between those pressures which are, and those which are not, in Daube's words, "consonant with the dignity and responsibility of free life."[12] I would explain this as follows: there are certain basic freedoms and rights which we possess which *entitle* us (morally) to certain things (or states of affairs). We would all, no doubt, draw up different lists of these rights and freedoms; but included in them would be safety of person, freedom of conscience and religion, a right to a certain level of education, and, for some of us, a right to some level of health care. When the "reward" is such as only to give us the necessary conditions of these rights and freedoms — when all that the reward does is to bring us up to a level of living to which we are entitled, and of which we have been deprived by man — then the "reward," I

think, constitutes duress. A reward which accrues to one who has achieved this level, or who can easily achieve it (other than by taking the reward-option), and which hence serves only to grant us "luxury" items, does not constitute duress, and hence does not render choice unfree, no matter how great this reward may be.

The rewards above the moral subsistence level are true rewards. In contrast, we may say (with some touch of metaphor) that the "rewards" which only bring us up to the level to which we were in any event entitled are properly viewed as functioning as *threats*: "Do this, or stay where you are" — when you should not have been "where you are" in the first place.

The astronaut, Evel Knievel, and the upper-middle-class street-crosser are being granted "luxury" items, and hence are capable of giving free consent. But consider a man who will not be admitted to the hospital for treatment unless he agrees to be a subject in an experiment (unrelated to his treatment). Those who feel, as I do, that we are, here and now, morally entitled to medical treatment would agree, I trust, that this illegitimate option coerces the man into agreeing. Or consider a man who has religious scruples against donating blood, who takes his daughter to a hospital for treatment. He is told that the doctors will not treat her unless the family donates a certain amount of blood. His freedom has been nullified: his "consent" to donating blood is morally invalid.[13] Similarly, the college student whose grade is contingent upon his participation in the instructor's psychological experiments is not validly consenting to serve. He is entitled to have his grade based upon his classroom work.

It yet remains to apply this distinction to our original problem, prison experimentation. The application will not be attempted here, for we would first need to be clear in our minds what rights and freedoms a prisoner is entitled to. I would not hesitate to say, though, that when a situation is created whereby a prisoner can only receive decent health care by participating in an experiment, he is being coerced into that experiment. I would have little hesitation in claiming that if subjecting himself to experimentation is the only way in which a prisoner could learn a trade which may be used "outside," then that prisoner is being coerced, his consent is not free. When we take into account the condition of our society, these would seem to be reasonable entitlements for the prisoner. Other rewards — for example, higher pay—may or may not constitute rewards above the moral subsistence level; if they are, then consent in light of these rewards could be freely offered. Perhaps too much has been said already; judgments like these must be made in an individualized fashion, one which is sensitive to the realities of prison life.

NOTES

The research for this paper was begun during an internship at the Institute of Society, Ethics and the Life Sciences in the month of June, 1973. I gratefully acknowledge the help of Drs. Daniel Callahan, Marc Lappé, Peter Steinfels, and Robert Veatch, of the Institute, who helped make my internship profitable and enjoyable. My wife Barbara read the manuscript and suggested a number of needed changes.

1. For examples of a similar method applied to different problems, see Thomas I. Emerson, *Toward A General Theory of the First Amendment* (New York: Vintage Books, 1967).

2. "Brain Surgery in Aggressive Epileptics," in *Hastings Center Report,* February 1973.

3. See the insert to Alexander M. Capron's call for a moratorium on prison experimentation, "Medical Research in Prisons," *Hastings Center Report,* June 1973. The insert is a report from *The New York Times,* April 15, 1973, and reads in part: "Ninety-six of the 175 inmates at Lancaster County prison have written to a newspaper here protesting a recent decision by the state to halt all medical experiments on state prisoners. In their letter to the *Lancaster New Era,* they urged that state to allow the research [which] did not harm them and enabled them to pay off their fines and court costs."

4. See Henry K. Beecher, *Research and the Individual: Human Studies* (Boston: Little, Brown, 1970), 56. Professor Beecher notes a study of prison inmates, who, for participation in an experiment involving malaria, received pay but no reduction of sentence. Half of the volunteers cited "altruism" rather than money as their motive for volunteering. Those inmates who did not volunteer "expressed or implied respect for those who did volunteer."

5. *Cobbs* v. *Grant,* 502 P. 2d 1, 11.

6. Alexander M. Capron, "Legal Rights and Moral Rights," in Hilton, *et al.,* eds., *Ethical Issues in Human Genetics* (Plenum Press, 1973), 228.

7. If this sort of explanation were given as a matter of course in *all* experiments, this might still further reduce the problem of artifacts. The remarks, it should

be noted, are directed towards medical experiments. By and large, they are inapplicable to, say, experiments in social psychology.

8. The counter-suggestion may be made that children cannot *really* make choices. This would, I think, put too great a weight upon the requirement of voluntarism. We would be recruiting the concepts of choice and volition to do a job which they have not been designed for.

9. I am speaking of course in the moral, not the legal, context. It may be that in an emergency a child may, in the absence of his parents, give legally valid consent.

10. This gives us the link between "responsible" in the dispositional sense explained here, and "responsible" in the blame-sense of the word ("I'll hold you responsible for that.").

11. The *caveat* must be added: natural contingencies do not have, as their *sole* result, the rendering of a person unfree, in the sense which vitiates consent: a man's brain tumor can make the man an idiot, schizophrenia can make a man insane, but these do not so much affect a person's volition as they do disturb his entire psychic structure.

12. David Daube, quoted in Beecher, 146.

13. *In re Gault,* 387 U.S. 1 (1967).

Ciarlariello v. Schacter

This decision deals with the question under what circumstances a patient may be taken to have withdrawn consent. In this case the patient, Ms. C., had undergone an angiogram for a suspected bleed into the brain that led to recurring headaches. This first angiogram had indicated a particular area in her brain might contain an aneurism. On the recommendation of her physician, Mrs. C. consented to a second angiogram. This angiogram was performed by Dr. Greco.

... Prior to the commencement of the [*second*] test, Dr. Greco spoke with Mrs. Ciarlariello and explained why the test was required, and how it was to be performed. He outlined what sensations she might experience as the injections were

made. ... He then explained the risks involved in the use of the dye [that is injected in angiograms to make the bloodvessels show up on the test], which included the possibility of a skin rash, and on rare occasions death, blindness, stroke and paralysis. Mrs. Ciarlariello appeared to understand all that was said to her and to consent to the procedure.

Dr. Greco then proceeded with the test. Some time after the procedure began, Mrs. Ciarlariello began moaning and yelling. Her breathing became very rapid and she flexed her legs. Dr. Greco immediately inquired as to the source of her discomfort but she could not respond because her breathing was developing into hyper-

Ciarlariello v. Schacter [1993] 2 S.C.R. 119.

ventilation. ... Dr. Keller [her attending physician], who heard the noise ... noted that the patient was hyperventilating and that her limbs were rigid. This, according to the medical evidence, is characteristic of a condition called "tetany" or "carpo-pedal spasm" and results from unchecked hyperventilation. Mrs. Ciarlariello controlled her breathing, began to calm down and said, "Enough, no more, stop the test."

At this point, the test, which had been interrupted by this episode, was stopped, and the catheter was withdrawn from the abdominal artery although it remained in Mrs. Ciarlariello's body. Dr. Greco explained to Dr. Keller that he had completed both carotid arteries. Dr. Keller then talked to Mrs. Ciarlariello trying to reassure her and calm her. Mrs. Ciarlariello complained that her right hand was numb. On examination she was not able to move or grasp with it. The left hand was also weak, although to a lesser degree.

Dr. Keller concluded that Mrs. Ciarlariello's weakness resulted from the tetany which in turn had been caused by the hyperventilation. Dr. Keller tested Mrs. Ciarlariello's sensory functions with pinpricks to her arms and legs. She could feel the pinpricks everywhere, including her right hand. Dr. Keller then tested Mrs. Ciarlariello's motor functions in all four extremities. Her left hand grip had returned to normal. The strength in both legs was normal as was the strength in both arms; but the right hand remained weak. Her temperature perception on arms and legs with a hot towel was normal.

Dr. Keller decided that the ... weakness in the right hand, was purely a motor problem rather than a sensory one. She concluded that the cause of the weakness in the right hand was the tetany which in turn resulted from the hyperventilation. She felt strengthened in that conclusion by the improvement in all the extremities which, with the exception of the right hand, had returned to normal. She fully expected that the right hand would also improve.

By this time Mrs. Ciarlariello had ceased moving; she was quiet and co-operative. She had responded unhesitatingly to questions during the examination of her arms and legs. Dr. Keller then explained to Mrs. Ciarlariello that one more area needed investigation and this would require another five minutes of the test procedure. Dr. Keller asked her if she wished the test completed and she replied, "Please go ahead."

Dr. Keller, administered the final injection. Mrs. Ciarlariello suffered an immediate reaction to the injection of the dye which rendered her a quadriplegic. Dr. Keller testified that such a reaction was extremely rare and that never, before or since, had she seen such a reaction.

Mrs. Ciarlariello brought an action in the Supreme Court of Ontario against the respondent physicians. ...

In the present case, there can be no doubt that the doctors involved conducted themselves in an exemplary manner. ... The only ... question is whether Mrs. Ciarlariello's withdrawal of her consent during the second angiogram required the doctors to repeat their complete explanations concerning this procedure in order to obtain her consent to proceed. In general terms, the question can be put in this way: to what extent must disclosure be made to the patient who, during the course of a procedure, withdraws consent, in order to resume the procedure with the informed consent of the patient? In order to answer that question, it will be necessary to first consider the effect of the withdrawal of consent....

...[G]enerally if there is any question as to whether the patient is attempting to withdraw consent, it will be incumbent upon the doctor to ascertain whether the consent has in fact been withdrawn. ... If, during the course of a medical procedure a patient withdraws the consent to that procedure, then the doctors must halt the process. This duty to stop does no more than recognize every individual's basic right to make decisions concerning his or her own body....

...[I]f it is found that the consent is effectively withdrawn during the course of the proceeding then it must be terminated. This must be the result except in those circumstances where the medical evidence suggests that to terminate the process would be either life threatening or pose immediate and serious problems to the health of the patient....

If sedatives or other medication were administered to the patient then it must be determined if the patient was so sedated or so affected by the medication that consent to the procedure could not effectively have been withdrawn. The question whether a patient is capable of withdrawing consent will depend on the circumstances of each case....

Once a patient withdraws consent to the procedure the question then becomes under what circumstances a valid consent to the continuation of the process can be given. ...

There is no doubt that when a patient is lying on a table and is in the very process of undergoing a surgical procedure, it is not the most desirable point at which to obtain their consent to the continuation of that procedure. Obviously, doctors should avoid obtaining consents under such circumstances. It is difficult, however, to determine beforehand what they should do when such a scenario arises. ...

The appropriate approach is ... to focus on what the patient would like to know concerning the continuation of the process once the consent has been withdrawn. Looking at it objectively, a patient would want to know whether there had been any significant change in the risks involved or in the need for the continuation of this process which had become apparent during the course of the procedure. In addition, the patient will want to know if there has been a material change in circumstances which could alter the patient's assessment of the costs or benefits of continuing the procedure. ... Changes may arise during the course of the procedure which are not at all relevant to the issue of consent. Yet, the critical question will always be whether the patient would want to have the information pertaining to those changes in order to decide whether to continue....

There had been no significant change in circumstances since the procedure had been stopped. ... There were no additional factors which had arisen which needed to be brought to the attention of the patient. Mrs. Ciarlariello was, therefore, capable of giving her consent to the continuation of the procedure based on the earlier disclosures. This she did....

...[T]he trial judge very carefully considered the ability of Mrs. Ciarlariello to comprehend the medical information.... He took into account Mrs. Ciarlariello's difficulties with the English language, and the stress that she was undergoing. ... [A]lthough a translator was not present during the angiogram, in light of her demonstrated ability to adequately comprehend the language, it was appropriate to conclude that Mrs. Ciarlariello had given a valid consent to the continuation of the procedure....

The appellants' action against the respondents in battery must fail....

The appellants' action in negligence must also fail. When a patient withdraws consent during a procedure to its continuation the procedure must be stopped unless to do so would seriously endanger the patient. However, the patient may still consent to the renewal or continuation of the process. That consent must also be informed. Although it may not be necessary that the doctors review with the patient all the risks involved in the procedure, the patient must be advised of any material change in the risks which has arisen and would be involved in continuing the process. In addition, the patient must be informed of any material change in the circumstances which could alter his or her assessment of the costs or benefits of continuing the procedure. Here, there had been no material change in the circumstances and a valid consent was given to the continuation of the process....

Accordingly, the appeal must be dismissed.

FURTHER READINGS

Donagan, Alan. "Informed Consent in Therapy and Experimentation." *The Journal of Medicine and Philosophy* 2:4 (December 1977) 319.

Faden, Ruth R. and Tom L. Beauchamp. *A History and Theory of Informed Consent.* New York and Oxford: Oxford University Press, 1986.

Ingelfinger, Franz J. "Informed (But Uneducated) Consent." *The New England Journal of Medicine* 287 (August 31, 1972) 465–466.

Kelly v. Hazlett (1976), 15 O.R. (2d) 290, 1 C.C.L.T.1, 75 D.L.R. (3d) 536 (H.C.).

Kluge, E.-H. W. *Biomedical Ethics in the Canadian Context.* Prentice Hall: Scarborough, Ont., 1991, Chapter 7.

Law Reform Commission of Canada. Working Paper 26, *Medical Treatment and the Criminal Law.* Ottawa: Queen's Printer, 1980.

Mallary, S.D., B. Gert and C.M. Culver. "Family Coercion and Valid Consent." *Theoretical Medicine* 7:2 (1986) 123-126.

Mulloy v. HopSang, (1935) W.W.R. 714 (Alberta Supreme Court, App.Div).

Patenaude, Andrea Farkas, Joel M. Rappeport and Brian R. Smith. "Physician's Influence on Informed Consent for Bone Marrow Transplantation." *Theoretical Medicine* 7(1986) 165–179.

Picard, E. *Legal Liability of Doctors and Hospitality in Canada.* Toronto: Carswell, 1984, Chapter 3, "Consent."

Salgo v. Leyland Stanford, Jr., University Board of Trustees (1957), 317 p. 2d., 270.

Somerville, M. *Consent to Medical Care.* Study Paper for the Law Reform Commission of Canada (Ottawa, 1980).

CHAPTER 7
CONSENT AND THE INCOMPETENT PATIENT

INTRODUCTION

The last selection in the previous chapter touched on the issue of competence. This notion is very important when it comes to informed consent. The paradigm case of informed consent involves a health care professional and someone who is adult, who can understand what is being said, and who can react appropriately. However, many times the patient is not competent in that sense. For instance, the patient may be a young child, or someone who is physiologically mature but mentally severely disabled. In these sorts of cases, someone has to make the decision for the incompetent person. But who?

Traditionally, it was assumed that the family or next-of-kin played that role. With the rise of modern medicine, as the decision-making function was gradually assumed by the physician even in ordinary contexts, it became the practice to let the physician assume the role of decision-maker for incompetent persons. In the last 20 years, the pendulum has swung the other way. The family has again become the primary decision-maker for incompetent persons.

However, the family may not always function appropriately in this regard. The case of *re S.D.*, excerpts from which are reproduced below, illustrates the court's concerns in this regard.

In his article, Eike-Henner W. Kluge examines some of the difficulties that attend a purely legally oriented approach to proxy decision making. The matter is explored further by Christine Harrison, Nuala P. Kenny, Mona Sidarous and Mary Rowell who address some recent developments in the ethics of informed consent concerning children. Traditionally it had been believed that children are by definition incompetent and cannot give (or refuse) consent to health care. The last few years have seen a change in this perspective. There are several reasons for this. First, Section 15 of the Charter of Rights and Freedoms explicitly prohibits discrimination on the basis of age. Second, Canadian case law has recognized for some time the category of a *mature* or *emancipated minor* who, although under the age of majority, nevertheless was able to make all sorts of decisions—including health care decisions—on her or his own behalf. Third, ethical analysis of the notion of competence and of the right to self-determination has suggested that the ability to make health care decisions does not inherently depend on age but on maturity, the ability to comprehend and reason, and the possession of appropriate values. While younger children may lack these qualities, as they become older this changes and they steadily increase in their decision-making capabilities.

These developments have led to a reevaluation of the legal perspective on decision making by children[1] and to a redrafting of the relevant provincial statutes. The article by Harrison, Kenny, Sidarous and Rowell explores some of the implications of this change for decision making in the acute-care setting. It comes to the conclusion that even though a child may not be fully competent, if at all possible the wishes of the child should nevertheless be respected.[2] It may be interesting to compare the position on saving the life of a child as stated by the Court in *re S.D.*[3] with the perspective advanced in this article. It may also be interesting to explore how well it accords with the position adopted by Tri-Council in its Code of Ethical Conduct for Research Involving Human Subjects.[4]

NOTES

1. *Re L.D.K.* (1985) R.F.L. (2d) 164. This is a case where wishes of a 12-year-old to refuse transfusions that were necessary for chemotherapy to be effective were respected. A similar position on the rights of competent children to accept or refuse medical treatment was taken by the courts in *re Y.A.* (19.7.1993) (Nfld.S.C. [Unif. Fam. Ct.]).

2. For another intersting discussion of volitional competence in children, see X. Plaus and B.R. Brissenden, "On adolescence and informed consent," *Health Law in Canada* 14(3),1994: 68-73.

3. See *infra.*

4. See *infra,* chapter 10.

Re S.D.

The subject of these proceedings is a severely retarded boy approaching 7 years, who shortly after birth suffered profound brain damage through meningitis which inflamed the lining of his brain and left him with no control over his faculties, limbs or bodily func-

---

Re S.D. (1983) 3 W.W.R. 618 (B.C.S.C.).

tions. At the age of 5 months life-support surgery was performed by implanting a shunt which is a plastic tube which drains excess cerebro-spinal fluid from the head to another body cavity from which it is expelled or absorbed.

As perceived by his parents the boy is legally blind, with atrophied optic nerves, partly deaf, incontinent, cannot hold a spoon to feed himself, cannot stand, walk, talk or hold objects. They say that he has no method of communicating with his environment and think he is in pain. The sounds he makes are too soft to be heard from any distance. He is subject to seizures despite anti-convulsant medication. He is restrained by splints which are bandages on his arms to keep his elbows straight so that he cannot chew on his hands and roughly handle his face. Staff carry him from bed to wheelchair, which has a molded "insert" to ensure he is held securely and he is belted in with a hip belt.

This description applies to his condition as it existed when he was a patient in Sunnyhill Hospital before the shunt stopped operating. About 6 weeks ago a blockage in the shunt was detected and the parents gave their consent to remedial surgery but, after a day's reflection, withdrew their consent on the ground that the boy should be allowed to die with dignity rather than continue to endure a life of suffering. They continue to maintain that position.

Because of the parent's refusal the Superintendent of Family and Child Service … considered this child "in need of protection" and acted … to apprehend him. …

Following apprehension, the Superintendent, … presented a written report to the Provincial Court of British Columbia and asked for an order that the custody of the child be retained by him pending a hearing to determine whether the child was in need of protection. Following 5 days of hearing and a weekend's contemplation and writing, the Provincial Court Judge read in open court a 29-page oral judgment on 14 March 1983 which ordered the Superintendent to return the child to his parent's custody. The Judge identified the issue as:

> … who may exercise an incompetent's right to refuse life sustaining treatment if no directive exists and the incompetent is unable to do so?

The Judge appears to have held that this right belongs in the family, in consultation with their medical advisors. Where treatment would serve "only to prolong a life inflicted with an incurable condition" rather than cure or improve the patient's condition, the interest of the state in the preservation of life is overridden by the wishes of the people whose duty it is to make the decision.

Adopting the distinction between treatment that "cures" and treatment that simply "prolongs life where there is no hope of recovery" the Judge found that the shunt revision fell into the latter category.

The Judge found that the shunt revision in S.'s case constituted an "extraordinary surgical intervention," and not "necessary medical attention." Since S. was therefore not deprived of "necessary medical attention" there was no basis for the belief that S. was not a "well-cared-for and loved child," and she concluded that she should order that he be returned to his parents under s.11(2)(b) of the Family and Child Service Act. S.11 sets out the procedure for review of the Superintendent's decision to apprehend a child pending a hearing on the question of whether the child is in need of protection. The Judge also held that the shunt revision would constitute a violation of S.'s right not to be subjected to cruel and unusual treatment under s.12 of the Canadian Charter of Rights and Freedoms. …

I think that the Superintendent's petition is accurate in contending that the learned Judge:

1) Held that a life saving operation does not amount to necessary medical attention as defined in s.1.

2) Did not consider as paramount the safety and well-being of the child as required in s.2.

3) Held that the shunt revision constituted cruel and unusual punishment under s.12 of the Canadian Charter of Rights and Freedoms.

4) Did not consider s. 7 of the Charter.

By referring to the proceedings in Provincial Court and to the disposition of those proceedings I have done so for narrative reasons only because, as I conceive it, the *parens patriae* jurisdiction of the Supreme Court in this matter takes precedence over the proceedings in Provincial Court and allows this court to act as if the matter came before it in the first instance. Confirmation of this view is contained in s.21 of the Act.

Nothing in this Act limits the inherent jurisdiction of the Crown, through the Supreme Court, over infants, as parens patriae, and the Supreme Court may rescind a permanent order where it is satisfied that to do so is conducive to a child's best interest and welfare.

...

In considering the application of the *parens patriae* jurisdiction I recognize that the central concern is to discover what is in S.'s best interest. This is not a "right to die" situation where the courts are concerned with people who are terminally ill from incurable conditions. Rather it is a question of whether S. has the right to receive appropriate medical and surgical care of a relatively simple kind which will assure to him the continuation of his life, such as it is.

I am satisfied that the laws of our society are structured to preserve, protect and maintain human life and that in the exer-cise of its inherent jurisdiction this court could not sanction the termination of a life except for the most coercive reasons. The presumption must be in favour of life. Neither could this court sanction the wilful withholding of surgical therapy where such withholding could result not necessarily in death but in a prolongation of life for an indeterminate time but in a more impoverished and more agonizing form.

I do not think that it lies within the prerogative of any parent or of this court to look down upon a disadvantaged person and judge the quality of that person's life to be so low as not to be deserving of continuance.

The matter was well put in an American decision — *re Weberlist* (1974), 360 N.Y.S. (2d) 783, 79 Misc. 2d 753 (N.Y. Co, Ct.), where Justice Asch said at p. 787:

> There is a strident cry in America to terminate the lives of other people — deemed physically or mentally defective.... Assuredly, one test of civilization is its concern with the survival of the unfittest, a reversal of Darwin's formulation.... In this case, the court must decide what its ward would choose, if he were in a position to make a sound judgment. ...

This last sentence puts it right. It is not appropriate for an external decision-maker to apply his standards of what constitutes a livable life and exercise the right to impose death if that standard is not met in his estimation. The decision can only be made in the context of the disabled person viewing the worthwhileness or otherwise of his life in its own context as a disabled person — and in that context he would not compare his life with that of a person enjoying normal advantages. He would know nothing of a normal person's life having never experienced it.

...

I respect and have given anxious consideration to the views of the parents. In so doing I must give some weight to the fact that they were divorced in mid-1980 after extended matrimonial discord. Also I must give weight to my conclusion based on the evidence that they thought S. better dead long before the need for the critical decision arose about replacement of the shunt. Despite the evidence of highly qualified professionals, in whom I place great reliance, they are satisfied S. will promptly die if treatment is denied. My finding is that it is by no means a certainty that death will soon follow and a real possibility exists that his life will go on indefinitely but in pain and progressive deterioration. I must reject their assertion that they would consent to the operation if they could be assured that he would thereafter be comfortable and free of pain when at the same time they reject the opinions of competent professionals that such will probably be the case. I believe that their minds are firmly made up and closed shut.

I regret having to make such findings.

Further, I find that the professionals who have been treating and observing S. since late 1982 are better qualified than they are to assess his condition and capacities because they, the parents, have hardly seen him. I do not criticize them for this but simply observe it as a fact.

I cannot accept their view that S. would be better off dead. If it is to be decided that "it is in the best interests of S. that his existence cease," then it must be decided that, for him, non-existence is the better alternative. This would mean regarding the life of a handicapped child as not only less valuable than the life of a normal child, but so much less valuable that it is not worth preserving. I tremble at contemplating the consequences if the lives of disabled persons are dependent upon such judgments.

To refer back to the words of Templeman, L.J., I cannot in conscience find that this is a case of severe proved damage "where the future is so certain and where the life of the child is so bound to be full of pain and suffering that the court might be driven to a different conclusion." I am not satisfied that "the life of this child is demonstrably going to be so awful that in effect the child must be condemned to die." Rather I believe that "the life of this child is still so imponderable that it would be wrong for her to be condemned to die."

There is not a simple choice here of allowing the child to live or die according to whether the shunt is implanted or not. There looms the awful possibility that without the shunt the child will endure in a state of progressing disability and pain. It is too simplistic to say that the child should be allowed to die in peace.

In conclusion I order that interim custody be granted to the Superintendent pending a hearing pursuant to s.13 of the Family and Child Service Act and while in that interim custody the surgical procedure be carried out pursuant to the authority of this court. The matter is remitted to the Provincial Court for the s.13 hearing.

After "Eve": Whither Proxy Decision Making?

Eike-Henner W. Kluge

One of the most difficult situations that physicians may face is one involving an incompetent patient. Normally, following what could be called a fiduciary model of the physician-patient relationship, physicians may feel that they have fulfilled their professional obligation when they have advised the patient of the various pertinent modalities of treatment, expressed an opinion and made a recommendation, and have done all this in language that the patient can and does understand. Whatever decision the patient then makes will be legally and ethically acceptable. If it should not accord with the physician's own better judgement, he or she may of course attempt to reason and persuade but not coerce; and all other things being equal, the physician may not overrule the patient's determination. *Reibl v. Hughes*[1] is very clear on that point. If all else fails and the physician cannot in good conscience accept the patient's decision, there is always the option of referring the patient to another physician and withdrawing from the case.[2] At no point, however, with the exceptions of emergency and therapeutic privilege, is the physician called on to assume the role of proxy decision-maker or to examine the ethical acceptability of the decision itself.

The case of the incompetent patient, however, is different. Here the physician must assume an evaluative role. As front-line workers, so to speak, physicians have to examine the way in which the proxy decision-makers — usually the next-of-kin — make the decision in order to assure themselves that it is the product of reflective consideration and not the offhand result of a hasty reaction. Furthermore, they must consider the criteria used by the proxy decision-makers in reaching the decision in order to make sure that they do not simply reflect the proxies' own standards, feelings or expectations but rather are ethically appropriate. When there is any doubt, the physician must engage the appropriate administrative or legal channels to prevent what may be an unacceptable exercise of proxy authority.[3]

To some degree, of course, this is a matter of subjective assessment on the part of the physician, but not entirely so. In cases in which the patient was once competent but is competent no longer, the physician will balance the quality of life expected from the various treatment options against the wishes and expectations expressed by the patient when competent in order to assess the reasonableness or acceptability of the particular proxy decision. The testimony of next-of-kin as well as formal and informal data to which the physician may have access will provide invaluable assistance. As to situations in which there is no evidence that the patient expressed preferences when competent, the physician will proceed on the basis of the quality-of-life standards that are currently accepted by the ordinary person, standards that are based not on the concept of social utility (whether defined within the ambit of the immediate family or social grouping or

Eike-Henner W. Kluge, "After 'Eve': Whither proxy decision making?" — Reprinted from, by permission of the publisher, *Canadian Medical Association Journal*, 137 (October 15, 1987) 715-720.

drawn more widely to include society as a whole) but rather on criteria that flow from the concept of the patient as a person. The physician will take into account the distinction between the continuation or sustaining of merely biologic life and support of the patient as a person who has (or retains the capacity for) sapient cognitive awareness and the possibility of meaningful social interaction.[4] Again, while this will involve a certain amount of subjectivity on the part of the physician, it need not and does not occur in complete isolation. Physicians can draw on the more or less standard perception of quality of life that prevails in society and are aided by their sensitivity to the cost of the various treatment options to the patient in purely human terms. Their professional knowledge of the nature and likelihood of the outcomes expected from the various modalities of treatment is invaluable, as is their awareness of what other, competent patients under similar circumstances have decided. Together, all this gives the physician a fairly good idea of what the ordinary reasonable person would decide under similar circumstances and provides a basis against which to measure the proxy decision. And although this sort of approach may present difficulties on occasion, it generally is workable and presents no serious ethical problems.

As to the case of the currently incompetent patient who never has been competent but in all likelihood will become competent in the future — i.e., an otherwise normal child — it, too, does not present the physician with fundamentally new issues. The physician will proceed on the assumption that, all other things being equal, the child's sensible experience and qualitative perception of the world is essentially like that of an adult and that the factor of incompetence involves the cognitive and judgemental plane. It is therefore entirely appropriate for the physician to take into account the child's subjective expressions (insofar as they are present or available) and balance them against the objective standard of what a reasonable person would decide when considering the proxy decision. The function of the proxy is to supply the cognitive and judgemental want of the child. Consequently, if the physician finds that the proxy decision-maker has introduced his or her own non-standard values in making the decision, the physician must challenge the decision. The situation becomes a little more complicated when the child has given assent in a particular direction, but even here it is not a matter of purely subjective evaluation. The assent must be seen as guiding, although not necessarily determining, depending on the facts of the cases.[5,6] Finally, in all cases of doubt, the courts must be the ultimate forum of appeal.

THE RADICALLY CONGENITALLY INCOMPETENT PATIENT

The case of the congenitally incompetent patient who, so far as medical science can tell, not only is barely at the limits of sapient cognitive awareness but also in all probability will never become competent, is radically different. The sort of balancing of subjective expression against an objective standard that can at least be attempted in other cases seems inappropriate here. This is so not because the patient is not reasonable — no incompetent patient is — but because the presumption on which such balancing is based may be false in such cases. The quality of life of the radically congenitally incompetent patient may be so fundamentally different from the norm that both the use of the objective standard of what a reasonable person would decide as a balance and the attempt to use the patient's own subjective expression would be untoward. The very significance of the latter may be fundamentally misconstrued because it would be based on the world experience of the physician, someone who fits the norm of the reasonable person. Consequently, there exists a danger that the use of the objective standard would violate the individuality of the patient and that the attempt to circumvent this by using subjective indicators from the patient would be so out of line with his or her actual experience that any treatment decision based on these criteria would be experienced as cruel and unusual treatment.[7,8]

If this is true, the physician who monitors proxy decisions made for radically congenitally incompetent patients is faced with a serious problem: What criteria — indeed, what evaluative approach — ought he or she to apply?

THE STEPHEN DAWSON DECISION

It was at least in part for this reason that the 1983 British Columbia Supreme Court decision *Re Stephen Dawson*[9] was welcomed by some members of the medical community. The case concerned a 7-year-old boy who had contracted meningitis shortly after birth, suffered severe brain damage and become hydrocephalic and as a consequence was exceedingly retarded, with no control over his faculties or limbs. At 5 months of age a shunt had been inserted and had been revised over the years, and at the time of application to the courts revision was again required. The reason for the court intervention was that the parents, as proxy decision-maker, had initially agreed to the revision, but after taking into account what they considered to be appropriate quality-of-life considerations from the perspective of the ordinary person — considerations involving the capac-

ity for sapient cognitive awareness, the possibility of relatively pain-free and physically comfortable existence, and the potential for meaningful social interaction — and after consultation with a pediatric neurosurgeon they had withdrawn their permission. The superintendent of child welfare for the province intervened, and the matter came to trial in provincial court. The test used by the court to evaluate the parents' decision was whether, under the circumstances, the proposed revision constituted extraordinary treatment. The court decided in the affirmative and held in favour of the parents. On appeal to the British Columbia Supreme Court, the decision was reversed and an order for treatment was made. Stephen subsequently received treatment and continues to live.

It was the reasoning stated by the British Columbia Supreme Court that made the decision so important for the medical community. For the first time in Canadian medicolegal history the courts issued a ruling that explicitly addressed the question of what criteria and approach a proxy decision-maker and a physician should use when dealing with a congenitally incompetent person. Mr. Justice L. McKenzie, who decided the issue, ruled 1) that a congenitally incompetent person does not lose the rights to health care normally enjoyed by other persons simply in virtue of his or her incompetence; 2) that the duty of exercising this right normally rests in the parents as appropriate proxy decision-makers; 3) that their decision-making authority is appropriately challenged when it is not exercised in the best interests of the incompetent person; and 4) that what counts as being in the best interests of the incompetent person must not be determined from the point of view of the objective reasonable person. Rather, 5) it must be determined from the perspective of the incompetent person. As Judge McKenzie put it, "I do not think that it lies within the prerogative of any parent or of this court to look down upon a disadvantaged person and judge the quality of that person's life to be so low as not to be deserving of continuance." Quoting with approval Judge Asch in the U.S. case *In the Matter of Eugene Weberlist* ("In this case, the court must decide what its ward would choose, if he were in a position to make a sound judgment.") he went on to say:

> This last sentence puts it right. It is not appropriate for an external decision-maker to apply his standards of what constitutes a livable life and exercise the right to impose death if that standard is not met in his estimation. The decision can only be made in the context of the disabled person viewing the worthwhileness or otherwise of his life in its own context as a disabled person — and in that context he would not compare his life with that of a person enjoying normal advantages. He would know nothing of a normal person's life having never experienced it.

In adopting this position, Judge McKenzie was enunciating what had become known as a substituted-judgement approach to proxy decision making for congenitally incompetent persons. As one U.S. commentator put it, proxy decision-makers should try to put themselves as much as possible into the situation of the incompetent person and then decide in the way and from the perspective from which the latter would decide, were he or she able.[10]

The Stephen Dawson case injected an element of clarity into the Canadian context. The Canadian physician faced with the question of how to proceed in these sorts of cases now had definite guidelines on how to interpret "best interests" considerations and evaluate the appropriateness of a particular proxy decision. However, while definitive and clarifying, Judge McKenzie's decision was not without problems, some of which I pointed out at the time.[11] In the context of proxy decision making the most important problem was the concept of a substituted-judgement approach itself. As I said then, the demand that the perspective of the congenitally incompetent person should constitute the basis of quality-of-life considerations by the proxy decision-maker and that any acceptance or rejection of medical treatment should be grounded on this basis is not only unworkable in practical terms but also and, indeed above all, logically incoherent. If the incompetent person lacks sapient cognitive awareness — or, less severely, if he or she lacks any standards or criteria — then, trivially, neither standards nor criteria can be ascribed to the person. That fact is definitive of the situation in which such people find themselves and characterizes their very nature. It is therefore logically impossible to determine what their wishes are or would be if they could make them known. To proceed otherwise is to do one of two things: to assume that despite this lack they have standards or criteria after all — a flat contradiction — or to project some other standards or criteria into the situation by substitution and thereby treat incompetent people as though they were not incompetent. In either case, however, the very concept of substituted judgement, of viewing the situation from the perspective of the incompetent person, "in its own context," is a fiction.

If this analysis was correct, the position of the physician faced with a congenitally incompetent patient was not improved but rather was worsened by the Stephen Dawson case: uncertainty over how to proceed had indeed been replaced by certainty, but at the price of logical impossibility.

THE CASE OF "EVE"

Then came *Eve v. Mrs. E.,*[12] which altered the whole picture. On the facts, the case was entirely different from that of Stephen

Dawson. "Eve" was a 24-year-old moderately retarded woman suffering from extreme expressive aphasia. She was described to the courts as an extremely pleasant and affectionate person who, being physically adult, was capable of being attractive to and attracted by men. Her mother, of advancing years, feared that Eve might become pregnant, and since Eve was unable to take care of a child, the mother saw herself faced with the prospect of having to care for Eve's progeny. She found this unmanageable. She also felt that both pregnancy and childbirth would be incomprehensible to Eve. Consequently, acting as proxy decision-maker, she requested that Eve be sterilized.

The court of first instance rejected the request. It ruled that except for clinically therapeutic reasons, parents or other appropriate proxy decision-makers could not give valid proxy consent to such a procedure. On appeal to the Supreme Court of Prince Edward Island, the judgement was reversed and sterilization by hysterectomy was ordered. However, leave was granted to appeal the decision to the Supreme Court of Canada. On Oct. 23, 1986, that court handed down its ruling. It reinstated the trial court's order and rejected sterilization. Mr. Justice La Forest, writing the unanimous decision of the court, gave two reasons. One dealt with the historical nature of the *parens patriae* powers of the court. Here the thrust of Mr. Justice La Forest's deliberations was that these powers could be exercised only in the best interests of the incompetent person, no matter what the position of society or next-of-kin. The second reason was an attempt to clarify the way in which such best interests could be determined. He here focused on the position advanced by the attorneys for Mrs. E. They had argued that as proxy decision-maker Mrs. E. had the duty to exercise Eve's rights for her and had argued further that, indeed, these rights ought to be exercised on the basis of what would be in Eve's best interests. However,

they insisted that Eve's best interests could be determined only in a subjective fashion: by approximating as closely as possible the kind of situation in which Eve found herself and then making the kind of decision that she herself would make. In other words, they reasoned that a "substituted-judgement" approach to the determination of "best interests" would be appropriate "because it places a higher value on the individuality of the incompetent person."[12] Using such an approach, they argued, would result in a decision for sterilization.

For the purposes of this essay, it is irrelevant whether the logic of Mrs. E.'s position is valid. What is important is the court's reaction to the line of reasoning. While accepting the concept of best interests as appropriate, the court roundly rejected the contention that best interests could be appropriately determined with the substituted-judgement approach. In fact, the court brusquely rejected the concept of substituted judgement itself. Substituted judgement, it reasoned, is an attempt to determine what choice the incompetent person would make were he or she able. However, the court stated,[12]

> Choice presupposes that a person has the mental competence to make it. It may be a matter of debate whether a court should have the power to make the decision if that person lacks the mental capacities to do so. But it is obviously a fiction to suggest that a decision so made is that of the incompetent, however much the court may try to put itself in her place. What the incompetent would do if she or he could make a choice is simply a matter of speculation.

Mr. Justice La Forest went on to speak of "the sophistry embodied in the argument favouring substituted judgment" and quoted with approval from *Matter of Eberhardy* (a U.S. case), in which the court had stated[13]:

We conclude that the question is not choice because it is sophistry to refer to it as such, but rather the question is whether there is a method by which others, acting on behalf of the person's best interests and in the interests, such as they may be, of the state, can exercise the decision.

Neither the U.S. court nor the Supreme Court of Canada went on to detail such a method. They agreed in their focus on best interests considerations. One thing, however, was clear: by characterizing the substituted-judgement approach as legal "legerdemain," the Supreme Court effectively ruled out the very test enjoined by the Stephen Dawson case.

Of course, it could be argued that all this holds only for sterilization, that it leaves all other cases unaffected. That, however, is unlikely for three reasons. First, it would contradict the very *raison d'être* of Supreme Court decisions. They are, and are supposed to be, models for general types of cases. While *Eve v. Mrs. E.* is representative of sterilization cases, it is also and, indeed, above all representative of a type of case that deals with the problem of proxy decision making for incompetent people. All cases of proxy decision for such people are thereby affected. The fact that the court itself saw it in this light is evidenced by the fact that the precedential cases it considered and cited in reaching its decision were drawn from a whole spectrum of cases proposing medical procedures for incompetent people, not only those advocating sterilization. Second, the fact that the Supreme Court intended its decision to have wider ambit is indicated by the fact that its rejection of substituted judgement is not explicitly directed to sterilization cases. It is couched independently of that issue in response to the argument that a substituted-judgement approach as such "is to be preferred to the best interests test because it places a higher value on the individuality of the mentally incompetent person."[12] In other words, it was a reply to the argument that because the substituted-judgement approach is the appropriate test for incompetent people in general, it should also be used in this case. It is to this general claim that the court replied in the negative. Its rejection, therefore, has general implications. Finally, there is this to consider. Undoubtedly there are many strands intertwined in this case. However, to construe the rejection of substituted judgement in a limited fashion is to ascribe to the Supreme Court the position that different principles of law and of ethics hold for the very same problem — proxy decision making — in different material cases. Not only would that undermine the very notion of the uniformity of legal and ethical principles, but also it lacks basis in any of the court's dicta.

I suggest, therefore, that *Eve v. Mrs. E.* ought to be seen as having general import. But if that is the case, it presents the Canadian physician with a problem: How to interpret best interests? The fact that the court recalled with approval Lord Eldon's remarks in *Wellesley v. Wellesley* ("It has always been the principle of this court, not to risk damage to children ... which it cannot repair"[12]) may be considered guiding. However, that merely pushes the interpretational uncertainty onto the word "damage." Did the court intend this to apply to physiologic damage only, or did it intend to encompass psychologic, mental and emotional deficit as well as other repercussions? There are indications that it intended the wider construal; for example, it inveighed against a "grave intrusion on the physical and mental integrity of the person"[12] and included "health problems, religious upbringing and protection against harmful association."[12] But we do lack a really explicit statement.

The physician is thus once again left in a domain of uncertainty. Only three — negative — guidelines are clear: physicians may not use a substituted-judgement approach to evaluate the appropriateness of proxy decisions; they may not accept a decision based on the proxy decision-maker's own idiosyncratic standards; and they may not use their own values, standards and expectations.

ATTEMPT AT A RESOLUTION

However, both the reasoning advanced in *Re Stephen Dawson* and that given in *Eve v. Mrs. E.* do point in the direction in which more positive criteria may be sought.[14] These stem not from the assumption of equality of life experience, which is the contentious concept, but from the assumption that whatever his or her handicap, the radically and congenitally incompetent patient is still a person. If this assumption is true — and here only incontrovertible evidence of the permanent lack of capability for sapient cognitive awareness can count as an indication to the contrary — that patient has the same panoply of rights as all other persons. More important, it follows that he or she must be treated as a person in all respects. This in turn means that the quality of life that the patient faces in the future as well as the quality at the present time, while it may be admitted to differ in degree of sophistication from that of the competent person, nevertheless cannot be held to differ in kind: no matter what the difference in degree, the quality itself, in its very nature, must be that of a person. This, however, immediately entails that the evaluative criteria that are appropriate in the case of all other persons must be applied here as well. Not, of course, in a straightforward fashion. That would be to ignore the difference in degree between the

respective qualities of life. Rather, what it means is that the physician must use the quality of life of an otherwise healthy person with similar type and degree of incompetence as an evaluative baseline and consider the relative changes that would result in that quality under the various treatment options being considered. In this it is appropriate for the physician to take into account the incompetent person's subjective expressions of satisfaction with physical life, the psychologic affect and other attendant factors, and balance these against the likelihood of retention of or improvement in sapient cognitive awareness, the possibility of meaningful social interaction at that level and the cost of the various options to the patient in purely human terms. Let us call this a comparative quality-of-life coefficient. The physician must then do a similar evaluation, with due alteration of detail, for an ordinary competent patient with a similar medical problem to determine what the comparative quality-of-life coefficient would be in his or her case. The physician must then compare the two coefficients. If, on balance, the comparative quality-of-life coefficient for the incompetent patient is the same as or higher than that for the competent patient, and if in the case of the latter the decision would normally be in favour of treatment (or of some specific form of treatment), the decision must be in favour of treatment for the incompetent patient as well. If the proxy decision-maker's decision is against treatment, the physician must oppose it, if necessary through administrative and judicial channels. In all other cases, he or she need not.

This way of approaching the problem provides a procedure that can be implemented in practice. At the same time, however — or perhaps precisely because of this — it allows us to reconcile *Eve v. Mrs. E.* with *Re Stephen Dawson*. For, in this way, Judge McKenzie's injunction to consider the situation of the radically congenitally incompetent person in the "context of the disabled person" can be given an interpretation that avoids the sophistry of substituted judgement while satisfying Mr. Justice La Forest's conclusion that the "best interests" of the person should be guiding.

A FINAL PROBLEM

At the same time, however, the case of Eve leaves the health care professional with a problem. The considerations that I have sketched are appropriate from the perspective of the incompetent person and under the *parens patriae* powers of the court. Ethically, however, they are insufficient. Medical decisions, after all, are not made in a vacuum, nor can health care decisions be reached in isolation from the overall context in which they must be implemented. The resources that will be involved in health care decisions and their distribution have ineluctable social implications. It is here that *Eve v. Mrs. E.* fails. By being focused narrowly within the *parens patriae* doctrine as traditionally understood, the decision paints an unrealistic picture. The rights of the incompetent person must never be less than those of the competent person solely by virtue of their incompetence, to be sure. However, justice and equality demand that they not be more either. It is ethically unacceptable to engage in reverse discrimination

that accords a favoured ethical status to the incompetent person solely by virtue of his or her incompetence. That, however, would in fact occur if the powers of Eve's rights, as captured in the best-interests clause as expressed in the judgement, were to be given automatic precedence over the rights of others; if, in the words of Mr. Justice La Forest, we were to "sympathize with Mrs. E." but insist, as he did, that in cases such as these only the rights of the incompetent person are decisive.[12] The point of *Eve v. Mrs. E.* and analogous court actions surely is to insist that the rights of the incompetent person must be given due weight because incompetent people are persons. That, however, also means that with due alteration of detail their rights must be treated as subject to the same balancing process to which the rights of all other persons are subject under similar conditions. By rejecting the weight of the competing rights of Mrs. E. and the rest of society, Mr. Justice La Forest has created a special class of persons who are immune from the restrictive and balancing considerations that apply to everyone else. This seems to suggest that the physician who monitors proxy decisions for such people must refrain from taking into account the considerations of equity and justice that guide the allocation of resources in all other cases. Not only are the ethics of this highly questionable, but also it may lead to a distributive nightmare.

NOTES

1. *Reibl v. Hughes,* 14 CCLT 1 (SCC 1980).
2. *Code of Ethics,* Can Med Assoc, Ottawa, 1978: 15.
3. Dickens, B.: The role of the family in surrogate medical consent. *Health Law Can* 1980; 1 (3): 49-52.
4. Keyserlingk, E.W.: Sanctity of life or quality of life. In *The Context of Ethics, Medicine and Law,* Law Reform Commission of Canada, Ottawa, 1979: 49-72.

5. McCormick, R.A.: Proxy consent in the experimentation situation. *Perspect Biol Med* 1974; 18: 2-20.

6. Ramsey, P.: *The Patient As Person,* Yale U Pr, New Haven, Conn., 1970: 1-58.

7. *Superintendent of Belchertown State School v. Saikewicz,* 370 NE (2d) 417 (Mass 1977).

8. Annas, G.: Reconciling Quinlan and Saikewicz: decision making for the terminally ill incompetent. *Am J Law Med* 1979; 4: 367-396.

9. *Re Stephen Dawson,* 3 WWR 618 (BC SC 1983) reversing 3 WWR 597 (BC Prov Ct 1983).

10. Annas, G.: The incompetent's right to die: the case of Joseph Saikewicz. *Hastings Cent Rep* 1978; 8 (1): 21-23.

11. Kluge, E.-H.W.: In the matter of Stephen Dawson: right v. duty of health care. *Can Med Assoc J* 1983; 129: 815-818.

12. *Eve v. Mrs. E.,* SCC, judgement handed down Oct 23, 1986, SCR 16654.

13. *Matter of Eberhardy,* 307 NW (2d) 881 (Wis 1981).

14. Magnet, J.E., Kluge, E.-H.W.: *Withholding Treatment From Defective Newborn Children,* Brown Legal Pub., Cowansville, PQ, 1985: 3-306.

Involving Children in Medical Decisions

Christine Harrison, Nuala P. Kenny, Mona Sidarous, Mary Rowell

Eleven-year-old Samantha is a bright, loving child who was treated for osteosarcoma in her left arm. The arm had to be amputated, and Samantha was given a course of chemotherapy. She has been cancer-free for 18 months and is doing well in school. She is self-conscious about her prosthesis and sad because she had to give away her cat, Snowy, to decrease her risk of infection. Recent tests indicate that the cancer has recurred and metastasized to her lungs. Her family is devastated by this news but do not want to give up hope. However, even with aggressive treatment Samantha's chances for recovery are less than 20%.

Samantha adamantly refuses her treatment. On earlier occasions she had acquiesced to treatment only to struggle violently when it was administered. She distrusts her health care providers and is angry with them and her parents. She protests, "You already made me give up Snowy and my arm. What more do you want?" Her parents insist that treatment must continue. At the request of her physician, a psychologist and psychiatrist con-

C. Harrison, N.P. Kenny, M. Sidarous and M. Rowell, "Bioethics for clinicians: 9. Involving children in medical decisions" — Reprinted from, by permission of the publisher, *CMAJ* 156:6 (March 15, 1997) 825-828.

duct a capacity assessment. They agree that Samantha is probably incapable of making treatment decisions; her understanding of death is immature and her anxiety level very high. Nursing staff are reluctant to impose treatment; in the past Samantha's struggling and the need to restrain her upset them a great deal.

ETHICS

Traditionally, parents and physicians have made all medical decisions on behalf of children. However, just as the concept of informed consent has developed over the last 30 years with respect to competent adult patients, so new ways of thinking about the role of children in medical decision making have evolved.

Ethical principles that provide guidance in the care of adults are insufficient in the context of caring for children.[1-3] Issues related to the voluntariness of consent, the disclosure of information, capacity assessment, treatment decisions and bereavement are more complex, as is the physician's relationship with the patient and the patient's family.[3,4] Adult models presume that the patient is autonomous and has a stable sense of self, established values and mature cognitive skills; these characteristics are undeveloped or underdeveloped in children.

Although it is important to understand and respect the developing autonomy of a child, and although the duty of beneficence provides a starting point for determining what is in the child's best interest, a family-centred ethic is the best model for understanding the interdependent relationships that bear upon the child's situation.[5] A family-centred approach considers the effects of a decision on all family members, their responsibilities toward one another and the burdens and benefits of a decision for each member, while acknowledging the special vulnerability of the child patient.

A family-centred approach presents special challenges for the health care team, particularly when there is disagreement between parent and child. Such a situation raises profound questions about the nature of the physician-patient relationship in pediatric practice. Integrity in this relationship is fundamental to the achievement of the goal of medicine,[6] which has been defined as "right and good healing action taken in the interest of a particular patient."[7] In the care of adults, the physician's primary relationship is with the particular capable patient. The patient's family may be involved in decision making, but it is usually the patient who defines the bounds of such involvement....

The assumption that parents best understand what's in the interest of their child is usually sound. However, situations can arise in which the parents' distress prevents them from attending carefully to the child's concerns and wishes. Simply complying with the parents' wishes in such cases is inadequate. It is more helpful and respectful of the child to affirm the parents' responsibility for the care of their child while allowing the child to exercise choice in a measure appropriate to his or her level of development and experience of illness and treatment. This approach ... recognizes the child as the particular patient to whom the physician has a primary duty of care.... [and] seeks to harmonize the values of everyone involved in making the decision.[6]

LAW

...The patient's right to refuse even life-saving medical treatment is recognized in Canadian law[8,9] and is premised on the patient's right to exercise control over his or her own body.

... In common law and under the statutory law of some provinces patients are presumed capable regardless of age unless shown otherwise; in other provinces an age at which patients are presumed capable is specified.[10] When a child's capacity is in doubt an assessment is required.

In the case of children who are incapable of making their own health care decisions, parents or legal guardians generally have the legal authority to act as surrogate decision-makers. The surrogate decision-maker is obliged to make treatment decisions in the best interest of the child. Health care providers who believe that a surrogate's decisions are not in the child's best interest can appeal to provincial child welfare authorities. The courts have the authority to assume a *parens patriae* role in treatment decisions if the child is deemed to be in need of protection.... Every province has child welfare legislation that sets out the general parameters of the "best interest" standard. Courts are reluctant to authorize the withholding or withdrawal of medical treatment, especially in the face of parental support for such treatment....

Most children fall into one of three groups with respect to their appropriate involvement in decision making.[11-12]... Preschool children have no significant decision-making capacity and cannot provide their own consent. As surrogate decision-makers, parents should authorize (or refuse authorization) on their child's behalf, basing their decisions on what they believe to be in the child's best interest....

Children of primary-school age may participate in medical decisions but do not have full decision-making capacity. They may indicate their assent or dissent without fully understanding its implications. Nonetheless they should be provided with information appropriate to their level of comprehension. Although the child's parents should authorize or refuse to authorize treatment, the child's assent should be sought and any strong and sustained dissent should be taken seriously.[13]...

Many adolescents have the decision-making capacity of an adult.[14,15] This capacity will need to be determined for each patient in light of his or her

- ability to understand and communicate relevant information;
- ability to think and choose with some degree of independence;
- ability to assess the potential for benefit, risks or harms as well as to consider consequences and multiple options; and
- achievement of a fairly stable set of values.[16]

Many children and adolescents, particularly those who have been seriously ill, will need assistance in developing an understanding of the issues and in demonstrating their decision-making capacity. Age-appropriate discussions, perhaps with the assistance of teachers, chaplains, play therapists, nurses, psychologists or others skilled in communicating with children, are helpful....

Physicians should ensure that good decisions are made on behalf of their child patients. Although the interests of other family members are important and will influence decision making, the child's interests are most important and are unlikely to be expressed or defended by the child himself or herself. Anxious, stressed or grieving family members may need assistance in focusing on what is best for the child. This may be especially difficult when a cure is no longer possible; in such cases a decision to stop treatment may seem like a decision to cause the child's death.

Whether or not the child participates, the following considerations should bear upon a treatment decision concerning that child:

- The potential benefits to the child
- The potential harmful consequences to the child, including physical suffering, psychological or spiritual distress and death

- The moral, spiritual and cultural values of the child's family....

For Samantha, resuming aggressive treatment will have a serious negative effect on her quality of life. The chances of remission are small, yet a decision to discontinue treatment will likely result in her death. Because death is an irreversible harm, and decisions with serious consequences require a high level of competence in decision making,[17] the capacity required would be very high. It has been determined that Samantha does not have this capacity.

Nevertheless, Samantha is included in discussions about her treatment options, and her reasons for refusing treatment are explored.[18] Members of the team work hard to re-establish trust. They and Samantha's parents come to agree that refusing treatment is not necessarily unreasonable; a decision by an adult patient in similar circumstances to discontinue treatment would

certainly be honoured. Discussions address Samantha's and her parents' hopes and fears, their understanding of the possibility of cure, the meaning for them of the statistics provided by the physicians, Samantha's role in decision making and her access to information. They are assisted by nurses, a child psychologist, a psychiatrist, a member of the clergy, a bioethicist, a social worker and a palliative care specialist....

Opportunities are provided for Samantha and her family to speak to others who have had similar experiences, and staff are given the opportunity to voice their concerns.

Ultimately, a decision is reached to discontinue chemotherapy and the goal of treatment shifts from "cure" to "care."... Samantha returns home, supported by a community palliative care program, and is allowed to have a new kitten. She dies peacefully.

NOTES*

1. Ruddick W. Parents and life prospects. In: O'Neill 0., Ruddick W., editors. *Having Children: Philosophical and Legal Reflections on Parenthood*. New York: Oxford University Press; 1979: 124.

2. Nelson, J.L. Taking families seriously. *Hastings Center Report* 1992; 22:6.

3. Hardwig J. What about the family? *Hastings Center Report* 1990; 20(2):5-10.

4. Leikin S. A proposal concerning decisions to forgo life-sustaining treatment for young people. 7 Pediatr 1989; 115:17-22.

5. Mahowald M. *Women and Children in Health Care*. New York, Oxford University Press; 1993: 187,189.

6. Hellmann J. In pursuit of harmonized values: patient/parent-pediatrician relationships. In: Lynch A., editor. *The "Good" Pediatrician: An Ethics Curriculum for Use in Canadian Pediatrics Residency Programs*. Toronto: Pediatric Ethics Network; 1996.

7. Pellegrino E.D. Toward a reconstruction of medical morality: the primacy of the act of profession and the fact of illness. 7 *Med Philos* 1979; 4:47.

8. *Malette v. Shulman* [1990], 67 DLR (4th) (Ont CA).

---

* These notes have been renumbered to aid the reader.

9. Art. II CCQ.

10. Etchells E., Sharpe G., Elliott C., Singer P.A. Bioethics for clinicians 3: Capacity. *Can Med Assoc J* 1996; 155:657-61.

11. Broome M.E., Stieglitz V.A. The consent process and children. *Res Nurs Health* 1992; 15:147-52.

12. Erlen J.A. The child's choice: an essential component in treatment decisions. *Child Health Care* 1987; 1 S. 156-60.

13. Baylis F. The moral weight of a child's dissent. *Ethics Med Pract* 1993; 3 (1):23.

14. Weithorn L.A., Campbell S.B. The competency of children and adolescents to make informed treatment decisions. *Child Dev* 1982; 53:1589-98.

15. Lewis C.C. How adolescents approach decisions: changes over grades seven to twelve and policy implications. *Child Dev* 1981; 52:538-44.

16. Brock D.W. Children's competence for health care decision making. In: Kopelman L.M., Moskop J.C., editors. *Children and Health Care: Moral and Social Issues*. Dordrecht (Holland): Kluwer Academic Publishers; 1989: 181-212.

17. Drane J.F. The many faces of competency. *Hastings Center Report* 1985; 15(2): 17-21.

18. Freyer D.R. Children with cancer: special considerations in the discontinuation of life-sustaining treatment. *Med Pediatr Oncol* 1992; 20:136-42.

FURTHER READINGS

American College of Physicians. "Cognitively Impaired Subjects." *Annals of Internal Medicine* 111: 10 (Nov. 15, 1989), 843–848.

Buchanan, Allen E. and Dan W. Brock. *Deciding for Others: The Ethics of Surrogate Decision Making*. Cambridge and New York: Cambridge University Press, 1989.

Gaylin, W. and R. Macklin, eds. *Who Speaks for the Child? The Problems of Proxy Consent*. New York and London: Plenum Press, 1982.

Keyserlingk, Edward W. *The Unborn Child's Right to Prenatal Care: A Comparative Law Perspective*. Montreal: McGill Legal Studies No. 5, 1984.

Savage, H. and Carla McKague. "Competency and Proxy Decision-Making," from H.Savage and Carla McKague, *Mental Health Law in Canada*. Toronto and Vancouver: Butterworths, 1987, 114-124.

Wikler, D. "Paternalism and the Mildly Retarded." *Philosophy and Public Affairs* 8 (1979) 337–392.

CHAPTER 8
ADVANCE DIRECTIVES

INTRODUCTION

Contemporary ethics agrees, and Canadian law emphasizes, that every person has the right to decide whether to accept or reject health care. The person may not be in a position to exercise that right because of mental disability, lack of capacity, etc.; however, in such cases a duly empowered proxy decision-maker will take over the decision-making role. This proxy or substitute decision-maker will then make a decision that is in the best interests of the incompetent person, using the objective reasonable person standard: i.e., using the values that an objective reasonable person would use if he or she were in a position similar to that of the incompetent person.

However, not all situations involving incompetent persons are the same. We can distinguish three different kinds of cases: cases where the now incompetent person was never competent; cases where the now incompetent person was previously competent but did not express any wishes about what should happen to him or her if he or she ever became incompetent and health care decisions had to be made; and cases where the now incompetent person was previously competent and *did* say what should happen to him or her if he or she ever became incompetent and health care decisions had to be made.

The increasing shift towards patient autonomy in patient decision making (see chapter 6) has led to a change in the traditional position. It is now generally accepted that competent persons have the right to decide what health care they will receive when they are no longer competent but health decisions have to be made. This may be problematic. For instance, what should be done if someone is bleeding to death and a simple medical procedure (e.g., a transfusion) would save her life, but she has previously expressed the wish—in writing— that she did not want any blood? How does the attending physician know whether the person has not changed her mind at the last minute? Or that she really meant it? Is letting the patient die compatible with the physician's duty to save lives? The landmark case of *Malette v. Shulman* below addresses these questions. It states that if the *advance directive* that the patient has given is specific to the situation in question and is unambiguous, then it must be followed—even if this means that the patient will die.

However, not all advance directives are as specific as the refusal of blood. Some deal with a whole range of interventions that the patient does or does not want; others merely indicate the values that should be followed when making a decision on behalf of the patient; still others stipulate neither interventions nor the values to be followed, but instead identify who the proxy decision-makers should be; and still others involve a combination of any or all of these. A wide variety of advance directives has emerged since *Malette v. Shulman*. Not all of them are helpful to the health care professional who is faced with an incompetent patient for whom a decision must be made. The article by Peter Singer *et al.* examines some of the complexities of the situation from the perspective of a health care professional.

In this context, it should be noted that most Canadian provinces have passed or are planning to pass laws that specify the legal status of advance directives, the form they should take, and the mechanisms that should exist for recording them. The last, in particular, is important: an advance directive is of very little use if the emergency response team is unaware of it, or if it is not part of the patient record that is accessible to the professional who is looking after the patient. In light of the discussion on the rights of children to participate in health care decision making, it may interesting to speculate whether children should also have the right to make binding advance directives.

Malette v. Shulman

I

In the early afternoon of June 30, 1979, Mrs. Georgette Malette, then age 57, was rushed, unconscious, by ambulance to the Kirkland and District Hospital in Kirkland Lake, Ontario. She had been in an accident. The car in which she was a passenger, driven by her husband, had collided head-on with a truck. Her husband had been killed. She suffered serious injuries.

On arrival at the hospital, she was attended by Dr. David L. Shulman, a family physician practising in Kirkland Lake who served two or three shifts a week in the emergency department of the hospital and who was on duty at the time. Dr. Shulman's initial examination of Mrs. Malette showed, among other things, that she had severe head and face injuries and was bleeding profusely. The doctor concluded that she was

---

Malette v. Shulman (1990) 72 O.R. (2d) 417 (C.A.) pp. 17–42.

suffering from incipient shock by reason of blood loss, and ordered that she be given intravenous glucose followed immediately by Ringer's Lactate. The administration of a volume expander, such as Ringer's Lactate, is standard medical procedure in cases of this nature. If the patient does not respond with significantly increased blood pressure, transfusions of blood are then administered to carry essential oxygen to tissues and to remove waste products and prevent damage to vital organs.

At about this time, a nurse discovered a card in Mrs. Malette's purse which identified her as a Jehovah's Witness and in which she requested, on the basis of her religious convictions, that she be given no blood transfusions under any circumstances. The card, which was not dated or witnessed, was printed in French and signed by Mrs. Malette. Translated into English, it read:

NO BLOOD TRANSFUSION!

As one of Jehovah's Witnesses with firm religious convictions, I request that no blood or blood products be administered to me under any circumstances. I fully realize the implications of this position, but I have resolutely decided to obey the Bible command: "Keep abstaining ... from blood." (Acts 15:28, 29). However, I have no religious objection to use the nonblood alternatives, such as Dextran, Haemaccel, PVP, Ringer's Lactate or saline solution.

Dr. Shulman was promptly advised of the existence of this card and its contents.

Mrs. Malette was next examined by a surgeon on duty in the hospital. He concluded, as had Dr. Shulman, that to avoid irreversible shock, it was vital to maintain her blood volume. He had Mrs. Malette transferred to the X-ray department for X-rays of her skull, pelvis and chest.

However, before the X-rays could be satisfactorily completed, Mrs. Malette's condition deteriorated. Her blood pressure dropped markedly, her respiration became increasingly distressed, and her level of consciousness dropped. She continued to bleed profusely and could be said to be critically ill.

At this stage, Dr. Shulman decided that Mrs. Malette's condition had deteriorated to the point that transfusions were necessary to replace her lost blood and to preserve her life and health. Having made that decision, he personally administered transfusions to her, in spite of the Jehovah's Witness card, while she was in the X-ray department and after she was transferred to the intensive care unit. Dr. Shulman was clearly aware of the religious objection to blood manifested in the card carried by Mrs. Malette and the instruction that "NO BLOOD TRANSFUSION!" be given under any circumstances. He accepted full responsibility then, as he does now, for the decision to administer the transfusions.

Some three hours after the transfusions were commenced, Mrs. Malette's daughter, Celine Bisson, who had driven to Kirkland Lake from Timmins, arrived at the hospital accompanied by her husband and a local church elder. She strongly objected to her mother being given blood. She informed Dr. Shulman and some of the other defendants that both she and her mother were Jehovah's Witnesses, that a tenet of their faith forbids blood transfusions, and that she knew her mother would not want blood transfusions. Notwithstanding Dr. Shulman's opinion as to the medical necessity of the transfusions, Mrs. Bisson remained adamantly opposed to them. She signed a document specifically prohibiting blood transfusions and a release of liability. Dr. Shulman refused to follow her instructions. Since the blood transfusions were, in his judgment, medically necessary in this potentially life-threatening situation, he believed it his professional responsibility as the doctor in charge to ensure that his patient received the transfusions. Furthermore, he was not satisfied that the card signed by Mrs. Malette expressed her current instructions because, on the information he then had, he did not know whether she might have changed her religious beliefs before the accident; whether the card may have been signed because of family or peer pressure; whether at the time she signed the card she was fully informed of the risks of refusal of blood transfusions; or whether, if conscious, she might have changed her mind in the face of medical advice as to her perhaps imminent but avoidable death.

As matters developed, by about midnight Mrs. Malette's condition had stabilized sufficiently to permit her to be transferred early the next morning by air ambulance to Toronto General Hospital where she received no further blood transfusions. She was discharged on August 11, 1979. Happily, she made a very good recovery from her injuries.

II

In June, 1980, Mrs. Malette brought this action against Dr. Shulman, the hospital, its executive director and four nurses, alleging, in the main, that the administration of blood transfusions in the circumstances of her case constituted negligence and assault and battery and subjected her to religious discrimination. ... With respect to Dr. Shulman, the learned judge concluded that the Jehovah's Witness card validly restricted his right to treat the patient, and there was no rationally founded basis upon which the doctor could ignore that restriction. Hence, his administration of blood transfusions constituted a battery on the plaintiff. The judge awarded her damages of $20,000 but declined to make any award of costs.

Dr. Shulman now appeals to this court from that judgment. Mrs. Malette cross-appeals the judge's dismissal of the action against the hospital and his order with respect to costs.

... I should perhaps underscore the fact that Dr. Shulman was not found liable for any negligence in his treatment of Mrs. Malette. The judge held that he had acted "promptly, professionally and was well-motivated throughout" and that his management of the case had been "carried out in a competent, careful and conscientious manner" in accordance with the requisite standard of care. His decision to administer blood in the circumstances confronting him was found to be an honest exercise of his professional judgment which did not delay Mrs. Malette's recovery, endanger her life or cause her any bodily harm. Indeed, the judge concluded that the doctor's treatment of Mrs. Malette "may well have been responsible for saving her life."

Liability was imposed in this case on the basis that the doctor tortiously violated his patient's rights over her own body by acting contrary to the Jehovah's Witness card and administering blood transfusions that were not authorized. His honest and even justifiable belief that the treatment was medically essential did not serve to relieve him from liability for the battery resulting from his intentional and unpermitted conduct....

III

What then is the legal effect, if any, of the Jehovah's Witness card carried by Mrs. Malette? Was the doctor bound to honour the instructions of his unconscious patient or, given the emergency and his inability to obtain conscious instructions from his patient, was he entitled to disregard the card and act according to his best medical judgment?

To answer these questions and determine the effect to be given to the Jehovah's Witness card, it is first necessary to ascertain what rights a competent patient has to accept or reject medical treatment and to appreciate the nature and extent of those rights.

The right of a person to control his or her own body is a concept that has long been recognized at common law. The tort of battery has traditionally protected the interest in bodily security from unwanted physical interference. Basically, any intentional nonconsensual touching which is harmful or offensive to a person's reasonable sense of dignity is actionable. Of course, a person may choose to waive this protection and consent to the intentional invasion of this interest, in which case an action for battery will not be maintainable. No special exceptions are made for medical care, other than in emergency situations, and the general rules governing actions for battery are applicable to the doctor-patient relationship. Thus, as a matter of common law, a medical intervention in which a doctor touches the body of a patient would constitute a battery if the patient did not consent to the intervention. Patients have the decisive role in the medical decision-making process. Their right of self-determination is recognized and protected by the law. As Justice Cardozo proclaimed in his classic statement: "Every human being of adult years and sound mind has a right to determine what shall be done with his own body; and a surgeon who performs an operation without his patient's consent commits an assault, for which he is liable in damages": *Schloendoff v. Society of New York Hospital*, 211 N.Y. 125 (1914).

The doctrine of informed consent has developed in the law as the primary means of protecting a patient's right to control his or her medical treatment. Under the doctrine, no medical procedure may be undertaken without the patient's consent obtained after the patient has been provided with sufficient information to evaluate the risks and benefits of the proposed treatment and other available options. The doctrine presupposes the patient's capacity to make a subjective treatment decision based on her understanding of the necessary medical facts provided by the doctor and on her assessment of her own personal circumstances. A doctor who performs a medical procedure without having first furnished the patient with the information needed to obtain an informed consent will have infringed the patient's right to control the course of her medical care, and will be liable in battery even though the procedure was performed with a high degree of skill and actually benefitted the patient.

The right of self-determination which underlies the doctrine of informed consent also obviously encompasses the right to refuse medical treatment. A competent adult is generally entitled to reject a specific treatment or all treatment, or to select an alternate form of treatment, even if the decision may entail risks as serious as death and may appear mistaken in the eyes of the medical profession or of the community. Regardless of the doctor's opinion, it is the patient who has the final say on whether to undergo the treatment. The patient is free to decide, for instance, not to be operated on or not to undergo therapy or, by the same token, not to have a blood transfusion. If a doctor were to proceed in the face of a decision to reject the treatment, he would be civilly liable for his unauthorized conduct notwithstanding his justifiable belief that what he did was necessary to preserve the patient's life or health. The doctrine of informed consent is plainly intended to ensure the freedom of individuals to make choices concerning their medical care. For this freedom to be meaningful, people must have the right to make choices that accord with their own values regardless of how unwise or foolish those choices may appear to others....

IV

The emergency situation is an exception to the general rule requiring a patient's prior consent. When immediate medical treatment is necessary to save the life or preserve the health of a person who, by reason of unconsciousness or extreme illness, is incapable of either giving or withholding consent, the doctor may proceed without the patient's consent. The delivery of medical services is rendered lawful in such circumstances either on the rationale that the doctor has implied consent from the patient to give emergency aid or, more accurately in my view, on the rationale that the doctor is privileged by reason of necessity in giving the aid and is not to be held liable for so doing. On either basis, in an emergency the law sets aside the requirement of consent on the assumption that the patient, as a reasonable person, would want emergency aid to be rendered if she were capable of giving instructions.

On the facts of the present case, Dr. Shulman was clearly faced with an emergency. He had an unconscious, critically ill patient on his hands who, in his opinion, needed blood transfusions to save her life or preserve her health. If there were no Jehovah's Witness card he undoubtedly would have been entitled to administer blood transfusions as part of the emergency treatment and could not have been held liable for so doing. In those circumstances he would have had no indication that the transfusions would have been refused had the patient then been able to make her wishes known and, accordingly, no reason to expect that, as a reasonable person, she would not consent to the transfusions.

However, to change the facts, if Mrs. Malette, before passing into unconsciousness, had expressly instructed Dr. Shulman, in terms comparable to those set forth on the card, that her religious convictions as a Jehovah's Witness were such that she was not to be given a blood transfusion under any circumstances and that she fully realized the implications of this position, the doctor would have been confronted with an obviously different situation. Here, the patient, anticipating an emergency in which she might be unable to make decisions about her health care contemporaneous with the emergency, has given explicit instructions that blood transfusions constitute an unacceptable medical intervention and are not to be administered to her. Once the emergency arises, is the doctor none the less entitled to administer transfusions on the basis of his honest belief that they are needed to save his patient's life?

The answer, in my opinion, is clearly no. A doctor is not free to disregard a patient's advance instructions any more than he would be free to disregard instructions given at the time of the emergency. The law does not prohibit a patient from withholding consent to emergency medical treatment, nor does the law prohibit a doctor from following his patient's instructions. While the law may disregard the absence of consent in limited emergency circumstances, it otherwise supports the right of competent adults to make decisions concerning their own health care by imposing civil liability on those who perform medical treatment without consent.

The patient's decision to refuse blood in the situation I have posed was made prior to and in anticipation of the emergency. While the doctor would have had the opportunity to dissuade her on the basis of his medical advice, her refusal to accept his advice or her unwillingness to discuss or consider the subject would not relieve him of his obligation to follow her instructions. The principles of self-determination and individual autonomy compel the conclusion that the patient may reject blood transfusions even if harmful consequences may result and even if the decision is generally regarded as foolhardy. Her decision in this instance would be operative after she lapsed into unconsciousness, and the doctor's conduct would be unauthorized. To transfuse a Jehovah's Witness in the face of her explicit instructions to the contrary would, in my opinion, violate her right to control her own body and show disrespect for the religious values by which she has chosen to live her life....

V

The distinguishing feature of the present case — and the one that makes this a case of first impression — is, of course, the Jehovah's Witness card on the person of the unconscious patient. What then is the effect of the Jehovah's Witness card?

In the appellant's submission, the card is of no effect and, as a consequence, can play no role in determining the doctor's duty toward his patient in the emergency situation existing in this case. The trial judge, the appellant argues, erred in holding both that the Jehovah's Witness card validly restricted the doctor's right to administer the blood transfusions, and that there was no rationally founded basis for ignoring the card. The argument proceeds on the basis, first, that, as a matter of principle, a card of this nature could not operate in these circumstances to prohibit the doctor from providing emergency health care and, second, that in any event, as a matter of evidence, there was good reason to doubt the card's validity.

The appellant acknowledges that a conscious rational patient is entitled to refuse any medical treatment and that a doctor must comply with that refusal no matter how ill-advised he may believe it to be. He contends, however, to quote from his factum, that "a patient refusing treatment regarded by a doctor as being medically necessary has a right to be advised by the doctor, and the doctor has a concomitant duty to advise the patient of the risks associated with that refusal." Here, because of the patient's unconsciousness, the doctor had no opportunity to advise her of the specific risks involved in refusing the blood transfusions that he regarded as medically necessary. In those circumstances, the appellant

argues, it was not possible for the doctor to obtain, or for the patient to give, an "informed refusal." In the absence of such a refusal, the argument proceeds, Dr. Shulman was under a legal and ethical duty to treat this patient as he would any other emergency case and provide the treatment that, in his medical judgment, was needed to preserve her health and life. In short, the argument concludes, Mrs. Malette's religiously motivated instructions, prepared in contemplation of an emergency, directing that she not be given blood transfusions in any circumstances, were of no force or effect and could be ignored with impunity.

In challenging the trial judge's finding that there was no rationally founded evidentiary basis for doubting the validity of the card and ignoring the restriction contained in it, the appellant puts forth a number of questions which he claims compel the conclusion that he was under no duty to comply with these instructions. He argues that it could properly be doubted whether the card constituted a valid statement of Mrs. Malette's wishes in this emergency because it was unknown, for instance, whether she knew the card was still in her purse; whether she was still a Jehovah's Witness or how devout a Jehovah's Witness she was; what information she had about the risks associated with the refusal of blood transfusion when she signed the card; or whether, if she were conscious, she would refuse blood transfusions after the doctor had an opportunity to advise her of the risks associated with the refusal.

... I share the trial judge's view that, in the circumstances of this case, the instructions in the Jehovah's Witness card imposed a valid restriction on the emergency treatment that could be provided to Mrs. Malette and precluded blood transfusions.

I should emphasize that in deciding this case the court is not called upon to consider the law that may be applicable to the many situations in which objection may be taken to the use or continued use of medical treatment to save or prolong a patient's life. The court's role, especially in a matter as sensitive as this, is limited to resolving the issues raised by the facts presented in this particular case. On these facts, we are not concerned with a patient who has been diagnosed as terminally or incurably ill who seeks by way of advance directive or "living will" to reject medical treatment so that she may die with dignity; neither are we concerned with a patient in an irreversible vegetative state whose family seeks to withdraw medical treatment in order to end her life; nor is this a case in which an otherwise healthy patient wishes for some reason or other to terminate her life. There is no element of suicide or euthanasia in this case.

Our concern here is with a patient who has chosen in the only way possible to notify doctors and other providers of health care, should she be unconscious or otherwise unable to convey her wishes, that she does not consent to blood transfusions. Her written statement is plainly intended to express her wishes when she is unable to speak for herself. There is no suggestion that she wished to die. Her rejection of blood transfusions is based on the firm belief held by Jehovah's Witnesses, founded on their interpretation of the Scriptures, that the acceptance of blood will result in a forfeiture of their opportunity for resurrection and eternal salvation. The card evidences that "as one of Jehovah's Witnesses with firm religious convictions" Mrs. Malette is not to be administered blood transfusions "under any circumstances"; that, while she "fully realize[s] the implications of this position," she has "resolutely decided to obey the Bible command"; and that she has no religious objection to "non-blood alternatives." In signing and carrying this card Mrs. Malette has made manifest her determination to abide by this fundamental tenet of her faith and refuse blood regardless of the consequences. If her refusal involves a risk of death, then, according to her belief, her death would be necessary to ensure her spiritual life.

Accepting for the moment that there is no reason to doubt that the card validly expressed Mrs. Malette's desire to withhold consent to blood transfusions, why should her wishes not be respected? Why should she be transfused against her will? The appellant's answer, in essence, is that the card cannot be effective when the doctor is unable to provide the patient with the information she would need before making a decision to withhold consent in this specific emergency situation. In the absence of an informed refusal, the appellant submits that Mrs. Malette's right to protection against unwanted infringements of her bodily integrity must give way to countervailing societal interests which limit a person's right to refuse medical treatment. The appellant identifies two such interests as applicable to the unconscious patient in the present situation: first, the interest of the state in preserving life and, second, the interest of the state in safeguarding the integrity of the medical profession.

VI

The state undoubtedly has a strong interest in protecting and preserving the lives and health of its citizens. There clearly are circumstances where this interest may override the individual's right to self-determination. For example, the state may in certain cases require that citizens submit to medical procedures in order to eliminate a health threat to the community or it may prohibit citizens from engaging in activities which are inherently dangerous to their lives. But this interest does not prevent a competent adult from refusing life-preserving medical treatment in general or blood transfusions in particular.

The state's interest in preserving the life or health of a competent patient must generally give way to the patient's stronger interest in directing the course of her own life. As indicated earlier, there is no law prohibiting a patient from declining necessary treatment or prohibiting a doctor from honouring the patient's decision. To the extent that the law reflects the state's interest, it supports the right of individuals to make their own decisions. By imposing civil liability on those who perform medical treatment without consent even though the treatment may be beneficial, the law serves to maximize individual freedom of choice. Recognition of the right to reject medical treatment cannot, in my opinion, be said to depreciate the interest of the state in life or in the sanctity of life. Individual free choice and self-determination are themselves fundamental constituents of life. To deny individuals freedom of choice with respect to their health care can only lessen, and not enhance, the value of life. This state interest, in my opinion, cannot properly be invoked to prohibit Mrs. Malette from choosing for herself whether or not to undergo blood transfusions.

Safeguarding the integrity of the medical profession is patently a legitimate state interest worthy of protection. However, I do not agree that this interest can serve to limit a patient's right to refuse blood transfusions. I recognize, of course, that the choice between violating a patient's private convictions and accepting her decision is hardly an easy one for members of a profession dedicated to aiding the injured and preserving life. The patient's right to determine her own medical treatment is, however, paramount to what might otherwise be the doctor's obligation to provide needed medical care. The doctor is bound in law by the patient's choice even though that choice may be contrary to the mandates of his own conscience and professional judgment. If patient choice were subservient to conscientious medical judgment, the right of the patient to determine her own treatment, and the doctrine of informed consent, would be rendered mean-

ingless. Recognition of a Jehovah's Witness's right to refuse blood transfusions cannot, in my opinion, be seen as threatening the integrity of the medical profession or the state's interest in protecting the same.

In sum, it is my view that the principal interest asserted by Mrs. Malette in this case — the interest in the freedom to reject, or refuse to consent to, intrusions of her bodily integrity — outweighs the interest of the state in the preservation of life and health and the protection of the integrity of the medical profession. While the right to decline medical treatment is not absolute or unqualified, those state interests are not in themselves sufficiently compelling to justify forcing a patient to submit to nonconsensual invasions of her person. The interest of the state in protecting innocent third parties and preventing suicide are, I might note, not applicable to the present circumstances.

VII

The unique considerations in this case arise by virtue of Mrs. Malette's aim to articulate through her Jehovah's Witness card her wish not to be given blood transfusions in any circumstances. In considering the effect to be given the card, it must, of course, be borne in mind that no previous doctor-patient relationship existed between Dr. Shulman and Mrs. Malette. The doctor was acting here in an emergency in which he clearly did not have, nor could he obtain, her consent to his intervention. His intervention can be supported only by resort to the emergency doctrine which I outlined in Part IV of these reasons.

Under that doctrine, the doctor could administer blood transfusions without incurring liability, even though the patient had not consented, if he had no reason to believe that the patient, if she had the opportunity to consent, would decline. In those circumstances, it could be assumed that the patient, as a reasonable person, would consent to aid being rendered if she were able to give instructions. The doctor's authority to make decisions for his patient is necessarily a limited authority. If he knows that the patient has refused to consent to the proposed procedure, he is not empowered to overrule the patient's decision by substituting his decision for hers even though he, and most others, may think hers a foolish or unreasonable decision. In these circumstances the assumption upon which consent is set aside in an emergency could no longer be made. The doctor has no authority to intervene in the face of a patient's declared wishes to the contrary. Should he none the less proceed, he would be liable in battery for tortiously invading the patient's bodily integrity notwithstanding that what he did may be considered beneficial to the patient.

In this case, the patient, in effect, issued standing orders that she was to be given "NO BLOOD TRANSFUSION!" in any circumstances. She gave notice to the doctor and the hospital, in the only practical way open to her, of her firm religious convictions as a Jehovah's Witness and her resolve to abstain from blood. Her instructions plainly contemplated the situation in which she found herself as a result of her unfortunate accident. In light of those instructions, assuming their validity, she cannot be said to have consented to blood transfusions in this emergency. Nor can the doctor be said to have proceeded on the reasonable belief that the patient would have consented had she been in a condition to do so. Given his awareness of her instructions and his understanding that blood transfusions were anathema to her on religious grounds, by what authority could he administer the transfusions? Put another way, if the card evidences the patient's intent to withhold consent, can the doctor none the less ignore the card and subject the patient to a procedure that is manifestly contrary to her express wishes and unacceptable to her religious beliefs?

At issue here is the freedom of the patient as an individual to exercise her right to refuse treatment and accept the consequences of her own decision. Competent adults, as I have sought to demonstrate, are generally at liberty to refuse medical treatment even at the risk of death. The right to determine what shall be done with one's own body is a fundamental right in our society. The concepts inherent in this right are the bedrock upon which the principles of self-determination and individual autonomy are based. Free individual choice in matters affecting this right should, in my opinion, be accorded very high priority. I view the issues in this case from that perspective.

VIII

The appellant's basic position, reduced to its essentials, is that unless the doctor can obtain the patient's informed refusal of blood transfusions he need not follow the instructions provided in the Jehovah's Witness card. Nothing short of a conscious, contemporaneous decision by the patient to refuse blood transfusions — a decision made after the patient has been fully informed by the doctor of the risks of refusing blood in the specific circumstances facing her — will suffice, the appellant contends, to eliminate the doctor's authority to administer emergency treatment or, by the same token, to relieve the doctor of his obligation to treat this emergency patient as he would any other. ...

In my opinion, it is unnecessary to determine in this case whether there is doctrine of informed refusal as distinct from the doctrine of informed consent. In the particular doctor-patient relationship which arose in these emergency circumstances it is apparent that the doctor could not inform the patient of the risks involved in her prior decision to refuse consent to blood transfusions in any circumstances. It is apparent also that her decision did not emerge out of a doctor-patient relationship. Whatever the doctor's obligation to provide the information needed to make an informed choice may be in other doctor-patient relationships, he cannot be in breach of any such duty in the circumstances of this relationship. The patient manifestly made the decision on the basis of her religious convictions. It is not for the doctor to second-guess the reasonableness of the decision or to pass judgment on the religious principles which motivated it. The fact that he had no opportunity to offer medical advice cannot nullify instructions plainly intended to govern in circumstances where such advice is not possible. Unless the doctor had reason to believe that the instructions in the Jehovah's Witness card were not valid instructions in the sense that they did not truly represent the patient's wishes, in my opinion he was obliged to honour them. He has no authorization under the emergency doctrine to override the patient's wishes. In my opinion, she was entitled to reject in advance of an emergency a medical procedure inimical to her religious values.

The remaining question is whether the doctor factually had reason to believe the instructions were not valid. ... On my reading of the record, there was no reason not to regard this card as a valid advance directive. Its instructions were clear, precise and unequivocal, and manifested a calculated decision to reject a procedure offensive to the patient's religious convictions. The instructions excluded from potential emergency treatment a single medical procedure well known to the lay public and within its comprehension. ... The card undoubtedly belonged to and was signed by Mrs. Malette; its authenticity was not questioned by anyone at the hospital and, realistically, could not have been questioned. The trial judge found, "[t]here [was] no basis in evidence to indicate that the card [did] not represent the current intention and instruction of the card holder" [p. 268 O.R., p. 43 D.L.R.].

There was nothing to give credence to or provide support for the speculative inferences implicit in questions as to the current strength of Mrs. Malette's religious beliefs or as to the circumstances under which the card was signed or her state of mind at the time. The fact that a card of this nature was carried by her can itself be taken as verification of her continuing and current resolve to reject blood "fully realiz-[ing] the implications of this position."

In short, the card on its face set forth unqualified instructions applicable to the circumstances presented by this emergency. In the absence of any evidence to the contrary, those instructions should be taken as validly representing the patient's wish not to be transfused. If, of course, there were evidence to the contrary — evidence which cast doubt on whether the card was a true expression of the patient's wishes — the doctor, in my opinion, would be entitled to proceed as he would in the usual emergency case. In this case, however, there was no such contradictory evidence. Accordingly, I am of the view that the card had the effect of validly restricting the treatment that could be provided to Mrs. Malette and constituted the doctor's administration of the transfusions a battery.

With respect to Mrs. Malette's daughter, I would treat her role in this matter as no more than confirmatory of her mother's wishes. The decision in this case does not turn on whether the doctor failed to follow the daughter's instructions. Therefore, it is unnecessary, and in my view would be inadvisable, to consider what effect, if any, should be given to a substitute decision, purportedly made by a relative on behalf of the patient, to reject medical treatment in these circumstances.

One further point should be mentioned. The appellant argues that to uphold the trial decision places a doctor on the horns of a dilemma, in that, on the one hand, if the doctor administers blood in this situation and saves the patient's life, the patient may hold him liable in battery while, on the other hand, if the doctor follows the patient's instructions and, as a consequence, the patient dies, the doctor may face an action by dependants alleging that, notwithstanding the card, the deceased would, if conscious, have accepted blood in the face of imminent death and the doctor was negligent in failing to administer the transfusions. In my view, that result cannot conceivably follow. The doctor cannot be held to have violated either his legal duty or professional responsibility towards the patient or the patient's dependants when he honours the Jehovah's Witness card and respects the patient's right to control her own body in accordance with the dictates of her conscience. The onus is clearly on the patient. When members of the Jehovah's Witness faith choose to carry cards intended to notify doctors and other providers of health care that they reject blood transfusions in an emergency, they must accept the consequences of their decision. Neither they nor their dependants can later be heard to say that the card did not reflect their true wishes. If harmful consequences ensue, the responsibility for those consequences is entirely theirs and not the doctor's.

Finally, the appellant appeals the quantum of damages awarded by the trial judge. In his submission, given the findings as to the competence of the treatment, the favourable results, the doctor's overall exemplary conduct and his good faith in the matter, the battery was technical and the general damages should be no more than nominal. While the submission is not without force, damages of $20,000 cannot be said to be beyond the range of damages appropriate to a tortious interference of this nature. The trial judge found that Mrs. Malette suffered mentally and emotionally by reason of the battery. His assessment of general damages was clearly not affected by any palpable or overriding error and there is therefore no basis upon which an appellate court may interfere with the award.

X

In the result, for these reasons I would dismiss the appeal and the cross-appeal, both with costs.

Advance Directives: Are They an Advance?

Advance Directives Seminar Group, Centre for Bioethics, University of Toronto

An advance directive is a document intended to govern the kind of life-sustaining treatment that a competent person will receive if he or she later becomes incompetent.[1] An instruction directive, also called a living will, contains a person's preferences regarding the use of life-sustaining treatments. A proxy directive, also called a durable power of attorney for health care, contains a person's preferences regarding who is to make

Peter Singer, Eileen Ambrosio, Shelley Birenbaum, Arthur Fisher, David Hughes, A.H. Khan, P. Khan, Pat Rundle, John Senn, Ross Upshor, Jo-Ann P. Wilson, Frederick H. Lowy, Eric Meslin, Carol Nash, Nitsa Kohut, Michelle Mullen, Hussein Z. Noorani, Nancy Ondrusek, Sharon Rea, Mehran Sam and Linda R. Shaw. "Advance directives: Are they an advance? — Reprinted from, by permission of the publisher, *CMAJ* 146:2 (1992) 127-134.

decisions about life-sustaining treatment on his or her behalf. The two types — instruction and proxy — can be combined into a single document....

Should advance directives be supported in principle? If so, how should they be designed? Who should be offered one? When should advance directives be updated? What should be done if patients change their minds? How should implementation be enforced? How should consideration of their use be promoted?

SHOULD ADVANCE DIRECTIVES BE SUPPORTED IN PRINCIPLE?

Arguments in Favour

Five arguments support the use of advance directives. First, because they permit competent people to project their preferences regarding life-sustaining treatment onto situations of future incompetence, advance directives extend people's autonomy. Studies have found that most patients want to discuss life-sustaining treatment with their physicians[6-9] and that 93% of outpatients and 89% of the public want advance directives.[10] Moreover, making an advance directive is itself an exercise of autonomy — people may benefit from knowing that they have done all they can to decide about treatment issues in the event of incompetence.

Second, advance directives promote the fair treatment of incompetent patients by conveying their prior wishes. Since competent patients have the right to forgo life-sustaining treatments[3,4] justice requires that incompetent patients also have this right and not be treated differently.

Third, advance directives may reduce the emotional anguish to the patient's family members by relieving them of the obligation to make life-or-death treatment decisions or, at least, by assuring them that they are making the decision the patient would have wanted them to make.

Fourth, advance directives may reduce the psychologic distress of health care providers who do not know whether to provide life-sustaining treatment (that patients may not have wanted) or not to provide such treatment (that patients may have wanted).[11]

Finally, advance directives may increase physician-patient communication. They provide a framework and focus for discussion of medically and ethically relevant issues.

Arguments Against

Seven arguments oppose the use of advance directives.[12] First, people who have become incompetent, such as those in a persistent vegetative state, are greatly changed from when they were competent, and the decisions they would make if they could communicate might be different. It may be inappropriate to project the autonomous wishes of competent people onto future situations of incompetence.

Second, justice does not require equal treatment of groups that vary in morally relevant ways. Competent patients are fully autonomous; incompetent patients are not. This may represent a morally relevant difference.

Third, people change their minds and may forget to change their directives, in which case care may be provided that the patient does not want or would adamantly reject if he or she could.

Fourth, most advance directives are biased toward refusal of treatment. If vulnerable groups are selectively encouraged to complete them, directives may become an instrument of discrimination. Moreover, it might be assumed that patients who have not completed a directive want life-sustaining treatment to be provided.

Fifth, policies on advance directives may restrict patients' rights. In the United States some states allow only patients who are terminally ill to complete advance directives, and some exclude artificial feeding from the types of treatments that may be contained in an advance directive.

Sixth, advance directives may lead to inappropriate choices if situations arise that the person did not foresee or consider. There may be a medical advance that would restore the person to full health. Conversely, treatment may be futile in a particular situation, and yet the person requested it in the directive when the hopelessness of the situation was not apparent.

Finally, by substituting a written form for physician-patient dialogue, advance directives may undercut the goal of informed consent — extensive and open discussion between patients and health care professionals.

Balancing the Arguments

There are arguments of autonomy and justice that support and oppose the use of advance directives. The remaining arguments in favour — families' emotional anguish, the distress of health care professionals and improved communication — reflect anecdotal experience but will require empirical validation. The remaining arguments against — changing preferences, the biased design of advance directive forms, applicability to patients who are not terminally ill, inappropriate treatment choices and undermining of the patient-health care professional dialogue — are practical issues of implementation. We conclude that although advance directives may be desirable in principle, if they are not carefully designed and implemented they may have undesirable effects in practice.

HOW SHOULD ADVANCE DIRECTIVES BE DESIGNED?

Refusals of or Requests for Life-sustaining Treatments?

Some instruction directives permit patients only to refuse, not to request, life-sustaining treatment. ... The Medical Directive[13] permits patients to decline or request life-sustaining treatment and has options that include "undecided" and "I want a therapeutic trial."[13]... Since the goal is to record for the future the preferences of competent patients, it seems unreasonable to offer advance directives that provide only for refusal. Advance directives should permit patients to refuse or request life-sustaining treatment.

Treatment Preferences or General Life Values?

Instruction directives can focus on preferences or values. By preference we mean a specific choice of the use of life-sustaining treatments in identified clinical situations. The Medical Directive permits its patients to choose or refuse 11 specific treatments in four specified clinical situations.[13] By value we mean a person's attitudes toward various aspects of human life such as physical and mental functioning, pain, social interaction, other elements of quality of life and medical technology. Another directive, the Values History,[14] contains a series of questions about "attitude toward life" and "personal relationships."

Value-based directives may be easier for patients to complete, because they do not require a knowledge of health problems or medical treatments. However, preference-based directives may be easier for health care professionals to interpret and implement because they provide more explicit directions regarding treatment. It is difficult to know how to balance these conflicting goals. Since values and preferences represent fundamentally different, but complementary, approaches, instruction directives should contain both these components.

Instruction or Proxy Directive?

It is difficult to design instruction directives to anticipate all possible clinical situations. Proxy directives avoid this problem by allowing the proxy to make an informed choice based on the clinical circumstances, but not everyone has a potential proxy he or she can trust. Because instruction and proxy directives complement one another we recommend that patients be offered both in one document. People who do not want to consider the use of life-sustaining treatments and prefer to entrust someone else with decision-making authority should complete only the proxy component. People without proxies whom they trust should complete only the instruction component.

Can a Specific Advance Directive Be Recommended?

Many advance directive documents are currently available and have been developed by a number of bodies.... We cannot recommend any one document over another since empirical data would be needed for comparison: Which directive is preferred (and why) by patients, families and health care providers? Which is most likely to ensure that patients receive the care they request when they become incapacitated? Such questions are in urgent need of research. Who should be offered an advance directive?

Who Should Be Offered an Advance Directive?

Advance directives could be offered not only to people who have requested information about them but also to the public, patients admitted to hospital, patients who have specific target conditions, and people who are making or updating their testamentary wills. (By "offering" we mean systematically providing information about and the opportunity to complete an advance directive with assistance when necessary.)

Information about advance directives and even the forms themselves could be distributed with drivers' licences, health cards, income tax returns and census questionnaires, at post offices or through mass mailing. Information could also be provided through special toll-free telephone numbers. The main advantage of this approach is that it would reach all those who might need life-sustaining treatment; for example, young adults admitted to hospital unconscious after a motor vehicle accident. Moreover, it would meet an egalitarian standard of justice, since all citizens would be offered the opportunity to complete a directive. The disadvantage is that language, literacy and educational barriers may prevent many people from understanding the directives and completing them appropriately.

Advance directives could be offered to all patients at the time of hospital admission, as required by the patient self-determination provisions of 1990.[2] An advantage of this approach is that patients admitted to hospital are more likely than members of the public to need advance directives. Many patients have conditions with foreseeable clinical courses, and discussions can be focused on the life-sustaining treatments that they might need; the choices are not as hypothetical and abstract as they are for healthy people. There are several drawbacks: discussions might be distressing to sick patients; advance directives cannot be completed by patients who are incompetent at the time of admission; patients in the midst of a medical emergency may not understand the choices being offered; the hospital environment is potentially coercive, and if facilities are obliged to offer advance directives the different versions developed may prove to be a problem if the patient is subsequently transferred to another facility.

Another group to be offered advance directives could be patients with specific illnesses. Such patients could be chronically or terminally ill or have such illnesses as early Alzheimer's disease, acquired immunodeficiency syndrome, end-stage renal disease or amyotrophic lateral sclerosis. The advance directive would embody a considered and authentic choice since patients would be in the situation to which their instructions apply. Because these patients have likely already considered their death, their completing a directive may not be distressing and may provide comfort by returning to them control over the future course of treatment. Moreover, such patients may be the most receptive to advance directives. They are likely to have a relationship with a physician who can raise the topic of life-sustaining treatment in a sensitive manner and at an appropriate time. On the other hand, an advance directive may distress some patients, especially in emergencies, when there is only limited time to consider the choice. Health care providers may not want to raise the issue of advance directives because of the time involved, the lack of reimbursement or the emotional stress of such discussions. The criteria for target groups may be difficult to define, and identifying an already vulnerable group of patients as being in need of advance directives could be considered discriminatory.

People who are making or updating their wills (testators) could be offered an advance directive. In this way a large number of people would be reached. Testators are already thinking about their death and so are likely to be receptive to discussing such issues. The lawyers involved often have their clients' trust, a detailed knowledge of their personal affairs and experience in discussing intimate and delicate matters with them. They are also experienced in recognizing people whose competence is likely to be challenged, so that such clients can be referred for medical or psychiatric assessment and their competence documented convincingly in case of a later challenge. One disadvantage of offering these people an advance directive is the implicit suggestion that a will concerning disposal of property is of equal importance to a will concerning "disposal" of a person's life and that they can be dealt with through a similar process. Another is that without the assistance of a physician, lawyers often cannot properly draft or discuss specific instruction directives.

Patients who are chronically or terminally ill are most likely to become incompetent and therefore have the most urgent need for an advance directive. People making or updating their wills are already thinking about death and so may be more receptive. We do not claim that these are the only groups to whom advance directives should be offered or that physicians and lawyers are the only people who should be offering them.

WHEN SHOULD ADVANCE DIRECTIVES BE UPDATED?

Advance directives should be updated when people change their minds about their choices. Moreover, a policy of regular updating may increase the confidence of health care professionals and families that they are following the patients' most current wishes. An adequate advance directive process must have some mechanism whereby changes can be easily incorporated and made known to all involved parties.

How often and under what circumstances people change their minds regarding the content of their advance directive is an empirical question. Four studies have examined the stability of preferences for life-sustaining treatment. Everhart and Pearlman[15] found that for critically ill patients these preferences at the time of discharge from an intensive care unit and 1 month later were stable. Silverstein and associates[16] reported that patients with amyotrophic lateral sclerosis changed their preferences over a 6-month period. Emanuel and collaborators found that on average the durability over 6 to 12 months of patients' preferences regarding situation-treatment choices in the Medical Directive was 87%. Teno, Mor and Fleishman[17] found moderate stability over 1 year of the preferences of patients with human immunodeficiency virus infection (m = 0.16 to 0.35).

We believe that updating should be done when there is a change in the patient's clinical status (improvement or deterioration), when the patient is admitted to a health care facility, when it is deemed appropriate by the physician or lawyer and when there is a major event such as divorce, death of a spouse, birth of children or move to a new jurisdiction. In addition, for patients in institutions advance directives should be considered part of the medical record in the same way details of medication are; as such, they would be subject to review on a semi-annual or annual basis.

It is probably unnecessary to set fixed periods after which advance directives are automatically null and void. A lesson from the decision in the Malette case[5] is that when people complete a directive their preferences will now be taken seriously. Linking advance directives to other documents (e.g., a driver's licence) may ensure

that people review their directives regularly. However, they should be informed at the time they complete an advance directive that it is not cast in stone, that if they change their mind they should change their directive and that all those who are aware of the earlier directive should be informed of the change.

WHAT SHOULD BE DONE IF PATIENTS CHANGE THEIR MINDS?

When patients complete advance directives they are, presumably, competent. When they change their minds later they may be competent or they may not. (The terms "competent" and "incompetent" are the subjects of considerable philosophic, medical and legal discussion[18,19] that is beyond the scope of this article.)

If a competent patient is able to communicate a preference that is contradictory to the one in the advance directive physicians should honour the later preference. Informed consent is a process and not an event, and patients have the right to change their minds. Safeguards should ensure that the patient did not change his or her mind under duress, but there is no reason to be more suspicious of changes of preference than of advance directives themselves....

A patient who is incompetent and able to communicate is controversial. Some members of our group held, that the patient's last competent wish, not the wish expressed during the state of incompetence, should be followed regardless of whether the patient had recently declined a previously requested treatment or recently requested a previously declined treatment. The rationale is the overriding priority of autonomy as embodied in the advance directive. Others argued that the physician should act generally in favour of preserving life. If the patient initially declined treatment but later requested it, then treatment should be given. If the patient initially requested treatment but later declined it, then again treatment should be given. The rationale is that in the face of contradictory evidence about the patient's authentic wishes the physician should err in favour of preserving life because wrongful death is worse than wrongful life.[20] If time permits we recommend broad consultation with the family, other health care professionals and possibly institutional ethics committees or consultants.

Since the patient who is incompetent and unable to communicate is unable to express a change in preference, this situation, too, is more theoretic than practical.

HOW SHOULD IMPLEMENTATION BE ENFORCED?

A recent study by Danis and colleagues[21] has shown that 75% of patients received the type of care that they requested in an advance directive. Was this rate of compliance too low, too high, or just right? How should compliance with patients' advance directives be enforced? We considered three mechanisms: legislation, case law and a system of graded referral through ethics committees and administrative tribunals. (The problem of conscientious objection to a patient's treatment has been addressed elsewhere.[22,23])

First, compliance with advance directives could be enforced through sanctions contained in provincial legislation and buttressed by federal legislation, including the Criminal Code and the Canadian Charter of Rights and Freedoms.... The perceived benefits of legislative sanctions depend on one's view of the problem that advance directives attempt to address. If one believes that patients' preferences are usually unknown but if they were known health care professionals would act in good faith to carry them out, then legislative sanctions are unnecessary. If one believes that even if patients' preferences were known health care professionals would not follow them, then legislative sanctions are necessary.

There are potential hazards to legislative sanctions. Patients' directives may be followed even if there is evidence that the patient had changed his or her mind, perhaps as a result of the clinical circumstances. Sanctions may deter health care professionals from offering advance directives to their patients because they fear that they will be forced to follow the poorly considered or inauthentic wishes of the patients who complete them. Finally, health care professionals are generally skeptical of legal solutions to patient care problems, and the presence of heavy-handed legislative sanctions may cause them to abandon the entire project of advance directives.

Some would argue that legislation that recognizes advance directives without ensuring that they will be followed is unnecessary. However, a clear benefit of such legislation is its symbolic value: the message that society approves of advance directives. Legislation would likely promote the use of these documents. It would dispel the concerns of health care professionals regarding the legality of advance directives. (It could also provide immunity from civil prosecution or disciplinary action for physicians who follow patients' advance directives.) It would offer an opportunity for public education through the news media as the proposed legislation is debated in provincial legislatures or the federal parliament.

Second, compliance with advance directives could be enforced solely by the common law and the courts. However, the adversarial nature of the courtroom is not well suited to the human problems of the hospital or clinic, and family lawyers increasingly realize that conflicts are best resolved outside the courts. Moreover, if all cases of disagreement were referred to the courts an already burdened system would be overloaded. Access to the court system requires financial resources that many families may not possess.

Finally, compliance could be enforced by graded referral, which occupies a middle ground between legislative sanctions and common-law solutions. Legislation could establish a process of selective referral of cases in which the health care professional wishes to deviate from or seek clarification about the patient's advance directive or in which there is conflict between providers and family members regarding its implementation. Such a system would operate at three levels. First, cases involving conflict would be referred to the institutional ethics committee.[24] Second, cases not thus resolved would be referred to a professional disciplinary board or multidisciplinary administrative tribunal. (The advantage of a professional disciplinary board administered by licensing bodies... is that these bodies are already in place and have a mandate to protect the public; the advantage of creating an administrative tribunal is that it would be constituted specifically to address the problem of advance directives.) Third, decisions made by the administrative tribunal or disciplinary body could be appealed to the courts. Such appeal procedures are well established.

Neither legislative sanctions nor common-law solutions alone satisfactorily address the problem of noncompliance with patients' advance directives. We recommend legislation without sanctions for noncompliance in addition to a system of graded referral of individual cases.

HOW SHOULD CONSIDERATION OF THE USE OF ADVANCE DIRECTIVES BE PROMOTED?

There are no published data on how many Canadians have completed advance directives. U.S. surveys have shown that 9% of people in Wisconsin[25] and 15% of Americans overall[26] have completed such documents. How can more people be given the opportunity to consider the use of advance directives? (By "considering their use" we mean offering people the opportunity to complete advance directives; a public policy focusing solely on encouraging people to complete them might foster coercion and violate the principle of self-determination on which advance directives are based.)

Consideration of the use of advance directives could be promoted by public education, professional education, policy in health care facilities, legislation and remuneration. Public education (which may include advertisements in the media) should not be used merely to direct or encourage people to complete a directive but also to inform them of the problem that such directives seek to address, their purpose, the main types of directives, the procedures for completing them and where people can turn for further information.

The professional education of health care providers, lawyers and all other counsellors on advance directives complements public education. Health care professionals should be aware of the legal status of advance directives, the need to raise the topic of directives at an appropriate time, effective methods of communication during their completion and the limitations of advance directives. Lawyers should understand the clinical situations and life-sustaining treatments involved and the need to refer clients for further discussion of their health to their physicians. Professional organizations whose members are called on to assist people to complete advance directives should make educational programs on this topic available to their members.

It may be appropriate for facilities to develop a policy of making advance directives available to patients, especially if the facility also provides education for health care providers. Only education can ensure that there are staff trained to assist patients to complete directives and that physicians and other members of the health care team are prepared to implement the directives appropriately when they come into effect.

Legislation recognizing the validity of advance directives could ensure that the documents are legally binding and protect physicians and other health care providers from civil liability for following them. (The Criminal Code should also be amended to protect them from criminal liability.) If the legal validity of advance directives is confirmed physicians may be more willing to recommend them to their patients and the public more willing to complete them.

Remuneration of health-care professionals for time spent discussing advance directives may encourage their use. It is likely that under provincial health care insurance plans at present such discussions qualify for remuneration as routine office visits or counselling. However, if advice on directives were an item in the fee schedule more physicians might be encouraged to offer it. (The perception may remain that when there is a financial incentive patients may be coerced into completing advance directives.) Remuneration of lawyers will tend to be driven more by client demand than by public policy. However, policy-makers should encourage publicly funded legal clinics to provide clients with advance directives; in addition, they should include advance directives among the services for which legal-aid remuneration is available and encourage private legal service plans (like those provided by unions) to include advance directives among the services offered.

Public and professional education is necessary to facilitate the introduction of advance directives. Legislation, institutional policies and remuneration all play a role in clarifying the official status of these documents and encouraging their use. Asked to pick a single best strategy, we prefer public education. A combined strategy that makes use of several or all of the options may be even better. For example, public education would be more effective if the legal validity of advance directives were established and health care providers were educated about advance directives, so that patients requesting them could be accommodated. Despite the focus on legislation in the public debate, other steps are necessary to promote the appropriate use of advance directives.

CONCLUSIONS

1. In principle, advance directives are a valuable method for people to express their preferences about life-sustaining treatment.

2. In design, directives should permit refusal of and requests for life-sustaining treatment. Instruction directives should be framed in terms of specific treatment preferences and general life values. Combined directives are preferable to instruction or proxy directives alone. No specific directive can be recommended.

3. Advance directives should be offered to anyone who requests them. Chronically or terminally ill patients will need them most, and clients who are making or updating their testamentary wills may be receptive to the idea of completing one.

4. Advance directives should be updated on the person's request, when there is a change in clinical status or admission to a health care facility, when deemed appropriate by a physician or lawyer and when the person undergoes a major life change. Those completing a directive should be advised to revise it if their preferences for life-sustaining treatment or the identity of the proxy decision-maker changes.

5. If competent people change their preferences, the most recently expressed wishes should be followed. If incompetent patients change the preferences expressed while they were competent, it is questionable whether the physician should follow the original wishes or those that would preserve the patient's life.

6. Advance directives should be enforced through a system of graded referral of controversial cases to institutional ethics committees, administrative tribunals or professional disciplinary boards and the courts.

7. Consideration of the use of advance directives should be promoted through public and professional education, health facility policy, legislation and remuneration.

... Other important questions remain: How will advance directives be made transportable, that is, made available when they are needed? Which people are best placed to give advice about advance directives?

Are advance directives an advance? We believe that they are. However, as we realized and as will become apparent when advance directives are more broadly used, they contain many limitations. Having identified and addressed some of these limitations, we hope that the introduction of advance directives in Canada will proceed with due caution.

NOTES*

1. Singer P.A., Siegler M. Elective use of life-sustaining treatments. In Stollerman G.H. (ed): *Advances in Internal Medicine,* vol 36. Yr Bk Med Pubs, New York, 1991: 57-79.

2. Omnibus Budget Reconciliation Act, 1990 (U.S. Public Law 101-508), s 42069 4751.

3. *Cruzan v. Director, Missouri Department of Health* (1990), II 0 SCt 2841.

4. *Attorney-General of B.C.v. Astaforoff,* 6 CCC, 3d 498 (BCCA 1983).

5. *Malette v. Shulman* (1990), 72 OR (2d) 417 (Ont CA).

6. Lo B., McLeod G.A., Saika G.: Patient attitudes to discussing life-sustaining treatment. *Arch Intern Med* 1986; 146: 1613-1615.

7. Shmerling R.H., Bedell S.E., Lilienfeld A. *et al.*: Discussing cardiopulmonary resuscitation: a study of elderly outpatients. *J Gen Intern Med* 1988; 3: 317-321.

8. Frankl D., Oye R.K., Bellamy P.E.: Attitudes of hospitalized patients toward life-support: a survey of 200 medical patients. *Am J Med* 1989; 86: 645-648.

---

* These notes have been renumbered to aid the reader.

9. Gamble E.R., McDonald P.J., Lichstein P.R.: Knowledge, attitudes and behavior of elderly persons regarding living. *Arch Intern Med* 1991; 151: 277-280.

10. Emanuel L.L., Barry M.J., Stoeckle J.D. *et al.*: Advance direcctives for medical care—a case for greater use. *N Engl J Med* 1991; 324: 889-895.

11. Pellegrino E.D., Thomasma D.C.: *For the Patient's Good—The Restoration of Beneficence in Health Care*, Oxford U Pr, New York, 1989: 136-147.

12. Fisher R.H., Meslin E.M.: Should living wills be legalized? *Can Med Assoc J* 1990; 142: 23-26.

13. Emanuel L.L., Emanuel E.J.: The Medical Directive: a new comprehensive advance care document. *JAMA* 1989; 261: 3288-3293.

14. Lambert P., Gibson J.M., Nathanson P.: The Values History: an innovation in surrogate medical decision making. *Law Med Health Care* 1990; 3: 202-212.

15. Everhart M.A., Pearlman R.A.: Stability of patient preferences regarding life-sustaining treatments. *Chest* 1990; 97: 159-164.

16. Silverstein M.D., Stocking C.B., Antel J. *et al.*: Amyotrophic lateral sclerosis and life-sustaining therapy: patients' desires for information, participation in decision making, and preferences for life-sustaining therapy. *Mayo Clin Proc* 1991; 66: 906-913.

17. Teno J., Mor V., Fleishman J.: Stability of preferences among patients with HIV-related disease [abstr]. *Clin Res* 1991; 39: 632A.

18. Weisstub D.N.: *Enquiry on Mental Competency, Final Report.* Queen's Printer for Ontario, Toronto, 1990.

19. Appelbaum P.S., Grisso T.: Assessing patients' capacities to consent to treatment. *N Engl J Med* 1988; 319: 1635-1638.

20. Singer P.A., Lowy F.H.: Refusal of life-sustaining treatment: the Malette case and decision-making under uncertainty. *Ann R Coll Physicians Surg Can* 1991; 24: 401-403.

21. Danis M., Southerland L.I., Garrett J.M. *et al.*: A prospective study of advance directives for life-sustaining care. *N Engl J Med* 1991; 324: 882-888.

22. *Making Health Care Decisions: A Report on the Ethical and Legal Implications of Informed Consent in the Patient-Practitioner Relationship,* vol 1. President's Commission for the Study of Ethical Problems in Medicine and Biomedical and Behavioral Research, Washington, 1982.

23. Miles S.H., Singer P.A., Siegler M.: Conflicts between patients' wishes to forgo treatment and the policies of health care facilities. *N Engl J Med* 1989; 321: 48-50.

24. Singer P.A., Pellegrino E.D., Siegler M.: Ethics committees and consultants. *J Clin Ethics* 1990; I: 263-267.

25. Shapiro R.S., Tavill F., Rivkin G. *et al.*: Living will in Wisconsin. *Wis Med J* 1986; 85: 17-23.

26. Harvey L.K., Shubat S.C.: *Physician and Public Attitudes.* Am Med Assoc, Chicago, 1989: 113.

FURTHER READINGS

Childress, James F. *Who Should Decide? Paternalism in Health Care*. Oxford and New York: Oxford University Press, 1982.

Emanuel, Ezekiel J. and Linda L. Emanuel. "Living Wills: Past, Present and Future." *Journal of Clinical Ethics* 1:1 (Spring 1990) 9-19.

Hackler, C., R. Moseley and D.E. Vawter, eds. *Advance Directives in Medicine*. New York: Praeger, 1989, 141-145.

Kuhse, Helga. *The Sanctity of Life Doctrine in Medicine: A Critique*. Oxford: Clarendon Press, 1987.

Law Reform Commission of Canada, Working Paper 46. *Omission, Negligence and Endangering*. Ottawa: Law Reform Commission, 1985.

Law Reform Commission of Canada, Report 20. *Euthanasia, Aiding Suicide and Cessation of Treatment*. Ottawa: Minister of Supply and Services, 1983.

Maguire, Daniel, *Death by Choice*. New York: Doubleday, 1974.

Nova Scotia Medical Consent Act, 1988, c.14, s.1.

Picard, Ellen. *Legal Liability of Doctors and Hospitals in Canada*. Toronto: Carswell, 1984.

Rosner, F. *Modern Medicine and Jewish Law*. N.Y.: Yeshiva University, 1972.

Schmeiser, Douglas A. "Living Wills and Medical Treatment of the Terminally Ill." *Health Management Forum* 2:3 (Fall 1989) 32-37.

Society for the Right to Die. *Handbook of Living Will Laws*. New York: Society for the Right to Die, 1987.

CHAPTER 9
INFORMATION AND
MEDICAL TREATMENT

INTRODUCTION

When we think of informed consent, we usually think of getting sufficient information about a procedure or undertaking to be able to make an informed and competent choice. We usually don't think about the fact that the choice that we make is really informed if, and only if, we know not only the treatment options but also our own health status or condition.

However, to know what our health status is, we have to have an overview of our own clinical picture; and in most cases we can get this only from our health care records: that is, from the records that detail the medically relevant findings that health care professionals — and especially physicians — have made about our health. Patient-rights groups have therefore maintained for some time that since informed consent is not really possible if patients do not know their own health care records, patients should have the right to see their records and to have copies made of them if they so wish.

The organizations that represent health care professionals — in particular, the Canadian Medical Association — have tended to resist this. First of all, they have argued that these records were never intended for patients: only for the attending physician or for other physicians. And following the line that a little knowledge is a dangerous thing, they have gone on to say that patients don't know enough about how to interpret these health care records, and therefore would jump to the wrong conclusions. They have also argued that patients might actually be harmed by finding out what is in their records. Physicians cannot allow this to happen. The primary obligation of physicians is to look out for the welfare of the patient. Finally, they have maintained that the patient record belongs to the physician because it is the physician who originated it.

If the courts are any indication, Canadian society does not agree with this. We find a graphic illustration of this in the New Brunswick case of *McInerney v.*

MacDonald. It sets out that under normal circumstances a patient does indeed have the right of access to her or his records. It is simply part of the evolving societal insistence on individual autonomy; an insistence that appears to reflect a deontological ethical perspective. At the same time, it does not address a major issue that has been worrying health care professionals ever since: What if the records contain confidential information about *other* people? Another question is, What about third-party access? For example, what if a patient gives a lawyer or an insurance company authorization to have access to her or his records? Do the patients really understand what this means? Especially in the case of insurance companies? Should health care professionals worry about this? Should health care institutions?

Howard Brody, who is a physician, deals with an entirely different subject that also falls under the heading of informed consent. Health care professionals sometimes deliberately mislead their patients. Physicians form the major group who does this. For example, they do it when they lead their patients to believe that the prescriptions they give them or the treatments they recommend are causally effective for the patients' conditions, when in actuality this is not the case.

Sometimes there appear to be good practical reasons for doing this. For instance, the patients may not actually have anything physiologically wrong with them at all, yet they *feel* ill. It may also be that there is no known treatment that is causally effective, yet there is a chance that the simple fact of prescribing something or of doing something will have a beneficial effect.

In these and similar cases, the physicians may be banking on what is known as the "placebo" effect to make the patients feel better. That is to say, they may be hoping that the psychosomatic effect of doing *something* will help the patients. Nurses and other health care professionals also deceive the patients when they go along with this.

Of course, not all cases of deliberate deception are like this. There is the case of the addict who is convinced that no method of treatment will help. The physician gradually weakens the injection of morphine with a saline solution — and after a while the patient is completely weaned. Are practices like this unethical? Brody looks at some of the issues that are involved.

McInerney v. MacDonald

The judgement was delivered by Mr. Justice La Forest...

The central issue in this case is whether in the absence of legislation a patient is entitled to inspect and obtain copies of his or her medical records upon request....

The appellant raises two issues in this appeal: (1) Are a patient's medical records

McInerney v. MacDonald 93 D.L.R. (4th) 415.

prepared by a physician the property of that physician or are they the property of the patient? (2) If a patient's medical records are the property of the physician who prepares them, does a patient nevertheless have the right to examine and obtain copies of all documents in the physician's medical record, including records that the physician may have received which were prepared by other physicians?...

I am prepared to accept that the physician, institution or clinic compiling the medical records owns the physical records. This leaves the remaining issue of whether the patient nevertheless has a right to examine and obtain copies of all documents in the physician's medical records....

Of primary significance is the fact that the records consist of information that is highly private and personal to the individual. It is information that goes to the personal integrity and autonomy of the patient. ...[S]uch information remains in a fundamental sense one's own, for the individual to communicate or retain as he or she sees fit....

A physician begins compiling a medical file when a patient chooses to share intimate details about his or her life in the course of medical consultation. The patient "entrusts" this personal information to the physician for medical purposes....[C]ertain duties do arise from the special relationship of trust and confidence between doctor and patient. Among these are the duty of the doctor to act with utmost good faith and loyalty, and to hold information received from or about a patient in confidence.... When a patient releases personal information in the context of the doctor-patient relationship, he or she does so with the legitimate expectation that these duties will be respected....

The fiduciary duty to provide access to medical records is ultimately grounded in the nature of the patient's interest in his or her records. As discussed earlier, information about oneself revealed to a doctor acting in a professional capacity remains, in a fundamental sense, one's own. The doctor's position is one of trust and confidence. The information conveyed is held in a fashion somewhat akin to a trust. While the doctor is the owner of the actual record, the information is to be used by the physician for the benefit of the patient. The confiding of the information to the physician for medical purposes gives rise to an expectation that the patient's interest in and control of the information will continue....

The trust-like "beneficial interest" of the patient in the information indicates that, as a general rule, he or she should have a right of access to the information and that the physician should have a corresponding obligation to provide it. The patient's interest being in the information, it follows that the interest continues when that information is conveyed to another doctor who then becomes subject to the duty to afford the patient access to that information.

There is a further matter that militates in favour of disclosure of patient records. As mentioned earlier, one of the duties arising from the doctor-patient relationship is the duty of the doctor to act with utmost good faith and loyalty. If the patient is denied access to his or her records, it may not be possible for the patient to establish that this duty has been fulfilled. As I see it, it is important that the patient have access to the records for the very purposes for which it is sought to withhold the documents, namely, to ensure the proper functioning of the doctor-patient relationship and to protect the well-being of the patient. If there has been improper conduct in the doctor's dealings with his or her patient, it ought to be revealed. The purpose of keeping the documents secret is to promote the proper functioning of the relationship, not to facilitate improper conduct.

Disclosure is all the more important in our day when individuals are seeking more information about themselves. It serves to reinforce the faith of the individual in his or her treatment. The ability of a doctor to provide effective treatment is closely related to the level of trust in the relationship. A doctor is in a better position to diagnose a medical problem if the patient freely imparts personal information. The duty of confidentiality that arises from the doctor-patient relationship is meant to encourage disclosure of information and communication between doctor and patient. In my view, the trust reposed in the physician by the patient mandates that the flow of information operate both ways....

While patients should, as a general rule, have access to their medical records, this policy need not and, in my mind, should not be pursued blindly. The related duty of confidentiality is not absolute. ... For example, "there may be cases in which reasons connected with the safety of individuals or of the public, physical or moral, would be sufficiently cogent to supersede or qualify the obligations prima facie imposed by the confidential relation." Similarly, the patient's general right of access to his or her records is not absolute. The patient's interest in his or her records is an equitable interest arising from the physician's fiduciary obligation to disclose the records upon request. As part of the relationship of trust and confidence, the physician must act in the best interests of the patient. If the physician reasonably believes it is not in the patient's best interests to inspect his or her medical records, the physician may consider it necessary to deny access to the information....In my view, the onus properly lies on the doctor to justify an exception to the general rule of access....

If a physician objects to the patient's general right of access, he or she must have reasonable grounds for doing so. Although I do not intend to provide an exhaustive analysis of the circumstances in which access to medical records may be denied,

some general observations may be useful. I shall make these in a response to a number of arguments that have been advanced by the appellant and in the literature for denying a patient access to medical records. These include: (1) disclosure may facilitate the initiation of unfounded lawsuits; (2) the medical records may be meaningless; (3) the medical records may be misinterpreted; (4) doctors may respond by keeping less thorough notes; and (5) disclosure of the contents of the records may be harmful to the patient or a third party.

The argument that patients may commence unfounded litigation if they are permitted to examine their medical records is not a sufficient ground for withholding them....Denial of access may actually encourage unfounded lawsuits. If a lawsuit is started, a patient can generally obtain access to his or her records under rules of civil procedure relating to discovery of documents. Thus, if a patient strongly wishes to see his or her records, one way of achieving this result is to commence an action before ascertaining whether or not there is a valid basis for the action....

The arguments that the records may be meaningless or that they may be misinterpreted do not justify non-disclosure in the ordinary case. If the records are, in fact, meaningless, they will not help the patient but neither will they cause harm. It is always open to the patient to obtain assistance in understanding the file....If it is possible that the patient will misconstrue the information in the record (for example, misinterpret the relevance of a particular laboratory test), the doctor may wish to advise the patient that the medical record should be explained and interpreted by a competent health care professional....

The concern that disclosure will lead to a decrease in the completeness, candour and frankness of medical records, can be answered by reference to the obligation of a physician to keep accurate records. A failure to do so may expose the physician to liability for professional misconduct or negligence. It is also easy to exaggerate the importance of this argument....

Non-disclosure may be warranted if there is a real potential for harm either to the patient or to a third party. This is the most persuasive ground for refusing access to medical records. However, even here, the discretion to withhold information should not be exercised readily. Particularly in situations that do not involve the interests of third parties, the court should demand compelling grounds before confirming a decision to deny access.... Non-disclosure can itself affect the patient's well-being. If access is denied, the patient may speculate as to what is in the records and imagine difficulties greater than those that actually exist. In addition, the physical well-being of the patient must be balanced with the patient's

right to self-determination. Both are worthy of protection. ...

Since I have held that the tangible records belong to the physician, the patient is not entitled to the records themselves. Medical records play an important role in helping the physician to remember details about the patient's medical history. The physician must have continued access to the records to provide proper diagnosis and treatment. Such access will be disrupted if the patient is able to remove the records from the premises.

Accordingly, the patient is entitled to reasonable access to examine and copy the records, provided the patient pays a legitimate fee for the preparation and reproduction of the information. Access is limited to the information the physician obtained in providing treatment. It does not extend to information arising outside the doctor-patient relationship....

The Lie That Heals: The Ethics of Giving Placebos

Howard Brody

The 170-year-long debate in the medical literature about the ethics of prescribing placebos in medical therapeutics needs to be reevaluated in light of recent placebo research and improved understanding of the placebo effect as an integral part of the doctor-patient relationship. It has traditionally been assumed that deception is an indispensible component of successful placebo use. Therefore, placebos have been attacked because they are deceptive, and defended on the grounds that the deception is illusory or that the beneficent intentions of the physician justify the deception. However, a proper understanding of the placebo effect shows that deception need play no essential role in eliciting this powerful therapeutic modality; physicians can use nondeceptive means to promote a positive placebo response in their patients.

H. Brody, "The Lie That Heals: The Ethics of Giving Placebos," *Annals of Internal Medicine* 97:1 (1982).

The debate over whether it is ethical for physicians to prescribe placebos for patients has surfaced at intervals in the medical literature since the 19th century. Because traditional oaths and codes of ethics are silent on this issue, physicians taking a stand on placebo use have been unable to appeal to authority and have been prompted to develop original and often highly creative moral arguments. Although these arguments deserve review simply as an often-neglected feature of medical history, they also require critical reexamination in light of two recent developments. The first is the awakening of experimental interest in the placebo effect, and a gradual reconceptualization of placebo phenomena to recognize their pervasiveness as part of medical practice.[1] The second is the emphasis in contemporary medical ethics of individual rights and patient autonomy in the doctor-patient relationship,[2-4] leading to the rejection of many paternalistic assumptions previously thought to justify medical deception.[5]

PLACEBOS AND THE PLACEBO EFFECT

"An empiric oftentimes, and a silly chirurgeon, doth more strange cures than a rational physician ... because the patient puts his confidence in him," Robert Burton wrote in 1628,[6] showing that at least by Renaissance times physicians appreciated the power of the imagination and expectation to change bodily states and to cure disease. In 1785 Benjamin Franklin led a commission to investigate Mesmer's animal magnetism and, in a series of elegant experiments, showed that the subjects' imagination was the most important factor in explaining the bizarre effects and miraculous cures attributed to that practice.[7] Physicians were not reluctant to take advantage of this phenomenon by prescribing medications thought to be pharmacologically inert

when no specific remedy was indicated. Thomas Jefferson wrote to Dr. Casper Wistar in 1807, "One of the most successful physicians I have ever known, has assured me, that he used more of bread pills, drops of colored water, and powders of hickory ashes, than of all other medicines put together."[8]

The contemporary era of placebo research began with the adoption of the double-blind controlled trial as the standard experimental method in the 1940s; subsequent findings on the placebo effect have been reviewed extensively.[1,9-13] Whenever a supposedly inert treatment is used in an experimental situation, 30% to 40% of subjects can be expected to show some benefit from the placebo treatment.[9] The pattern of the response to placebo typically resembles the pharmacologic findings of active drug responses.[14] In one study of the effect of both clofibrate and placebo on cholesterol level and cardiovascular mortality, those control subjects who reliably took their placebos showed lower cholesterol and reduced mortality compared with their less compliant counterparts.[15] Placebo response is not limited to the patient's subjective experience; placebos alter laboratory values and other measures of objective physiologic change.[16] Although placebos are commonly thought of primarily as pain relievers, virtually all potentially reversible symptoms and diseases that have been investigated in double-blind studies show some response to placebo — including diabetes,[17] angina pectoris,[18] and malignant neoplasms.[19] Placebos can also cause many of the same side effects seen with active medication.[20,21] For all these reasons it is impossible to use placebo response to distinguish between a real, organic symptom and a symptom that is "all in the patient's head," although the myth to the contrary still persists.[22]

From an early focus on attempting to elucidate the "personality type" of persons who react to placebos (which failed in part because the same person may respond or fail to respond to placebo in different circumstances),[9] attempts to understand placebo phenomena have shifted to a broader approach to factors in the doctor-patient relationship, in the overall situational context, and in the cultural background.[23-29] It has become more clear that whatever happens when a patient gets better after ingesting a sugar pill also happens to some degree whenever the patient receives a pharmacologically potent treatment within a supportive healing relationship; that at least some of the symptom relief that follows administration of the active treatment arises from emotional and symbolic factors. That is, the placebo effect pervades much of medical practice even when no placebo has been used.

For example, when meprobamate, phenobarbital, and placebo were administered blindly to anxious patients, the two pharmacologically active drugs were clearly superior to placebo when administered by a physician who had confidence in the drugs' efficacy and who was viewed by the subjects as supportive; the drugs and placebo showed no difference when administered by a less supportive and more skeptical physician. Subjects of the first physician also showed more overall symptom relief.[30] It is reasonable to suspect, then, that when the family physician prescribes decongestants for a viral upper respiratory infection, some of the patient's symptom relief is due to the pharmacologic action of the drug, but some is also due to the emotional support of the doctor-patient relationship, the doctor's confirmation and legitimization of the illness, and the reassurance that the symptoms do not represent something more serious than a bad cold.

DEFINITIONS

The expanded concept of the placebo effect just described makes it undesirable to have the definition of "placebo effect" totally dependent on the definition of "placebo." The following definitions may serve satisfactorily for our purposes: The placebo effect is the change in the patient's condition that is attributable to the symbolic import of the healing intervention rather than to the intervention's specific pharmacologic or physiologic effects; a placebo is a form of medical therapy, or an intervention designed to simulate medical therapy, that is believed to be without specific activity for the condition being treated, and that is used either for its symbolic effect or to eliminate observer bias in a controlled experiment. It is worth recalling here that although the sugar pill is cited as the paradigm case of placebo use, any medical treatment, including such diverse techniques as surgery[31] and biofeedback[32] can function as a placebo.

Another useful distinction uses the terms "pure" and "impure" placebos. A pure placebo, such as a lactose pill or a saline injection, is totally without pharmacologic potency. An impure placebo has some pharmacologic properties, but these are not relevant to the current circumstances and the treatment is used solely for its psychologic effect. Common examples are thyroid, vitamin B12, and penicillin, when used in patients who do not have hypothyroidism, pernicious anemia, or bacterial infections, respectively.

PLACEBOS AND DECEPTION

Jefferson said of the use of bread pills and drops of colored water in 1807, "It was certainly a pious fraud."[8] Subsequent writers, including physicians, philosophers, and scientists, have adopted widely divergent positions on the ethics of giving placebos.[33] All authorities, however, are agreed on one point — if there is an ethical problem in therapeutic use of placebos, the problem is that of deception. This agreement in turn arises from a shared assumption about how placebos are typically used in clinical practice, which will be called here the "traditional use" of placebos. In the traditional use, the physician administers a treatment known to him or her to be without pharmacologic potency; but the physician either tells or allows the patient to believe that the treatment has such potency. It is further assumed in the traditional-use model that the patient's false belief in the potency of the treatment is essential for the placebo effect to occur.[34-36]

Enough has already been said about the recently expanded concept of the placebo effect to call the traditional-use model into question on several counts. However, the bulk of the medical literature on the ethics of placebos accepts this model as a given. Hence, to do justice to most of the arguments offered by physicians for and against placebo use, the traditional-use model must form the point of departure. In a subsequent section, the ethical position that results from replacing the traditional model with the expanded concept will be considered.

It will be most convenient to survey first the arguments offered against placebo use, as these assume that deception is generally wrong, and that it is just as wrong (if indeed not worse) when encountered in medicine as when encountered elsewhere in life. Next, arguments in favor of placebo use can be investigated to see how successfully they defuse the deception issue.

ARGUMENTS AGAINST PLACEBOS

It is standard in modern writings on medical ethics to oppose placebo use because it represents a specific instance of the more general issue of patient deception.[2,3,5,37,38] The value of avoiding deception is grounded in the more basic values of the autonomy and dignity of the individual patient. The basic idea is that of moral reciprocity. We generally wish that other people treat us in a manner that shows their respect for us as persons; and this entails that they not use manipulation or deception on us, even if they judge the results to be for our own good. If we are to regard our patients as our moral equals and to respect their dignity as persons, we are similarly prohibited from practicing deception or manipulation on them.

This line of reasoning is most at home in the context of a deontologic or duty-based ethical theory. Deception is condemned because it violates an *a priori* moral rule — *a priori* because the rule appeals to the very nature of our beings (that is, persons deserving respect) rather than to the good or bad consequences of our actions. Appeal to duty and to moral rule has always been a popular mode of argument. Thus one medical editor[39] wrote in 1885, "Physicians ... cannot always tell the plain truth to a patient without injuring him. It should be the rule of ... life, however, to be straightforward and candid. Therefore, we say that placebos should be ... rarely, if ever, prescribed." Describing the characteristics of the trustworthy and virtuous physician, the writer concluded, "We venture to say that such a man would not find it necessary to keep a polychromatic assortment of sugar pills in his closet."

This commentator explicitly rejects an argument from consequences — at times, indeed, being truthful may injure patients. But more basic than negative consequences is the *a priori* "rule of ... life," which in the 19th century was closely tied to concepts of virtue and gentlemanly conduct, and hence truthfulness.

Other physicians, however, have been uncomfortable with *a priori* appeals and have preferred a utilitarian mode of argument, demanding to be shown that placebo use, generally applied, would lead to a net increase in unhappiness over happiness for all concerned. Among many adopting a utilitarian stand, the most articulate and forceful was Richard C. Cabot, best known today as originator of the clinicopathologic conferences of the Massachusetts General Hospital, but in his day an innovative writer on medical ethics as well as on medicine, and holder of the Chair of Professor of Social Ethics at Harvard University in addition to his medical appointment.[40] Cabot[41] rejected an *a priori* approach to issues of truth and falsehood — "you will notice I am not now arguing that a lie is, in itself and apart from its consequences, a bad thing" — but felt that the negative consequences of placebo use condemned the practice. The obvious short-range consequence occurred when the patient discovered the deception and lost trust in the physician. True, it was probable in any single case that the physician would not be found out; but Cabot[41] rejoined, "Is it good for us as professional men to have our reputations rest on the expectation of not being found out?"

But Cabot[41] was much more concerned about the long range consequences of creating unhealthy public attitudes toward medicine and medications:

The majority of placebos are given because we believe that the patient will not be satisfied without them. He has learned to expect medicine for every symptom and without it he simply won't get well. True, but who taught him to expect a medicine for every symptom? He was not born with that expectation. He learned it from an ignorant doctor who really believed it.... It is we physicians who are responsible for perpetuating false ideas about disease and its cure ... and with every placebo that we give

we do our part in perpetuating error, and harmful error at that.

Cabot elsewhere[42] stated even more bluntly, "Placebo giving is quackery." He concluded[41] that in general the negative consequences of placebo use outweighed the positive; but that placebos could be justified in some rare cases:

No patient whose language you can speak, whose mind you can approach, needs a placebo. I give placebos now and then ... to Armenians and others with whom I cannot communicate, because to refuse to give them would create more misunderstandings, a falser impression, than to give them. The patient will think that I am refusing to treat him at all; but if I can get hold of an interpreter and explain the matter, I tell him no lies in the shape of placebos.

Another more recent commentator reflected on both the occasional justification for giving placebos, and the rarity with which such a case ought to arise: "Some patients are so unintelligent, neurotic, and inadequate as to be incurable, and life is made easier for them by a placebo." Then, paraphrasing an earlier commentator,[43] he concluded: "It has been said that the use of placebos is in inverse ratio to the combined intelligences of patient and doctor."[44]

In assessing the consequences of placebo use as a general policy, one should note the tendency of deception to multiply itself, and the need to cover up for the original lie. Prescribing placebos now involves insuring the complicity of the nurse, the pharmacist, and all other parties to the prescription. There is also the problem of setting a fee for the placebo prescription — if too high, then someone will appear to be making an unjustified profit from deception; if too low, the deception may inadvertently be discovered. It may be more for such mundane reasons and not out of any increased ethical insight that the use of totally inert medicines like lactose pills has declined once physicians stopped dispensing their own drugs. In more recent times, fear of lawsuits may also have played a role.

ARGUMENTS FOR PLACEBOS

Deceptive or not, placebos have in fact been widely administered by practicing physicians, and to many the fascinating power of the body to respond to purely symbolic interventions seemed too potent a therapeutic tool to pass up. A number of commentators have tried to give a formal justification for placebo use. Once again, two general moral approaches have been used. For the deontologist, the force of the moral rule against deception cannot be denied; so it must be argued either that the deception rule does not properly apply to the placebo case, or that other moral rules may mitigate it. The utilitarian may calculate all the good consequences attributable to placebos, and argue (or assume) that these outweigh the evils of deception. For each of these attempts at justification, however, the placebo opponents have had a ready and generally persuasive reply.

First, one may forthrightly deny that placebo use need involve deception by the physician. This position, while occasionally alluded to,[45] is seldom stated explicitly in the medical literature; but it is frequently encountered in debate and discussion among physicians. It is usually argued that if the physician tells the patient that a sugar pill is morphine or penicillin, he is guilty of an outright and unethical lie. But if he administers the pill with a noncommittal statement, such as, "This pill will make you feel much better," he has not deceived the patient; any false beliefs result from the patient's deceiving himself and

are not the moral responsibility of the physician: "should a patient become suspicious …, the therapist need only give an honest evasion, rather than a lie."[36]

Richard Cabot[41] attacked this and other arguments defending medical practices that mislead the patient by stating, *"a true impression,* not certain words literally true, is what we must try to convey." By way of fleshing out Cabot's objection, it may be acknowledged that what counts as deception may be dependent on the norms and expectations associated with particular social settings. For instance, when we go to the theater and see Mark Twain reading from *Huckleberry Finn,* we do not consider ourselves to have been deceived when we discover he is a cleverly made-up actor. We may then ask whether the clinical setting is one of those special social situations where creating a false impression by deliberate misdirection does not count as deception. Cabot appears to have assumed that a patient may reasonably expect in that setting that, if a drug or other treatment is given, it is selected for its pharmacologic potency for the patient's condition. It also seems reasonable to assume that the patient will not expect that the physician will specifically name the treatment — the patient is accustomed to receiving pills alluded to by the physician merely as "an antibiotic" or "a decongestant," but these remedies are still assumed by the patient to be pharmacologically potent. One may then conclude that if the physician prescribes an inert pill and conceals this from the patient by verbal misdirection, he has violated these legitimate patient expectations and is guilty of deception; the special nature of the clinical setting gives no license for creating a false impression in this manner.

Legal backing[46] for Cabot's argument comes with the characterization of the physician-patient relationship as a fiduciary one, in which one party assumes a special responsibility to look out for the best interests of the other. "Where a person sustains toward others a relation of trust and confidence, his silence when he should speak, or his failure to disclose what he ought to disclose, is as much a fraud in law as an actual affirmative false representation."[47]

Still, the physician is not responsible for false beliefs the patient may bring into the encounter, if the physician has taken no action to cause those beliefs[48,49]; how far the physician's duty extends to dispel those false beliefs, if they do not lead directly to health-threatening behavior, is an interesting ethical question in itself. What is the physician's duty toward the patient who arrives with a firmly entrenched belief in the therapeutic and preventive powers of vitamins, and asks the physician to recommend a good daily vitamin supplement? This patient harbors a false belief, and energetic and prolonged discussion from the physician might mitigate or dispel it. But this reeducation seems hardly worth the effort, given the low probability of harm and the (presumed) low readiness of the patient to assimilate the new information. Thus the postulated duty not to create false beliefs in the patient by one's words or actions need not imply a more onerous duty to seek out and dispel all the false beliefs the patient may have acquired elsewhere.

Second, the placebo advocate may admit that placebos as traditionally used involve deception, but still insist that this use is ethically justified. Social practice recognizes a class of deceptions called white lies, which are felt to be essentially harmless because of their innocuous content and benign motivation.[50] Even if the special circumstances of medical practice do not automatically permit out-and-out deception, it still seems to be the case that many partial truths or euphemisms are appropriate. For example, proper supportive care of the cancer patient seeking some hope to mitigate the frightening diagnosis calls for a somewhat slanted presentation emphasizing the

potential gains from therapy, not merely for a listing of the 5-year survival statistics.

But a problem in including placebos in the category of white lies is that what counts as a white lie is fairly well demarcated by social convention; otherwise anyone uttering a falsehood, however blatant, could excuse his act by claiming it was "only a white lie." Members of society are thus in effect forewarned about this practice and, if they choose to ask their friends how their new hats or ties look on them, they can be said to have given at least implied consent to any white lie that results. By contrast, the traditional-use model assumes that knowledge of the lie will be restricted to the medical profession, lest placebos lose their effectiveness with wider publicity. Recipients of the so-called white lie are therefore systematically excluded from any knowledge of the existence of this practice, and they have no opportunity to challenge questionable uses of placebo deception by reference to generally accepted social norms and limits. This would make placebo use morally suspect in a way that the usual white lies are not.

Leslie[51] attempted to justify placebo deception in a similar fashion: "There is a fine line of distinction between the words, *deception* and *deceit* ... deceit implies blameworthiness whereas deception does not necessarily do so...." Leslie emphasized the benign intent of the physician and offered as an analogy a magician practicing sleight of hand to entertain an audience. But Bok[50] has emphasized that the supposedly benign intent of the person doing the lying, and the expected value of the resulting benefits, often look very different from the perspective of the person being lied to. The audience choosing voluntarily to witness the magician's performance can weigh for themselves the degree of deception, the intent, and the value of the benefits; the patient in the traditional-use model of placebos is denied this opportunity. (It may in fact be argued that the magic show is not "deception" at all, as any reasonably well informed person knows what goes on at such events and is not fooled in any substantive way.) Thus, Leslie is either merely asserting that some deceptions are justified and others are not, without giving any arguments to prove that placebos belong in the justified category; or else his "fine line" between deception and deceit is so fine as to escape attention altogether.

All this discussion of justified and unjustified deception, however, may seem pointless to the pragmatic physician who adopts the traditional use of placebos merely because it can benefit the patient. By this pragmatic view, either the physician's duty not to deceive is of no moral concern at all, or else it is far outweighed by the much stronger duty to benefit the patient — a duty which, Veatch[38] has argued, has dominated the so-called Hippocratic ethical tradition in medicine to the unwarranted exclusion of other, equally rational moral considerations. This view has gained added impetus since the recent wave of research described above, showing the extent and frequency of placebo responses. The pragmatic approach has been further bolstered by research linking the placebo response to endorphins.[52] Because endorphins function primarily in analgesia, and because, as was noted above, the placebo response is not limited to pain, this endorphin research really provides a very limited account of the physiologic means by which placebos may exert their effects. But to the uncritical medical mind, the identified biochemical basis for some placebo responses has somehow made the whole placebo issue suddenly respectable. (Shapiro[53] discovered in an informal survey that negativism toward placebo use among physicians correlated with greater age, private rather than academic practice, and nonparticipation in clinical research.)

In this setting, the placebo advocate may attribute, rightly or wrongly, several false beliefs to the person who argues against placebo use. The opponent of placebos may be thought to believe: that placebos really do not work, or work only for a limited number of medical conditions; that some pharmacologically active remedy exists for all conditions, so that the doctor who prescribes a placebo is automatically withholding the "correct" drug; or that any treatment that works by psychologic mechanisms is thereby inferior to a treatment that works by biochemical means. As we saw, ethical concern over placebos does not depend on any of these false assumptions, yet placebo opponents are still sometimes labeled as if their arguments ran contrary to modern scientific medicine. It may have been a mistaken attribution of these false beliefs that led a distinguished investigator of the placebo response[54] to characterize as "oft-quoted but fatuous" one of the better recent papers[55] offering arguments of the sort first used by Cabot.

One could, of course, offer a utilitarian counter-attack to Cabot[41] and contend that he had miscalculated the likelihood and the severity of the various consequences of placebo use. But any balanced view of the pros and cons makes this a remote possibility. First, if past studies are reliable, only 30% to 40% of patients will respond to placebo positively. Second, even though lactose can be expected to have fewer toxic effects than active drugs, placebo side effects and even addiction do periodically occur. Finally, even if one rejects these considerations, one is still left with the long-range consequences Cabot predicted — a public conditioned to look for the cure for all ills in a bottle of medicine, and to neglect prevention and a healthy lifestyle in favor of a medical quick fix.

But most pragmatic authors do not even attempt a balanced utilitarian consideration. If anything, they are content with a crude risk-benefit ratio: Anything that benefits the patient is good; placebos have been shown in scientific trials to benefit patients; therefore, placebos should be used, at least in selected sorts of cases. A frequent hidden assumption is that the only harm worth considering in this crude pragmatic calculus is direct physical harm such as that due to a toxic drug reaction. Less tangible harms — risks to doctor-patient trust, unhealthy views about drug-taking, and decreased opportunity for the patient to make choices about his own care — are simply left out of the equation.[34,36,43,56-65] The nature of the risk-benefit calculus is further illustrated by those authors who list specific contraindications or limitations for placebo use,[33,34,51] for instance, the concern that overuse of placebos will lead to diminished diagnostic vigilance[57] or that the placebo-treated patient will be more resistant to definitive psychotherapy.[66]

Placebo use may thus be cautiously endorsed because of its success, without raising ethical qualms:

> I knew a surgeon years ago who thought nothing of performing an oblique lower right quadrant incision, then suturing without entering the abdominal cavity in patients who had emotional problems manifested by pain in the abdomen. His results were excellent and as one might expect his operative mortality and morbidity were exceptionally low.... Certainly this is not common and I doubt whether anyone else would have done such procedures. However, I am certain that thousands of appendectomies and hysterectomies are done yearly as placebos. In retrospect, though at the time I was horrified at what he had done, and still am aware of the possible grave consequence, I am inclined to admire his courage.[63]

The unnecessary-surgery argument indicates that the less scientifically inclined physician may inadvertently use therapy that actually can benefit the patient only through the placebo effect. One may then argue that it is better for the physician to use a pure placebo rather than an impure placebo. Prescribing pure placebos at least promotes full knowledge (for the physician, at least) of the approach being taken; impure placebos promote unscientific medicine and expose the patient to increased risk of toxic reactions.[43,57,60]

> If deception is involved in the case of the pure placebo, it applies to only one person, namely, the patient, for the physician knows that the agent is devoid of all but psychotherapeutic properties. But when we use [an impure placebo] there is the danger of deceiving two people.... The doctor may come to think that the agent has potency when, in fact, it has none. That danger is real....[67]

Other authors are vaguely concerned about the deception issue but feel it to be merely a semantic problem: "If placebo therapy is regarded as a form of deception, then, of course, an ethical dilemma arises.... What is needed is a redefinition of placebo or nonspecific effects in psychologic or psychotherapeutic terms."[27] "If we give patients a placebo as an honest psychotherapeutic device, we can be considered fulfilling [our] primary responsibility."[63] But just because a substance is used for its symbolic properties does not eliminate the possibility of morally blameworthy deception:

> We like to think that our patients bring us their symptoms and problems for our consideration, expecting thoughtful and honest advice. With ... the declining influence of the Church, the doctor's value to the community as an impartial and educated adviser has become as important as the priest's used to be. The placebo is a form of deception and a

betrayal of trust equivalent to the sale of bottles of ditch-water as water of the River Jordan.[44]

There is, however, another form of defense for placebos that does not look at a weighing of the good and bad consequences, but rather at the nature of the implied expectations in the doctor-patient relationship. Placebo use is unjustified if the patient's proper expectation is "that the physician will give me the chance to be informed about the treatment"; but not if the expectation is "that the physician will choose on my behalf the treatment most likely to help." Thus it is argued that placebo use "does not amount to deception of the patient who trusts the doctor to order whatever he considers is most likely to be of benefit."[45]

There is nothing illogical about an expectation that gives the physician this extensive a blank check. But it is unlikely that most patients have such an expectation, at least in modern times, and specifically in relation to placebos. On the contrary, the indignation with which most people respond on learning they have received placebo surreptitiously is strong evidence against any widespread acceptance of this much paternalism. An individual patient, of course, may negotiate such an arrangement with his or her physician; but that hardly justifies the blanket attribution of paternalistic expectations to patients generally.

AN ALTERNATIVE POSITION: PLACEBO EFFECT WITHOUT DECEPTION

Of all the positions above, opposition to placebo use unless there are especially strong extenuating circumstances in a specific case is ethically most sound; the other positions either evade the deception issue or fail to disarm its legitimate force. But one must recall that all of these arguments assume the traditional-use model, which holds that the deception is an essential ingredient for successful placebo treatment. The considerations noted at the beginning of this paper, however, based on newer placebo research and appropriate redefinition of the terms "placebo effect" and "placebo," point the way to an effective separation of deception and the placebo effect in clinical practice. Once deception is eliminated (and not merely glossed over) the ethical problem is defused.

One excellent and commonplace example of nondeceptive use of placebos occurs in properly designed double-blind research with informed consent. The research subject is ignorant as to whether he or she is actually receiving placebo or the experimental drug; but he or she has been fully informed of the experimental design, about the use of placebos in the study, and about the risks and benefits associated with the design. If free consent is given based on that information, no deception has occurred and all the criteria for ethical research have been met. Unfortunately there are a few experiments, more commonly occurring in social science research, where deception about the nature of the experimental design is essential if the data are to be valid. Whether and with what consent arrangements such studies may be ethically conducted requires additional analysis.[68]

The first empirical rejection of the traditional-use model of the placebo response was a nonblind placebo trial.[69] Thirteen of 14 psychiatric outpatients with somatic symptoms who completed a week's trial of sugar pills, having been openly informed that they were sugar pills and that many patients experienced relief with such medication, experienced objective symptom reduction. Such a study, of course, has severe limitations, and this work has not been replicated. But a more recent survey of placebo therapeutics gives several case reports of successful placebo therapy in patients who were openly informed that they were receiving pharmacologically inert substances.[70] Furthermore, Norman Cousins,[71] in describing the response of his mysterious connective tissue disease to a combination of high-dose ascorbic acid, laughter, and positive thinking, commented, "It is quite possible that this treatment — like everything else I did — was a demonstration of the placebo effect." Here is anecdotal testimony that a well-informed patient may be aware of the mental or symbolic effect of a therapy and still experience major bodily changes.

Whereas possibilities for nondeceptive use of placebos are theoretically intriguing and are of some limited clinical applicability, the nondeceptive use of the placebo effect has much more important practical implications, because some element of the placebo effect exists in every clinical encounter even when no placebo is used.[1,23,25,28,29] An analysis of the symbolic elements of the physician-patient relationship suggests that a clinical approach that makes the illness experience more understandable to the patient, that instills a sense of caring and social support, and that increases a feeling of mastery and control over the course of the illness, will be most likely to create a positive placebo response and to improve symptoms.[24,26,29] Empirical support for this thesis is provided by a study of the effect of the anesthesiology pre-operative visit on postoperative pain. The control group received a standard visit whereas the experimental group received teaching about the nature of postoperative pain, advice on simple techniques to avoid pain and increase relaxation, and reassurance that back-up medication was available from the nurses. The experimental group required half as much pain medication and were able to be discharged an average of 2 days earlier. These investigators[72] — who used no inert substances and who committed no deceptions on the subjects — described their results as illustrating "a placebo effect without a placebo." Once clinicians realize the extent to which simple information and encouragement can elicit a positive placebo response and thus supplement the pharmacologic effects of any active medication, the perceived need to use deception or inert medication in clinical practice ought to be markedly diminished.

CONCLUSION

The placebo, as traditionally used, could be called the lie that heals. But a satisfactory understanding of the nature of the placebo effect shows that the healing comes not from the lie itself, but rather from the relationship between healer and patient, and the latter's own capacity for self-healing via symbolic and psychological approaches as well as via biological intervention.

For some time medical science has looked almost exclusively at technical means of diagnosis and treatment; the doctor-patient relationship that forms the setting for their application has been naïvely viewed as a noncontributory background factor, relegated to the amorphous realm of the "art of medicine," or simply ignored. In this setting, the placebo effect has inevitably been viewed as a nuisance variable, interfering with our ability to elicit "clean data" from clinical trials; and deception in medicine has been seen either as an unimportant side issue or as a tolerated means toward another end. But, as the doctor-patient relationship is rediscovered as a worthy focus for medical research and medical education, the placebo effect assumes center stage as one approach to a more sophisticated understanding of this relationship.[73] Deception is avoided, as ethically inappropriate and as a threat to the long-term stability of the relationship; and clinicians turn to alternative, nondeceptive ways to elicit positive placebo responses in all patient encounters at the same time that they apply the most appropriate medical technology.

NOTES

1. Brody, H. *Placebos and the Philosophy of Medicine.* Chicago: University of Chicago Press; 1980.

2. Beauchamp, T.H., Childress, J.F. *Principles of Biomedical Ethics.* New York: Oxford University Press; 1979.

3. Brody, H. *Ethical Decisions in Medicine*, 2nd ed. Boston: Little, Brown & Co.; 1981.

4. Buchanan, A. Medical paternalism. *Philosophy and Public Affairs.* 1978;7:370-90.

5. Reiser, S.J. Words as scalpels: Transmitting evidence in the clinical dialogue. *Ann Intern Med.* 1980;92:837-42.

6. Burton, R. *The Anatomy of Melancholy.* New York: Empire State Book Co.; 1924:168.

7. *Report of Dr. Benjamin Franklin and Other Commissioners Charged by the King of France with the Examination of the Animal Magnetism, As Now Practised at Paris.* London: J. Johnson; 1785. Fabin's Bibliotecha Americana, microcard #25 579.

8. Ford P.L., ed. *The Writings of Thomas Jefferson.* Vol. IX. New York: Putnam; 1898:78-85.

9. Beecher, H.K. The powerful placebo. *JAMA.* 1955;159:1602-6.

10. Kurland, A.A. Placebo effect. In: Uhr, L., Millar, J.G., eds. *Drugs and Behavior.* New York: John Wiley; 1960:156-65.

11. Berg, A.O. Placebos: A brief review for family physicians. *J Fam Pract.* 1977;5:97-100.

12. Shapiro, A.K., Morris, L.A. The placebo effect in medical and psychological therapies. In: Garfield, S.L., Bergin, A.E., eds. *Handbook of Psychotherapy and Behavior Change.* 2nd ed. New York: John Wiley; 1978.

13. Turner, J.L., Gallimore, R., Fox, C. *Placebo: An Annotated Bibliography.* Available from: UCLA, Neuropsychiatric Institute, Center for the Health Sciences, 760 Westwood Plaza, Los Angeles, CA 90024.

14. Lasagna, L., Laties, V.G., Dohan, J.L. Further studies on the "pharmacology" of placebo administration. *J Clin Invest.* 1958;37:533-7.

15. The Coronary Drug Project Research Group. Influence of adherence to treatment and response of cholesterol on mortality in the Coronary Drug Project. *N Engl J Med.* 1980;303:1038-41.

16. Wolf, S. Affects of suggestion and conditioning on the action of chemical agents in human subjects — the pharmacology of placebos. *J Clin Invest.* 1950;29:100-9.

17. Singer, D.L., Hurwitz, D. Long-term experience with sulfonylureas and placebo. *N Engl J Med.* 1967;277:450-6.

18. Benson, H., McCallie, D.P. Angina pectoris and the placebo effect. *N Engl J Med.* 1979;300:1424-9.

19. Klopfer, B. Psychological variables in human cancer. *J Projective Techniques.* 1957;21:331-40.

20. Wolf, S., Pinsky, R.H. Effects of placebo administration and occurrence of toxic reactions. *JAMA.* 1954;155:339-41.

21. Honzak, R., Horackova, E., Culik, A. Our experience with the effect of placebo in some functional and psychosomatic disorders. *Activitas Nervosa Superior.* 1972;14:184-5.

22. Goodwin, J.S., Goodwin, J.M., Vogel, A.V. Knowledge and use of placebos by house officers and nurses. *Ann Intern Med.* 1979;91:106-10.

23. Modell, W. *The Relief of Symptoms.* Philadelphia: WB Saunders; 1955.

24. Adler, H.M., Hammett, V.B.O. The doctor-patient relationship revisited. An analysis of the placebo effect. *Ann Intern Med.* 1973;78:595-8.

25. Benson, H., Epstein, M.D. The placebo effect: a neglected asset in the care of patients. *JAMA.* 1975;232:1225-7.

26. Cassell, E.J. The healer's art: A new approach to the doctor-patient relationship. Philadelphia: JB Lippincott; 1976.

27. Gallimore, R., Turner, J.L. Contemporary studies of placebo phenomena. In: Jarvik, M.E., ed. *Psychopharmacology in the Practice of Medicine.* New York: Appleton-Century-Crofts; 1977:45-57.

28. Silber, T.J. Placebo therapy: The ethical dimension. *JAMA.* 1979;242:245-6.

29. Brody, H., Waters, D.B. Diagnosis is treatment. *J Fam Pract.* 1980;10:445-9.

30. Uhlenhuth, E.H., Canter, A., Neustadt, J.O., Payson, H.E. The symptomatic relief of anxiety with meprobamate, phenobarbital, and placebo. *Am J Psychiatry.* 1959;115:905-10.

31. Beecher, H.K. Surgery as placebo: A quantitative study of bias. *JAMA.* 1961;176:1102-7.

32. Stroebel, E.F., Glueck, B.C. Biofeedback treatment in medicine and psychiatry: An ultimate placebo? *Semin Psychiatry.* 1973;5:379-93.

33. Shapiro, A.K. Attitudes toward the use of placebos in treatment. *J Nerv Ment Dis.* 1960;130:200-9.

34. Abramowitz, E.W. The use of placebos in the local therapy of skin diseases. *NY State J Med.* 1948;48:1927-30.

35. Hofling, C.K. The place of placebos in medical practice. *GP.* 1955;11(6):103-7.

36. Fischer, H.K., Dlin, B.M. The dynamics of placebo therapy: A clinical study. *Am J Med Sci.* 1956;232:504-12.

37. Simmons, B. Problems in deceptive medical procedures: An ethical and legal analysis of the administration of placebos. *J Med Ethics.* 1978;4:172-81.

38. Veatch, R.M. *A Theory of Medical Ethics.* New York: Basic Books; 1981.

39. Placebos. *Med Record.* 1885;27:576-7.

40. Burns, C.R. Richard Clarke Cabot and reformation in American medical ethics. *Bull Hist Med.* 1977;51:353-68.

41. Cabot, R.C. The use of truth and falsehood in medicine: An experimental study. *Am Med.* 1903;5:344-9.

42. Cabot, R.C. The physician's responsibility for the nostrum evil. *JAMA.* 1906;47:982-3.

43. Platt, R. Two essays on the practice of medicine. *Lancet.* 1947;253:305-7.

44. Handfield-Jones, R.P.C. A bottle of medicine from the doctor. *Lancet.* 1953;265:823-5.

45. Placebo therapy. *Practitioner.* 1964;192:590.

46. Brody, H. The physician-patient contract: Ethical and legal aspects. *J Legal Med.* 1976;4:25-30.

47. *Perkins v. First National Bank of Atlanta.* 143 SE 2d 474: Georgia; 1975.

48. McDermott, J.F. A specific placebo effect encountered in the use of dexedrine in hyperactive child. *Am J Psychiatry.* 1965;121:923-4.

49. Cassel, C., Jameton, A.L. Power of the placebo: a dialog on principles and practice. *Art of Medication.* 1980;1(3):22-7.

50. Bok, S. *Lying: Moral Choice in Public and Private Life.* New York: Pantheon; 1978.

51. Leslie, A. Ethics and the practice of placebo therapy. *Am J Med.* 1954;16:854-62.

52. Levine, J.D., Gordon, N.C., Fields, H.L. The mechanism of placebo analgesia. *Lancet.* 1978;2:654-7.

53. Shapiro, A.K. The use of placebos: A study of ethics and physicians' attitudes. *Psychiatry in Med.* 1973;4:17-29.

54. Lasagna, L. The powerful cipher. *The Sciences.* 1980;20(20):31-2.

55. Bok, S. The ethics of giving placebos. *Sci Am.* 1974;231(5):17-23.

56. Carter, A.B. The placebo: Its use and abuse. *Lancet.* 1953;265:823.

57. The humble humbug [Editorial]. *Lancet.* 1954;267:321.

58. Wayne, E.J. Placebos [Abstract]. *Br Med J.* 1956;2:157.

59. Lasagna, L. Placebos. *Sci Am.* 1956;193:(7)68-71.

60. Koteen, H. Use of a "double-blind" study investigating the clinical merits of a new tranquilizing agent. *Ann Intern Med.* 1957;47:978-89.

61. Atkinson, E.C. Dummy tablets [letter]. *Br Med J.* 1958:1:1478.

62. Branson, H.K., Ward, R. The place of the placebo in geriatric nursing. *Hosp Management.* 1964:98(6):34, 37.

63. Shure, N. The placebo in allergy. *Ann Allergy.* 1965;23:368-76.

64. Thrift, C.B., Traut, E.F. Further studies on placebo management of skeletal disease. *Ill Med J.* 1966;129:683-5.

65. Sicé, J. Evaluating medication [Letter]. *Lancet*. 1972;2:651.

66. Salfield, D.J. The placebo. *Lancet*. 1953;265:940.

67. Wolff, H.G., DuBois, E.F., Cattell, M., et al. Conferences on therapy: The use of placebos in therapy. *NY State J Med*. 1946;46:1718-27.

68. Soble, A. Deception in social science research: Is informed consent possible? *Hastings Cen Rep*. 1978;8(October):40-6.

69. Park, L.C., Covi, L. Nonblind placebo trial: An exploration of neurotic outpatients' response to placebo when its inert content is disclosed. *Arch Gen Psychiatry*. 1965;12:336-45.

70. Vogel, A.V., Goodwin, J.S., Goodwin, J.M. The therapeutics of placebo. *Am Fam Physician*. 1980;22(1):105-9.

71. Cousins, N. Anatomy of an illness (as perceived by the patient). *N Engl J Med*. 1976;295:1458-63.

72. Egbert, L.D., Battit, G.E., Welch, C.E., Bartlett, M.K. Reduction of postoperative pain by encouragement and instruction of patients. *N Engl J Med*. 1964;270:825-7.

73. Jensen, P.S. The doctor-patient relationship: Headed for impasse or improvement? *Ann Intern Med*. 1981;95:769-71.

FURTHER READINGS

Beauchamp, T.L. and J.F.Childress. *Principles of Biomedical Ethics*. New York and Oxford: Oxford University Press, 1979.

Emson, H. E. *The Doctor and the Law*. Toronto: Butterworths, 1989.

Engelhardt, Jr., H.T. *Foundations of Bioethics*. New York and Oxford: Oxford University Press, 1986.

Jospe, M. *The Placebo Effect in Healing*. Lexington, Mass: Health, 1978.

Kluge, E.-H.W. "Placebos: Some Ethical Considerations." *Canadian Medical Association Journal* 1990; 142 (4) 293-295.

Lipkin, M. "Suggestion and Healing." *Perspectives in Biology and Medicine* 20 (1984) 121–126.

Mallary, S.D., B. Gert and C.M. Culver. "Family Coercion and Valid Consent." *Theoretical Medicine* 7: 2 (June, 1986) 123–126.

Parks, L.C. and L. Covi. "Non-Blind Placebo Trials." *Archives of General Psychiatry*. 124 (1965) 334-45.

Savage, H. and Carla McKague. *Mental Health Law in Canada*. Toronto and Vancouver: Butterworths, 1987.

Simmons, Beth. "Problems in Deceptive Medical Procedures: An Ethical and Legal Analysis of the Administration of Placebos." *Journal of Medical Ethics* 4 (1978) 172–181.

Spiro, H.K. *Doctors, Patients and Placebos*. New Haven: Yale University Press, 1986, 33.

CHAPTER 10
RESEARCH AND EXPERIMENTATION INVOLVING COMPETENT PERSONS

INTRODUCTION

The usual view of health care is that when patients go to see their physicians, they will be prescribed therapies, investigative procedures or other types of interventions that are well established with known effectiveness, outcomes and side effects.

However, there are times when there is no established or validated treatment for a particular condition; where there is no proven investigative procedure and no well-established way of proceeding. Sometimes the only thing that physicians can do is recommend something that in the end is really unproven or experimental. This raises several issues. For instance, who should make the decision to proceed? On what basis? How much information should be disclosed? Should the patient be coerced? May the patient ever be deceived?

For years, the Medical Research Council of Canada set the standards that federally funded projects involving research with human subjects should follow.[1] In the last few years it was realized that research with human beings could not be readily distinguished into medical as opposed to engineering or socially oriented research: the areas frequently overlapped. As a result, the Medical Research Council of Canada, the Natural Sciences and Engineering Research Council of Canada, and the Social Sciences and Humanities Research Council of Canada formed a combined working group and came up with an integrated set of guidelines. The major portions of these guidelines, formulated as a Code, are reproduced below. This new Code has not been finalized at time of writing but is already being used to guide the evaluation of research protocols in most Canadian research establishments. This Code emphasizes informed and autonomous decision making. In so doing, it reasserts the fundamental principle of complete disclosure that was already announced by the courts in *Halushka v. The University of Saskatchewan*, excerpts from which are included below. *Halushka* is one of the few legal cases in North America that deal with consent and disclosure in the experimental/research setting and as such has set the standard.

In arriving at their respective positions, the three Councils and the courts were guided by the so-called Nuremberg Code: a code for research or experimentation on human subjects that was developed by the Allies after the Second World War when they sat in judgment on physicians and other health care professionals of Nazi Germany who had used prisoners and civilians as though they were experimental animals. They were also guided by the Declaration of Helsinki: a proclamation originally issued by the World Medical Association in 1964 and since amended several times to keep up with changes in the socioethical understanding of the medical profession worldwide. Excerpts from the most recent version of the Declaration are included below.

However, the ethics of research involving human subjects involves more than merely informed consent. There is also the question whether the research should be undertaken in the first place: Is it really necessary to expose volunteers to risk in order to acquire information, or is the information sufficiently well known? Is the information worth the risk in the first place? These are some of questions that are addressed by Benjamin Freedman in his classic article on experimental equipoise.

NOTE

1. Medical Research Council of Canada, *Guidelines on Research Involving Human Subjects* (Ottawa: Minister of Supply and Services, 1987).

Draft Code of Ethical Conduct for Research Involving Humans

Medical Research Council of Canada, Natural Sciences and Engineering Research Council of Canada, and the Social Sciences and Humanities Research Council of Canada

INFORMED CHOICE

Article 1.1

Research with prospective participants may only begin if they or any authorized third parties are given the opportunity to make an informed choice about participation and only when their consent is thereby secured and thereafter maintained throughout their participation in the research.

Article 1.2

Incompetent individuals, or those who are not free to make voluntary choices, may only be recruited when the knowledge sought cannot be obtained from competent individuals or from those who are able to make voluntary choices.

Article 1.3

Research involving incompetent individuals is acceptable under special circumstances. In such cases, enrolment in research or continued participation requires that the researcher explain to the REB [Research Ethics Board] how third party authorization and the participants' assent will be obtained, and how the participants' best interests will be protected. In addition:

(a) when individuals are incompetent, third party authorization must be obtained. Such authorization must not be given by the researcher or any other member of the research team;

(b) the authorization of a relevant third party to permit recruitment of an incompetent participant for research is valid only while the participant remains incompetent; and

(c) should participants become competent during the research project, their informed choice must be sought.

Article 1.4

The assent or dissent of incompetent individuals must be respected by researchers. Normally, assent is a necessary condition for research to proceed and dissent is a sufficient condition for the research to stop, unless there are sufficient compensating benefits for the participant that can only be provided through research participation.

Article 1.5

In the absence of a prior directive, incompetent individuals, or individuals who are of doubtful competence or those who are unable to make voluntary choices, should

---

The Medical Research Council of Canada, the Natural Sciences and Engineering Research Council of Canada, and the Social Sciences and Humanities Research Council of Canada, Draft Code of Ethical Conduct for Research Involving Humans (Ottawa, 1997).

not be included in research that exposes them to risks beyond the threshold for normally acceptable risk without the potential for greater benefits for them. (For exceptions to this Article, see Articles 1.7 and 1.8.)

Article 1.6

For participants who made an informed choice when competent, but who later become incompetent, participation in research is permissible provided a prior directive and/or specific authorization is in place.

Article 1.7

Consent to research in emergency or life-threatening situations may be forgone when the patient is unable to give consent and third party authorization cannot be secured in sufficient time. The researchers must only address questions concerning the condition that caused the emergency or life-threatening situation and must not expose the participant to more than reasonable additional anticipated harms over standard efficacious care.

Article 1.8

When research has commenced without the informed choice of the participant or the third party authorization, in accordance with Article 1.7, a now competent participant or the authorized third party must be informed of the research participant status as soon as possible. Informed consent or authorization must be obtained for continuation in the project and for subsequent examinations or tests related to the study.

Article 1.9

Researchers must provide sufficient information to prospective participants or authorized third parties so that they can make an informed choice. Throughout the informed choice process, the researcher must ensure that prospective participants are given adequate opportunities to discuss and contemplate their participation. At the commencement of the informed choice process, researchers or their qualified designated representatives must provide prospective participants, either verbally or in writing, with the following:

(a) information that the individual or collectivity is being invited to participate in a research project;

(b) a comprehensible statement of the research purpose, the identity of the researcher, the expected duration and nature of participation, and a description of research procedures;

(c) a comprehensible description of reasonably foreseeable harms and benefits that may arise from research participation;

(d) an assurance that prospective participants are free not to participate, have the right to withdraw at any time without prejudice to pre-existing entitlements, and will be given continuing and meaningful opportunities for deciding whether or not to continue to participate; and

(e) the possibility of commercialization of research findings, and the presence of any apparent or actual conflict of interest on the part of researchers, their institutions or sponsors.

If signed consent is required, the participant must be given a copy of such consent form and any relevant written information.

There must be no statement that by consenting, participants waive any legal rights or waive rights other than those specified in the consent form.

In light of (b) and (c), REBs may require researchers to provide prospective participants with additional information.

Article 1.10

REB review is required for research involving naturalistic observation. However, if the naturalistic observation takes place in a public setting or in a setting that is normally open to public observation, then the REB would not normally require informed choice of those observed.

Article 1.11

Researchers must justify to the REB the use of either partial disclosure of deception and must show that:

(a) partial disclosure or deception is the only feasible method for realizing research objectives;

(b) nothing will be withheld from the participants that might, if divulged, cause them to refuse to participate; and

(c) prospective participants will be informed about the magnitude, probability, and general characteristics of any risks they may be exposed to by the research.

Article 1.12

For research involving the use of partial disclosure or deception, the REB, in accord with a proportionate approach to ethics assessment:

(a) may require debriefing following participation when the risk of harm to participants is within the threshold for normally acceptable risk;

(b) must require debriefing following participation when the risk of harm to participants is above the threshold for normally acceptable risk;

(c) may require that the researcher provide the participants a second opportunity for consent when the risk of harm to those participants is above the threshold for normally acceptable risk; and

(d) may require that participants be given the opportunity to withdraw their data from the study when the risk of harm to participants is above the threshold for normally acceptable risk.

RESEARCH ETHICS BOARDS

Article 2.1

The REB must be vested by its institution with the authority to approve, reject, propose modifications to or terminate all proposed or ongoing research involving humans within the institution's jurisdiction on grounds of the ethical considerations set forth in this Code.

Article 2.2

Terms of reference shall be adopted for each REB which must include:

(a) protecting participants from research harms;

(b) respecting the duties and rights of researchers; and

(c) reviewing proposed and ongoing research to ensure that it complies with this Code.

Article 2.3

The minimum acceptable membership of an REB is five members, including both men and women, of whom:

(a) at least two members have broad expertise in the methods or in the areas of research that are covered by the REB;

(b) at least one member who is knowledgeable in the discipline of ethics;

(c) at least one member is a lawyer; and

(d) at least one member has no affiliation with the institution, but is recruited from the community served by the institution and, if possible, from potential participants.

The institution's legal counsel must not be a member of the REB.

Article 2.4

REB decisions concerning research ethics must be reached in face-to-face meetings, and must be based upon review of fully detailed research proposals or, where applicable, progress reports.

Article 2.5

The REB must function impartially and provide reasoned and appropriately documented written decisions. When an REB is considering a negative decision, it must provide the researcher with all the reasons for doing so and give the researcher an opportunity to reply.

Article 2.6

Minutes of all REB meetings must be prepared and maintained by the REB. These minutes shall clearly document the REB's decisions and the reasons for them, and will be accessible to authorized representatives of the institution, researchers, and funding agencies to assist those conducting internal and external audits or research monitoring and to facilitate appeals.

Article 2.7

All ongoing research must be subject to continuing ethics review. The rigor of this review must follow the principle of a proportionate approach to ethics assessment. The minimal requirement for continuing review is submission to the REB of a brief final report at the conclusion of the project.

Article 2.8

As part of each research proposal submitted for REB review, the researcher must propose to the REB the continuing review process deemed appropriate for that project.

Article 2.9

When submitting a proposal for multi-centre research, the researcher must distinguish between core elements of the research and those elements that can be altered to comply with local requirements without invalidating the pooling of data.

Article 2.10

When research is to be performed outside the jurisdiction of the institution which employs the researcher, the researcher must obtain approval of the institution's REB as well as the approval of the REB (if any) having responsibility where the research is to be done.

Article 2.11

Researchers have the right to request reconsideration by the REB of decisions affecting their research.

Article 2.12

Should an institution permit review of an REB decision by an appeal board, that board must be within the same institution and its membership must meet the requirements of Article 2.3 of this Code. No ad hoc appeal boards are permitted.

PRIVACY, CONFIDENTIALITY AND ACCESS TO PERSONAL RECORDS, SECONDARY USE OF DATA, AND DATA LINKAGE

Article 3. 1

The researcher must secure REB approval for access to private information obtained directly from participants or from the secondary use of data that identifies them. The researcher must demonstrate to the REB that adequate provision has been made for keeping private information confidential. REB approval is not required for access to information in the public domain, including archival documents.

Article 3.2

The researcher must provide adequate information to prospective participants to enable them to make informed choices regarding participation in the research. Specifically, researchers must inform participants about:

(a) conditions under which identifying information will be released to third parties and the identities of those third parties;

(b) any modes of observation (e.g., photographs or videos) or access to information (e.g., sound recordings) in the research that allows identification of particular participants;

(c) any anticipated secondary uses of data from the research;

(d) any anticipated linkage of data gathered in the research with other data about participants, whether that data are contained in public or private records; and

(e) provisions for confidentiality in publication resulting from the research.

Article 3.3

Researchers may gain access to identifying information from databases if they have demonstrated to the satisfaction of the REB that:

(a) identifying information is essential to the research; and

(b) they have taken appropriate measures to protect the privacy of the individuals, to ensure the confidentiality of the data, and to minimize harms to participants.

Article 3.4

If identifying information is involved, REB approval must be sought for secondary uses of data. REB approval is not required for access to non-identifying data.

Article 3.5

Depending on the sensitivity of the information and on feasibility, the REB may also require that a researcher's access to secondary use of data be dependent on:

(a) the informed consent of those who contributed data; or

(b) an appropriate strategy for informing the participants; or

(c) consultation with a representative group of those who contributed data.

Article 3.6

When researchers wish to contact individuals from whom data were obtained, permission must be secured from the REB prior to contact.

Article 3.7

Data linkage that may identify research participants must be approved by the REB.

CONFLICT OF INTEREST

Article 4.1

Researchers and REB members must disclose conflicts of interest, real or apparent, to the REB.

CLINICAL TRIALS

Article 5.1

Phase I non-therapeutic clinical trials must undergo both stringent review and continuous monitoring by an REB independent of the clinical trials' sponsor.

Article 5.2

In combined Phase I/II therapeutic clinical trials, researchers and REBs must carefully examine the integrity of the selection, recruitment, and informed choice and consent processes. Where appropriate, the REB may require an independent monitoring process.

Article 5.3

REBs must examine the budgets of all clinical trials.

Article 5.4

The use of placebos in clinical trials is ethically unacceptable where clearly effective therapies or interventions are available.

INCLUSIVENESS IN RESEARCH

Article 6.1

Researchers must not discriminate against prospective or actual research participants on the basis of culture, religion, race, mental or physical disability, ethnicity, sex or age.

Article 6.2

Researchers and REBs must endeavor to distribute equitably the potential benefits of research. Accordingly, depending on the themes and objectives of the research, researchers and REBs must:

(a) select and recruit research participants from disadvantaged social, ethnic, racial, and mentally or physically disabled groups; and

(b) ensure that the design of the research reflects appropriately the participation of these groups.

Article 6.3

Researchers and REBs must endeavor to distribute equitably the potential benefits of research. Accordingly, depending on the themes and objectives of the research, researchers and REBs must:

(a) select and recruit women from disadvantaged social, ethnic, racial and mentally or physically disabled groups; and

(b) ensure that the design of the research reflects appropriately the participation of this group.

Article 6.4

No woman should be automatically excluded from relevant research.

Article 6.5

Depending on the theme and objectives of the research project, the researcher must justify to the REB the use of age as a criterion for the inclusion or exclusion of research participants.

Article 6.6

Infants, children and adolescents should not be excluded from participating in research which is potentially directly beneficial to them as individual participants and, with appropriate safeguards, indirectly beneficial to them as a group.

HUMAN GENETIC RESEARCH

Article 8.1

The genetics researcher must seek informed choice from the individual and report results to that individual. As genetic research involves the family and/or the community in terms of family history, linkage, and other studies, a potential tension exists between the individuals, their families, and the group. Therefore, informed choice must also involve those social structures as far as is practical and possible.

Article 8.2

The researcher and the REB must ensure that the results of genetic testing and genetic counselling records are protected from access by third parties unless consent is given by the participant. Family information in databanks must be coded by number without the possibility of identification of participants within the bank itself.

Article 8.3

Researchers and genetic counsellors involving families and groups in genetic research studies must reveal potential harms to the REB and outline how such harms will be dealt with as part of the research project.

Article 8.4

Genetics researchers and the REB must ensure that the research protocol makes provision for access to genetic counselling for the participants, where appropriate.

Article 8.5

Research on gene alteration must be limited to somatic cells and tissues. Neither research on germline gene alteration nor non-therapeutic use of gene alteration in humans is permitted.

Article 8.7

Because the banking of genetic material poses potential harms to individuals, their families, and the collectivities to which they may belong, researchers must satisfy the REB and prospective research participants that they have addressed the issues involved in banking of genetic data including confidentiality, privacy, storage, use of the data, and results to come, withdrawal by the participant, and future contact of participants, families, and collectivities.

REPRODUCTION, INFERTILITY, EMBRYOS AND FETUSES

Article 9.1

The researcher must obtain informed consent from the individual from whom human reproductive cells were obtained for the research use of those cells and tissues.

Article 9.2

No research will be carried out on ova or sperm that have been obtained through commercial transactions.

Article 9.3

Research must not be carried out with the intent of creating hybrid species which could survive by such means as mixing human gametes with cells or tissues of other species, or vice versa.

Article 9.4

Human zygotes and embryos must not be specifically created for research purposes; however, research that involves human zygotes and embryos will be ethically acceptable if:

   (a) the ova and sperm from which they were formed are obtained in accordance with articles 9.1, 9.2 and 9.3;

   (b) the research does not involve the genetic alteration of human zygotes/embryos; and

   (c) zygotes or embryos exposed to any manipulations not directed specifically to the ongoing normal development will not be transferred for continuing pregnancy.

Article 9.5

In keeping with international consensus, the researcher must restrict research on human zygotes and embryos to the first 14 days of development.

Article 9.6

Ectogenesis, cloning of human beings, formation of animal/human hybrids, or the transfer of zygotes/embryos between humans and other species are all unacceptable.

HUMAN TISSUE

Article 10.1

The informed choice of a living donor, or authorized third party in the case of incompetent individuals or, when the donor is deceased, a prior directive or third party authorization, must be sought and consent must be secured in order to acquire and use human tissue for research purposes.

Article 10.2

In collecting tissue for research, the researcher must provide donors with information about the:

(a) manner in which tissue will be taken, the safety and invasiveness of acqui-

sition, and the duration and conditions of preservation;

b) potential uses for the tissue including any commercial uses;

c) safeguards to protect the individual's privacy and confidentiality; and

(d) identifying information attached to specific tissue, and its potential traceability.

Article 10.3

When identification is possible, researchers must seek permission from individuals, authorized third parties or, when appropriate, the collectivities in question for the use of their previously collected tissue. The provisions of article 10.2 also apply here. Further, when the individuals who, after making an informed choice, provided previously collected tissue for research are not individually identifiable (anonymous and anonymized tissue), and when there are no potential harms to them, there is no need to seek donors' permission to use their tissue for research purposes unless legislation so requires.

Equipoise and the Ethics of Clinical Research

Benjamin Freedman

There is widespread agreement that ethics requires that each clinical trial begin with an honest null hypothesis.[1,2] In the simplest model, testing a new treatment B on a defined patient population P for which the current accepted treatment is A, it is necessary that the clinical investigator be in a state of genuine uncertainty regarding the comparative merits of treatments A and B for population P. If a physician knows that these treatments are not equivalent, ethics requires that the superior treatment be recommended. Following Fried, I call this state of uncertainty about the relative merits of A and B "equipoise."[3]

B. Freedman, "Equipoise and the Ethics of Clinical Research," *New England Journal of Medicine* 1987; 317: 141-145.

Equipoise is an ethically necessary condition in all cases of clinical research. In trials with several arms, equipoise must exist between all arms of the trial otherwise the trial design should be modified to exclude the inferior treatment. If equipoise is disturbed during the course of a trial, the trial may need to be terminated and all subjects previously enrolled (as well as other patients within the relevant population) may have to be offered the superior treatment. It has been rigorously argued that a trial with a placebo is ethical only in investigating conditions for which there is no known treatment[2]; this argument reflects a special application of the requirement for equipoise. Although equipoise has commonly been discussed in the special context of the ethics of randomized clinical trials,[4,5] it is important to recognize it as an ethical condition of all controlled clinical trials, whether or not they are randomized, placebo-controlled or blinded.

The recent increase in attention to the ethics of research with human subjects has highlighted problems associated with equipoise. Yet, as I shall attempt to show, contemporary literature, if anything, minimizes those difficulties. Moreover, there is evidence that concern on the part of investigators about failure to satisfy the requirements for equipoise can doom a trial as a result of the consequent failure to enroll a sufficient number of subjects.

The solutions that have been offered to date fail to resolve these problems in a way that would permit clinical trials to proceed. This paper argues that these problems are predicated on a faulty concept of equipoise itself. An alternative understanding of equipoise as an ethical requirement of clinical trials is proposed, and its implications are explored.

Many of the problems raised by the requirement for equipoise are familiar. Shaw and Chalmers have written that a clinician who "knows, or has good reason, to believe," that one arm of the trial is superior may not ethically participate.[6] But the reasoning or preliminary results that prompt the trial (and that may themselves be ethically mandatory)[7] may jolt the investigator (if not his or her colleagues) out of equipoise before the trial begins. Even if the investigator is undecided between A and B in terms of gross measures such as mortality and morbidity, equipoise may be disturbed because evident differences in the quality of life (as in the case of two surgical approaches) tip the balance.[3-5,8] In either case, in saying "we do not know" whether A or B is better, the investigator may create a false impression in prospective subjects, who hear him or her as saying "no evidence leans either way," when the investigator means "no controlled study has yet had results that reach statistical significance."

Late in the study — when P values are between 0.05 and 0.06 — the moral issue of equipoise is most readily apparent,[9,10] but the same problem arises when the earliest comparative results are analyzed.[11] Within the closed statistical universe of the clinical trial, each result that demonstrates a difference between the arms of the trial contributes exactly as much to the statistical conclusion that a difference exists as does any other. The contribution of the last pair of cases in the trial is no greater than that of the first. If, therefore, equipoise is a condition that reflects equivalent evidence for alternative hypotheses, it is jeopardized by the first pair of cases as much as by the last. The investigator who is concerned about the ethics of recruitment after the penultimate pair must logically be concerned after the first pair as well.

Finally, these issues are more than a philosopher's nightmare. Considerable interest has been generated by a paper in which Taylor *et al.*[12] describe the termination of a trial of alternative treatments for breast cancer. The trial foundered on the problem of patient recruitment, and the investigators trace much of the difficulty in enrolling patients to the fact that the investigators were not in a state of equipoise regarding the arms of the trial. With the increase in concern about the ethics of research and with the increasing presence of this topic in the curricula of medical and graduate schools, instances of the type that Taylor and her colleagues describe are likely to become more common. The requirement for equipoise thus poses a practical threat to clinical research.

RESPONSES TO THE PROBLEMS OF EQUIPOISE

The problems described above apply to a broad class of clinical trials, at all stages of their development. Their resolution will need to be similarly comprehensive. However, the solutions that have so far been proposed address a portion of the difficulties, at best, and cannot be considered fully satisfactory.

Chalmers' approach to problems at the onset of a trial is to recommend that randomization begin with the very first subject.[11] If there are no preliminary, uncontrolled data in support of the experimental treatment B, equipoise regarding treatments A and B for the patient population P is not disturbed. There are several difficulties with this approach. Practically speaking, it is often necessary to establish details of administration, dosage, and so on, before a controlled trial begins, by means of uncontrolled trials in human subjects. In addition, as I have argued above, equipoise from the investigator's point of view is likely to be disturbed when the hypothesis is being formulated and a protocol is being prepared. It is then, before any subjects have been enrolled, that the information that the investigator has assembled makes the experimental treatment appear to be a reasonable gamble. Apart from these problems,

initial randomization will not, as Chalmers recognizes, address disturbances of equipoise that occur in the course of a trial.

Data-monitoring committees have been proposed as a solution to problems arising in the course of the trial.[13] Such committees, operating independently of the investigators, are the only bodies with information concerning the trial's ongoing results. Since this knowledge is not available to the investigators, their equipoise is not disturbed. Although committees are useful in keeping the conduct of a trial free of bias, they cannot resolve the investigators' ethical difficulties. A clinician is not merely obliged to treat a patient on the basis of the information that he or she currently has, but is also required to discover information that would be relevant to treatment decisions. If interim results would disturb equipoise, the investigators are obliged to gather and use that information. Their agreement to remain in ignorance of preliminary results would, by definition, be an unethical agreement, just as a failure to call up the laboratory to find out a patient's test results is unethical. Moreover, the use of a monitoring committee does not solve problems of equipoise that arise before and at the beginning of a trial.

Recognizing the broad problems with equipoise, three authors have proposed radical solutions. All three think that there is an irresolvable conflict between the requirement that a patient be offered the best treatment known (the principle underlying the requirement for equipoise) and the conduct of clinical trials; they therefore suggest that the "best treatments" requirement be weakened.

Schafer has argued that the concept of equipoise, and the associated notion of the best medical treatment, depend on the judgment of patients rather than of clinical investigators.[14] Although the equipoise of an investigator may be disturbed if he or she favors B over A, the ultimate choice of treatment is the patient's. Because the patient's values may restore equipoise, Schafer argues, it is ethical for the investigator to proceed with a trial when the patient consents. Schafer's strategy is directed toward trials that test treatments with known and divergent side effects, and will probably not be useful in trials conducted to test efficacy or unknown side effects. This approach, moreover, confuses the ethics of competent medical practice with those of consent. If we assume that the investigator is a competent clinician, by saying that the investigator is out of equipoise, we have by Schafer's account said that in the investigator's professional judgment one treatment is therapeutically inferior — for that patient, in that condition, given the quality of life that can be achieved. Even if a patient would consent to an inferior treatment, it seems to me a violation of competent medical practice, and hence of ethics, to make the offer. Of course, complex issues may arise when a patient refuses what the physician considers the best treatment and demands instead an inferior treatment. Without settling that problem, however, we can reject Schafer's position. For Schafer claims that in order to continue to conduct clinical trials, it is ethical for the physician to offer (not merely accede to) inferior treatment.

Meier suggests that "most of us would be quite willing to forego a modest expected gain in the general interest of learning something of value."[15] He argues that we accept risks in everyday life to achieve a variety of benefits, including convenience and economy. In the same way, Meier states, it is acceptable to enroll subjects in clinical trials even though they may not receive the best treatment throughout the course of the trial. Schafer suggests an essentially similar approach.[5,14] According to this view, continued progress in medical knowledge through clinical trials requires an explicit abandonment of the doctor's fully patient centered ethic.

These proposals seem to be frank counsels of desperation. They resolve the ethical problems of equipoise by abandoning the need for equipoise. In any event, would their approach allow clinical trials to be conducted? I think this may fairly be doubted. Although many people are presumably altruistic enough to forego medical treatment in the interest of science, many are not. The numbers and proportions required to sustain the statistical validity of trial results suggest that in the absence of overwhelming altruism, the enrollment of satisfactory numbers of patients will not be possible. In particular, very ill patients, toward whom many of the most important clinical trials are directed, may be disinclined to be altruistic. Finally, as the study by Taylor *et al.*[12] reminds us, the problems of equipoise trouble investigators as well as patients. Even if patients are prepared to dispense with the best treatment, their physicians, for reasons of ethics and professionalism, may well not be willing to do so.

Marquis has suggested a third approach. "Perhaps what is needed is an ethics that will justify the conscription of subjects for medical research," he has written. "Nothing less seems to justify present practice."[4] Yet, although conscription might enable us to continue present practice, it would scarcely justify it. Moreover, the conscription of physician investigators, as well as subjects, would be necessary, because, as has been repeatedly argued, the problems of equipoise are as disturbing to clinicians as they are to subjects. Is any less radical and more plausible approach possible?

THEORETICAL EQUIPOISE VERSUS CLINICAL EQUIPOISE

The problems of equipoise examined above arise from a particular understanding of that concept, which I will term "theoretical equipoise." It is an understanding that is both conceptually odd and ethically irrelevant. Theoretical equipoise exists when, overall, the evidence on behalf of two alternative treatment regimens is exactly balanced. This evidence may be derived from a variety of sources, including data from the literature, uncontrolled experience, considerations of basic science and fundamental physiologic processes and perhaps a "gut feeling" or "instinct" resulting from (or superimposed on) other considerations. The problems examined above arise from the principle that if theoretical equipoise is disturbed, the physician has, in Schafer's words, a "treatment preference" — let us say, favoring experimental treatment B. A trial testing A against B requires that some patients be enrolled in violation of this treatment preference.

Theoretical equipoise is overwhelmingly fragile; that is, it is disturbed by a slight accretion of evidence favoring one arm of the trial. In Chalmers' view, equipoise is disturbed when the odds that A will be more successful than B are anything other than 50 percent. It is therefore necessary to randomize treatment assignments beginning with the very first patient, lest equipoise be disturbed. We may say that theoretical equipoise is balanced on a knife's edge.

Theoretical equipoise is most appropriate to one-dimensional hypotheses and causes us to think in those terms. The null hypothesis must be sufficiently simple and "clean" to be finely balanced: Will A or B be superior in reducing mortality or shrinking tumors or lowering fevers in population P? Clinical choice is commonly more complex. The choice of A or B depends on some combination of effectiveness, consistency, minimal or relievable side effects, and other factors. On close examination, for example, it sometimes appears that even trials that purport to test a single hypothesis in fact involve a more complicated, portmanteau measure, e.g., the "therapeutic index" of A

versus B. The formulation of the conditions of theoretical equipoise for such complex, multidimensional clinical hypotheses is tantamount to the formulation of a rigorous calculus of apples and oranges.

Theoretical equipoise is also highly sensitive to the vagaries of the investigator's attention and perception. Because of its fragility, theoretical equipoise is disturbed as soon as the investigator perceives a difference between the alternatives — whether or not any genuine difference exists. Prescott writes, for example, "It will be common at some stage in most trials for the survival curves to show visually different survivals," short of significance but "sufficient to raise ethical difficulties for the participants."[16] A visual difference, however, is purely an artifact of the research methods employed: when and by what means data are assembled and analyzed and what scale is adopted for the graphic presentation of data. Similarly, it is common for researchers to employ interval scales for phenomena that are recognized to be continuous by nature, e.g., five-point scales of pain or stages of tumor progression. These interval scales, which represent an arbitrary distortion of the available evidence to simplify research, may magnify the differences actually found, with a resulting disturbance of theoretical equipoise.

Finally, as described by several authors, theoretical equipoise is personal and idiosyncratic. It is disturbed when the clinician has, in Schafer's words, what "might even be labeled a bias or a hunch," a preference of a "merely intuitive nature."[14] The investigator who ignores such a hunch, by failing to advise the patient that because of it the investigator prefers B to A or by recommending A (or a chance of random assignment to A) to the patient, has violated the requirement for equipoise and its companion requirement to recommend the best medical treatment.

The problems with this concept of equipoise should be evident. To understand the alternative, preferable interpretation of equipoise, we need to recall the basic reason for conducting clinical trials: there is a current or imminent conflict in the clinical community over what treatment is preferred for patients in a defined population P. The standard treatment is A, but some evidence suggests that B will be superior (because of its effectiveness or its reduction of undesirable side effects, or for some other reason). (In the rare case when the first evidence of a novel therapy's superiority would be entirely convincing to the clinical community, equipoise is already disturbed.) Or there is a split in the clinical community, with some clinicians favoring A and others favoring B. Each side recognizes that the opposing side has evidence to support its position, yet each still thinks that overall its own view is correct. There exists (or, in the case of a novel therapy, there may soon exist) an honest, professional disagreement among expert clinicians about the preferred treatment. A clinical trial is instituted with the aim of resolving this dispute.

At this point, a state of "clinical equipoise" exists. There is no consensus within the expert clinical community about the comparative merits of the alternatives to be tested. We may state the formal conditions under which such a trial would be ethical as follows: at the start of the trial, there must be a state of clinical equipoise regarding the merits of the regimens to be tested, and the trial must be designed in such a way as to make it reasonable to expect that, if it is successfully concluded, clinical equipoise will be disturbed. In other words, the results of a successful clinical trial should be convincing enough to resolve the dispute among clinicians.

A state of clinical equipoise is consistent with a decided treatment preference on the part of the investigators. They must simply recognize that their less-favored treatment is preferred by colleagues whom they consider to be responsible and competent.

Even if the interim results favor the preference of the investigators, treatment B, clinical equipoise persists as long as those results are too weak to influence the judgment of the community of clinicians, because of limited sample size, unresolved possibilities of side effects, or other factors. (This judgment can necessarily be made only by those who know the interim results — whether a data-monitoring committee or the investigators.)

At the point when the accumulated evidence in favor of B is so strong that the committee or investigators believe no open-minded clinician informed of the results would still favor A, clinical equipoise has been disturbed. This may occur well short of the original schedule for the termination of the trial, for unexpected reasons. (Therapeutic effects or side effects may be much stronger than anticipated, for example, or a definable subgroup within population P may be recognized for which the results demonstrably disturb clinical equipoise.) Because of the arbitrary character of human judgment and persuasion, some ethical problems regarding the termination of a trial will remain. Clinical equipoise will confine these problems to unusual or extreme cases, however, and will allow us to cast persistent problems in the proper terms. For example, in the face of a strong established trend, must we continue the trial because of others' blind fealty to an arbitrary statistical bench mark?

Clearly, clinical equipoise is a far weaker — and more common — condition than theoretical equipoise. Is it ethical to conduct a trial on the basis of clinical equipoise, when theoretical equipoise is disturbed?

Or, as Schafer and others have argued, is doing so a violation of the physician's obligation to provide patients with the best medical treatment?[4,5,14] Let us assume that the investigators have a decided preference for B but wish to conduct a trial on the ground that clinical (not theoretical) equipoise exists. The ethics committee asks the investigators whether, if they or members of their families were within population P, they would not want to be treated with their preference, B? An affirmative answer is often thought to be fatal to the prospects for such a trial, yet the investigators answer in the affirmative. Would a trial satisfying this weaker form of equipoise be ethical?

I believe that it clearly is ethical. As Fried has emphasized,[3] competent (hence, ethical) medicine is social rather than individual in nature. Progress in medicine relies on progressive consensus within the medical and research communities. The ethics of medical practice grants no ethical or normative meaning to a treatment preference, however powerful, that is based on a hunch or on anything less than evidence publicly presented and convincing to the clinical community. Persons are licensed as physicians after they demonstrate the acquisition of this professionally validated knowledge, not after they reveal a superior capacity for guessing. Normative judgments of their behavior, e.g., malpractice actions, rely on a comparison with what is done by the community of medical practitioners. Failure to follow a "treatment preference" not shared by this community and not based on information that would convince it could not be the basis for an allegation of legal or ethical malpractice. As Fried states: "[T]he conception of what is good medicine is the product of a professional consensus." By definition, in a state of clinical equipoise, "good medicine" finds the choice between A and B indifferent.

In contrast to theoretical equipoise, clinical equipoise is robust. The ethical difficulties at the beginning and end of a trial are therefore largely alleviated. There remain difficulties about consent, but these too may be diminished. Instead of emphasizing the lack of evidence favoring one arm over another that is required by theoretical equipoise, clinical equipoise places the emphasis in informing the patient of the honest disagreement among expert clinicians. The fact that the investigator has a "treatment preference," if he or she does, could be disclosed; indeed, if the preference is a decided one, and based on something more than a hunch, it could be ethically mandatory to disclose it. At the same time, it would be emphasized that this preference is not shared by others. It is likely to be a matter of chance that the patient is being seen by a clinician with a preference for B over A, rather than by an equally competent clinician with the opposite preference.

Clinical equipoise does not depend on concealing relevant information from researchers and subjects, as does the use of independent data-monitoring committees. Rather, it allows investigators, in informing subjects, to distinguish appropriately among validated knowledge accepted by the clinical community, data on treatments that are promising but are not (or, for novel therapies, would not be) generally convincing, and mere hunches. Should informed patients decline to participate because they have chosen a specific clinician and trust his or her judgment — over and above the consensus in the professional community — that is no more than the patients' right. We do not conscript patients to serve as subjects in clinical trials.

THE IMPLICATIONS OF CLINICAL EQUIPOISE

The theory of clinical equipoise has been formulated as an alternative to some current views on the ethics of human research. At the same time, it corresponds closely to a preanalytic concept held by many in the research and regulatory communities. Clinical equipoise serves, then, as a rational formulation of the approach of many toward research ethics; it does not so much change things as explain why they are the way they are.

Nevertheless, the precision afforded by the theory of clinical equipoise does help to clarify or reformulate some aspects of research ethics; I will mention only two.

First, there is a recurrent debate about the ethical propriety of conducting clinical trials of discredited treatments, such as Laetrile.[17] Often, substantial political pressure to conduct such tests is brought to bear by adherents of quack therapies. The theory of clinical equipoise suggests that when there is no support for a treatment regimen within the expert clinical community, the first ethical requirement of a trial — clinical equipoise — is lacking; it would therefore be unethical to conduct such a trial.

Second, Feinstein has criticized the tendency of clinical investigators to narrow excessively the conditions and hypotheses of a trial in order to ensure the validity of its results.[18] This "fastidious" approach purchases scientific manageability at the expense of an inability to apply the results to the "messy" conditions of clinical practice. The theory of clinical equipoise adds some strength to this criticism. Overly "fastidious" trials, designed to resolve some theoretical question, fail to satisfy the second ethical requirement of clinical research, since the special conditions of the trial will render it useless for influencing clinical decisions, even if it is successfully completed.

The most important result of the concept of clinical equipoise, however, might be to relieve the current crisis of confidence in the ethics of clinical trials. Equipoise, properly understood, remains an ethical condition for clinical trials. It is consistent with much current practice. Clinicians and philosophers alike have been premature in calling for desperate measures to resolve problems of equipoise.

NOTES

I am indebted to Robert J. Levine, MD, and to Harold Merskey, MD, for their valuable suggestions.

1. Levine R.J. *Ethics and Regulation of Clinical Research*, 2nd ed. Baltimore: Urban & Schwarzenberg, 1986.
2. *Idem.* The use of placebos in randomized clinical trials. *IRB: Rev Hum Subj Res* 1985; 7(2):I-4.
3. Fried C. *Medical Experimentation: Personal Integrity and Social Policy.* Amsterdam: North-Holland Publishing, 1974.
4. Marquis D. Leaving therapy to chance. *Hastings Cent Rep* 1983; 13(4):40-7.
5. Schafer A. The ethics of the randomized clinical trial. *N Engl J Med* 1982; 307:719-24.
6. Shaw L.W., Chalmers T.C. Ethics in cooperative clinical trials. *Ann NY Acad Sci* 1970; 169:487-95.
7. Hollenberg N.K., Dzau V.J., William G.H. Are uncontrolled clinical studies ever justified? *N Engl J Med* 1980; 303:1067.
8. Levine R.J., Lebacqz K. Some ethical considerations in clinical trials. *Clin Pharmacol Ther* 1979; 25:728-41.
9. Klimt C.R., Canner P.L. Terminating a long-term clinical trial. *Clin Pharmacol Ther* 1979; 25:641-6.
10. Veatch R.M. Longitudinal studies, sequential designs and grant renewals: what to do with preliminary data. *IRB: Rev Hum Subj Res* 1979; 1(4):I-3.

11. Chalmers T. The ethics of randomization as a decision-making technique and the problem of informed consent. In: Beauchamp T.L., Walters L., eds. *Contemporary Issues in Bioethics*. Encino, Calif.: Dickenson, 1978: 426-9.

12. Taylor K.M., Margolese R.G., Soskolne C.L. Physicians' reasons for not entering eligible patients in a randomized clinical trial of surgery for breast cancer. *N Engl J Med* 1984; 310:1363-7.

13. Chalmers T.C. Invited remarks. *Clin Pharmacol Ther* 1979; 25:649-50.

14. Schafer A. The randomized clinical trial: for whose benefit? *IRB: Rev Hum Subj Res* 1985; 7(2):4-6.

15. Meier P. Terminating a trial—the ethical problem. *Clin Pharmacol Ther* 1979; 25:633-40.

16. Prescott R.J. Feedback of data to participants during clinical trials. In: Tagnon H.J., Staquet M.J., eds. *Controversies in Cancer: Design of Trials and Treatment*. New York: Masson Publishing, 1979: 55-61.

17. Cowan D.H. The ethics of clinical trials of ineffective therapy. *MB: Rev Hum Subj Res* 1981; 3(5):10-1.

18. Feinstein A.R. An additional basic science for clinical medicine: The limitations of randomized trials. *Ann Intern Med* 1983; 99;544-50.

Halushka v. University of Saskatchewan et al.

Saskatchewan Court of Appeal, Woods, Brownridge and Hall, J.J.A.

May 4, 1965.

HALL, J.A.:

... The respondent reported to the anaesthesia department at the University Hospital and there saw the appellant Wyant. The conversation which ensued concerning the proposed test was related by the respondent as follows:

> Doctor Wyant explained to me that a new drug was to be tried out on the Wednesday following. He told me that electrodes would be put in my both arms, legs and head and that he assured me that it was a perfectly safe test it had been conducted many times before. He told me that I was

not to eat anything on Wednesday morning that I was to report at approximately nine o'clock, then he said it would take about an hour to hook me up and the test itself would last approximately two hours, after the time I would be given fifty dollars, pardon me, I would be allowed to sleep first, fed and then given fifty dollars and driven home on the same day.

The appellant Wyant also told the respondent that an incision would be made in his left arm and that a catheter or tube would be inserted into his vein.

436 Dominion Law Reports 53 (2d).

The respondent agreed to undergo the test and was asked by the appellant Wyant to sign a form of consent. ... The respondent described the circumstances surrounding the signing, ... saying:

> He then gave me a consent form, I skimmed through it and picked out the word "accident" on the consent form and asked Doctor Wyant what accidents were referred to, and he gave me an example of me falling down the stairs at home after the test and then trying to sue the University Hospital as a result. Being assured that any accident that would happen to me would be at home and not in the Hospital I signed the form.

The test contemplated was known as "The Heart and Blood Circulation Response under General Anaesthesia," and was to be conducted jointly by the appellants Wyant and Merriman, using a new anaesthetic agent known commercially as "Fluoromar." This agent had not been previously used or tested by the appellants in any way.

The respondent returned to the University Hospital on August 23, 1961, to undergo the test. The procedure followed was that which had been described to the respondent and expected by him, with the exception that the catheter, after being inserted in the vein in the respondent's arm, was advanced towards his heart. When the catheter reached the vicinity of the heart, the respondent felt some discomfort. The anaesthetic agent was then administered to him. ... Eventually the catheter tip was advanced through the various heart chambers out into the pulmonary artery where it was positioned....

At 12:25 the respondent suffered a complete cardiac arrest.

The appellants Wyant and Merriman and their assistants took immediate steps to resuscitate the respondent's heart by manual massage. To reach the heart an incision was made from the breastbone to the line of the arm-pit and two of the ribs were pulled apart. A vasopressor was administered as well as urea, a drug used to combat swelling of the brain. After one minute and thirty seconds the respondent's heart began to function again....

In ordinary medical practice the consent given by a patient to a physician or surgeon, to be effective, must be an "informed" consent freely given. It is the duty of the physician to give a fair and reasonable explanation of the proposed treatment including the probable effect and any special or unusual risks....

In my opinion the duty imposed upon those engaged in medical research ... to those who offer themselves as subject for experimentation ... is at least as great as, if not greater than, the duty owed by the ordinary physician or surgeon to his patient. There can be no exceptions to the ordinary requirements of disclosure in the case of research as there may well be in ordinary medical practice. The researcher does not have to balance the probable effect of lack of treatment against the risk involved in the treatment itself. The example of risks being properly hidden from a patient when it is important that he should not worry can have no application in the field of research. The subject of medical experimentation is entitled to a full and frank disclosure of all the facts, probabilities and opinions which a reasonable man might be expected to consider before giving his consent. The respondent necessarily had to rely upon the special skill, knowledge and experience of the appellants, who were, in my opinion, placed in the fiduciary position....

Although the appellant Wyant informed the respondent that a "new drug" was to be tried out, he did not inform him that the new drug was in fact an anaesthetic of which he had no previous knowledge, nor that there was risk involved with the use of an anaesthetic. Inasmuch as no test had been previously conducted using the anaesthetic agent "Fluoromar" to the knowledge of the appellants, the statement made to the respondent that it was a safe test which had been conducted many times before, when considered in the light of the medical evidence describing the characteristics of anaesthetic agents generally, was incorrect and was in reality a non-disclosure.

The respondent was not informed that the catheter would be advanced to and through his heart but was admittedly given to understand that it would be merely inserted in the vein in his arm. While it may be correct to say that the advancement of the catheter to the heart was not in

itself dangerous and did not cause or contribute to the cause of the cardiac arrest, it was a circumstance which, if known, might very well have prompted the respondent to withhold his consent. The undisclosed or misrepresented facts need not concern matters which directly cause the ultimate damage if they are of a nature which might influence the judgment upon which the consent is based.

The explanation ... given by the appellant Wyant to the respondent could be misleading and could well serve to distract the respondent from a proper appraisal of his position....

The appeal is dismissed with costs.

Declaration of Helsinki

Recommendations Guiding Physicians in Biomedical Research Involving Human Subjects

World Medical Association

INTRODUCTION

It is the mission of the physician to safeguard the health of the people. His or her knowledge and conscience are dedicated to the fulfillment of this mission.

The Declaration of Geneva of the World Medical Association binds the physician with the words, "The Health of my patient will be my first consideration," and the International Code of Medical Ethics declares that, "A physician shall act only in the patient's interest when providing medical care which might have the effect of weakening the physical and mental condition of the patient."

The purpose of biomedical research involving human subjects must be to improve diagnostic, therapeutic and prophylactic procedures and the understanding of the aetiology and pathogenesis of disease.

In current medical practice most diagnostic, therapeutic or prophylactic procedures involve hazards. This applies especially to biomedical research.

Medical progress is based on research which ultimately must rest in part on experimentation involving human subjects.

Adopted by the 18th World Medical Assembly, Helsinki, Finland, June 1964, and amended by the 29th World Medical Assembly, Tokyo, Japan, October 1975; 35th World Medical Assembly, Venice, Italy, October 1983; 41st World Medical Assembly, Hong Kong, September 1989; and the 48th General Assembly, Somerset West, Republic of South Africa, October 1996.

In the field of biomedical research a fundamental distinction must be recognized between medical research in which the aim is essentially diagnostic or therapeutic for a patient, and medical research, the essential object of which is purely scientific and without implying direct diagnostic or therapeutic value to the person subjected to the research.

Special caution must be exercised in the conduct of research which may affect the environment, and the welfare of animals used for research must be respected.

Because it is essential that the results of laboratory experiments be applied to human beings to further scientific knowledge and to help suffering humanity, the World Medical Association has prepared the following recommendations as a guide to every physician in biomedical research involving human subjects. They should be kept under review in the future. It must be stressed that the standards as drafted are only a guide to physicians all over the world. Physicians are not relieved from criminal, civil and ethical responsibilities under the laws of their own countries.

BASIC PRINCIPLES

1. Biomedical research involving human subjects must conform to generally accepted scientific principles and should be based on adequately performed laboratory and animal experimentation and on a thorough knowledge of the scientific literature.

2. The design and performance of each experimental procedure involving human subjects should be clearly formulated in an experimental protocol which should be transmitted for consideration, comment and guidance to a specially appointed committee independent of the investigator and the sponsor provided that this independent committee is in conformity with the laws and regulations of the country in which the research experiment is performed.

3. Biomedical research involving human subjects should be conducted only by scientifically qualified persons and under the supervision of a clinically competent medical person. The responsibility for the human subject must always rest with a medically qualified person and never rest on the subject of the research, even though the subject has given his or her consent.

4. Biomedical research involving human subjects cannot legitimately be carried out unless the importance of the objective is in proportion to the inherent risk to the subject.

5. Every biomedical research project involving human subjects should be preceded by careful assessment of predictable risks in comparison with foreseeable benefits to the subject or to others. Concern for the interests of the subject must always prevail over the interests of science and society.

6. The right of the research subject to safeguard his or her integrity must always be respected. Every precaution should be taken to respect the privacy of the subject and to minimize the impact of the study on the subject's physical and mental integrity and on the personality of the subject.

7. Physicians should abstain from engaging in research projects involving human subjects unless they are satisfied that the hazards involved are believed to be predictable. Physicians should cease any investigation if the hazards are found to outweigh the potential benefits.

8. In publication of the results of his or her research, the physician is obliged to preserve the accuracy of the results.

Reports of experimentation not in accordance with the principles laid down in this Declaration should not be accepted for publication.

9. In any research on human beings, each potential subject must be adequately informed of the aims, methods, anticipated benefits and potential hazards of the study and the discomfort it may entail. He or she should be informed that he or she is at liberty to abstain from participation in the study and that he or she is free to withdraw his or her consent to participation at any time. The physician should then obtain the subject's freely given informed consent, preferably in writing.

10. When obtaining informed consent for the research project the physician should be particularly cautious if the subject is in a dependent relationship to him or her or may consent under duress. In that case the informed consent should be obtained by a physician who is not engaged in the investigation and who is completely independent of this official relationship.

11. In case of legal incompetence, informed consent should be obtained from the legal guardian in accordance with national legislation. Where physical or mental incapacity makes it impossible to obtain informed consent, or when the subject is a minor, permission from the responsible relative replaces that of the subject in accordance with national legislation.

Whenever the minor child is in fact able to give a consent, the minor's consent must be obtained in addition to the consent of the minor's legal guardian.

12. The research protocol should always contain a statement of the ethical considerations involved and should indicate that the principles enunci-

ated in the present declaration are complied with.

MEDICAL RESEARCH COMBINED WITH PROFESSIONAL CARE (CLINICAL RESEARCH)

1. In the treatment of the sick person, the physician must be free to use a new diagnostic and therapeutic measure, if in his or her judgement it offers hope of saving life, reestablishing health or alleviating suffering.

2. The potential benefits, hazards and discomfort of a new method should be weighed against the advantages of the best current diagnostic and therapeutic methods.

3. In any medical study, every patient — including those of a control group, if any — should be assured of the best proven diagnostic and therapeutic method. This does not exclude the use of inert placebo in studies where no proven diagnostic or therapeutic method exists.

4. The refusal of the patient to participate in a study must never interfere with the physician-patient relationship.

5. If the physician considers it essential not to obtain informed consent, the specific reasons for this proposal should be stated in the experimental protocol for transmission to the independent committee (1, 2).

6. The physician can combine medical research with professional care, the objective being the acquisition of new medical knowledge, only to the extent that medical research is justified by its potential diagnostic or therapeutic value for the patient.

NON-THERAPEUTIC BIOMEDICAL RESEARCH INVOLVING HUMAN SUBJECTS (NON-CLINICAL BIOMEDICAL RESEARCH)

1. In the purely scientific application of medical research carried out on a human being, it is the duty of the physician to remain the protector of the life and health of that person on whom biomedical research is being carried out.

2. The subject should be volunteers — either healthy persons or patients for whom the experimental design is not related to the patient's illness.

3. The investigator or the investigating team should discontinue the research if in his/her or their judgement it may, if continued, be harmful to the individual.

4. In research on man, the interest of science and society should never take precedence over considerations related to the well-being of the subject.

FURTHER READINGS

Annas, G.J., L.H. Glantz and B.F. Katz. *Informed Consent to Human Experimentation: The Subject's Dilemma.* Cambridge, Mass.: Ballinger Publication Co., 1977.

Beecher, H.K. "Ethics in Clinical Research." *New England Journal of Medicine* 274 (1966), 1354-60.

Beecher, H.K. *Experimentation in Man.* Springfield, Ill.: Charles C. Thomas, 1959.

Cohen, C. "Medical Experimentation on Prisoners." *Perspectives in Biology and Medicine.* Vol. 21, No. 3 (Spring 1978), 357-372.

Dickens, B. "What is a Medical Experiment?" *Canadian Medical Association Journal* 113 (Oct. 4, 1975), 635-639.

Donagan, A. "Informed Consent in Therapy and Experimentation." *The Journal of Medicine and Philosophy.* 2:4 (1977) 307-329.

Frenkel, D.A. "Human Experimentation: Codes of Ethic." *Legal Medical Quarterly* 1: 1 (1977) 7-14.

Freund, P.A., ed. *Experimentation with Human Subjects.* New York: American Academy of Arts and Sciences, 1970.

Halushka v. The University of Saskatchewan (1965), 53 D.L.R.(2d) 436.

Katz, Jay. *Experimenting With Human Beings.* New York: Russell Sage Foundation, 1972.

Kluge, E.-H. W. *Biomedical Ethics in the Canadian Context.* Scarborough, Ont.: Prentice Hall, 1991, Chapter 7.

Law Reform Commission of Canada. Working Paper 61, *Biomedical Experimentation Involving Human Subjects.* Ottawa, 1989.

Levine, Robert J. *Ethics and Regulation of Clinical Research.* New Haven and London: Yale University Press, 1988.

Medical Research Council of Canada. *Guidelines on Research Involving Human Subjects 1987.* Ottawa: Minister of Supply and Services, 1987.

National Commission for the Protection of Human Subjects of Biomedical and Behavioral Research. *The Belmont Report: Ethical Principles for the Protection of Human Subjects of Research.* Washington, D.C.: U.S. Government Printing Office, 1978, pub. no. 78-0012.

Nuremberg Code. *The Trials of War Criminals before the Nuremberg Military Tribunal.* Washington DC: U.S. Government Printing Office, 1948.

Park, *et al.* "Effects of Informed Consent in Research Patients and Study Results." *Journal of Nervous and Mental Diseases* 195 (1976) 349-357.

CHAPTER 11
RESEARCH AND EXPERIMENTATION INVOLVING PERSONS WITH DIMINISHED COMPETENCE

INTRODUCTION

It is difficult to act as proxy decision-maker in the ordinary therapeutic setting. The problems are compounded when the treatment that is suggested is experimental or innovative in nature. Nevertheless, sometimes there is no choice but to involve such incompetent subjects in experimental protocols. The factors that make them incompetent may be the very reasons why the protocol is developed in the first place.

For instance, children differ from adults not simply because they are younger, smaller and know less. In many cases, their organs function differently from the way adults' organs function. This is important when it comes to trying to determine how drugs work on children. We cannot simply scale down the dosage proportionally on the basis of size and body-weight. The pharmacokinetic function of the drug, the metabolization process, etc. may be quite different. Therefore, children really are the only subjects on whom we can find out how a drug works on children.

Similar remarks apply to people who suffer from organic psychiatric diseases, as well as the elderly. There are conditions that strike mainly elderly persons. Alzheimer's disease is a good example. The disease typically leaves the stricken individual incompetent. Therefore such a person cannot meet the ordinary standards of informed consent. Yet to exclude this population group from research and experimentation is to exclude precisely the group about whom we need data if we are going to be able to develop appropriate methods of treatment.

The Law Reform Commission of Canada suggests that experimenting on and doing research with human subjects is both ethical and legal. In its working paper, *Biomedical Experimentation Involving Human Subjects*, the Commission addresses the issue — but at the same time maintains that special safeguards should be in place. The selection from *Biomedical Experimentation* outlines some of the safeguards envisioned by the Commission. It presents the Commission's perspective on experimenting with prisoners, children, the mentally disabled, and embryos and foetuses. Since the function of the Law Reform Commission is to suggest legislation to the Minister of Justice, the considerations it raises are of considerable importance.

Barry Brown considers the topic from the point of view of elderly populations. Since most of us will fall into this category of elderly, this selection may be of special interest.

Biomedical Experimentation Involving Human Subjects [selected excerpts]

Law Reform Commission of Canada

SPECIAL CASES

I. PRISONERS

In the last few years a great deal has been written about experimentation on prisoners, and in the United States the topic has been the subject of lively legal and ethical debate. The major relevant international documents, the Nuremberg Code and the Helsinki Declaration, do not expressly prohibit the use of prison populations in scientific and medical research. Furthermore, a comparison between the first draft and the version finally adopted at Helsinki in 1964 shows that the total ban on the use of prisoners found in the initial draft was deliberately omitted from the final version. On the other hand, the resolution passed by the United Nations General Assembly on December 18, 1982,[1] clearly appears to prohibit it, as does a resolution of the Council of Europe.[2]

A number of studies, including those conducted by the Belmont Commission of which we spoke above, have shown that experimentation on prisoners is a phenomenon almost exclusively confined to the United States.[3] European countries, including France[4] and the Federal Republic of Germany,[5] expressly prohibit this practice. England and most other countries, although they do not prohibit it, do not engage in it. In Canada, it appears to be prohibited in federal and provincial institutions. For instance, section 21 of the *Regulation respecting Houses of Detention*[6] made under the *Act respecting Probation and Houses of Detention*[7] reads as follows:

> 21.   An imprisoned person may not be subjected to medical and scientific experiments that may be detrimental to his mental or physical integrity.[8]

Law Reform Commission of Canada, [selections from] Working Paper 61 *Biomedical Experimentation Involving Human Subjects* (Ottawa: Minister of Supply and Services, 1989).

Experimentation on prisoners in the United States really began during World War II with the pharmacological testing of treatments for infectious diseases that might be contracted by members of the armed forces. Various abuses came to light during the 1950s and 1960s and were strongly denounced. In some states the practice was completely banned. In its recommendations the Belmont Commission took a position somewhere between permissiveness and total prohibition. It considered that an unconditional ban on experimentation involving prisoners was inappropriate, but that certain precautions should be taken to ensure that consent would be freely given. Based on these recommendations, DHEW [Department of Health, Education & Welfare] issued regulations which are even more restrictive than those proposed by the Belmont Commission.[9]

In the course of its investigations, the Belmont Commission made a number of interesting observations. First, contrary to what might be expected, almost all of the more recent experiments on prisoners involved the testing of medications or new cosmetic products that involved little risk. Next, payments to prisoners for their participation were always very small, making it doubtful whether economic incentives played much of a role in obtaining their consent. Finally, the Commission noted that in most cases the same experiments could have been conducted as rigorously and successfully using subjects from the general population.

Why are prisoners so attractive to researchers? The answer is simple. Prisoners are a captive population leading a routine existence. Their lifestyle greatly facilitates the administration of research protocols and the collection of data, especially where the research is related to new medications and pharmaceutical products.

Both advocates and adversaries of the legalization of research using prisoners advance substantial arguments in support of their positions. The main argument of those who oppose legalization is as follows: in experimentation (where the subject derives no personal benefit), it is absolutely essential that consent be freely given. The fact that the prisoner is in a prison environment means that there are several reasons why he is unable to give free consent. He is more susceptible to undue influence; his motive for participating is often not disinterested, but rather related to his hopes for improving his lot (breaking the monotony, earning money or privileges, making a good impression on authorities, obtaining early release, having his sentence reduced or being granted parole). His being deprived of freedom makes his consent suspect and, given the possibilities for abuse, justifies an outright ban.

Proponents of the opposite view argue that an outright ban on the use of prisoners is discriminatory and unfair. They note that, in general, prisoners are highly motivated and that performing a socially useful, altruistic act that gives them a sense of self-worth is often an expression of their desire to make amends. They also argue that, while participation in an experiment should never be linked to a reduced sentence or parole, the desire to break the monotony of prison life or to improve one's lot is perfectly legitimate. Finally, one can only speak of coercion where there really is a threat. To offer a prisoner a tempting reward for his participation is not to threaten but merely to encourage, and does not in any way undermine his freedom to choose.

Nevertheless, no one would seriously dispute that the voluntary nature of a prisoner's consent must be considered more critically than in the case of a person having the exercise of his freedom. It must also be admitted that, except for research on the condition of prisoners themselves, prison populations tend to be used more out of convenience than out of scientific necessity. The same type of research can be conducted in the same manner on subjects who are not imprisoned, even though with more difficulty.

The mere existence of additional difficulties is not, in our opinion, a sufficient reason for legalizing experimentation on prisoners. We believe that the danger of abuse is too great. The fact that prisoners, unlike children or the mentally ill, do not constitute a distinct biomedical group, and that there will always be uncertainty about how free their consent is, whatever precautions may be taken, in our opinion also justifies a formal ban on the use of prisoners as experimental subjects and thus the maintenance of the status quo. Faced with this dilemma, the Commission believes it is necessary to consider the issue further before taking a position either in favour of a total ban or of acceptance under some conditions of experimentation on prisoners in Canadian prisons. We are also very interested in hearing from concerned parties and the public.

II. CHILDREN

...

Experiments involving children continue to be highly controversial. The legal profession is sharply divided on the issue.[10] There is agreement on only one point: experimentation of a therapeutic nature, that is to say which offers a reasonable hope of benefiting the child (such as the testing of a new medication in the treatment of leukemia) is legitimate and legal under ordinary conditions because its ultimate aim is to provide an individual benefit. Where the controversy arises is with respect to non-therapeutic experimentation.

Before we consider the arguments in support of each position, a few remarks are in order. First, everyone agrees that experimentation on children should be prohibit-

ed where adults capable of giving consent could be used just as well. Second, it is clear that from a scientific standpoint some experiments can be performed only on children. This is true for most research on childhood diseases (such as infantile leukemia, cystic fibrosis, chorea) and on certain congenital deformities. The issue must be faced squarely: an outright ban on any research involving children would limit the growth of scientific knowledge concerning these diseases and disorders and thereby adversely affect the development of cures and remedies, so the stakes are considerable.

Everyone agrees that a child is more vulnerable than an adult because it is impossible for him to weigh all the factors that should guide him in making a decision. The same holds true for an adult whose mental faculties are impaired. Whatever solution is chosen, in a society such as ours the law must, because of the possibilities for abuse, provide enhanced protection for its most vulnerable members.

This issue was the subject of a controversy between two American theologians, Ramsey[11] and McCormick.[12] Ramsey opposed any type of non-therapeutic experimentation involving children. He considered children incapable of adhering to the objectives pursued by the researcher. He felt it would be immoral to allow consent by a representative (parent or guardian), since non-therapeutic experimentation could not be of direct benefit to the child. The preservation of the health and enhancement of the well-being of a child were the only objectives to which a third party could consent on that child's behalf. Since non-therapeutic experimentation serves neither of these purposes, it should be totally prohibited.

McCormick and others[13] replied to this reasoning with two arguments. First, they advanced the notion of social utility. To ban all research involving children would be to condemn other children, since advances in the treatment of childhood diseases would no longer be possible. Second, although consent remains an important and even vital element, it should not necessarily be the one and only factor. Essentially, consent is given to indicate acceptance of the risks inherent in an experiment; the risk factor should thus be the major focus in any debate on the subject. In the name of what principle, it could then be asked, should there be a ban on an experiment of major scientific value and which involves no risk for the child? For those who support the second position, the legality of experimentation on children must therefore be determined primarily in terms of the risk involved in the experiment. Consent in the form of parental permission should continue to be required. However, if the risks involved in an experiment are humanly acceptable, the impossibility of obtaining the subject's own consent should not be used to justify an absolute ban.

... In Canada, as elsewhere, there is a tendency to reject a total ban on non-therapeutic experimentation involving children. We believe that this is a reasonable position and that a complete ban is not called for. We also believe that the ethical and legal guarantees proposed in some of the above-mentioned models are highly desirable.

Recommendation

4. The Commission recommends that the legality of non-therapeutic biomedical experimentation involving children should be recognized in a general federal statute on experimentation, provided that all the following conditions are met:

(a) the research is of major scientific importance and it is not possible to properly conduct it using adult subjects capable of giving consent;

(b) the research is in close, direct relation to infantile diseases or pathologies;

(c) the experiment does not involve any serious risks for the child;

(d) the consent of a person having parental authority and of an independent third party (a judge, an ombudsman or the child's lawyer) is obtained; and

(e) where possible, the consent of the child should be obtained. Moreover, whatever the child's age, his refusal should always be respected.

III. THOSE WITH MENTAL DISORDERS

Experimentation on persons with a mental disorder or illness raises problems similar in some respects to those raised by experimentation on prisoners and in other respects to those raised by experimentation on children. In effect, such persons are often not free, and the observations we made in connection with prisoners therefore apply to them. But regardless of whether or not they are confined, their situation resembles that of children in that they are in theory incapable of giving valid consent.

It is therefore not surprising that issues affecting those with mental disorders and children are frequently discussed together, since the principles that apply to the one generally apply to the other.

First, for the same reasons that experimentation on prisoners has been banned, experimentation on confined, mentally disordered people should be banned where the choice of subjects is based solely on grounds of ease of observation and analysis of results.

It should also be pointed out that the mentally disordered do not form as well-defined a group as, for instance, children. It is a very heterogeneous group and includes people who are institutionalized as well as those who are not. If the term mental disorder is taken in a broad sense, the category also includes those in a state of irreversible coma. Finally, mental disorder and mental illness may be temporary or permanent, and can vary greatly in severity, to the extent that one affected person may be absolutely incapable of understanding an experiment and giving his consent, whereas another may have this capability.

... An absolute ban on experimentation involving the mentally deficient can be objected to on the same grounds that we discussed in connection with children: it precludes certain kinds of desirable progress in the treatment of mental illnesses. On the other hand, and again as in the case of children, permitting experimentation with no restrictions requires disregarding the basic condition that consent be obtained, at least where the handicap is such as to deprive the subject of all discernment. As the Cameron affair at McGill University's Allan Memorial Institute clearly shows, abuses are possible and, because the mentally deficient form a more heterogeneous group, they are probably even more vulnerable than children. If law and ethics are to allow experimentation on the mentally deficient, strict requirements must therefore be laid down.

In the Commission's opinion, non-therapeutic biomedical experimentation should be allowed on persons with a mental deficiency, but it should be surrounded with ethical and legal guarantees.

Recommendation

5. The legality of non-therapeutic biomedical experimentation on mentally deficient persons should be recognized, in a general federal statute on experimentation provided that the following conditions are met:

(a) the research is of major scientific importance and it is not possible to properly conduct it using adult subjects capable of giving consent;

(b) the research is in close, direct relation to the subject's mental illness or deficiency;

(c) the research does not involve any serious risks for the subject;

(d) the consent of the incompetent person's representative and of an independent third party (a judge, an ombudsman or the incompetent person's lawyer) is obtained; and

(e) where possible, the incompetent person's consent is to be obtained, and his refusal is always to be respected.

IV. EMBRYOS AND FOETUSES

The ethical and legal issues raised by research on embryos and foetuses are extremely complex, and as likely as not to provoke highly emotional responses because they are linked to the controversy surrounding abortion and each person's own position on the subject. Moreover, experimentation on embryos and foetuses touches on a very difficult philosophical, theological and ethical problem: the beginning of human life.[14] At what moment in the development of the product of conception are we dealing with a human being or a human person? What value should society place on embryonic and foetal life?

The Law Reform Commission, in Working Paper 58, *Crimes Against the Foetus*, defined the term foetus as "the product of a union in the womb of human sperm cells and egg cells at all stages of its life prior to becoming a person": the term does not therefore include embryos fertilized *ex utero*. This is the meaning the word will have here.

Historically, experimentation began on the foetus. According to a special report of the Belmont Commission, it has taken four main directions.[15] First, research on the physiology and development of foetal tissue, hence on the growth of the foetus. Second, research relating to the diagnosis and detection of foetal diseases and congenital deformities. Third, some research has been done on foetal therapy and pharmacology, in particular on the possible effects of certain medications. This type of research, it should be said, is mainly retrospective and based on observation of aborted foetuses. It is this type of research that led to the discovery that the German measles vaccine could penetrate the placental barrier in women and have a teratological effect on the foetus, which was not the case with monkeys. Finally, there is research on foetuses that are not viable outside the womb, to determine whether they can be saved by somehow reproducing the uterine environment. This research has sometimes been described in layman's terms as the creation of an "artificial womb." As well, recent developments in France and the United States include experiments using the thymus glands of dead foetuses to produce a growth hormone, and those using foetal tissue to research the etiology of cancer.

Directly connected with the problem of experimentation on foetuses is the use of tissues from dead foetuses for the treatment of some diseases. Some current research offers hope that the implantation in the brain of certain foetal tissues or substances could have curative properties in the case of, for instance, Alzheimer's disease and Parkinson's disease. It should be noted in this connection that in principle these bodily substances are taken only from dead foetuses and that in strictly legal terms the taking of tissue from corpses is already regulated. From an ethical standpoint, however, there are those who object to the practice for a number of reasons. First, there is the connection with abortion, around which, as we know, there is nothing resembling a social consensus. Second,

some fear that society will come to close its eyes to the production of foetuses solely for tissues and substances. The problem is complex and will not be dealt with here since it is, strictly speaking, outside the bounds of biomedical experimentation.

In addition to the above, research is also being done on *in vitro* fertilization techniques using embryos a few days old. Not every embryo formed as a result of *in vitro* fertilization is necessarily reimplanted. The ethical and legal problems posed by surplus embryos are complex. May they be frozen? Destroyed? Experimented on? The situation of the embryo is in fact different from that of the foetus. It should be remembered that at a few days old the embryo consists of just a few undifferentiated cells. Although it possesses life, it is not viable and, because of the total absence of even a primitive nervous system, it cannot feel any pain. Embryo research is also of real interest, making possible a better understanding of the very process of the creation and development of human life. It has important consequences for embryo conservation and freezing techniques as well as for the development of artificial reproductive technologies. Finally, with regard to genetic research, it makes possible the hope that one day ways will be found to repair the errors of nature and to correct genetic deficiencies in as yet unborn infants. This set of problems has given rise to a number of studies.[16]

B. General Principles Governing Experimentation on Embryos and Foetuses

The Commission is of the opinion that any policy in the area of non-therapeutic biomedical experimentation should have to comply with certain fundamental principles. The first is respect for all forms of human life, whatever its stage of development. The rules governing experimentation should therefore also reflect respect for the sanctity of human life from its beginnings.

Second, the law should never treat embryos and foetuses as mere objects. Accordingly, their commercialization or the commercialization of research on them should be strictly prohibited, although this prohibition should clearly not extend to the use of embryonic or foetal tissue for therapeutic purposes.

Third, it seems clearly unethical to allow the creation of embryos solely for experimental purposes. In other words, only surplus embryos conceived in connection with an *in vitro* fertilization program and not reimplanted should be used in experiments rather than simply be destroyed. We will return to this question below.

Fourth, the Commission is of the opinion that, with respect to experimentation on foetuses, research policy should be clearly dissociated from abortion policy. A woman's right to have an abortion and her decision to do so does not necessarily mean that science may freely dispose of the aborted foetus. Consequently, the prospect of abortion should not affect the criteria determining the admissibility and legitimacy of research. However, if an experiment has been found to be ethically acceptable for foetuses in general, it seems legitimate to prefer to conduct it on a foetus to be aborted rather than on one intended to be brought to term, since this would decrease the risks even further.

Fifth, the Commission considers it important that permissible types of research be strictly defined. Like many others, the Commission is of the opinion that some experiments should by their very nature be considered unethical and contrary to public policy.

It is important to establish controls for monitoring embryo and foetal research.

Within the broad framework established by legislation, there should be provision for ensuring that research is ethical before it is undertaken. It is also necessary to ensure that it remains ethical during the period of experimentation and, once the experimentation has been completed, to ascertain the ethical value of the lessons to be learned for the future. The Commission is of the opinion that peer review is absolutely indispensable, as being the only way of properly evaluating the scientific aspects of a protocol and ensuring that it is ethical. It is also of the opinion that the ethics committees that presently approve research would do well both to include members from other disciplines (ethicists and jurists) and to play a wider role. In effect, in most cases these committees now do nothing more than accept or reject protocols. Once they approve an experiment because they consider it ethical, they have no authority to monitor it.

Finally, there is the question of the consent of parents to do research on their embryos or foetuses. The issue is even more sensitive when the foetus is in the womb, but the problem remains the same.

With respect to the question of consent, one thing is clear from the outset: no experiments should be allowed on a foetus *in utero* without the mother's free and informed consent. But is it useful, necessary or even desirable to obtain the father's consent as well? Three positions are possible. According to the first, the mother's consent should be sufficient, since she is in the best possible position to make an informed decision, and requiring the father's consent could be perceived as an undue restriction on the woman's rights over her own body.

The second position is to the opposite effect: non-therapeutic experimentation is purely elective and the child to be born is also the father's child. Requiring his consent is considered as providing additional protection.

Finally, there are some who, arguing that it is sometimes difficult if not impossible to identify the father, consider that where he is known, the mother's consent should still suffice unless he objects to the experiment.

Upon consideration, the Commission is of the opinion that the consent of both parents should be necessary. It seems important, on the one hand, to underline the fact that a child has two parents and hence to grant the father the right of refusal and, on the other hand, to respect his moral, religious or personal reasons for withholding consent. We would also extend this rule to experimentation on embryos since the underlying reasoning applies in that case as well.

Recommendation

6. Non-therapeutic biomedical experimentation on embryos and foetuses should be recognized, in a general federal statute on experimentation, provided that all the following conditions are met:

(a) the experimentation has received the prior approval of a multidisciplinary ethics committee responsible for ensuring that the research is ethical and scientifically genuine and having direct authority to monitor and control it;

(b) the embryo or foetal research is carried out in centres or hospitals recognized by the appropriate public authorities; and

(c) the consent of both parents of the embryo or foetus has been obtained.

C. The Differences Between the Embryo and the Foetus

From a biological standpoint, there are differences between an embryo and a foetus. It is known that, in the current state of science, the embryo cannot continue to develop outside the womb beyond a certain period of time. On the other hand, the development of the foetus is a slow process ending in the birth of a person: at a certain point, the foetus is endowed with nervous perception; at another, the foetus is viable even if expelled from its mother's body. For this reason, it seems to us essential to distinguish between these two stages in the development of the product of conception, each of which gives rise to different scientific, ethical and legal questions despite their undeniable common denominator: the existence of a potential human being.

1. Experimentation on Embryos

As we mentioned above, embryo research (we are speaking here of embryos fertilized *ex utero*: see the definition of the foetus given above) is currently being carried out on embryos produced by *in vitro* fertilization as a solution to the problem of sterility and which end up not being reimplanted. What might come to mind here is, of course, the deliberate creation of embryos solely for purposes of scientific research, something that will be that much easier when science discovers how to freeze oocytes. Researchers with frozen sperm and oocyte banks at their disposal will in theory no longer have to rely on the therapeutic process of *in vitro* fertilization for a supply of embryos. However, for the time being most jurists and ethicists look askance at the production of embryos for purely experimental purposes. They consider it to be in conflict with the respect due to human life even in a primitive state. The situation is not the same with respect to surplus embryos. There are three possibilities for embryos that are not reimplanted in the woman who provided the oocyte required for their creation: they could be destroyed, donated to another sterile couple or, before being destroyed, be used for research. The

Commission is of the view that, if circumstances do not permit donation, experimentation to advance knowledge seems to be preferable to outright destruction.

Recommendation

7. (1) The creation of embryos solely for purposes of scientific research should be prohibited and punished as a criminal offence.

The fate of the embryo that has been used for experimental purposes poses another problem. As we will see further on, the current international consensus is that the period during which research may be carried out should be limited (to fourteen days, generally speaking). Furthermore, the Commission agrees with the unanimous opinion of medical and legal authorities that embryos that have already been used for experimental purposes should not be reimplanted in a woman. The risk that such experimentation would leave traces is indeed too great.

Recommendation

7. (2) The re-implantation of embryos that have been used for experimental purposes should be prohibited and subject to criminal penalty.

Let us now return to the main problems raised by embryo research. The first question is to determine how standards relating to embryo experimentation should be defined by law. The view of the Commission is that not all types of research on embryos should be permitted. Moreover, the scientific community itself disapproves of certain types of research, and in this it has the support of ethicists and of all the governmental and quasi-governmental reports on the subject. Among these types of research are cloning, ectogenesis, parthenogenesis, and the crossing of human and animal gametes. The

Commission shares this point of view and considers that certain types of research on embryos should be prohibited and criminally punished. A description and a complete list of them should be drawn up in consultation with the scientific community.

Recommendation

7. (3) Certain types of experimentation on embryos, in particular cloning, ectogenesis, parthenogenesis, and the crossing of human and animal gametes, should be prohibited by criminal law; a complete list of types of experiment should be drawn up after consultation with scientific authorities.

The second question involves determining until what point *in vitro* research on embryos is ethically acceptable. Currently there is some international consensus that a limit of fourteen (sometimes seventeen) days should be imposed. In scientific terms the figure is, of course, arbitrary, but a number of reasons can be put forward to justify it. To begin with, after fourteen days of cellular development the embryo *ex utero* cannot be reimplanted. Furthermore, it is at this point that it becomes known if the embryo is going to twin. Finally, it is towards the fourteenth or even the seventeenth day that the neural tube, that is to say the central nervous system, begins to develop.

While we are aware that this fourteen-day limit is arbitrary the Commission nevertheless considers that, given the current state of knowledge, it is appropriate to agree to a standard that enjoys broad international support, if only to ensure that research done in Canada will be as respected as that done in the rest of the world.

Recommendation

8. (1) Experimentation on embryos should be prohibited after the fourteenth day of embryonic development.

Like sperm, the human embryo may be frozen. Medical science has already produced living children from embryos that had been frozen. However, freezing raises certain problems. First, science does not yet really know what the effects of prolonged freezing are. Second, if freezing extends over a long period of time, the very principle of generations may be disrupted: think of the prospect — science fiction for the time being, but already theoretically possible — of the reimplantation some fifty years hence of an embryo created in 1989. Such difficulties have prompted most countries to impose time limits on freezing. Given the current state of knowledge, these limits are of course completely arbitrary. However, a figure of five years seems to meet with more or less general approval. The Commission agrees with this position.

Recommendation

8. (2) The freezing of embryos should be allowed, but it should not be prolonged for more than five years.

2. Experimentation on Foetuses

Non-therapeutic biomedical experimentation on foetuses also raises sensitive questions. Some criteria are the same as for experimentation on embryos (authorization by an ethics committee, prior approval of the team or centre, the impossibility of obtaining the same results by experimentation on animals or adults, consent of both parents). But the foetus also poses a special problem that should be dealt with in somewhat more detail.

Experimentation on the foetus may take place either inside or outside the mother's womb. In *ex utero* experimentation, a new factor comes into play: either the foetus is dead or doomed because nonviable, or else it is viable. In the case of an already dead foetus, experiments are presently limited to the taking of foetal tissue. As we have seen, the law requires various kinds of authorization. If on the other hand the foetus is viable, from both a legal and ethical standpoint it must be treated as a human being with all the rights of a person.

In effect, a foetus that has proceeded completely and permanently from its mother's body becomes a "person" as defined in the Law Reform Commission's proposed new Criminal Code. In this connection, the reader is referred to Working Paper 58, *Crimes Against the Foetus*. Therefore the conditions set out above in the case of experimentation involving children apply.

Unlike the embryo, which is to be destroyed in any event, a foetus inside the womb raises the question of whether the risks are proportionate to the expected benefits. As we have seen, in the case of competent adults the law requires that there be no serious risk to life or health. Naturally, this requirement should continue to apply to the mother whose body is subjected, even indirectly, to an experiment that primarily concerns the foetus. That said, the Commission considers that when it is impossible for experimental subjects themselves to give consent, they should be provided with additional protection. For children and the incompetent, the Commission recommended that experimentation be allowed where it did not involve serious risk. Since the whole life, integrity and health of the unborn child can be compromised by experimentation on the foetus, the Commission considers acceptable only those experiments involving no risk or only minimal risk, this being defined as a risk normally associated with pregnancy.

Recommendation

9. The only experiments on the foetus that should be considered acceptable are those involving no risk or only minimal risk, this being defined as a risk normally associated with pregnancy.

NOTES*

1. Resolution 37-194 (111th plenary session), December 18, 1982. "The Principles of Medical Ethics relevant to the role of health personnel, particularly physicians, in the protection of prisoners against torture and other cruel, inhuman, or degrading treatment" appear in (1983) 37:3 *WHO CHRONICLE* at 91-92.

2. Resolution 73-5, February 12, 1987.

3. See National Commission for the Protection of Human Subjects of Biomedical and Behavioral Research, *Research Involving Prisoners* (Washington, D.C.: Department of Health, Education & Welfare, 1976).

4. *Code de procédure pénale*, art. D380(3) and Law of 20 December 1988, art. 209.3.

5. Medicines Act, August 24, 1976. Bundesgesetzblatt 1, 2445.

6. R.R.Q. 1981, c. P-26, r.1 art. 21.

7. R.S.Q. 1977, c. P-26.

8. For federal regulations, see: *Penitentiary Service Regulations*, C.R.C., c. 1251.

9. See National Commission for the Protection of Human Subjects of Biomedical and Behavioral Research, *supra*, note 3.

10. See the first report of the Medical Research Council of Canada, *Guidelines on Research Involving Human Subjects* (Ottawa: Supply and Services Canada, 1987) at 9.

11. P. Ramsey, *The Patient as Person: Explorations in Medical Ethics* (New Haven: Yale University Press, 1970); "The Enforcement of Morals: Non-Therapeutic Research on Children" (1976) 6:4 *Hast. Cent. Rep.* 21; "Children as Research Subjects: A Reply" (1977) 7:2 *Hast. Cent. Rep.* 40.

12. R.A. McCormick, "Proxy Consent in the Experimentation Situation" (1974) 18 *Perspectives in Biology and Medicine* 2; "Experimentation in Children: Sharing in Sociality" (1976) 6:6 *Hast. Cent. Rep.* 41.

13. See B. Freedman, "A Moral Theory of Consent" (1975) 5:4 *Hast. Cent. Rep.* 32; H.K. Beecher, *Research and the Individual: Human Studies* (Boston: Little, Brown, 1970) at 63.

14. M. Rivet, "Le droit à la vie ou l'hominisation du XXI^c siècle: l'éthique et le droit répondant à la science," in D. Turp and G.A. Beaudoin, eds., *Perspectives canadiennes et européennes des droits de la personne* (Cowansville, Que.: Yvon Blais, 1986) at 445.

15. National Commission for the Protection of Human Subjects of Biomedical and Behavioral Research, *Research on the Fetus: Report and Recommendations* (Bethesda, Md.: The Commission, 1975).

16. For Britain, see *inter alia, Report of the Committee of Inquiry into Human Fertilization and Embryology,* Warnock Report (London: HMSO, 1984).

   For the Federal Republic of Germany, see the report of the Benda Commission,

---

*These notes have been renumbered to aid the reader.

Fecondation in vitro, analyse du genome et therapie genetique, Rapport Benda (Paris: La Documentation française, 1987).

For Australia, see the *Report on the Disposition of Embryos Produced by In Vitro Fertilization; Report of the Special Committee Appointed by the Queensland Government Inquiry into the Laws Relating to Artificial Insemination, In Vitro Fertilization and Other Matters*, 1984; *South Australia Report on Artificial Insemination and Related Matters*, 1984.

For France, see *Sciences de la vie: de l'éthique au droit.*

For Canada, Ontario Law Reform Commission, *Report on Human Artificial Reproduction and Related Matters,* Ontario Law Reform Commission (Toronto: The Commission, 1985), vol. II, Recommendation 31 at 281; Medical Research Council of Canada, *Guidelines on Research Involving Human Subjects,* at 9; Barreau du Québec, *Les enjeux éthiques et juridiques des nouvelles technologies de reproduction* (Montréal, 1988).

Proxy Consent for Research on Incompetent Elderly

Barry F. Brown

In the past decade, the ethical issues of research with the elderly have become of increasing interest in gerontology, medicine, law, and biomedical ethics. In particular, the issue has been raised whether the elderly deserve special protection as a dependent group (Ratzan 1980). One of the most profound difficulties in this area of reflection is that of the justification of proxy consent for research on borderline or definitely incompetent patients.

Some diseases of the elderly, such as Alzheimer's disease, cause senile dementia: devastating for the patient and family and, in future, a considerable burden for society. This condition, in turn, renders a patient incapable of giving informed, vol-untary consent to research procedures designed to learn about the natural history of the disease, to control it, and to find a cure. The research must be done on human subjects, since there is not as yet a suitable animal model; indeed some feel that there never can be such a model. A protection of the patient, rooted in concern for his best interests, from procedures to which he cannot give consent gives rise to a paradox: "If we can only perform senile dementia research using demented patients, but should not allow them to participate because they are incompetent, then we are left in a quandary. We cannot ethically conduct senile dementia research using demented patients because they are incom-

Barry F. Brown, "Proxy Consent for Research on Incompetent Elderly," from James E. Thornton and Earl R. Winkler, eds., *Ethics and Aging: The Right to Live, The Right to Die,* (Vancouver: The University of British Columbia Press, 1988) 183-193.

petent; but we cannot technically perform it using competent subjects because they are not demented" (Ratzan 1980: 36). Such a position seems to protect demented patients at the expense of their exposure, as a class, to prolonged misery or death.

If the patient cannot give consent, is the proxy consent of relatives ethically valid? That is, do the relatives have the moral right or capacity to give consent for procedures that may not offer much hope for the patient in that they may not offer a direct benefit to him?

Such procedures have by recent convention been called non-therapeutic. They might offer a possible benefit for other sufferers in the future, but little hope of benefit for *this* patient, here and now.

At present, an impasse has developed regarding such research. It appears that such procedures might be illegal under criminal laws on assault. If the research is strictly non-therapeutic, then no benefit is to be found for the patient-subject. If the requirement of therapeutic experimentation is that a direct, or fairly immediate, improvement in the patient's condition is the sole benefit that could count, then it is difficult to see how this could be discovered. For unlike the case of a curable disease or research on preventive measures for childhood diseases, such as polio, the Alzheimer's patients suffer from a presently terminal illness. Studies of the causation of this condition may hold little or no hope of alleviating the condition in them. There appears to be no present or future benefit directly accruing to them. Others may benefit, but they likely will not. Thus, it seems, there is no benefit in view.

If, in fact, such procedures, even relatively innocuous ones, are illegal, then such research cannot go ahead. If so, such persons will remain "therapeutic orphans" just as surely as infants and children unless proxy consent is valid. If proxy consent is also legally invalid, then the legal challenge

to this impasse may be either legislative or judicial. In either case, ethical arguments must be offered as justification for the case that proxy consent is or ought to be legally valid. The following explorations are a contribution to that debate.

Can some kind of benefit for the demented be found in research that offers no immediate hope of improvement? I believe that it can, but the nature of that benefit will be unfamiliar or unacceptable to those who are sure that there are only two mutually exclusive alternatives: a utilitarian conception of the social good pitted against a deontological notion of the individual's rights.

Contemporary biomedical ethics routinely employs three principles in its effort to resolve such dilemmas (Reich 1970; Beauchamp & Childress 1983). These are the principle of beneficence, which demands that we do good and prevent harm; the principle of respect for persons (or the principle of autonomy), from which flows the requirement of informed consent; and the principle of justice, which demands the equitable distribution of the benefits and burdens of research. But the first two obviously conflict with each other in human experimentation: the principle of beneficence, which mandates research to save life and restore health, especially if this is seen as directed to the good of society, is in tension with the principle of respect for persons, which requires us to protect the autonomy of subjects. Moreover, the principle of beneficence requires us not only to benefit persons as patients through research, but also to avoid harming them as research subjects in the process. So there is an internal tension between moral demands created by the same principle. Finally, demented patients are no longer fully or sufficiently autonomous. Standard objections to paternalism do not apply. Consequently paternalism of the parental sort is not inappropriate, but rather necessary in order to protect the interest of the patient.

Simple application of these principles, therefore, will not provide a solution. Underlying the manner in which they are applied are radically different conceptions of the relationship of the individual good to the societal or common good.

In the present framework of philosophical opinion, there appear to be two major positions. On the one hand, some consequentialist arguments for non-therapeutic research justify non-consensual research procedures on the grounds that individual needs are subordinate to the general good conceived as an aggregate of individual goods. This good, that of the society as a whole, can easily be seen to take precedence over that of individuals. This is especially so if the disease being researched is conceptualized as an "enemy" of society. On the other hand, a deontological position argues that the rights of the individual take precedence over any such abstract general good as the advancement of science, the progress of medicine, or the societal good. In this view, to submit an individual incapable of giving or withholding consent to research procedures not for his own direct benefit is to treat him solely as a means, not as an end in himself. In this debate, one side characterizes the general good proposed by the other as much too broad and inimical to human liberty; the other sees the emphasis on individual rights as excessively individualistic or atomistic.

There are strengths and weaknesses in both approaches. The consequentialist rightly insists on a communal good, but justifies too much; the deontologist rightly protects individual interests, but justifies too little. I contend that if we are to resolve the dilemma concerning the incompetent "therapeutic orphan," it is necessary to go between these poles. In order to do so, I wish to draw upon and develop some recent explorations concerning non-therapeutic research with young children. In at least one important respect, that of incompe-tence, children and the demented are similar. We ought to treat similar cases similarly. I wish also to argue that research ethics requires: (1) a conception of the *common good* that is at once narrower than that of society as a whole and yet transcends immediate benefit to a single individual; and (2) a conception of the common good that sees it not in opposition to the individual good but including it, so that the good is seen as distributed to individuals.

THE LESSON OF RESEARCH WITH CHILDREN

As to the first, we may learn much from the discussions concerning research with children, particularly as they bear upon the distinction between therapeutic and non-therapeutic experimentation. In the 1970s a spirited debate took place between the noted ethicists Paul Ramsey and Richard McCormick on the morality of experimentation with children (Ramsey 1970, 1976, 1977; McCormick 1974, 1976). Ramsey presented a powerful deontological argument against non-therapeutic experimentation with children. Since infants and young children cannot give consent, an essential requirement of the canon of loyalty between researcher and subject, they cannot be subjected ethically to procedures not intended for their own benefit. To do so, he contended, is to treat children solely as means to an end (medical progress), not as ends in themselves (Ramsey 1970).

McCormick, arguing from a natural law position similar to that developed in the next section, argued that since life and health are fundamental natural goods, even children have an obligation to seek to preserve them. Medical research is a necessary condition of ensuring health, and this is a desirable social goal. Consequently children, as members of society, have a duty in social justice to wish to accept their share of the burdens of participating in research that promises benefit to society and is of minimal or no risk. Thus the parents' proxy consent is a reasonable presumption of the child's wishes if he were able to consent (McCormick 1974).

There are two major puzzles generated by this debate over non-therapeutic research in children. First, Ramsey stressed that the condition to which a child may be at risk need not reside within his skin, but could be an epidemic dread disease. Thus, testing of preventive measures such as polio vaccine on children is justified; indeed it counts for Ramsey as therapeutic. This is interesting for several reasons. First, the therapeutic benefit may be indirect or remote, not necessarily immediate. Second, it embodies the concept of a group or population at risk smaller than society as a whole. Third, it apparently allows for considerable risk. There was a risk of contracting polio from the vaccine. Although the risk might have been slight statistically, the potential damage was grave. By Ramsey's own account, a slight risk of grave damage is a grave risk. Thus, he was prepared to go beyond the limit of minimal or no risk on the grounds that the polio vaccine was *therapeutic,* while McCormick attempted to justify *non-therapeutic* research on children, but confined the risk to minimal or none. It is odd that in the subsequent protracted debate, this difference was not contested.

The second major puzzle arises from McCormick's view that fetuses, infants, and children ought to participate in low- or no-risk non-therapeutic research in order to share in the burden of social and medical progress in order that all may prosper. Note that only *burdens* are to be shared, not benefits. This is because the topic by definition was non-therapeutic experimentation. By putting it this way he seemed to many to be subordinating the interests of such subjects

to a very broadly construed societal good. But let us remember that the argument for such research in the first place was that without it, infants and children would be "therapeutic orphans." That is, without pediatric research, there could be fewer and slower advances in pediatric therapy.

Although not of direct benefit, such research is intended for the long-term benefit of children, and is thus indirectly or remotely therapeutic. It is not conducted for "the benefit of society" or for "the advancement of medical science"; it is for children in the future. Otherwise, it could be carried out on adults. Thus, such research should be construed as done not in view of broad social benefit but for the benefit of children as a group or a sub-set of society. Of course, if advances are made in medicine for the sake of children, society benefits as well, but this is incidental and unnecessary. The sole justification is provided by the benefits now and to come for *children.* At the same time, such benefits set one of the limits for such research: it should be confined to children's conditions, and should not be directed at conditions for which the research may be done on competent persons.

THE COMMON GOOD OF A DISEASE COMMUNITY

Some of the hints arising from the foregoing debate can now be developed. It is indeed wrong to experiment on an incompetent person for "the benefit of society" if the research is unrelated to that person's disease and he is made a subject simply because he is accessible and unresistant. But is it necessarily unethical to conduct experiments on an incompetent person which attempt to discover the cause of the condition which causes the incompetence, and which may cure it or prevent it in others, even if he will not himself be cured?

In a "third way" of conceptualizing the relation between the individual and the group, the good in view is neither that of society as a whole nor that of a single individual. It involves the group of persons with a condition, such as Alzheimer's disease. Here I turn to a conception of the common good articulated by John Finnis of Oxford. Finnis defines the common good not as the "greatest good for the greatest number" but as "a set of conditions which enables the members of a community to attain for themselves reasonable objectives, or to realize reasonably for themselves the value[s] for the sake of which they have reason to collaborate with each other [positively and/or negatively] in a community" (Finnis 1980: 155).

The community may be either the complete community or the political one, or it may be specialized, such as the medical community, the research community, or the community of children with leukemia, and so on. The common good is thus not the sum total of individual interests, but an ensemble of conditions which enable individuals to pursue their objectives or purposes, which enable them to flourish. The purposes are fundamental human goods: life, health, play, esthetic experience, knowledge, and others. Relevant to this discussion are life, health, especially mental integrity, and the consequent capacity for knowledge, all of which are threatened by diseases which cause dementia.

For my purposes, the community should be considered to be, at a minimum, those suffering from Alzheimer's disease. They have, even if they have never explicitly associated with each other, common values and disvalues: their lost health and the remaining health and vitality they possess. It could be said with McCormick that if they could do so, they would reasonably wish the good of preventing the condition in their relatives and friends.

But the community may be rightly construed more broadly than this. It naturally includes families with whom the patients most closely interact and which interact in voluntary agencies devoted to the condition, the physicians who treat them, the nurses, social workers, and occupational therapists who care for them, and the clinical and basic researchers who are working to understand, arrest, cure, and prevent the disease.

The participation of the patient, especially the demented patient, may be somewhat passive. He is a member of the specialized community by accident, not by choice, unless he has indicated his wish to become a research subject while still competent. Efforts to determine what a demented or retarded person would have wished for himself had he been competent have been made in American court decisions involving an incompetent patient's medical care. These "substituted judgment" approaches may have some worth, especially if the patient had expressed and recorded his wishes while still competent.

An individual might execute a document analogous to a human tissue gift — a sort of pre-dementia gift, in which he would officially and legally offer his person to medical research if and when he became demented. This might alleviate the problem of access to some extent, but it has its own difficulties. A pre-dementia volunteer cannot know in advance what types of research procedures will be developed in future, and so cannot give a truly informed consent except to either very specific procedures now known or to virtually anything. Such a pre-commitment may give some support to the decision to allow him to be a subject. But that decision, I contend, is justified by the claim, if valid, that it is for the common good of the dementia-care-research community, of which he is a member and to which, it is presumed, he would commit himself if he were capable of doing so at the time.

It is true, of course, that one might not ever have wished to participate in research procedures. In this case, the individual should be advised to register his or her objection in advance, along the lines that have been suggested for objection to organ donation in those countries that have a system of presumed consent for such donation. This can be achieved by carrying a card on which such an opt-out is recorded, or by placing one's name on a registry which might be maintained by support organizations. I suggest that unless one opt out in this manner, in the early stages of the disease, he or she be considered to have opted-in. That is, there should be a policy of presumed consent. In any event, as experience with organ retrieval has shown, in the final analysis it is the permission of relatives that is decisive in both those cases in which an individual has consented and those in which he or she has not made his or her wishes known.

The other members of the community may not all know each other. They do, however, have common values and, to a considerable degree, common objectives. There can be a high level of deliberate and active interaction, especially if there is close communication between the researchers, family, and volunteers in the voluntary health agencies.

What, then, is the ensemble of conditions which constitute the common good of the Alzheimer's community? Insofar as the purposes of collaboration include the effort to cure or to alleviate the disease, the common good would embrace, in addition to caring health professionals, a policy of promoting research, its ethical review, a sufficient number of committed clinical and scientific researchers, the requisite physical facilities and funding (some or all of which may be within other communities such as hospitals and medical schools), availability of volunteers for research, an atmosphere of mutual trust between research and subject, and finally ongoing research itself. This list is not exhaustive.

If access to the already demented is not allowed, and if this is essential for research on the disease to continue, it may well be impossible to find the answers to key questions about the disease. The common good of the Alzheimer's community would be damaged or insufficiently promoted. Since the goods of life and mental health are fundamental goods, this insufficiency would be profound.

One essential aspect of this common good is distributive justice. Each patient-subject shares not only in the burdens of research in order that all may prosper, but also the benefits. The benefits are not necessarily improved care or cure for the subject, but generally improved conditions for all such patient-subjects: a more aggressive approach to research, improved knowledge of the disease, increased probabilities for a cure, and others. Since the individual participates wholly in that good, he will be deprived of it in its entirety if it is not pursued. The common good is not so much a quantity of benefits as a quality of existence. It can therefore be distributed in its fullness to each member of the community. So, too, each can suffer its diminution.

Richard McCormick (1974) left his description of the common good unnecessarily broad and sweeping. According to some natural law theorists (Maritain 1947) the common good is always a distributed good, not simply the sum of parts. It is construed as flowing back upon the individual members of the community, who are not simply parts of a whole but persons, to whom the common good is distributed in its entirety. Thus, not only can the common good of which McCormick speaks be narrowed to that of children as a group (equivalent to Ramsey's population at risk) but the benefits of such research can be seen as redistributed to the individuals of the group. The benefits are not to be taken in the sense of an immediately available therapy, but in the sense of improved general conditions under which a cure, amelioration, or prevention for all is more likely.

CONCLUSION

Some of these observations can now be applied to the case of the elderly demented. First, the debate showed the inadequacy of the simple distinction between therapeutic and non-therapeutic experimentation, which has been challenged on several grounds in past years. For example, May (1976: 83) includes diagnostic and preventive types of research under therapeutic experimentation, whereas Reich (1978: 327) observes that the terms "therapeutic" and "non-therapeutic" are inadequate because they do not seem to include research on diagnostic and preventive techniques. In the area of the development of experimental preventive measures such as vaccines for epidemic diseases, and in the area of diseases in which research is carried out on terminal patients with little or no expectation of immediate benefit for these patients, the distinction is somewhat blurred. In each case, there is a defined population at risk: one without the disease but at great risk of contracting it, the other with a disease but with little hope of benefiting from the research.

Such types of research seem to constitute an intermediate category: the "indirectly therapeutic," involving the hope of either prevention or alleviation or cure. This category as applied to dementia shows some characteristics of therapeutic experimentation in the accepted sense, since it is carried out on persons who are ill and it is directed to their own illness. But it also shares some properties of non-therapeutic research, since it is not for their immediate treatment and, therefore, benefit. The good to be achieved is more remote, both in time and in application, since it is less sharply located in the individual than is therapy as such.

It must be admitted that there is a difference between the testing of a vaccine for prevention of disease in young, healthy children and research on elderly, seriously ill patients. In the former, the child-subjects will benefit if the vaccine is successful, or at least be protected from harm. In the latter, the subjects will not benefit by way of prevention or cure of their disease, but rather simply by being part of a community in which those goals are being actively pursued. The identification of the demented patient's good with that common good is doubtless less concrete than the identification of the child's good with that of his peers. But it seems to me that underlying both these cases is a notion of the common good required to justify all cases of research that do not promise a hope of direct benefit to a person who is, here and now, ill.

Years ago, Hans Jonas (1969) noted that a physician-researcher might put the following question to a dying patient: "There is nothing more I can do for you. But there is something you can do for me. Speaking no longer as your physician but on behalf of medical science, we could learn a great deal about future cases of this kind if you would permit me to perform certain experiments on you. It is understood that you yourself would not benefit from any knowledge we might gain; but future patients would." Although greatly vulnerable and deserving of maximum protection, such a patient might be ethically approached to be a research subject, because the benefits to future patients are in a way a value to him: "At least that residue of identification is left him that it is his own affliction by which he can contribute to the conquest of that affliction, his own kind of suffering which he helps alleviate in others; and so *in a sense it is his own cause*" (Jonas 1969: 532, emphasis mine).

In this case, the individual apprehends a good greater than his personal good, less than that of society: that of his disease class, which is *his* good. Of course, the identification of which Jonas speaks is psychological: he would likely not agree with the approach herein outlined and might require that such participation be through a conscious, free choice of the patient. Nevertheless, it is a real, objective good which justifies his choice and prevents us from asking him to participate in research unrelated to his disease. Can a relative, a son or daughter perhaps, ethically make that decision for an incompetent, demented Alzheimer's patient? If so, it is because, in a sense, it is the patient's cause, the patient's good as a member of a community which justifies that choice. It is not a matter of enforcing a social duty or minimal social obligation here, but seeking a good that lies in the relationship one has to others with the same disease. That same good, as noted above, limits the participation of the subject to research related precisely to his disease, not to anything else.

What is the implication of this for risk and the limits of risk? As has been seen, some wish to allow for exposure of subjects to greater than minimal risk provided only that it is classified as "therapeutic" (though the subjects are not ill). Others, in spite of the fact that the research is intended for the benefit of a group at risk, classify it as nontherapeutic and limit the acceptable risk to minimal levels. Are these the only alternatives? One advisory group has allowed, in the case of the mentally incompetent, for a "minor increase over minimal risk" in such circumstances (National Commission for the Protection of Human Subjects 1978: 16). This is presumably permitted because the research is "of vital importance for the understanding or amelioration of the type of disorder or condition of the subjects" or "may reasonably be expected to benefit the subjects in future" (17). But what counts as minor increase in risk? Proposed research into Alzheimer's might involve invasive procedures such as brain biopsies, implantation of electrodes, spinal taps, and injections of experimental drugs. Are these of greater risk than that specified by the National Commission simply because they are invasive of the human brain? Or is there clear statistical risk of serious added damage to the brain? These are matters for empirical study. The invasiveness per se should not rule out a procedure. The major limitations should be whether the procedure is painful, causes anxiety, or adds to the already serious damage to the brain. If research involving procedures of greater risk than "minor increase over minimal" is ever to be justified, it must be so by the intent to avert the proportional evils of death or mental incapacity. If these are insufficient, then I fail to see what grounds might be available upon which to base a case for legislative change.

It is clear, then, that should such research be acceptable, it also demands that stringent protective procedures be established in order to ensure that the demented are not drafted into research unrelated to their disease class. This is because the standard, being broader than that of "direct or fairly immediate benefit," is open to an accordionlike expansion, and therefore to abuse. Such safeguards could include: rigorous assurance that the proxy's consent (in reality, simply a permission) is informed and voluntary, the provision of a consent auditor, and various layers of administrative review and monitoring, from a local institutional review board up to a judicial review with a guardian appointed to represent the patient-subject's rights. These procedures may prove to be onerous. But we are on dangerous ground, and as we try to avoid overprotection, which may come at the expense of improved therapy for all, we must also avoid opening up a huge door to exploitation.

REFERENCES

Beauchamp, T.L., & Childress, J.F. (1983). *Principles of Biomedical Ethics.* 2nd ed. New York: Oxford University Press.

Finnis, J. (1980). *Natural Law and Natural Rights.* Oxford: Clarendon Press.

Jonas, H. (1969). Philosophical reflections on experimenting with human subjects. In T. Beauchamp and L. Walters (Eds.), *Contemporary Issues in Bioethics.* 2nd ed. Belmont, CA: Wadsworth.

Maritain, J. (1947). *The Person and the Common Good.* New York: Charles Scribner's Sons.

May, W. (1976). Proxy consent to human experimentation. *Linacre Quarterly, 43,* 73-84.

McCormick, R. (1974). Proxy consent in the experimentation situation. *Perspectives in Biology and Medicine, 18,* 2-20.

McCormick, R. (1976). Experimentation in children: sharing in sociality. *Hastings Center Report, 6,* 41-46.

National Commission for the Protection of Human Subjects (1978). *Report and Recommendations: Research Involving Those Institutionalized As Mentally Infirm.* Washington, D.C.

Ramsey, P. (1970). *The Patient As Person.* New Haven: Yale University Press.

Ramsey, P. (1976). The enforcement of morals: Non-therapeutic research on children. *Hastings Center Report, 4,* 21-30.

Ramsey, P. (1977). Children as research subjects: a reply. *Hastings Center Report, 2,* 40-41.

Ratzan, R. (1980). "Being old makes you different": The ethics of research with elderly subjects. *Hastings Center Report, 5,* 32-42.

Reich, W. (1978). Ethical issues related to research involving elderly subjects. *Gerontologist, 18,* 326-37.

FURTHER READINGS

In the Matter of Kristie Lee F, P.C.C. (F.D.) Ontario (1072/88).

Coughlan, M.J. and E. Anscombe. "Using People," *Bioethics* 4:1 (1990) 55-65.

Levine, Robert J. *Ethics and Regulations of Clinical Research* (New Haven and London: Yale University Press, 1988) Chapters 10-13.

Mason, J.K. *Medico-Legal Aspects of Reproduction and Parenthood* (Brookfield, VT.: Gopwer, 1990) 280-296, "Consent to Treatment and Research in Children."

Medical Research Council of Canada. *Guidelines on Research Involving Human Subjects 1987* (Ottawa: Minister of Supply and Services, 1987).

National Commission for the Protection of Human Subjects of Biomedical and Behavioral Research. *The Belmont Report: Ethical Principles for the Protection of Human Subjects of Research* (Washington, D.C.: U.S. Government Printing Office, 1978) pub. no. 78–0012.

McCormick, R. "Proxy Consent in Experimentation Situations," *Perspectives in Biology and Medicine* 18:1 (1974).

Nicholson, Richard H., ed. *Medical Research With Children: Ethics, Law, and Practice* (New York and Tokyo: Oxford University Press, 1986).

Picard, E.I. *Legal Liability of Doctors and Hospitals in Canada* (Toronto: Carswell, 1984) Chapter 3, "Consent."

Ramsey, P. *The Ethics of Fetal Research* (New Haven: Yale University Press, 1975).

Superintendent of Belchertown State School v. Saikewicz, 370 N.E. (2d) C 417 (Mass. S.C. 1977).

Wasserstrom, R. "Ethical Issues Involved in Experimentation on the Non-Viable Human Foetus," National Commission for the Protection of Human Subjects of Biomedical and Behavioral Research, *Appendix: Research on the Foetus* (1975) DHEW No. (05) 76–128.

CHAPTER 12
PERSONHOOD

INTRODUCTION

Until fairly recently, the distinction between being a person and being a member of the species *homo sapiens* was of interest only to philosophers and theologians. It was generally assumed that any living human being was a person, and *vice versa*. Not only our tradition, but also our laws reflect that fact.[1]

Three recent developments in health care have challenged this assumption. First, medical technology such as respirators, kidney machines, etc. were developed to the point that people could be kept alive considerably beyond the time when otherwise they would have died. However, in many cases the people who were thus saved were left in a permanent vegetative coma, because their higher brain centres had been destroyed. These individuals were therefore biologically alive but without any possibility of a return to sentient cognitive awareness. In fact, in some cases, not only were their higher brain centres destroyed, but also the whole brain — and yet the bodies could be kept alive for a time. The question therefore arose, are these individuals still persons?

The thrust of the question was sharpened by the scarcity of medical resources. It therefore came to be asked whether it was ethically appropriate to spend scarce resources to sustain someone who was only biologically living when that would deprive others of appropriate and possibly beneficial health care.

A second development that influenced the debate and expanded it considerably was the advent of transplantation. It soon became evident that organs from living donors had a much better chance of not being rejected than organs from cadavers. This increased the pressure for examining the validity of the distinction between being biologically alive only, and being alive as a person.

Finally, the distinction between humanity and personhood was pressed when abortion became a public issue, and when the federal government attempted to draft abortion laws that satisfied the multicultural and multi-religious makeup of Canadian society. This pushed the debate about personhood to the beginning of human life. It forced an examination of the question of whether a human being is a person from the moment of conception, or acquires personhood at some later stage.

In the course of the debate, it became evident to many that the question of when someone is dead is really the question of when someone is *no longer* a person, and that this question could not ethically be divorced from the question of when someone is *already* a person. Whatever notion of personhood was ultimately to be developed, and however it was to be related to the concept of a human being, it would have to be applicable in a consistent fashion in both cases.

The selections below give an indication of the range of considerations that have been covered in the course of the debate. On the issue of developing personhood, one extreme is presented by Frances Rosenberg's editorial from the Association of Medical Women's *Newsletter*. The position paper of the Committee on Ethics of the Canadian Medical Association reflects an attempt by the senior advisory committee of organized Canadian medicine to steer a somewhat less radical course.

On the issue of when someone is no longer a person, the case of *R. v. Kitching and Adams* represents the perspective of Canadian law.

Finally, the discussion by Roland Puccetti, who is a philosopher, deals with the question of those who are in permanent vegetative state. These individuals do not meet the whole-brain criterion, yet there is no question that they no longer have the capacity for sentient cognitive awareness. Are they dead as persons? The issue is especially important in light of the chronic shortage of health care resources and the cost involved in keeping these individuals alive. The issues of resource allocation, right to health care, etc., dealt with by selections in preceding chapters, here become relevant.

NOTE

1. The political and legal position on personhood is another matter. It involves judicial recognition of individuals as having the rights that are normally associated with other individuals who are recognized as persons in a judicial sense. Women were not recognized as legal persons in Canada until 1929, when the Privy Council of Great Britain extended that recognition by stating that the word "person" contained in the British North America Act extended to women as well as men. It is interesting to note that in this sense, children are still not recognized as persons.

The Status of the Human Foetus

Canadian Medical Association, Committee on Ethics

Fertilization marks the beginning of human embryonic development. From its very beginning, therefore, a human foetus is a member of the species *Homo sapiens*. Physicians, scientists and ordinary members of the community agree on this point. Thereafter, however, opinions diverge. Some see no difference between being a human being in a biological sense (i.e., being a member of the species *Homo sapiens*) and being a human being or person in an ethical sense. Indeed, they characterize any attempt to draw such a distinction as untenable and pernicious. Others maintain that there is a difference. They believe that membership in the species *Homo sapiens* has only biological importance. They believe that what conveys ethical status is not membership in a biological species but the fulfillment of certain criteria. They maintain that these criteria involve such characteristics as the capacity for sapient cognitive awareness, the capacity for self-awareness, and the like.

The opposition between these two approaches has usually been cast as the opposition between a biologically and a functionally oriented notion of personhood. The biologically oriented position contends that human beings are persons in an ethical sense from the very moment of conception. The functionally oriented position maintains that only those living organisms who satisfy certain functional criteria — some of which have been mentioned — can be considered persons.

Recent developments have cast doubt on the acceptability of the biologically oriented position.[1] They have done so from a medical as well as from a legal perspective. Developments in medicine have reached a point where a biologically human being may be kept alive long after any semblance of sapient capacity has been irremediably destroyed. Medically, therefore, it has become appropriate to distinguish between a human being who is biologically alive but no longer a person, and someone who is biologically alive as well as a person. The acceptance of the Harvard criteria for the determination of brain death was but the professional recognition of this development. The concept has since been refined in various ways and has found legal acceptance in most jurisdictions.

In Canada, legal acceptance of brain-centred criteria for the determination of death occurred in the case of *Regina v. Kitching and Adams*.[2] The courts here recognized that while some human beings may be biologically alive, the fact that their brains are irreparably dysfunctional allows us to consider them legally dead and therefore persons no longer. At this time, only Manitoba has enacted a statute which fixes this distinction. However the distinction is generally accepted for most purposes in Canada as well as elsewhere.[3] Indeed, the practice of harvesting organs from biologically alive but brain-dead human beings would otherwise not be defensible: It would amount to murder.

"The status of the human foetus" — Reprinted from Reports to the General Council, by permission of the publisher, Canadian Medical Association, 1991; Appendix 7, 201-221. This material was a background document and does not reflect CMA policy.

These developments did not take place in isolation. They went hand-in-hand with a fundamental reorientation in ethical perspective. It became widely accepted as matter of general principle that what is ethically central to the issue of personhood is not whether a given individual is alive or even belongs to the species *Homo sapiens*. Instead, the possession of certain capacities became widely recognized as ethically central: specifically, the capacity for some level of self-awareness and sapient cognitive awareness.

By drawing on these historical developments, the Committee does not mean to equate a developing foetus with a brain-dead human being; nor does the Committee intend to suggest that the process of dying is an exact analogue as the process of gestation. The Committee recognizes that there are fundamental differences. They include the fact that a foetus is developing and has a potential for increased functioning, whereas this is precisely what is absent in the case of a brain-dead human being.

Nevertheless, the Committee feels that the analogy has a point. Abstracting from philosophical niceties that centre around the notion of potentiality itself, the analogy lies in the functional aspects of the case. Death is not an instantaneous event. It is a process of increasing dissolution and dysfunction. Brain cells die, and their death contributes to the dysfunction of the brain as a whole. At some point in this process, this dysfunction is so cumulative that a threshold is crossed. At that point the individual is said to be dead, the fact of continued cellular and even organic life notwithstanding.

The development of the human foetus also involves a functional gradation. The difference is that it occurs in reverse fashion. There is a gradual increase in neurological complexity from the first identifiable neural cells which do not as yet function in an integrated fashion, to the integrated brain structure of the foetus at term. The capacity for sapient cognitive awareness is absent at the beginning of that development. There is not even capacity for somatic sensation. These capacities are acquired as the neurological structure of the foetus grows and increases. They constitute as it were an inverse of the process of death. Consistency and equality require that if the integrated functioning presence of such structures, and the presence of such capacities, are deemed necessary for human beings to be considered persons, they must be applied to the human foetus as well as to human beings that have already been born.

The fact that the foetus has the potential for development may be thought to make a difference. However, the Committee on Ethics believes that is not the case. In the *first* place, a potential does not give whoever has that potential the same status as someone who actually exhibits the relevant characteristic. A fertilized and incubating egg is a foetal bird. For all that, however, the incubating egg does not have the same status, and in an intuitively clear sense is not materially the same, as the hatched bird which it will become. In order to attain that status, the foetal bird has to develop under appropriate conditions of incubation. To equate a fertilized and developing egg with a bird who has been hatched, and to treat them the same, is to ignore the very fundamental difference between the two: A difference that involves their present material natures.[4] Of course this does not prevent society from bestowing the same *legal* status on both, or from protecting the two by the same (or at least essentially similar) sanctions. However, that would be the result of a deliberate decision by society on societal or other grounds. Logically it would neither be necessary nor would it follow from the material nature of the case.

In the *second* place, to say that something has a potential by that very fact is to distinguish it from something in which the potential is actualized. Otherwise the distinction would be pointless. Therefore to say that the two have the same status — the same ethical status — requires a premise which says that something which has a mere potential and something in which this potential is actualized *should* be treated the same way. But that is the very point at issue. Simply to assert that their status is the same is to settle the matter by definition. It is to beg the question. An example may serve to illustrate the point: If someone who is a potential sufferer from Huntington disease (someone who carries the genetic determinant for it) has the same status as someone who is an actual sufferer from Huntington disease in virtue of that potentiality, then the potential sufferer should be treated the same way as the actual sufferer. However to treat the two in the same way would be entirely inappropriate: psychologically, socially and above all medically.[5]

The Committee therefore proposes the following:

Recommendation 1

A human foetus becomes a person when it meets the criteria for personhood that must be met by all other human beings.

Recommendation 2

These criteria are met when the foetal nervous system has developed to the point where it has the basic capacity for sapient cognitive awareness irrespective of level of sophistication.

These considerations suggest that while ethical considerations are always relevant with respect to the human foetus, they increase in gravity and change in nature as the gestation progresses. As the pregnancy progresses, the foetus increasingly becomes an object of ethical concern.[6,7] This means that in actions that impact on a human foetus, respect for the life of the foetus increasingly has to be balanced against the right to self-determination of the pregnant woman and to the integrity of her person. However, once the foetus has become a person, the ethical deliberations that are now appropriate no longer consist in a weighing of the value of respect for life of the foetus against the principle of autonomy of the pregnant woman. They now involve a balancing of the right to life against the right to integrity and self-determination. At this point the existence of competing rightclaims is no longer at issue. What is at issue is their relative strengths.

In other words, although a human foetus is an object of serious ethical concern prior to approximately twenty weeks, it is not the ethical equal of the mother before that time. The reason lies in the development of its functional capacity. If one were to depict this capacity on a linear scale, it could be represented as a line with variable but increasing slope. The line begins at a minimal level when fertilization occurs and rises steadily until around the twentieth week. According to current understanding, the line appears to cross a critical point of quantum-like proportions around that time. The reason is that according to current understanding it is around that time that the capacities of the foetus meet the minimal requirements that are otherwise considered necessary for someone to be considered a person.

What this means in practical terms may be illustrated by considering the case of a pregnant woman who requires medical treatment. Ethical considerations require that the attending physician take the life and welfare of the foetus into account when evaluating the treatment options for the woman no matter what the stage of development of the foetus.[8] The physician must balance the competing claims of the woman against considerations concerning the foetus. However, the strength of that balancing will not be uniform at all stages of foetal development. Instead, the weight given to foetal concerns in this balancing process will be functionally determined by the level of development of the foetus and the threat to the health of the pregnant woman.

Care must be taken not to understand this notion of balancing in too liberal a fashion. It does not mean that only passing and token consideration should be given to the foetus. Instead, it means that the reasoning process that leads to a medical decision must attempt a genuine balancing, with serious consideration being given to the foetus as well as to the pregnant woman. This is in keeping with the resolution of the 1989 General Council of the CMA which directed the Committee on Ethics to consider the proposition that "in the decision concerning an abortion, both parties must consider the existence of the unborn child and respect its rights." In any abortion counselling, therefore, or in any situation involving the human foetus, the status of that foetus must be taken into account.[9]

Furthermore, it should be kept in mind that history is replete with examples where individuals have been denied appropriate treatment because they have been denied the status of persons. The fate of women prior to their enfranchisement, of slaves, of ethnic and religious minorities in general are all-too familiar examples. The Committee is solicitous that not recognizing the foetus as an object of ethical concern from its very beginning may be seen in this light. It therefore wants to go on record as rejecting completely, emphatically and utterly the suggestion that any and all actions towards a foetus are licit simply because the foetus has not as yet been born. Society has certain standards and values which, while not ethical principles, nevertheless function as fundamental principles of acceptable conduct. One of these was referred to above. It is the principle of respect for human life. No human being, whatever its stage of development, may be deprived without good reason of the protection that this principle affords. Therefore it is the position of the Committee that all other things being equal the human foetus, whatever its stage of development, is also entitled to appropriate and respectful treatment.[10]

Among other things, this means that so far as the Committee is concerned, the standard of conduct to be observed towards a human foetus who has not as yet attained to the stage where it becomes a person must, as a minimal benchmark, satisfy the requirements embodied in humane legislation: The fact that a foetus does not have the same status as an ordinary member of society does not mean that it should be accorded even less respect than non-human living beings. Furthermore, the Committee believes that a human foetus which has not as yet attained to being an object of full-fledged ethical concern may be involved in undertakings that are of no benefit to itself only on the condition that there are overwhelming ethical reasons (rooted in the rights of extant and fullfledged members of society) that outweigh the considerations which stem from the principle of respect for human life. In other words, the Committee believes that the human foetus should not be involved in non-therapeutic endeavours or undertakings that are not mandated by overwhelming social or individual ethical considerations.

The Committee on Ethics therefore suggests the following as a further fundamental guideline for all actions involving the human foetus:

Recommendation 3

The principle of respect for human life is of fundamental importance in medical practice. Therefore any action involving a human foetus must always be evaluated in light of this principle,

and departures from it must always
be justified in terms of the principles
of medical ethics.

VIABILITY

So far, no reference has been made to the
concept of viability. The reason lies in the
dubious ethical validity that attaches to
the notion of viability itself.

In the foetal context, "viability" usually refers to the capacity of the foetus to stay
alive when removed from or independent
of the body of its mother. In a state of nature
and in the absence of medical intervention,
that capacity depends solely on the state of
the individual foetus: on its development,
its present capacities and the like. This is no
longer true in the contemporary setting.
Viability is no longer an independent variable which, all other things being equal,
finds its basis in the state of the foetus itself.
Given the advances of modern medicine and
technology, it has largely become a function
of the sophistication of the external supports that are available, on the readiness
to use them — as well as on the willingness
of society to use all available scientific
means to push back still further the current practical limits on sustaining life.

What this means in ethical terms is
that to consider viability as determinative
of the ethical status of anyone is to make
the ethical status of that individual dependent on the willingness of society to develop
and use means to use life support systems.
More specific to the foetal context, to attach
ethical significance to the notion of foetal
viability is to ignore the criteria for personhood that are considered relevant in all
other contexts. It is to replace considerations that depend on the state and development of the foetus with considerations that
depend on the sophistication of available
medical technology and on society's willingness to use it.

It is worth mentioning in this regard
that such an approach would constitute an
ethical anomaly: The fact that someone is
dependent on a respirator, a kidney
machine or other external support system
is generally not considered sufficient reason for not treating that individual as an
object of fullfledged ethical concern.
Consistency demands that the human foetus should not be treated differently.

Implications for the Physician

(a) With Respect to Everyday Practice

These considerations have important
consequences for physicians in actual practice. The first consequence, and in many
ways perhaps the most important, is that
such physicians ought to consider the foetus
an object of ethical concern almost from the
beginning, and that the foetus should be
considered a genuine patient at the latest at
twenty weeks gestation. This would hold
true irrespective of whether the foetus was
in utero or in an artificial environment.

Furthermore, current developments in
reproductive technology and reproductive
care, as well as advances in perinatal medicine and associated disciplines, have made
it clear that the fetal environment during
gestation has a profound effect on the development of the foetus itself. What is done
to the foetus — or, for that matter, to the
mother — may shape its later life profoundly. In anticipation of considerations
to be dealt with later, the Committee therefore suggests the following as a guiding
principle:

Recommendation 4

**A physician should always act on the
assumption that the foetus is likely to
become a person unless there are clear
indications to the contrary.**

(b) Indications to the Contrary

(i) However, there are cases where the exceptive clause of Consideration 5 will in fact be met. *For instance*, the foetus may suffer from such severe and irreparable congenital or other deficits that it will never fulfil the material requirements for becoming a person. In such cases, while the physician's actions should still be guided by respect for life, the physician's primary concern should be the pregnant woman.

Recommendation 5

When it is medically certain that the foetus will never become a person, the physician's obligations towards the foetus are those agreed to by the pregnant woman and otherwise owed living beings of a comparable level of development. The primary concern of the physician, however, should be the pregnant woman.

ii) A *second* indication to the contrary obtains when, according to the best medical knowledge available under the circumstances, the foetus suffers from such deficits that if it were to be born, its life would be tantamount to a continuous state of injury, or the life that the foetus could reasonably be expected to live would be describable only in terms of inhumanity, indignity and suffering.[11] In such cases, the aim of the physician should be to try to prevent the actualization of continuous and irremediable harm. The sorts of situations that would warrant such considerations may include Trisomy 13, Tay-Sachs, anencephaly and similar conditions that are usually grouped under the term "medical indications for abortion."

Recommendation 6

When, in the best understanding of the physician, the foetus can only attain an existence that is significantly lacking in human quality or one that is fraught with irremediable pain and suffering, then the physician may ethically terminate the pregnancy. The treatment of the mother should be from a humanitarian perspective, recognizing her loss. Under certain circumstances, termination of the foetus's existence even after 20 weeks gestation may be appropriate.

The last statement should be seen as a partial clarification of the CMA's current position on abortion, which states that "Elective termination of pregnancy after fetal viability may be indicated under exceptional circumstances."[12]

(iii) A *third* exceptive condition obtains when the pregnant woman's life is in danger and it is medically certain that her life can be saved — but only through a procedure that will kill the foetus.

In a case like this, the physician's primary obligation is towards the pregnant woman. However, the Principle of Autonomy entails that the woman has the right to decide whether she wishes her life to be saved or, alternatively, wants the life and welfare of the foetus to receive priority. The physician therefore has an obligation to try and determine the woman's wishes. Once these wishes have been determined, the physician must follow them. If it is not possible to ascertain what the woman's wishes are, Recommendation 5 takes over and the woman's life and welfare become the physician's primary concern.

Recommendation 7

When the physician is faced with a choice between the life of the pregnant woman and the life of the foetus and if the pregnant woman has indicated in a competent and informed fashion that the life of the foetus should be given priority, then the physician must follow those wishes.

Recommendation 8

When the physician is faced with a choice between the life of the pregnant woman and the life of the foetus and if there is no way of reasonably determining the wishes of the pregnant woman, the physician should attempt to save both. If that should prove to be unfeasible, the life of the mother should be the physician's first priority.

However, there may be cases where the course selected by the pregnant woman may conflict with the private values of the physician. In such cases, if the physician were to follow the wishes of the woman, the physician would be forced to go against his or her own conscience. However, the Code of Ethics of the Canadian Medical Association makes it clear, and indeed it is generally accepted, that all other things being equal, a physician has the right to follow his or her conscience in the conduct of his or her practice. Therefore if the values of the physician differ or likely to differ from those of the pregnant woman, and if that difference is likely to impact on the willingness or ability of the physician to respect the woman's wishes or to follow standard medical practice, then the physician has an obligation so to inform the woman at the inception of the physician-patient relationship.

This may present problems in individual cases. The process of communicating such personal values is always a delicate matter. However, it is a general and fundamental requirement of informed consent that a patient be informed of any relevant and important differences between the physician's standards and those of the general medical community, and that the patient must be told of any factors that are likely to affect the physician's ability to acquiesce in the patient's informed and competent directives based on the patient's values. These fundamental duties do not lapse in the case of pregnancy.

Recommendation 9

If the physician's private morality differs or is likely to differ from the generally accepted standards of society, or if the physician's private morality places the physician into conflict with the competent and informed value-directives of the pregnant woman (or if it is likely to do so) then the physician should inform the pregnant woman of that fact at the earliest appropriate opportunity. At that time, the physician should also inform the woman that she has the option to consult another physician.

Other Contexts

There remains a whole domain of actions that involve the foetus prior to twenty weeks gestation. Experimental protocols from the side of the physician, lifestyle and behaviour patterns from the side of the pregnant woman, etc. are here implicated.[13] In these cases a distinction should be drawn between situations where the foetus is intended (or expected) to complete the gestational period and ultimately be born, and situations where the intention (or expectation) is that this will not occur.

If the intention (or expectation) is that the foetus will develop to the point where it becomes a person, then any action or inaction that impacts negatively on the developmental chances of the foetus, whatever its stage of development, will be *prima facie* indefensible.

The reason lies in the ethics of causality. In general terms, the argument may be stated as follows: To initiate a train of events that predictably and foreseeably will have an injurious outcome, or to allow such a train of events to occur when it lies within the powers of the individual actor to prevent it without undue harm to the actor him- or herself, confers responsibility for that outcome on the actor.[14]

In the case of foetal development, knowingly to initiate a train of events that predictably and foreseeably will have this sort of outcome, or to allow such a train of events to occur when it lies within the powers of the individual to prevent it, is to initiate a train of events that predictably and foreseeably would result in harm to the foetus once it becomes a person. Anyone who finds her- or himself in such a position acquires a degree of responsibility for the outcome. The degree of responsibility that attaches to the person will be commensurate with the extent the individual's involvement (or deliberate failure to become involved) contributed to the outcome itself.

These considerations apply not only to the pregnant woman or the physician; they also are valid for all other persons whose actions or inactions have a measurable causal impact on the development of the foetus. Therefore they also apply to the medical staff, the nursing staff and anyone else who may be involved in an appropriate capacity. Still, in the medical setting it applies primarily to the physician. It is the physician who has ultimate responsibility for the medical environment. Therefore there lies a special ethical obligation on the attending physician not to ignore these considerations.[15]

Recommendation 10

When the foetus has become a person, or when there is the intention or reasonable expectation that the foetus will become a person, the physician has an obligation to try and prevent harm to the foetus insofar as that is compatible with other obligations the physician may have.

SPECIAL CONSIDERATIONS

(a) When it is not intended/expected that the foetus will survive beyond twenty weeks gestation.

Not all pregnancies are intended to go to term or are expected to do so. A pregnancy where the woman intends to have an abortion is an example of the former; a pregnancy where the constitution of the foetus is incompatible with survival beyond twenty weeks is an example of the latter. In cases such as these, non-therapeutic and research activities, when conducted prior to 20 weeks gestation and in accordance with otherwise applicable standards, are ethically permissible if certain conditions are met. These include the following:

(1) the pregnant woman and/or other appropriate alternate decision-maker has given informed consent; and

(2) the research protocol or procedure has been duly approved by an appropriate Ethics Review Board according to national and uniform guidelines set out by the Medical Research Council of Canada, the National Council on

Bioethics in Human Research, and any other relevant and applicable body; and

(3) the foetus will not survive beyond twenty weeks gestation.

Recommendation 11

Non-therapeutic, experimental, innovative or otherwise unusual procedures are permissible on a foetus with maternal and/or other appropriate consent if it is intended and certain that the foetus will never become a person and will never develop beyond twenty weeks gestation. Such procedures or undertakings, however, must meet all otherwise applicable standards of treatment and/or experimentation and must have been approved by an appropriate ethics review board. They should also be in keeping with Recommendation 3 above.

(b) Situations where the bodily integrity of the pregnant woman is the central issue.

The right to integrity of the person is a logical consequence of the Principle of Autonomy and Respect for Persons. It therefore follows that every person, irrespective of gender, age or other qualitative distinctions, has the right to insist on such integrity against all others. Nevertheless, no right is absolute. All are conditioned by the circumstances under which they arise and the circumstances in which they are claimed. Consequently there are situations where the right to the integrity of the person may be rendered ineffective and may be overruled by the competing and weightier rights of others.

Women who become pregnant are almost always willing to undergo a considerable measure of self-sacrifice in order to benefit their foetuses. The voluntary inception of a pregnancy itself, with all that this

entails, bears vivid testimony to this fact. Therefore the best way to assure that a conflict between maternal and foetal considerations does not arise in the first instance is to make every effort to ensure that pregnancies are wanted, and that mothers themselves are the beneficiaries of appropriate social, economic and psychological conditions. The benefits that would redound to the foetus from such a perspective will of course be quite patent.

Nevertheless, even under the best of circumstances, it may sometimes happen that a conflict between maternal and foetal interests arises. For instance, the pregnant woman may refuse to cooperate in the medical care designed to benefit the foetus, she may create a potentially hazardous environment for the foetus, or she may refuse to accept the need for a Caesarian delivery because of the implications that such undertakings have for the woman herself. In such cases, great care should be taken that the limitations of medical knowledge are taken into account, that due weight is given to the fallibility inherent in medical predictions of this nature, and that the limitations on the reliability of diagnostic procedures are factored into the equation.

Still, even when all of these factors are given due weight, the physician may be of the opinion that an intervention would be necessary for the sake of the foetus. In almost all cases, such a conflict will be resolvable through judicious and appropriate education and counselling of the pregnant woman, and through a conscientious and co-operative examination of the relevant options.[16] However, there may be cases where such a process will not lead to a resolution. This will be especially troublesome in the later stages of pregnancy when the foetus has become a person and a surgical or medical intervention is considered necessary to save the life of the foetus yet the woman claims the right of inviolability of her body. In such cases, it may be appropriate for the physician to request a judicial ruling to determine whether such a breach of personal integrity or interference with her autonomy should take place.

In emergency cases, where such a judicial review is not possible, the physician has the duty to do what is medically appropriate and possible under the circumstances, in keeping with the reasoning indicated above.[17] In defense of this, the physician may point to the doctrine of emergency, the principle of beneficence, and the fact that the foetus has become a person. Furthermore, failure to engage in the appropriate and medically indicated action may well constitute an abandonment of the foetal patient.

Recommendation 12

The physician's duty towards the foetus during the third trimester may require that the physician resort to the judicial process in order to try to ensure the survival and well-being of the foetus. Such a step should be taken only after due consideration of the gravity of such a step and after all alternatives that are reasonably available have been exhausted. In emergency contexts, the physician's duty is governed by the doctrine of emergency.[18]

CONCLUSIONS

The practice of medicine goes to the heart of human life. More than any other professional activity, therefore, medicine requires an exquisite adherence to ethical standards and a respect for the fundamental values that shape our social outlook. Recommendations 1–12 are an attempt to provide such standards and to implement such values. Doubtless, these Recommendations will strike some as restricting the interests of certain parties too severely; equally as predictably, they will strike others as not going far enough. The task of the Committee on Ethics is to combine ethical sensitivity with practicality. The preceding Recommendations are an attempt to do just that.

Approved by the Committee on Ethics, Canadian Medical Association; principal author, E.-H.W. Kluge, Director, Department of Ethics and Legal Affairs, Canadian Medical Association.

NOTES

1. The most noteworthy recent example is *R. v. Morgentaler* [1988] 1 S.C.R. 30.

2. *R. v Kitching and Adams* (1976), 32 C.C.C. (2d) 159, [1976] 6 W.W.R. 697.

3. The recent case of *R. v. Green* [1988] B.C.J. No. 1807, Vernon Registry No. 18024, June 27, 1988, does not contradict the reasoning in *Kitching and Adams*. As the presiding judge in *Green* made very clear, he rejected the position of *Kitching and Adams* specifically for legal reasons of practicality: reasons that do not obtain in the medical setting:

   > The suggestion that brain death or the irreversible cessation of brain function be the legal standard for determining when death occurs may be suitable in the medical context and even in the civil law context, but in my view it is a completely impractical standard to apply in the criminal law. ... If the onus is on the Crown to satisfy this jury beyond a reasonable doubt that Mr. Frie was still alive — that is to say that his brain function

had not yet irreversibly ceased — when the Accused Green "pumped" two bullets into him, it can be seen that such an onus would be impossible to discharge — unless someone had happened along with an EEG monitor and applied same to Mr. Frie either before or immediately after the two shots allegedly fired by Green.

As I have said both the medical profession and the Law Reform Commission are principally concerned with the moral and legal issues arising out of artificially sustained life and human transplant procedures. The legal issues raised are approached from what is primarily a civil law point of view — in other words the administration of the criminal law does not appear to have been of paramount concern in the approach taken by either group.

On the face of it I see no reason why the same legal definition of death must be applied in both a civil and criminal context. Indeed there are good reasons why the same criteria should not apply. The criminal law seeks to deter the incidence of, inter alia, violent crime by holding accountable those whose conduct endangers the lives and safety of others. The civil law, in the context under discussion, seeks to ensure that societies' moral and personal values are not compromised in the pursuit of bona fide efforts to prolong or save meaningful life.

4. This difference was traditionally recognized by the Judaeo-Christian Islamic religions, who characterized the conceptus as a "clot of blood" and accepted it as having a human ethical status only after a series of developments had occurred. The distinction between a potential person and an actual person was clearly recognized in canon law. See *Corpus Juris Canonici Emendatum et Notis Illustratum cum Glossae: Decretalium Gregori Papae Noni Compilatio* (Rome, 1585), *Glossa ordinaria,* Bk. 5, t. 12, c. 20, p. 1713. For a good historical discussion, see J. Donceel, "Abortion: Medicate v. Immediate Animation," *Continuum* 5 (Spring 1967) 167-171, and "Immediate Animation and Delayed Hominization," *Theological Studies* 13 (March 1970), 76-105; E.-H.W. Kluge, "St. Thomas, Abortion and Euthanasia," *Philosophical Research Archives* (September, 1981).

5. For a fuller discussion of the notion of potentiality and its ethical implications, see E.-H.W. Kluge, *The Ethics of Deliberate Death* (Yale University Press: New Haven and London, 1975), Chap. 1; H.T. Engelhardt, Jr., *The Foundations of Bioethics* (Oxford University Press: New York and Oxford, 1986) 110-113.

6. See Law Reform Commission Working Paper 58, 40 ff. *et pass.* for considerations along similar lines.

7. See H.T. Engelhardt, Jr., *The Foundation of Bioethics* (Oxford: Oxford University Press, 1986) Chap. 6; Paul Ramsey, *The Patient As Person* (New Haven and London: Yale University Press, 1977) Chap. 2; Helmut Thielicke, "The Doctor as Judge of Who Shall Live and Who Shall Die," in Kenneth Vaux, ed., *Who Shall Live? Medicine, Technology, Ethics* (Philadelphia, 1970); Karl Rahner, "Gedanken Ueber das Sterben," *Arzt und Christ* 15, 1969; etc.

8. Resolutions of the 122nd General Council of the Canadian Medical Association, Quebec City, 1989.

9. Resolutions of the 122nd General Council of the Canadian Medical Association, Quebec City, 1989.

10. For a recent discussion indicating agreement with according the fetus some status, see George J. Annas, "A French Homonculus in a Tennessee Court," *Hastings Center Report* 19:6 (Nov. Dec. 1989) 20-22, at 20 "Every national commission worldwide that has examined the status of the human embryo to date has placed it in this third category: neither people nor products, but nonetheless entities of unique symbolic value that deserves society's respect and protection."

11. For various discussions of this concept, see Margin Kohl, ed., *Infanticide and the Value of Life* (Buffalo: Prometheus, 1978); Ruth Macklin, *Mortal Choices: Bioethics in Today's World* (New York: Pantheon, 1987) Chapter 8, "The 'Best Interest' of the Child"; Richard A. McCormick, "To Save or Let Die: The Dilemma of Modern Medicine," *Journal of the American Medical Association* 229 (July 8, 1974); President's Commission for the Study of Ethical Problems in Medicine and Biomedical and Behavioral Research, *Deciding to Forego Life-Sustaining Treatment* (U.S. Gov't. Printing Office: Washington, 1983); Magnet and Kluge, *Withholding Treatment from Defective Newborn Children* (Cowansville: Brown Legal Publications, 1985) Chapter Three; etc.

12. CMA Policy Summary, "Induced Abortion."

13. For an extended discussion, see Edward E. Keyserlingk, "The Unborn Child's Right to Prenatal Care," *Health Law in Canada* 3:1 (1987) 10-21. See also Law Reform Commission, Working Paper 58, *Crimes Against the Foetus* (Law Reform Commission of Canada: Ottawa, 1989), 50 ff., "A New Foetus Title" 1. Foetal Destruction or Harm:

    (1) Everyone commits a crime who

    (a) purposely, recklessly or negligently causes destruction or serious harm to a foetus; or

    (b) being a pregnant woman, purposely causes destruction or serious harm to her foetus by any act or by failing to make reasonable provision for assistance in respect of delivery.

    The Committee differs from the Commission in that it believes that provision against causing harm should take into account the difference between a foetus that is intended or expected to go to term and a foetus where the opposite is expected or intended.

14. Cf. Law Reform Commission of Canada, Working Paper 46 *Omission, Negligence and Endangering* (Law Reform Commission of Canada: Ottawa, 1985). See also Working Paper 45, *Secondary Liability — Participation in Crime and Inchoate Offenses* (Law Reform Commission of Canada: Ottawa, 1985). See also E.-H.W. Kluge, *The Ethics of Deliberate Death* (Port Washington N.Y. & London: National University Publications, 1981) 12-13.

15. See Law Reform Commission, Working Paper 58, "A New Foetus Title."

16. See The American College of Obstetricians and Gynecologists, Committee on Ethics, "Patient Choice: Maternal-Fetal Conflict," *WHI* 1:1 (Fall, 1990) 13-15.

17. There has been an increase in court cases dealing with emergency requests for nonconsensual Caesarean sections. The various jurisdictions have split on whether such sections are legally allowable. However, the Committee sees a danger in equating what is ethical with what is legal. It does not believe that the law is necessarily an appropriate guide to what is or should be ethical behaviour. As an example, the Committee would point to the sterilization laws that were lately repealed by the various provinces, or the laws that declared women and children nonpersons. For a contrary view to the one expressed above, see George J. Annas, "Pregnant Women as Fetal Containers," *Hastings Center Report* 16:6 (December, 1986) 13-14.

18. It should be noted that Recommendation 12 does not constitute a novelty in the Canadian context. There are several Canadian court decisions that deal with the issue consideration [e.g., *Re Children's Aid Society of City of Belleville, Hastings Country and T et al.*]

Say "No" to Fetal Personhood

Frances Rosenberg

A woman is her fetus. Until the fetus is born, there is only one person, the mother.

Why has it become so easy for society to propose that a pregnant woman can be treated as more than one person? Perhaps the partial answer lies with the progressive fragmentation of the family and the individual that has followed industrialization. Increasingly, we live in two worlds. The private world (largely a world of women) is concerned with the "natural" areas of our lives; sex, reproduction and the emotional aspects of relationships. The public world, on the other hand, is primarily the domain of man, and is concerned, first and foremost, with production and efficiency. This is the world of work and business, where productivity takes precedence over feelings.[1] Concurrent with this division in family life, the individual has felt increasingly alienated from the community.

For men, the performance of work that has no apparent relationship to a larger whole has eroded their image of themselves as valuable members of society. For women, the displacement of family tradition on childbearing and rearing by societal authorities has reduced their perceived social stature.

When we move from the person as a whole to their parts we see increasing fragmentation. Women have long been compelled to disown their intelligence, given the widely held beliefs that brains and beauty do not mix and that beauty is the quality desired in women. More recently, parts of our bodies, including sperm, ova, and embryos can be moved from person to person, and out of and back into the same person.[1]

These processes for artificial reproduction have tended to obscure the integrity of mother and fetus that is intrinsic to natural reproduction.

Revised from "Editorial," *Newsletter of the Association of Medical Women of Canada*: "Say 'No' to Fetal Personhood," 1990.

Coupled with the fragmentation evident within society, there has been the production orientation of medicine toward childbearing in which the health care deliverers could be likened to factory management with women being the laborers and the infant the product. Contemporary efforts at returning childbirth to a more natural state fail to address the erosion of women's integrity that has resulted from the practice of "commodity oriented" obstetrics. One has but to read much that is written about artificial reproduction and fetal rights to realize that there has been little change in the attitude toward women's childbearing role.

Now here is the insidious thing ... we are all so shaped by the thinking that has given rise to the question of fetal rights and the implied fetal personhood that we find it very difficult to explore the issue. Yet we must if society is to be informed by the insight of women. We must transcend those beliefs and attitudes instilled by the forces that created this dilemma and express our feelings on this issue. We must examine for ourselves how it would feel if bureaucrats, doctors, lawyers, were determining how we should behave when we were pregnant and there were "pregnancy police" (a term now in use in the U.S.) to monitor our behaviour. If that would not be comfortable, then say "no" to fetal personhood. Trust your instinct and assert your womanhood. Let us reestablish organic unity between the fetus and the mother through the recognition of only one person prior to childbirth, the mother.

Frances Rosenberg MD PhD FRCP(C), Department of Laboratories, St. Paul's Hospital.

NOTE

1. See E. Martin, *The Woman in the Body*. Boston: Beacon Press (1987).

R. v. Kitching and Adams

Matas J.A. (dissenting in part) (Monnin J.A. concurring): — The appellants, Adams and Kitching, were charged with causing the death of D. G. Junor by means of an unlawful act, thereby committing manslaughter. They were convicted on the charge after a trial before Hunt J. and a jury, and were sentenced to penitentiary for five years and four years respectively. This is an appeal from conviction and sentence.

Around midnight, 23rd July 1975, Junor was seen at the Vibrations Discotheque, a bar attached to the St. Charles Hotel in Winnipeg. Junor ordered a drink, and shortly after was seen sitting in a chair with his feet up on another chair, his head slouched forward and his chin resting on his chest. (It became known later that Junor had a blood alcohol reading of 267 milligrams per 100 millilitres of blood.) One of the waiters employed at the Vibrations tried to rouse him but was unsuccessful.

Within a few minutes Junor was taken outside by two men and dropped onto the

---

R. v. Kitching and Adams (1976) 6 W.W.R. 697 (Manitoba Court of Appeal).

concrete sidewalk. A cab driver stationed near the hotel saw the manoeuvre and said that when Junor was dropped, his face hit the sidewalk, making a sound which was described as: "A. Just a squishy sound, like, say a tomato hitting against concrete."

...

An ambulance was called. On arrival, the ambulance attendant examined Junor, did not detect any sign of life and tried resuscitative procedures. Junor was taken to the Health Sciences Centre, with the procedures being continued. On arrival at the hospital, shortly after 1:00 a.m. on 24th July, Junor was examined by Dr. Donan, the resident in charge of the intensive care unit. Dr. Donan noted that the patient had no respiration, pulse, or activity of the heart. Seven minutes after continued resuscitative procedures, a pulse was obtained and respiration was restored. Junor was admitted to the intensive care unit. During the early morning he was attached to a respirator and to several monitoring devices.

At 7:00 a.m. on 24th July Dr. Tweed, an anaesthetist, examined Junor and found he was deeply unconscious, totally unresponsive to voice or deep painful stimulation and with no significant neurological signs. When removed from the respirator he breathed spontaneously but his breathing was shallow and inadequate. Dr. Tweed diagnosed a brain injury. At 11:30 p.m., the same day, Dr. Tweed found, in summary, that Junor had a complete absence of function at any level of his brain and that his outlook for recovery was hopeless.

Dr. A. J. Gomori, a neurologist, was called in as a consultant and he examined Junor in the early afternoon of 24th July and at 11:00 a.m. on 25th July. On the second examination, Dr. Gomori found that Junor was unable to breathe on his own, there was no evidence of response to external painful stimuli and there were no reflexes; Dr. Gomori could not detect any brain

stem function; all of this indicated "brain death" and no chance of any recovery.

In the early afternoon of 25th July Junor suffered a cardiac arrest, which normally would have ended his life. However, Junor's bodily functions were maintained until his kidneys could be removed for transplant purposes. The purpose of maintaining the bodily functions, latterly, was to preserve Junor's organs, not his life. After removal of the kidneys the artificial respirator was turned off; the EKG, monitoring the heart, continued to show electrical activity for 13 minutes.

The formal death certificate was completed upon removal of the kidneys.

Dr. J. R. Taylor, a pathologist, conducted an autopsy on the morning of 26th July 1975. He said there were two major findings: two hairline fractures of the base of the skull and extensive degenerative changes within the brain itself. The injuries to the skull and brain were consistent with a fall. According to Dr. Taylor, the principal injury was "the brain lesion, the total and absolute death of the brain." Dr. Taylor summarized his findings as follows:

Well, as I have said at the time of autopsy I found several things. He had an absence of kidneys for one thing. Incidently he had evidence of highly bronchial pneumonia. Thirdly, he had, and most significantly to my mind he had evidence of severe and irreversible brain injury at the time of death. How that injury came about can be interpreted in one of two ways. At least, but primarily it was I think due to a blow which was sufficient to crack his skull. It was sufficient to produce subarachnoid hemorrhage, and it might, but I can't prove this, it might have been sufficient at the time to have damaged this man's brain. It could have damaged the hypothalamus, or some other part of the brain. At the time of autopsy all I can suggest is one of two pathways of this finding of the final condition of the brain. Either it was caused at the time of the initial injury or the death of the brain was a result of a sequence of events starting with the injury and the brain swelling, compression of blood vessels, and from the compression of the blood vessels to the death of the brain, with the same final end result. At the time of autopsy it is not possible to say when or which pathway this man took. I think it would require other evidence of the state of his nervous system, the function especially of his hypothalamus at the time that he was admitted, to be able to elucidate and at this point I cannot expand on that factor.

The jury heard detailed evidence from all the doctors who were called by the Crown on the several tests given Junor and his progressive medical condition; as well, there was an exhaustive exploration of the difficult criteria for determining death and the basis for use of those criteria.

...

The question of the cause of death was left to the jury for their decision. They obviously decided, after weighing all the evidence, including the extensive medical testimony, and the judge's charge, that Junor had died as a result of acts of appellants. In my view, the learned trial judge, if anything, gave more credence than was warranted to the defence that death was caused by the doctors, in respect of the transplant.

O'Sullivan J.A.: — Counsel for the accused argued that their clients should not be convicted of manslaughter because there was a possibility on the evidence that the deceased, Mr. Junor, was killed not as a result of the acts of the accused, but as a result of the acts of doctors at Health Sciences Centre in Winnipeg, who removed the deceased's kidneys and shut off a life-supporting ventilator.

The actions of the accused took place on 24th July 1975 about 1:00 a.m., when Mr. Junor was dropped on the sidewalk while being taken out of the Vibrations.

On 25th July 1975, at about 1:00 p.m., the deceased's heart was beating spontaneously and his lungs were breathing with the help of a ventilator.

At that time the deceased's body was taken to an operating room and both kidneys were removed for potential transplantation.

About 2:10 p.m., following removal of the kidneys, the ventilator was shut off. The heart continued to beat on its own for 13 minutes. Then the heart stopped beating.

It was only after the kidneys were removed that Dr. W. A. Tweed certified the death of Mr. Junor. No one at Health Sciences Centre had pronounced him dead before the removal of the kidneys.

The contentions of counsel raise far-reaching questions of law relating to death, its definition, and the time of death.

By traditional criteria, there is no question that Mr. Junor was alive when his kidneys were removed. Traditionally, both law and medicine have been unanimous in saying that it is not safe to pronounce a man dead until after his vital functions have ceased to operate. The heart has always been regarded as a vital organ.

Since the introduction of organ transplantation, however, many physicians and moralists have sought to establish new and different criteria for determining the time and the fact of death.

It is apparent that the fresher the kidneys, the better chance the recipient will have. It is apparent that in the case of a heart transplant there is no use transplanting a dead heart. The heart must be alive if the recipient of it is to have any chance of life. The problem facing medicine and society in recent years is: How do you get a living heart out of a dead body? If a person is not dead until after his heart ceases to function, it is practically impossible to imagine a successful heart transplant except by taking a living heart out of a still living person. But this is abhorrent to the conscience of many people.

So a substantial body of medical opinion has come forward with the suggestion that the concept of death itself should be redefined.

Some have said, if a man is "as good as dead," we will call him "dead" and then there will be no ethical problem about taking out his vital organs.

Some doctors have said that a person is as good as dead, and is therefore dead, if he is in such a condition that it can be predicted with confidence that he will never again be able to be restored to meaningful life.

Others have advanced the proposition that death is not an event but a process and when the process of death reaches a stage where a doctor is of the opinion that the process is irreversible the person should be declared dead.

Dr. Tweed advanced this view in this case before the jury and the learned trial judge appears to have adopted it for he said to the jury, "It appears that death is a process, not an event, as I stated earlier."

This is a most controversial statement, at variance with centuries of religious tradition. It is a statement vigorously disputed in many medico-legal books, for example, in Grey's *Attorney's Textbook of Medicine*, (3d) 1975 (Supp.), vol. 1B, para. 29.11. Religion has taught us that death is an event. Dying may be a process, but death is an event. Except for some small sects, such as those in Rumania, who believe that death is a process during which the soul is in a state of suspended animation (hence, perhaps residing in vampire bats), the overwhelming weight of religious teaching all over the world is that the moment of death occurs when the soul leaves the body. This is true not only of Christians, who believe in the personal immortality of the individual soul and the immediacy of judgment after death, but also of eastern religions which believe in the transmigration of souls at the moment of death.

Furthermore, by common consent, it has been held by all civilized people that no one, for however laudable a purpose, has the right to dispatch a dying man so as to hasten his death. Most moralists agree that it is not wrong to withhold extraordinary treatment to prolong the life of a dying man. It is not wrong to let him die. But directly to dispatch him by cutting out his heart or his lungs or his kidneys is contrary to every principle of civilized morality, as held by large numbers of citizens.

Another large body of medical opinion, I think the most substantial body, accepts the fact that death is an event and not a process. They say that the criteria for "defining" death are really criteria for determining the manifestations of death. It is true that the fact of death is manifested where all the vital signs, including heartbeat, have ceased. But, they say, it is equally true that the fact of death is manifested if all activity of the brain has ceased for a sufficient period of time. If the brain of a man is dead, then it is safe to say that the whole man is dead. It is the activities operated through the brain which differentiate man from an animal. If the brain is dead, he is dead.

This approach has gained widespread support not only among doctors but among moralists as well and has received legislative recognition in some states and in the Province of Manitoba.

This opinion does not proceed on the principle that if a man will surely die, then it is safe to call him already dead. It operates on the principle that, if a man's brain is dead, he is dead.

The trouble is that it is not always obvious when brain death occurs. There are well documented cases where a man's brain has shown absolutely no sign of activity for two days or more and yet he has recovered and survived. This is particularly so where a man has ingested large quantities of central nervous system depressants such as barbiturates.

There has been a great deal of debate about this subject and the debate is likely to go on for some time.

Many eminent physicians, including an ad hoc committee of doctors of Harvard University, have established certain criteria for determining brain death. Among the requirements are flat EEGs taken 24 hours apart. The possibility of barbiturate consumption being excluded, they say that if there is no sign of brain activity during a 24-hour period, it is then safe to say that the brain is dead and hence that the man is dead.

In the case of the deceased, Mr. Junor, the Harvard criteria were not followed. Twenty-four hours before the kidney transplant there was evidence of brain stem activity. Neither were the criteria proposed by Cornell University doctors followed.

Faced with the difficulties inherent in establishing universally acceptable criteria for determining brain death, many doctors have said that the safe course is to have at least two doctors certify death before allowing removal of vital organs.

Thus, a world assembly on medicine held in Australia in 1968 said, "If transplantation of an organ is involved, the decision that death exists should be made by two or more physicians, and the physician determining the moment of death should in no way be immediately concerned with the performance of the transplantation."

Many hospitals have regulations requiring such certificates of death prior to removal of vital organs. According to the evidence, the Health Sciences Centre has no such protection for potential donors.

These questions are important and they may have to be considered by the courts some day. In my opinion, however, they were not properly before the court in the case before us.

The legal and ethical implications of the conduct of doctors are no doubt under constant and careful review by peer review committees, by the Colleges of Physicians and Surgeons, and by others.

I think it is regrettable that the doctors at Health Sciences Centre were subjected to the lengthy questioning in this case. I do not think that the trial in this case, or in cases similar to it, affords a suitable forum for discussing these important questions.

I think that counsel for the accused proceeded on a fundamental misconception of the law. They assumed that, if it could be shown that death resulted in this case from the removal of the kidneys, then the accused should be acquitted because there would be a reasonable doubt that they had been the cause of death.

The assumption underlying counsel's conduct in this case is that there can be only one cause of death. I think the law is that the conduct of a defendant in a criminal trial need not be shown to be the sole or "the effective" cause of a crime. It is sufficient if it is a cause. ...

I think the authorities are clear that there may be two or more independent operative causes of death.

Without in this case criticizing the doctors of Health Sciences Centre or suggesting that they were guilty of any improper conduct, I am of the opinion that their conduct was irrelevant to the questions before the jury. Even if it could be shown that the actions of the doctors constituted an operative cause of Mr. Junor's death — and I emphasize that I do not suggest that the evidence would support such a conclusion — still that would not exonerate the accused unless the evidence left a reasonable doubt that the accused's actions also constituted an operative cause of the deceased's death.

On that question, the evidence was overwhelming. Whether or not the kidneys had been removed, the deceased could not have lasted more than a short period of time even with artificial assistance.

The jury had to decide not whether the doctors were ethical or not but simply, did the accused cause the death of the deceased by unlawful means? The question of causation was put to the jury plainly; they decided that the accused did cause the death. The evidence was overwhelmingly in favour of their verdict.

On the matters raised by defence counsel on the subject of conviction, I am in substantial agreement with the reasons of my brother Matas.

I would not say, however, that the learned trial judge answered the jury's question satisfactorily. Although he said that criminal negligence was not the jury's major problem, it is obvious, I think, that the jury had directed its mind toward the possibility of finding the accused liable on the basis of their criminal negligence. I think the trial judge left the jury with the impression that they could convict the accused of manslaughter if they concluded that the accused caused death not by unlawful act but by criminal negligence.

The accused were acting in the course of a duty. Their actions amounted to the unlawful act of assault only if they used more force than was reasonably necessary.

A wanton and reckless disregard for the deceased's safety might have made the accused guilty of manslaughter by criminal negligence but they were not charged with that.

Had the charge been worded suitably, this distinction would not have been material. But the Crown chose to charge only manslaughter by unlawful act. Why the Crown did so we do not know. But the Crown is bound by the charge it brings. Otherwise the accused might be convicted of that of which they have had no proper notice.

Nevertheless, I am prepared to apply the provisions of s. 613(1)(*b*)(iii) because I am satisfied that the jury could not, as reasonable men, have done otherwise than find the accused guilty of manslaughter by unlawful act.

...

Does Anyone Survive Neocortical Death?

Roland Puccetti

A person is dead when an irreversible cessation of all that person's brain functions has occurred. The cessation of brain functions can be determined by the prolonged absence of spontaneous cardiac and respiratory functions.

> Law Reform Commission of Canada Working Paper 23 (1979, pp. 58-59)

An individual with irreversible cessation of all functions of the entire brain, including the brain stem, is dead.

> *Defining Death,* President's Commission ([15], p. 162)

One day on a very cold morning, I started the engine of my car without opening the garage door, then retreated to the kitchen to let it warm up. At that moment there was a long distance phone call from my publisher, and I spent a half hour haggling

Roland Puccetti, "Does Anyone Survive Neocortical Death?" in Richard M. Zaner, ed., *Death: Beyond Whole-Brain Criteria*. Dordrecht: Kluwer Academic Publishers, 1988, 75-90.

over the terms of a contract. Upon returning to the garage I found there, alongside the car, my dog Fido. Of course I immediately opened the automatic door and carried him outside into the fresh air. When I saw he wasn't breathing I pressed rhythmically on his chest cavity, and sure enough his heart and lungs started to respond. But still he did not wake up, so I took him to the vet's on the way to the university. The vet said Fido appeared to be comatose as a result of carbon monoxide poisoning, and advised that I prepare myself for the worst. He said it seemed the dog would not recover consciousness because the top of the brain was destroyed, although the brain stem must be intact, since Fido could breathe unaided. What should I do?

Now suppose I told you that I did the following. I took Fido home, made a special bed for him, shaved his body and fitted him with diapers, learned to feed him intravenously and nasogastrically, and arranged to have him turned in his bed often so he would not develop pressure sores. Evenings I would watch TV alongside Fido, stroking his warm body and listening to his breathing, though never again did he go for a walk with me, fetch the newspaper, bark, or do anything dogs normally do.[1] Would you think I am a rational person? Or worse, suppose I asked the vet to put Fido down for me and he replied that he couldn't do that to a comatose canine capable of spontaneous breathing, *because the law forbade it.* Would you think this a rational society?

If your answers to those questions are, as I think they would be, resoundingly negative, then presumably the main reason for your negative response is simply that my ministrations would do *no good* for Fido, who has permanently lost consciousness even if he is nonapneic; for the same reason, *no harm* can be done to him by stopping his breathing. In other words, a permanently unconscious dog is, for all practical purposes, a dead dog anyway.

Now change the above apocryphal story in just one detail. Instead of it being Fido on the garage floor, it is my neighbor's infant son, little Bobby. I rush him to a children's hospital, but with the same result. Now could what was agreed to be irrational behavior in Fido's case become rational in Bobby's case? That a human life is much more valuable and worth preserving at all costs is completely irrelevant, since we agreed before that the main consideration was simply that one can do neither good nor harm to an irreversibly comatose being, and that should hold true independently of his species identity.

Yet, and this is what I find amazing, a great number of otherwise very able people in the legal and health professions think just the opposite. But before we examine their arguments, let us get one point absolutely straight. No matter what your calling, any position you adopt on this issue is going to be a *philosophical* stand. For the question we are addressing here is quintessentially philosophical: namely, *what constitutes* (in this world anyway, to avoid begging religious questions) *personal death?* This does not mean a poll of professional philosophers will settle the matter, for by that standard the Earth must have been flat in the Middle Ages, before it became spherical again in the Renaissance. Nevertheless, you cannot offer argument as to when a person may be safely considered dead without doing philosophy. The question, of course, is whether you are doing philosophy well or badly. I begin with an example of what I consider bad philosophizing on this subject.

I. WALTON ON CEREBRAL VS. ENCEPHALIC DEATH

In his recent book [17], Douglas N. Walton asks why proponents of the cerebral or neocortical criterion of brain death are not even more selective.

The reply (that it is the cerebrum which mediates cognitive activity in the brain) is still not entirely satisfactory. However, it seems equally plausible to say that mental activity of the higher cognitive sort takes place essentially in the cerebral cortex, the thin membraneous *[sic]* substance that forms a mantle over the cerebrum. Why include the lobes of the cerebrum under the cortex if lower parts of the midbrain or the cerebellum and brain stem are excluded? ... [The cerebral death advocate] might argue that it is safer to include the whole cerebrum, because there is a possibility of indeterminacy or error. But then, if tutiorism (chancing error to be on the safe side) is brought in, why not be even safer and take into account the whole-brain ([18], p. 50)?

To which one can counter: if it is better to err on the side of safety, why not wait until complete somatic death (including, e.g., cartilage cells in the knee) occurs, thereby foregoing organ transplantation? The reason cerebral death includes the lobes of the cerebrum beneath the cortical surface is that these are composed of association fibers (white matter) that interconnect neocortical motor and sensory areas (grey matter); if these are selectively destroyed (e.g., in asphyxiation), the result is a shattered self with isolated conscious functions [5]. If, on the other hand, the neocortical surface is itself selectively destroyed, which as we shall see is the case with apallic syndrome, that is sufficient to obliterate all conscious functions.

The case for excluding other subcortical structures mentioned by Walton in passing has nothing at all to do with tutiorism anyway. The midbrain is of course just the top of the brain stem, where the superior and inferior colliculi trigger orientating reflexes related, respectively, to sources of visual and auditory stimuli: such reflexive responses do not require conscious mediation, as we all know from finding ourselves turned towards an abrupt movement in the peripheral visual field, or in the direction of a sudden sound, before such stimuli register in consciousness. If a brain structure does its job unconsciously, then there is no reason to think its integrity in a comatose patient is evidence of residual conscious functions. Similarly with the cerebellum, which preorchestrates complex bodily movements, and under therapeutic electrode stimulation does not yield clear sensations [3]. The cerebellum probably also stores learned subroutines of behavior, like swimming or typing: precisely the kinds of things you do better when not concentrating on them. Why then is it necessary for the cerebellum to be dead in order to have a dead person on your hands?

Yet Walton seems to think that everything above the level of C^1 [i.e., above a particular cellular level in the cerebellum] directly contributes to a conscious mental life. His attitude seems to be that if something moves, it must or at least might have a life of its own, with its own kind of feeling. For example, of the pupillary reflex mediated by the lower brain stem he says:

The pupillary reflex could, for all we know, indicate some presence of feeling or sensation even if the higher cognitive faculties are absent. Even if we cannot resolve the issue with the precision we would like and, indeed, just because of that, we should be on the safe side.... Following my tutiorist line of argument, it is clear that we cannot rule out the possibility that brain stem reflexes could indicate some form of sensation or feeling, even if higher mental activity is not present ([18], p. 69).

The statement fairly reeks of superstition. As we all know, when the doctor flashes his penlight on the eye, we do not feel the pupil contract, then expand again when he turns the light off. If not, then why in the world does Walton suppose that a deeply comatose patient feels anything in the same testing situation? The whole point of evolving reflexes like this, especially in large-brained animals that do little peripheral but lots of central information processing, is to shunt quick-response mechanisms away from the cerebrum so that the animal can make appropriate initial responses to stimuli *before* registering them consciously. If one could keep an excised human eye alive *in vitro* and provoke the pupillary reflex, the way slices of rat hippocampus have been stimulated to threshold for neuronal excitation, would Walton argue that the isolated *eye* might feel something as its pupil contracts?[2]

Apparently he would, since in his view the entire encephalon must be safely dead to justify a finding of personal death. The spinal cord, he agrees, presents no obstacle to a determination of death, because of the relative sparsity of its neurons and its accessibility to tactile stimuli exclusively. I quote:

> The upshot is that brain death should include the whole-brain but nothing more. I would add that specially if we emphasize the element of reflective selfconsciousness or awareness … the tactile stimuli accessible from the spinal cord need not be thought significant if, in the absence of a brain, there is no possibility of awareness of these stimuli. The presence of a tactile reflex by itself need not indicate mental activity or consciousness ([18], p. 75).

But what is sauce for the goose is sauce for the gander. Why does a pinprick in the foot or hand, provoking a withdrawal reflex in that limb because of residual electrical activity in the spinal arc nerve pathways, count as a tactile sensation in the case of a cerebrally dead patient, but not in the case of an encephalically dead one? For consider: there is no such thing as a non-localized tactile sensation; to the question, "Where did the accused touch you on your person?" there always is and must be a fairly specific answer. Even a statement like "I felt the spring sun warm my body all over, like a gentle kiss," is in a sense localized: it refers to all the skin surface on one side of the body, that facing the sun. Now what brain mechanism localizes sensations of touch? Surely it is the somatosensory strip posterior to the Rolandic fissure in both cerebral hemispheres (Brodmann's area 3), which is clearly gone in the cerebrally dead patient. No localization, no tactile sensation: thus Walton's unconcern for spinal cord-mediated nerve impulses from the skin surface is logically extendable to the entire subcortical architecture of the brain.

Walton nevertheless expresses deep puzzlement over this matter, and in fact at times comes perilously close to committing the Fallacy of Ad Ignorantium. For example, wondering whether perception or awareness might not occur in the absence of higher cognitive functions, he writes:

> It is hard to know how to define exactly what is meant by "higher cognitive faculties," so it is hard to be sure that we mean by this phrase something that definitely excludes all types of perception that might persist in deeper parts of the brain ([18], pp. 75-76).

But surely ignorance of whether a statement is true does not imply that we know it is false; the admitted complexity of the human brain does not carry with it the imputation that we cannot say *some* things about it with confidence. One thing I feel reasonably confident in stating is that sensations are not experienced without recruitment of populations of neurons in the grey matter on the cerebral cortical surface. And it is easy to see why this is so: the phylogenetic novelty of *neo*cortex is due to brain expansion in primates beginning about 50 million years ago to accommodate increasing intelligence, for where else could new cell layers appear but on the outer surface of the brain [9]? That being the case, sensation migrated there as well, and although deeper structures certainly contribute complexly to the sentient input, this is not transduced as sensation until, at a minimum, some 10,000 neurons are provoked to discharge on the surface of at least one cerebral hemisphere at the same time [16]. It is also plain why the contribution of subcortical mechanisms to this input does not itself implicate conscious perception. If it did, we would have sensations in *seriatum:* a baseball leaving the pitcher's hand would be seen as arriving by the hitter several times in succession as neural impulses course from retina to optic chiasm to geniculate body through the optic radiation to primary visual cortex in the occipital lobe. From an evolutionary viewpoint, that would be a recipe for disaster.

Walton makes the claim that, to be on the safe side, "we should presume that the whole-brain is required to produce mental activity" ([18], p. 74). Normally, of course, that is true, but from this it would hardly follow that, when the ultimate neuronal destination of neural input is no longer there, or is dead, sensations still occur. We can liken this proposal to having an express elevator that whisks passengers from the ground floor to executive offices on the top floor. If a nuclear strike blows off the top floor, it would be unreasonable to suppose that you could nevertheless conduct your business at still-standing intermediate floors. What Walton is doing is confusing the normally necessary contribution of subcortical mechanisms to sensation with the sufficient condition of neocortical functions.

In the case of the primary visual system in man this is indisputable: destruction of Brodmann's area 17 alone, say by shrapnel wounds, brings permanent total blindness [7]; whereas a peripherally blind person with intact visual cortex can be induced to experience visual sensations by direct electrode stimulation of that grey matter [2].

Probably the sensation we worry most about in irreversibly comatose patients is *pain.* Now Walton may know that depth electrode stimulation intended to relieve intractable "central" or "thalamic" pain (where the pain is not localized at all), indicates that there are discrete "pain centers" in the thalami [14,17], and these are certainly subcortical structures that could survive neocortical death. Would this fact not tend to show that such patients might nevertheless experience pain, in line with Walton's tutioristic cautions?

Such a suggestion would be, I think, doubly wrong. It is wrong, first, because it incorporates an excessively *homuncular* view of the relation between brain structures and conscious experience. The "little men in the thalami getting pain messages" picture is absurd: it is *we* who get the pains, not those structures. And it is wrong, secondly, because if the firing of thalamic pain centers by itself gave rise to pain experience, then it surely follows that if we could excise this tissue, keep it alive *in vitro,* stimulate it electrically to threshold for discharge and record the neurons' discharging, we would have to say that there is pain going on *in the vat!* Anyone who would believe this is beyond reason.

II. PEOPLE AS BRAIN STEMS

I want now to consider a specific case of neocortical death without brain stem death, in order to show the utter futility of acting on the stand Walton defends. There are many cases like this one, and in some somatic survival subsequent to cerebral destruction far surpasses the present case.[3] Nevertheless, the case history here is remarkably complete. I give it *in extenso* so that I cannot be accused of glossing over some crucial fact [8].

Case 8. The patient (Th. Sv.) was a female who had been born in 1936. In July 1960, at the age of 24, she suffered severe eclampsia during pregnancy with serial epileptic attacks, followed by deep coma and transient respiratory and circulatory failure. In the acute phase, Babinski signs were present bilaterally and there was a transitory absence of pupillary, corneal and spinal reflexes. A left-sided carotid angiogram showed a slow passage of contrast medium and signs of brain edema. An EEG taken during the acute phase did not reveal any electrical activity. The EEG remained isoelectric for the rest of the survival time (seventeen years). After the first three to four months the patient's state became stable with complete absence of all higher functions.

Examination ten years after the initial anoxic episode showed the patient lying supine, motionless, and with closed eyes. Respiration was spontaneous, regular and slow with a tracheal cannula. The pulse was regular. The systolic blood pressure was 75-100 mm. Hg. Severe flexion contractures had developed in all extremities. Stimulation with acoustic signals, touch or pain gave rise to primitive arousal reactions including eye-opening, rhythmic movement of the extremities, chewing and swallowing, and withdrawal reflexes. The corneal reflex was present on the left side. When testing was done on the right

side, transient horizontal nystagmus movements were elicited. Pupillary reflexes were present and normal on both sides. On passive movements of the head, typical vestibulo-ocular reflexes were elicited. The spinal reflexes were symmetrical and hyperactive. Patellar clonus was present bilaterally. Divergent strabismus was found when the eyes were opened (by the examiner). Measurement of the regional cerebral blood flow on the left side (ten years after the initial anoxic episode) showed a very low mean hemisphere flow of 9 ml/100g/min. The distribution of the flow was also abnormal, high values being found over the brain stem. The patient's condition remained essentially unchanged for seven more years and she died seventeen years after the anoxic episode after repeated periods of pulmonary edema.

Autopsy showed a highly atrophic brain weighing only 315 grams. The hemispheres were especially atrophied and they were in general transformed into thin-walled yellow-brown bags. The brain stem and cerebellum were sclerotic and shrunken. On the basal aspect some smaller parts of preserved cortex could be seen, mainly in the region of the unci. Microscopically the cerebral cortex was almost totally destroyed with some remnants of a thin gliotic layer and underneath a microcystic spongy tissue with microphages containing iron pigment. The basal ganglia were severely destroyed, whereas less advanced destruction was found in the subfrontal basal cortex, the subcallosal gyrus, the unci, the thalamus and hypothalamus, and in the subicular and entorhinal areas. In the cerebellum the Purkinji cells had almost completely disappeared and were replaced by glial cells. The granular layer was partly destroyed. The cerebellar white matter was partly demyelinated. In the brain stem some neurons had disappeared and a diffuse gliosis was found. Several cranial nuclei remained spared. The long sensory and motor tracts were completely demyelinated and gliotic, whereas transverse pontine tracts remained well myelinated ([8], pp. 196-198).

This clinical picture, confirmed by the autopsy findings, is known in the literature as "neocortical death without brain stem death," or more recently and appropriately, as "the apallic syndrome," for its characteristic feature is precisely destruction of the paleum, that cortical mantle of grey matter covering the surface of the cerebrum or telencephalon. As it happens, neurons composing the paleum are the most vulnerable to oxygen deprivation during transient cardiac arrest or, as in the above case, asphyxiation. Whereas in encephalic or whole-brain death, therefore including the brain stem that monitors respiration (which in turn provokes cardiac activity), the patient can be sustained on a ventilator for only up to a week in adults and two weeks in children before cardiac standstill, the apallic patient breathes spontaneously and demonstrates cephalic reflexes (also brain stem mediated), so that if fed nasogastrically or intravenously and kept free from infection, he or she can sustain somatic life for years or even decades after losing the top of the brain.

I said "somatic life," for without a paleum the basis for a conscious and hence a personal life in this world is gone forever. But then what are we doing supplying intensive care to apallic syndrome patients? For surely the quality of life in a patient like Th.Sv. during all those seventeen years differed not one jot from the quality of life of someone buried underground for seventeen

years. It was zero. Permanent unconsciousness is permanent unconsciousness whether the condition is associated with a body that lives by virtue of being able to breathe spontaneously or not. To deny this is to elevate spontaneous breathing to a principle of human life, something I find incredible. Yet this is actually the emerging consensus of the medico-legal community in North America, as indicated by my earlier quotations from the Reform Commission's Report in Canada for 1979, and the U.S. President's Commission's Report of 1981. Are there any good arguments to support this astonishing attitude?

The President's Commission goes out of its way to justify regarding a whole-brain dead person sustained on a respirator as a dead person whose organs are therefore freely transplantable, whereas cerebrally dead persons are still to be considered alive and requiring heroic maintenance procedures. Listen to this passage:

> While the respirator and its associated medical techniques do substitute for the functions of the intercostal muscles and the diaphragm, which without neuronal stimulation from the brain cannot function spontaneously, they cannot replace the myriad functions of the brain stem or of the rest of the brain. The startling contrast between bodies lacking *all* brain functions and patients with intact brain stems (despite severe neocortical damage) manifests this. The former lie with fixed pupils, motionless except for the chest movements produced by their respirators. The latter can not only breathe, metabolize, maintain temperature and blood pressure, and so forth, *on their own* but also sigh, yawn, track light with the eyes, and react to pain or reflex stimulation ([15], p. 35).

One is tempted to cry out: *So what?* I can not only breathe, metabolize, maintain temperature and blood pressure, *on my own,* but also sigh, yawn, and react to reflex stimulation (such as the patellar reflex) when in a deep, dreamless sleep. Admittedly I cannot track light with my eyes, or react to a pinprick in the foot, without awakening, but that is because, with an intact reticular formation and intact primary visual system, the light I am tracking causes visual sensations, and with an intact somatosensory strip a pinprick in the foot wakes me up because I feel it as such. The apallic syndrome patient *can* do both these things without awakening, of course, because those neocortical structures are permanently missing. In fact, he or she cannot do *anything* consciously anymore, because there is no one home in that head to wake up.[4]

This consideration seems to make no difference to members of the President's Commission, who then go on to say:

> It is not easy to discern precisely what it is about patients in this latter group that makes them alive while those in the other category are not. It is in part that in the case of the first category (i.e., absence of all brain functions) when the mask created by the artificial medical support is stripped away what remains is not an integrated organism but "merely a group of artificially maintained subsystems." Sometimes, of course, an artificial substitute can forge the link that restores the organism as a whole to unified functioning. Heart or kidney transplants, kidney dialysis, or an iron lung used to replace physically impaired breathing ability in a polio victim, for example, restore the integrated functioning of the organism as they replace the failed function of a part. Contrast such situations, however, with the hypothetical of a decapitated body treated so as to prevent the outpouring of blood and to gener-

ate respiration: continuation of bodily functions in that case would not have restored the requisites of human life ([15], pp. 35-36).

But what *are* the requisites of human life according to the President's Commission? Evidently they are the ability to breathe spontaneously, demonstrate cephalic reflexes, regulate body temperature, metabolism, and blood pressure, etc.: in other words, *to perform unaided the janitorial functions of the Central Nervous System, which requires no conscious direction or reflection whatsoever.* Thus by the standards of the Commission, a hypothetical decapitated human body treated so as to prevent the outpouring of blood, but with brain stem left intact so that these janitorial functions are performed unaided, qualifies as a live person with all the requisites of human life, whereas if someone lops off the stem and substitutes a mechanical respirator in its place, the patient becomes a dead person thereby. Again, what is the difference in quality of life, or even prospects for the quality of life, in the two cases? And again the answer seems undeniable: none whatever.

To sum up: either human life is rooted in brain stem function or it is rooted in the capacity for personal experience. If the former, then all vertebrate species are on an equal footing and what counts in medical ethics is just long-term organic functioning independently of our capacity to intervene. If the latter, then there is no ethically relevant difference in the status of encephalically and cerebrally dead people: they have both lost the neocortical basis of an ongoing personal life. The only surprising fact to come out of the apallic syndrome is, or should be, that corpses are really of two kinds: the vast majority that cannot breathe unaided, and a small minority that nevertheless can do this. Apneic or nonapneic, a corpse is still a corpse.

III. THE DIAGNOSTIC PROBLEM

In a still more recent writing Walton [19] returns to defense of the whole-brain criterion of death. He begins by restating his earlier scepticism about our ability to avoid negative error in diagnosis of the apallic syndrome. He says:

> However, physicians have not yet developed or tested proven, certainly safe criteria for the apallic syndrome or other so-called "vegetative states" more highly localized in dysfunction than whole-brain death. For the present, tutioristic reasoning dictates cleaving to criteria for whole-brain death ([19], p. 270).

I do not know what Walton understands by "certainly safe" criteria for diagnosis of apallic syndrome; since the practice of medicine is an empirical science, there is always room for error. However, an accumulation of diagnostic results like those given in the case of Th. Sv. seems strongly conclusive. If one can safely exclude the possibility of hypothermia or intoxication with a CNS depressive, which drastically lowers oxygen requirements of the neocortex, a repeated finding of diminished cerebral blood flow, to less than 20% of normal, is itself powerful evidence of pallial destruction. In fact Lassen *et al* [10]. reported firm correlations between increases in blood flow to specific regions of the cortex of patients in the waking, conscious state when problem solving, and also a significant overall increase in blood flow to the cerebrum as a whole of about 10 per cent during such activity. It therefore seems exceedingly unlikely that any kind of conscious experience is going on in a brain with use for less than a fifth of normal blood flow.[5]

However, with the advent of Positron Emission Tomography, all reasonable grounds for doubt can be removed. In PET scanning, the uptake of oxygen and particularly glucose in selective subregions of cerebral cortex can be measured and displayed in color on a video screen: yellow or green for normal metabolic activity, blue or purple for low or no uptake. Although as of a couple years ago the PET scan had apparently not been used to confirm a diagnosis of apallic syndrome [4], nothing could be safer, easier or more certain: the entire surface of the brain would be displayed in blue or purple. While such deep subcortical structures as the brain stem itself are not visualizable using the PET scan [11], the absence of apnea is by itself evidence of the integrity of the stem. So much for Walton's concerns about negative error in diagnosing apallic syndrome.

IV. SEEDS OF DOUBT

Before leaving Walton's contrary stand on this issue, I want to reply to two further points he makes in that more recent defense of the whole-brain criterion. Neither is really very important, but they illustrate the tendency in philosophical debate to sow confusion among your opponents by almost any means at hand.

First, Walton says that even in the face of a repeated isoelectric EEG, where there is not death of the whole-brain there can be *restoration* of cortical activity through reactivation of the brain stem arousal system. The imputation, of course, is that cortical destruction may itself be reversible. Where there is breath there is always hope.[6]

But Walton refers to only one case [6]. And he does not go on to say that the patient, victim of a motorcycle fall, was treated with electrode stimulation for only 19 days following five months' akinetic mutism, gave only partial signs of arousal, and at no time recovered spontaneous motor activity, leading to abandonment of the treatment. If this patient *had* recovered consciousness, then he could not have been correctly diagnosed as a case of post-traumatic apallic syndrome, for the fact is that no one, after age 16 or so, sprouts new central neurons. The failure in this case to secure sustained arousal is indeed confirmation of post-traumatic pallial destruction, and remains, sadly, incurable.

Walton's second fresh point in the debate alludes to findings by Lober (reported in [12]), that some people recovered from infantile hydrocephaly, thus growing up with severely reduced cerebral hemispheres, can nevertheless function well: an example being that of a university student, IQ 126, who gained first-class honors in mathematics. This Walton takes to be evidence that the neocortex is neither the sole seat of consciousness nor, perhaps, crucial to the return of conscious functions.

One wants to scream aloud a commonplace of clinical psychopathology: When neural plasticity enters the picture, all bets are off! The neural plasticity of the infant brain allows a lot less than the normal quantity of grey matter to take over a wide range of functions that are usually diffused in greater brain space. This is strikingly and uncontroversially demonstrated in complete hemispherectomy for infantile hemiplegia, where control of the whole body (except for distal finger movements in the arm contralateral to the missing half brain) is found in adulthood [1]. Furthermore, as Epstein has said (quoted in [12]), hydrocephalus is principally a disease of the *white* matter of the brain (the cerebral ventricles, swelled by overproduction of cerebrospinal fluid, disrupt the axons of association fibers around them). It is precisely the *sparing* of nerve cells in the grey matter, even in severe cases of hydrocephalus, that explains the retention of conscious functions and high-performance IQs.

To summarize against Walton on both these points, *for those who have a normal history of neocortical development,* the integrity of the neocortex is essential to the continuance of a mental, and hence a personal, life. It follows from this that pallial destruction is equivalent to personal demise, and this has nothing to do with a residual capacity for spontaneous respiration. Thus both the wholly brain dead and the cerebrally dead patient are dead people, and it is only superstition to make a vital dichotomy between them.

V. ETHICAL CONSIDERATIONS

Many who have followed me so far would nevertheless balk at the problem of disposing of human remains capable of breathing spontaneously. They would say that active intervention to stop the breathing prior to preparation for burial is not only presently illegal (laws can be changed, and already have, to facilitate organ harvesting), but morally murder; and it is often argued that passive (by the non-continuance of treatment) as opposed to active euthanasia is the more humane course.

Both these replies miss the point. You can stab a corpse, but you cannot *kill* it, for it is already dead whether breathing or not. If neocortical death is agreed to constitute personal death, then a firmly diagnosed apallic syndrome patient is in no better or worse situation than the encephalically dead patient sustained on a respirator, whom we all agree is dead though still breathing artificially. Similarly, "euthanasia" means "mercy killing," but one cannot be merciful to a cadaver, for cadavers are beyond pain and indeed all further experience of this world. Indeed, if it were *my* nonapneic remains causing the problem, I want to insist in advance that the breathing be stopped, for by treating my body as if *I* were still alive, hospital personnel would be stripping me of human dignity:

it is enough to have others change your diapers in the first years of life.[7]

Someone might suggest that the difference between defenders of the whole-brain criterion and defenders of the neocortical standard is that they envisage different logical subjects: the former taking that to be a still living, spontaneously breathing human *body,* the latter a *mind* now gone from this world. But if this were just a verbal dispute, it ought not to matter much to the disposal problem in a more enlightened age. But in fact it does matter. Those taking the first view would have to say to enquiring relatives and friends, "He's still alive but permanently unconscious, so we're going to let him die of dehydration, starvation, or infection, whichever comes first." Whereas those taking the second view, which is my own, would logically respond in words like these: "She's dead but her body is still breathing, so we're going to stop the breathing and prepare her body for burial."

Needless to say, the latter formulation seems to me less cruel.

NOTES

1. He might, however, occasionally wag his tail. Apparently this is spinal cord mediated, as dogs coming out of anesthesia often wag their tails. I owe this suggestion to John Fentress.

2. Of course no such contraction would occur, since the pupillary reflex is brain stem mediated; the point is strictly hypothetical.

3. McWhirter gives the following case: "The longest recorded coma was that undergone by Elaine Esposito (b. Dec. 3, 1934) of Tarpon Springs, Florida. She never stirred after an appendectomy on Aug. 6, 1941, when she was 6, in Chicago, Illinois, and she died Nov. 24, 1978 aged 43 years 357 days, having been in a coma for 37 years 111 days" ([13], p. 37).

4. Conversely, selective damage to the brain stem alone can produce a similar result, for without input from the brain stem's reticular activating system, untouched neocortical cells cannot be alerted to incoming stimuli and the patient never wakes up. In the apallic syndrome the lines, so to speak, are still up but no one is home; whereas with brain stem lesions sparing cells that monitor respiration, there is someone home but permanently slumbering because the lines are down. In either case a personal life in this world has ended, so the same remarks made in the section of this paper entitled "Ethical Considerations" will apply. It is perhaps confusion of the necessary contribution of the brain stem reticular formation to achieving conscious awareness with conscious awareness itself that motivates superstitious attitudes towards the apallic syndrome.

5. D. H. Ingvar has recently reported that cerebral blood flow in apallic patients has been measured using Xenon 133 gas inhalation and 254 scintillators that monitor oxygen and glucose uptake in as many square centimeters of superficial cerebral cortex on each side of the head. The video display is uniform: dark blue or purple on the entire screen, indicating little or no uptake of blood, because "these patients have no neocortex to supply with blood" (Ingvar, in a Symposium organized by the Faculty of Medicine, University of Montreal, entitled "Two Hemispheres: One Brain," on May 18, 1984).

6. An anatomist once suggested to me that there is hope for eventual restoration of cortical activity in experiments where embryonic fetal tissue has been successfully transplanted into homologous lesioned areas of the adult rat brain. While this may be encouraging with regard to treatment of, say, expressive aphasia, I do not see how one could hope to replace an entire neocortex that way; surely the survivor of such an operation would not be the original person.

7. This point was originally supplied by a former student of mine who has nursed apallic syndrome patients (name withheld).

BIBLIOGRAPHY

1. Basser, L. S.: 1962, "Hemiplegia of Early Onset and the Faculty of Speech with Special Reference to the Effects of Hemispherectomy," *Brain* 85, 427-460.

2. Brindley, G. A. and Lewin, W. S.: 1968, "The Sensations Produced by Electrical Stimulation of the Visual Cortex," *Journal of Physiology* 196, 479-493.

3. Cooper, I. S. et al.: 1974, "The Effect of Chronic Stimulation of Cerebellar Cortex on Epilepsy in Man," in I. S. Cooper, M. Riklan and R. S. Snider (eds.), *The Cerebellum, Epilepsy, and Behavior,* Plenum Press, New York and London, pp. 119-171.

4. Feindel, W.: 1982, Personal Communication.

5. Geschwind, N. et al.: 1968, "Isolation of the Speech Area," *Neuropsychologia* 6, 327-340.

6. Hassler, R. et al.: 1969, "Behavioural and EEG Arousal Induced by Stimulation of Unspecific Projection Systems in a Patient with Post-traumatic Apallic Syndrome," *Electroencephalography and Clinical Neurophysiology* 27, 306-310.

7. Holmes, G.: 1945, "The Organization of the Visual Cortex in Man," *Proceedings of the Royal Society* (Biology) 132, 348-361.

8. Ingvar, D. H. et al.: 1978, "Survival After Severe Cerebral Anoxia, with Destruction of the Cerebral Cortex: The Apallic Syndrome," *Annals of the New York Academy of Sciences* 315, 184-214.

9. Jerison, H. J.: 1973, *Evolution of the Brain and Intelligence,* Academic Press, New York and London.

10. Lassen, N. A. et al.: 1978, "Brain Function and Blood Flow," *Scientific American* 239, 62-71.

11. LeBlanc, M.: 1983, Personal Communication.

12. Lewin, R.: 1980, "Is Your Brain Really Necessary?" *Science* 210, 1232-1234.

13. McWhirter, N. D.: 1984, *Guinness Book of World Records,* Bantam, New York.

14. Melzack, R.: 1973, *The Puzzle of Pain,* Penguin, London.

15. President's Commission for the Study of Ethical Problems in Medicine and Biomedical and Behavioral Research: 1981, *Defining Death: Medical, Legal, and Ethical Issues in the Determination of Death,* U.S. Government Printing Office, Washington, D.C.

16. Puccetti, R.: 1981, "The Case of Mental Duality: Evidence from Split-brain Data and Other Considerations," *The Behavioral and Brain Sciences* 4, 92-123.

17. Sem-Jacobsen, C.: 1968, *Depth-Electrographic Stimulation of the Human Brain and Behavior,* Thomas, Springfield, Illinois.

18. Walton, D. N.: 1980, *Brain Death: Ethical Considerations,* Purdue University Press, West Lafayette, Indiana.

19. Walton, D. N.: 1981, "Epistemology of Brain Death Determination," *Metamedicine* 2, 259-274.

FURTHER READINGS

"A Definition of Irreversible Coma: Report of the Ad Hoc Committee of the Harvard Medical School to Examine the Definition of Death." *Journal of the American Medical Association* 205 (1968) 337.

Adamkiewicz, V.W. "What are the bonds between the fetus and the uterus?" *Canadian Nurse* 1976 Feb; 72 (2): 26-8.

Curran, W.J. "An historical perspective on the law of personality and status with special regard to the human fetus and the rights of women." *Milbank Memorial Fund Quarterly* 1983 Winter; 61 (1): 58-75.

Gillon, R. "Pregnancy, obstetrics and the moral status of the fetus." *Journal of Medical Ethics* 1988 Mar; 14 (1): 3-4.

Goldenring, J.M. "The brain-life theory: towards a consistent biological definition of humanness." *Journal of Medical Ethics* 1985 Dec; 11 (4): 198-204.

Jonas, Hans. "Against the Stream: Comments on the Definition and Redefinition of Death," in T.L. Beauchamp and S. Perlin, eds. *Ethical Issues in Death and Dying* (Englewood Cliffs, N.J.: Prentice Hall, 1978) 51-59.

Justin, R.G. and Rosner, F. "Maternal/fetal rights: two views." *Journal of the American Medical Women's Association* 1989 May-June; 44 (3): 90-5.

Kluge, E.H. "When caesarean section operations imposed by a court are justified." *Journal of Medical Ethics* 1988 Dec; 14 (4): 206-11.

Sharpe, Gilbert S. "Determination of Death," from G.S. Sharpe. *The Law and Medicine in Canada* (Toronto and Vancouver: Butterworths, 1987).

Strong, C. and Anderson, G. "The moral status of the near-term fetus." *Journal of Medical Ethics* 1989 Mar; 15 (1): 25-7.

The Canadian Medical Association. "Guidelines for the Diagnosis of Brain Death. *CMAJ* 136 (January 15, 1987) 220A-B.

Theoretical Medicine 5 (1984) 16. The whole issue devoted to the definition of death. Issue editor, D.A. Walton.

Tomlinson, Tom. "The Conservative Use of the Brain-Death Criterion: A Critique." *The Journal of Medicine and Philosophy* 9:4 (1984) 377-393.

Zaner, Richard M., ed. *Death: Beyond Whole-Brain* (Dordsrecht and Boston: Kluwer Academic Publishers, 1988).

CHAPTER 13
ABORTION

INTRODUCTION

Abortion is generally defined as the deliberate termination of a pregnancy prior to foetal viability.[1] While this definition makes no reference to killing or bringing about the death of the foetus, the usual reason for performing an abortion is not simply to terminate the pregnancy by removing the foetus from the uterus, but also to kill the foetus. Therefore in actual fact, in most cases the death of the foetus is precisely what is intended by performing the abortion. Since a human foetus is a human being, abortion is really an act of deliberate death. Abortion is therefore appropriately dealt with in this chapter.

Historically, abortions have been approached in a variety of ways. In Roman and Greek times they were not considered ethically reprehensible, because an unborn foetus was not a person in the eyes of the law.[2] Even early Christian writers such as St. Augustine and St.Thomas Aquinas more or less shared this view. In more recent times, abortion became a criminal misdemeanour and ultimately was considered an act of murder. It was considered defensible only under exceptional circumstances: specifically, when the life of the pregnant woman was threatened and the only way to save it was through an abortion. This exception was enshrined in Section 251 of the Criminal Code of Canada, which was struck down in 1988 by the Supreme Court of Canada in the famous case of *R. v. Morgentaler*. Excerpts from that case are reproduced below. Since 1988, Canada has not had any statute law specifically dealing with abortion.

Wayne Sumner presents a philosopher's perspective on abortion. In a classic Canadian discussion, he depicts the issue of abortion as involving a complex series of questions that deal with personhood, autonomy and a balance of social and individual rights.

Susan Sherwin presents a feminist point of view. She argues that any discussion of abortion that does not centre on the position of the woman as someone who is socially embedded in a male-oriented and male-dominated culture falsifies the issue. Sherwin's reasoning constitutes one of the more dominant voices in Canadian feminist-oriented bioethics.

NOTES

1. See Canadian Medical Association, Policy Statement on Abortion.

2. Roman civil law recognized the fiction that an unborn child *en ventre sa mère* is a person in the sense that it will inherit property left to it while still unborn. However, that status did not carry over into the criminal sphere, which defined legal personhood. In Canada, the fiction was first introduced into civil proceedings in *Léveillé v. Montreal Tramway*.

R. v. Morgentaler

Supreme Court of Canada

The Chief Justice — The principal issue raised by this appeal is whether the abortion provisions of the Criminal Code, R.S.C. 1970, c. C-34, infringe the "right to life, liberty and security of the person and the right not to be deprived thereof except in accordance with the principles of fundamental justice" as formulated in s. 7 of the Canadian Charter of Rights and Freedoms.

...

RELEVANT STATUTORY AND CONSTITUTIONAL PROVISIONS

Criminal Code

251. (1) Every one who, with intent to procure the miscarriage of a female person, whether or not she is pregnant, uses any means for the purpose of carrying out his intention is guilty of an indictable offence and is liable to imprisonment for life.

(2) Every female person who, being pregnant, with intent to procure her own miscarriage, uses any means or permits any means to be used for the purpose of carrying out her intention is guilty of an indictable offence and is liable to imprisonment for two years.

(3) In this section, "means" includes

(a) the administration of a drug or other noxious thing,

(b) the use of an instrument, and

(c) manipulation of any kind.

(4) Subsections (1) and (2) do not apply to

(a) a qualified medical practitioner, other than a member of a therapeutic abortion committee for any hospital, who in good

---

R.v.Morgentaler [1988] 1 S.C.R. 30, 63 O.R.(2d)281, 26 O.A.C. 1, 44 D.L.R.(4th) 385, 82 N.R. 1, 3 C.C.C.(3d)449, 62 C.R.(3d)1, 31 C.R.R.

faith uses in an accredited or approved hospital any means for the purpose of carrying out his intention to procure the miscarriage of a female person, or

(b) a female person who, being pregnant, permits a qualified medical practitioner to use in an accredited or approved hospital any means described in paragraph (a) for the purpose of carrying out her intention to procure her own miscarriage, if, before the use of those means, the therapeutic abortion committee for that accredited or approved hospital, by a majority of the members of the committee and at a meeting of the committee at which the case of such female person has been reviewed,

(c) has by certificate in writing stated that in its opinion the continuation of the pregnancy of such female person would or would be likely to endanger her life or health, and

(d) has caused a copy of such certificate to be given to the qualified medical practitioner.

(5) The Minister of Health of a province may by order

(a) require a therapeutic abortion committee for any hospital in that province, or any member thereof, to furnish to him a copy of any certificate described in paragraph (4) (c) issued, by that committee, together with such other information relating to the circumstances surrounding the issue of that certificate as he may require, or

(b) require a medical practitioner who, in that province, has procured the miscarriage of any female person named in a certificate described in paragraph (4) (c), to furnish to him a copy of that certificate, together with such other information relating to the procuring of the miscarriage as he may require.

(6) For the purposes of subsections (4) and (5) and this subsection

"accredited hospital" means a hospital accredited by the Canadian Council on Hospital Accreditation in which diagnostic services and medical, surgical and obstetrical treatment are provided;

"approved hospital" means a hospital in a province approved for the purposes of this section by the Minister of Health of that province;

"board" means the board of governors, management or directors, or the trustees, commission or other person or group of persons having the control and management of an accredited or approved hospital;

"qualified medical practitioner" means a person entitled to engage in the practice of medicine under the laws of the province in which the hospital referred to in subsection (4) is situated;

"therapeutic abortion committee" for any hospital means a committee, comprised of not less than three members each of whom is a qualified medical practitioner, appointed by the board of that hospital for the purpose of considering and determining questions relating to terminations of pregnancy within that hospital.

(7) Nothing in subsection (4) shall be construed as making unnecessary the obtaining of any authorization or consent that is or may be required, otherwise than under this Act, before any means are used for the purpose of carrying out an intention to procure the miscarriage of a female person.

A. The Canadian Charter of Rights and Freedoms

1. The Canadian Charter of Rights and Freedoms guarantees the rights and freedoms set out in it subject only to such reasonable limits prescribed by law as can be demonstrably justified in a free and democratic society.

7. Everyone has the right to life, liberty and security of the person and the right not to be deprived thereof except in accordance with the principles of fundamental justice.

...

III

...

B. Security of the Person

The law has long recognized that the human body ought to be protected from interference by others. At common law, for example, any medical procedure carried out on a person without that person's consent is an assault. Only in emergency circumstances does the law allow others to make decisions of this nature. Similarly, art. 19 of the Civil Code of Lower Canada provides that "The human person is inviolable" and that "No person may cause harm to the person of another without his consent or without being authorized by law to do so." "Security of the person," in other words, is not a value alien to our legal landscape. With the advent of the Charter, security of the person has been elevated to the status of a constitutional norm. This is not to say that the various forms of protection accorded to the human body by the common and civil law occupy a similar status. "Security of the person" must be given content in a manner sensitive to its constitutional position. The above examples are simply illustrative of our respect for individual physical integrity.

... Nor is it to say that the state can never impair personal securities interests. There may well be valid reasons for interfering with security of the person. It is to say, however, that if the state does interfere with security of the person, the Charter requires such interference to conform with the principles of fundamental justice.

... The case law leads me to the conclusion that state interference with bodily integrity and serious state-imposed psychological stress, at least in the criminal law context, constitute a breach of security of the person. It is not necessary in this case to determine whether the right extends further, to protect either interests central to personal autonomy, such as a right to privacy, or interests unrelated to criminal justice.

... Parliament could choose to infringe security of the person if it did so in a manner consistent with the principles of fundamental justice. The present discussion should therefore be seen as a threshold inquiry and the conclusions do not dispose definitively of all the issues relevant to s. 7. With that caution, I have no difficulty in concluding that the encyclopedic factual submissions addressed to us by counsel in the present application establish beyond any doubt that s. 251 of the Criminal Code is *prima facie* a violation of the security of the person of thousands of Canadian women who have made the difficult decision that they do not wish to continue with a pregnancy. At the most basic, physical and emotional level, every pregnant woman is told by the section that she cannot submit to a generally safe medical procedure that might be of clear benefit to her unless she meets criteria entirely unrelated to her own priorities and aspirations. Not only does the removal of decision-making power threaten women in a physical sense; the indecision of knowing whether an abortion will be granted inflicts emotional stress. Section 251 clearly interferes with a woman's bodily integrity in both a physical and emotional sense. Forcing a woman, by threat of criminal sanction, to carry a foetus to term unless she meets certain criteria unrelated to her own priorities and aspirations, is a profound interference with a woman's body and thus a violation of security of the person. Section 251, therefore, is required by the Charter to comport with the principles of fundamental justice.

... [T]he operation of the decision-making mechanism set out in s. 251 creates additional glaring breaches of security of the person. The evidence indicates that s. 251 causes a certain amount of delay for women who are successful in meeting its criteria. In the context of abortion, any unnecessary delay can have profound consequences on the woman's physical and emotional well-being.

More specifically, in 1977, the *Report of the Committee on the Operation of the Abortion Law* (the Badgley Report) revealed that the average delay between a pregnant woman's first contact with a physician and a subsequent therapeutic abortion was eight weeks (p. 146). Although the situation appears to have improved since 1977, the extent of the improvement is not clear. The intervener, the Attorney General of Canada, submitted that the average delay in Ontario between the first visit to a physician and a therapeutic abortion was now between one and three weeks. Yet the respondent Crown admitted in a supplementary factum filed on November 27, 1986, with the permission of the Court that (p. 3):

> ... the evidence discloses that some women may find it very difficult to obtain an abortion: by necessity, abortion services are limited, since hospitals have budgetary, time, space and staff constraints as well as many medical responsibilities. As a result of these problems a woman may have to apply to several hospitals.

> If forced to apply to several different therapeutic abortion committees, there can be no doubt that a woman will experience serious delay in obtaining a therapeutic abortion...

The entire process [of obtaining an abortion] was found to be protracted with women requiring three to seven contacts with health professionals. ... but in the case of abortion, the implications of any delay, according to the evidence, are potentially devastating. The first factor to consider is that different medical techniques are employed to perform abortions at different stages of pregnancy. The testimony of expert doctors at trial indicated that in the first twelve weeks of pregnancy, the relatively safe and simple suction dilation and curettage method of abortion is typically used in North America. From the thirteenth to the sixteenth week, the more dangerous dilation and evacuation procedure is performed, although much less often in Canada than in the United States. From the sixteenth week of pregnancy, the instillation method is commonly employed in Canada. This method requires the intra-amniotic introduction of prostaglandin, urea, or a saline solution, which causes a woman to go into labour, giving birth to a foetus which is usually dead, but not invariably so. The uncontroverted evidence showed that each method of abortion progressively increases risks to the woman.

... The second consideration is that even within the periods appropriate to each method of abortion, the evidence indicated that the earlier the abortion was performed, the fewer the complications and the lower the risk of mortality.

... It is no doubt true that the overall complication and mortality rates for women who undergo abortions are very low, but the increasing risks caused by delay are so clearly established that I have no difficulty in concluding that the delay in obtaining therapeutic abortions caused by the mandatory procedures of s. 251 is an infringement of the purely physical aspect of the individual's right to security of the person.

... The above physical interference caused by the delays created by s. 251, involving a clear risk of damage to the physical well-being of a woman, is sufficient, in my view, to warrant inquiring whether s. 251 comports with the principles of fundamental justice.

However, there is yet another infringement of security of the person. It is clear from the evidence that s. 251 harms the psychological integrity of women seeking abortions. A 1985 report of the Canadian Medical Association, discussed in the *[Report on Therapeutic Abortion Services in Ontario]* Powell Report, at p. 15, emphasized that the procedure involved in s. 251, with the concomitant delays, greatly increases the stress levels of patients and that this can lead to more physical complications associated with abortion.

... I have already noted that the instillation procedure requires a woman actually to experience labour and to suffer through the birth of a foetus that is usually but not always dead ... The psychological injury caused by delay in obtaining abortions, much of which must be attributed to the procedures set out in s. 251, constitutes an additional infringement of the right to security of the person.

... [T]he evidence demonstrates that the system established by the section for obtaining a therapeutic abortion certificate inevitably does create significant delays. It is not possible to say that delay results only from administrative constraints, such as limited budgets or a lack of qualified persons to sit on therapeutic abortion committees. Delay results from the cumbersome operating requirements of s. 251 itself. ... Although the mandate given to the courts under the Charter does not, generally speaking, enable the judiciary to provide remedies for administrative inefficiencies, when denial of a right as basic as security of the person is infringed by the procedure and administrative structures created by the law itself, the courts are empowered to act.

... In summary, s. 251 is a law which forces women to carry a foetus to term contrary to their own priorities and aspirations and which imposes serious delay causing increased physical and psycholog-

ical trauma to those women who meet its criteria. It must, therefore, be determined whether that infringement is accomplished in accordance with the principles of fundamental justice, thereby saving s. 251 under the second part of s. 7.

C. The Principles of Fundamental Justice

... A pregnant woman who desires to have an abortion must apply to the "therapeutic abortion committee" of an "accredited or approved hospital". Such a committee is empowered to issue a certificate in writing stating that in the opinion of a majority of the committee, the continuation of the pregnancy would be likely to endanger the pregnant woman's life or health. Once a copy of the certificate is given to a qualified medical practitioner who is not a member of the therapeutic abortion committee, he or she is permitted to perform an abortion on the pregnant woman and both the doctor and the woman are freed from any criminal liability.

... As is so often the case in matters of interpretation, however, the straightforward reading of this statutory scheme is not fully revealing. In order to understand the true nature and scope of s. 251, it is necessary to investigate the practical operation of the provisions.

... [T]he seemingly neutral requirement of s. 251(4) that at least four physicians be available to authorize and to perform an abortion meant in practice that abortions would be absolutely unavailable in almost one quarter of all hospitals in Canada.

Other administrative and procedural requirements of s. 251(4) reduce the availability of therapeutic abortions even further. For the purposes of s. 251, therapeutic abortions can only be performed in "accredited" or "approved" hospitals.

... [Furthermore t]he requirement that therapeutic abortions be performed only in "accredited" or "approved" hospitals effectively means that the practical availability of the exculpatory provisions of subs. (4) may be heavily restricted, even denied, through provincial regulation.

... A further flaw with the administrative system established in s. 251(4) is the failure to provide an adequate standard for therapeutic abortion committees which must determine when a therapeutic abortion should, as a matter of law, be granted. Subsection (4) states simply that a therapeutic abortion committee may grant a certificate when it determines that a continuation of a pregnancy would be likely to endanger the "life or health" of the pregnant woman. It was noted above that "health" is not defined for the purposes of the section.

... Various expert doctors testified at trial that therapeutic abortion committees apply widely differing definitions of health. For some committees, psychological health is a justification for therapeutic abortion; for others it is not. Some committees routinely refuse abortions to married women unless they are in physical danger, while for other committees it is possible for a married woman to show that she would suffer psychological harm if she continued with a pregnancy, thereby justifying an abortion. It is not typically possible for women to know in advance what standard of health will be applied by any given committee.

... It is no answer to say that "health" is a medical term and that doctors who sit on therapeutic abortion committees must simply exercise their professional judgment. A therapeutic abortion committee is a strange hybrid, part medical committee and part legal committee.

... The combined effect of all of these problems with the procedure stipulated in s. 251 for access to therapeutic abortions is a failure to comply with the principles of fundamental justice.

... The Crown argues in its supplementary factum that women who face difficulties in obtaining abortions at home can simply travel elsewhere in Canada to procure a therapeutic abortion. That submission would not be especially troubling if the difficulties facing women were not in large measure created by the procedural requirements of s. 251 itself. If women were seeking anonymity outside their home town or were simply confronting the reality that it is often difficult to obtain medical services in rural areas, it might be appropriate to say "let them travel". But the evidence establishes convincingly that it is the law itself which in many ways prevents access to local therapeutic abortion facilities. The enormous emotional and financial burden placed upon women who must travel long distances from home to obtain an abortion is a burden created in many instances by Parliament. Moreover, it is not accurate to say to women who would seem to qualify under s. 251(4) that they can get a therapeutic abortion as long as they are willing to travel.

... I conclude that the procedures created in s. 251 of the Criminal Code for obtaining a therapeutic abortion do not comport with the principles of fundamental justice.

...

V

... The appellants contended that the sole purpose of s. 251 of the Criminal Code is to protect the life and health of pregnant women. The respondent Crown submitted that s. 251 seeks to protect not only the life and health of pregnant women, but also the interests of the foetus. ... In my view, it is unnecessary for the purpose of deciding this appeal to evaluate or assess "foetal rights" as an independent constitutional value. Nor are we required to measure the full extent of the state's interest in establishing criteria unrelated to the pregnant woman's own priorities and aspirations.

What we must do is evaluate the particular balance struck by Parliament in s. 251, as it relates to the priorities and aspirations of pregnant women and the government's interests in the protection of the foetus.

Section 251 provides that foetal interests are not to be protected where the "life or health" of the woman is threatened. Thus, Parliament itself has expressly stated in s.251 that the "life or health" of pregnant women is paramount. The procedures of s. 251(4) are clearly related to the pregnant woman's "life or health" for that is the very phrase used by the subsection.

... I think the protection of the interests of pregnant women is a valid governmental objective, where life and health can be jeopardized by criminal sanctions. ... I agree that protection of foetal interests by Parliament is also a valid governmental objective. It follows that balancing these interests, with the lives and health of women a major factor, is clearly an important governmental objective.

... I am equally convinced, however, that the means chosen to advance the legislative objectives of s. 251 do not satisfy any of the three elements of the proportionality component of *R. v. Oakes.* The evidence has led me to conclude that the infringement of the security of the person of pregnant women caused by s. 251 is not accomplished in accordance with the principles of fundamental justice.

... I conclude, therefore, that the cumbersome structure of subs. (4) not only unduly subordinates the s. 7 rights of pregnant women but may also defeat the value Parliament itself has established as paramount, namely, the life and health of the pregnant woman. ...

CONCLUSION

Section 251 of the Criminal Code infringes the right to security of the person of many pregnant women. The procedures and administrative structures established in the section to provide for therapeutic abortions do not comply with the principles of fundamental justice. Section 7 of the Charter is infringed and that infringement cannot be saved under s. 1.

... Having found that this "comprehensive code" infringes the Charter, it is not the role of the Court to pick and choose among the various aspects of s. 251 so as effectively to re-draft the section. The appeal should therefore be allowed and s. 251 as a whole struck down under s. 52(1) of the Constitution Act, 1982. ...
Beetz J.:

... "Security of the person" must include a right of access to medical treatment for a condition representing a danger to life or health without fear of criminal sanction. If an act of Parliament forces a person whose life or health is in danger to choose between, on the one hand, the commission of a crime to obtain effective and timely medical treatment and, on the other hand, inadequate treatment or no treatment at all, the right to security of the person has been violated.

... With the greatest of respect, I cannot agree with the view that the therapeutic abortion committee is a "strange hybrid, part medical committee and part legal committee" as the Chief Justice characterizes it. ... The committee is not called upon to evaluate the sufficiency of the state interest in the foetus as against the woman's health. This evaluation of the state interest is a question of law already decided by Parliament in its formulation of s. 251(4).

... The wording of s. 251(4)(c) limits the authority of the committee. The word "health" is not vague but plainly refers to the physical or mental health of the pregnant woman. ...The standard is further circumscribed by the word "endanger." Not only must the continuation of the pregnancy affect the woman's life or health, it must endanger life or health, so that a committee that authorizes an abortion when this element is not present or fails to authorize it when it is present exceeds its authority. Finally, the expression "would or would be likely" eliminates any requirement that the danger to life or health be certain or immediate at the time the certificate is issued.

... Just as the expression of the standard in s. 251(4)(c) does not offend the principles of fundamental justice, the requirement that an independent medical opinion be obtained for a therapeutic abortion to be lawful also cannot be said to constitute a violation of these principles when considered in the context of pregnant women's right to security of the person. ... [B]y requiring that a committee state that the medical standard has been met for the criminal sanction to be lifted, Parliament seeks to assure that there is a reliable, independent and medically sound opinion that the continuation of the pregnancy would or would be likely to endanger the woman's life or health. ...

... [Although] the current mechanism in the Criminal Code does not accord with the principles of fundamental justice, [this] does not preclude, in my view, Parliament from adopting another system, free of the failings of s. 251(4), in order to ascertain that the life or health of the pregnant woman is in danger, by way of a reliable, independent and medically sound opinion.

Parliament is justified in requiring a reliable, independent and medically sound opinion in order to protect the state interest in the foetus. This is undoubtedly the objective of a rule which requires an independent verification of the practising physician's opinion that the life or health of the pregnant woman is in danger. It cannot be said to be simply a mechanism designed to protect the health of the pregnant woman ... Parliament requires this independent opinion because it is not only the woman's interest that is at stake in a decision to

authorize an abortion. The Ontario Court of Appeal alluded to this ... when it stated that "One cannot overlook the fact that the situation respecting a woman's right to control her own person becomes more complex when she becomes pregnant, and that some statutory control may be appropriate." The presence of the foetus accounts for this complexity. By requiring an independent medical opinion that the pregnant woman's life or health is in fact endangered, Parliament seeks to ensure that, in any given case, only therapeutic reasons will justify the decision to abort. The amendments to the Criminal Code in 1969 amounted to a recognition by Parliament, as I have said, that the interest in the life or health of the pregnant woman takes precedence over the interest of the state in the protection of the foetus when the continuation of the pregnancy would or would be likely to endanger the pregnant woman's life or health.

... I do not believe it to be unreasonable to seek independent medical confirmation of the threat to the woman's life or health when such an important and distinct interest hangs in the balance.

... I am of the view that there would still be circumstances in which the state interest in the protection of the foetus would require an independent medical opinion as to the danger to the life or health of the pregnant woman. Assuming without deciding that a right of access to abortion can be founded upon the right to "liberty," there would be a point in time at which the state interest in the foetus would become compelling. From this point in time, Parliament would be entitled to limit abortions to those required for therapeutic reasons and therefore require an independent opinion as to the health exception.

... Some delay is inevitable in connection with any system which purports to limit to therapeutic reasons the grounds upon which an abortion can be performed lawfully.... Furthermore, rules promoting the safety of abortions designed to protect the interest of the pregnant woman will also cause some unavoidable delay. It is only insofar as the administrative structure creates delays which are unnecessary that the structure can be considered to violate the principles of fundamental justice.... A fair structure, put in place to decide between those women who qualify for a therapeutic abortion and those who do not, should be designed with a view to efficiently meeting the demands which it must necessarily serve.

... Does the objective of protecting the foetus in s. 251 relate to concerns which are pressing and substantial in a free and democratic society? ... I am of the view that the protection of the foetus is and, as the Court of Appeal observed, always has been, a valid objective in Canadian criminal law. ... I think s. 1 of the Charter authorizes reasonable limits to be put on a woman's right having regard to the state interest in the protection of the foetus.

... The Crown must show that the means chosen in s. 251 are reasonable and demonstrably justified.... [N]ot only are some of the rules in s. 251 unnecessary to the primary objective of the protection of the foetus and the ancillary objective of the protection of the pregnant woman's life or health, but their practical effect is to undermine the health of the woman which Parliament purports to consider so important. Consequently, s. 251 does not meet the proportionality test....

... The gist of s. 251(4) is, as I have said, that the objective of protecting the foetus is not of sufficient importance to defeat the interest in protecting pregnant women from pregnancies which represent a danger to life or health. I take this parliamentary enactment in 1969 as an indication that, in a free and democratic society, it would be unreasonable to limit the pregnant woman's right to security of the person by a rule prohibiting abortions in all circumstances when her

life or health would or would likely be in danger. This decision of the Canadian Parliament to the effect that the life or health of the pregnant woman takes precedence over the state interest in the foetus is also reflected in legislation in other free and democratic societies.

... Finally, I wish to stress that we have not been asked to decide nor is it necessary,... to decide whether a foetus is included in the word "everyone" in s. 7 so as to have a right to "life, liberty and security of the person" under the Charter.

The reasons of McIntyre and La Forest J.J. were delivered by *McIntyre J.* (dissenting):

... The charge here is one of conspiracy to breach the provisions of s. 251 of the Criminal Code. There is no doubt, and it has never been questioned, that the appellants adopted a course which was clearly in defiance of the provisions of the Code and it is difficult to see where any infringement of their rights, under s. 7 of the Charter, could have occurred. There is no female person involved in the case who has been denied a therapeutic abortion and, as a result, the whole argument on the right to security of the person, under s. 7 of the Charter, has been on a hypothetical basis. The case, however, was addressed by all the parties on that basis and the Court has accepted that position.

... In considering the constitutionality of s. 251 of the Criminal Code, it is first necessary to understand the background of this litigation and some of the problems which it raises. Section 251 of the Code has been denounced as ill-conceived and inadequate by those at one extreme of the abortion debate and as immoral and unacceptable by those at the opposite extreme. There are those, like the appellants, who assert that on moral and ethical grounds there is a simple solution to the problem: the inherent "right of women to control their own bodies" requires the repeal of s. 251 in favour of the principle of "abortion on demand". Opposing this view are those who contend with equal vigour, and also on moral and ethical grounds, for a clear and simple solution: the inherent "right to life of the unborn child" requires the repeal of s. 251(4), (5), (6) and (7) in order to leave an absolute ban on abortions. The battle lines so drawn are firmly held and the attitudes of the opposing parties admit of no compromise.

... [Parliament has made an] attempt... to balance the competing interests of the unborn child and the pregnant woman. Where the provisions of s. 251(4) are met, the abortion may be performed without legal sanction. Where they are not, abortion is deemed to be socially undesirable and is punished as a crime.

... The values we must accept for the purposes of this appeal are those expressed by Parliament which holds the view that the desire of a woman to be relieved of her pregnancy is not, of itself, justification for performing an abortion.

... It is not for the Court to substitute its own views on the merits of a given question for those of Parliament.... [I]ts role is confined to deciding whether the solution enacted by Parliament offends the Charter. If it does, the provision must be struck down or declared inoperative, and Parliament may then enact such different provisions as it may decide.

... The Court must not resolve an issue such as that of abortion on the basis of how many judges may favour "pro-choice" or "pro-life". To do so would be contrary to sound principle and the rule of law affirmed in the preamble to the Charter which must mean that no discretion, including a judicial discretion, can be unlimited.

... It is said that a law which forces a woman to carry a foetus to term unless she meets certain criteria unrelated to her own priorities and aspirations interferes with security of her person.... All laws, it must be noted, have the potential for interference with individual priorities and aspirations. In fact, the very purpose of most legislation is to cause such interference. It is only when such legislation goes beyond interfering with priorities and aspirations, and abridges rights, that courts may intervene.

... In my view, it is clear that before it could be concluded that any enactment infringed the concept of security of the person, it would have to infringe some underlying right included in or protected by the concept. For the appellants to succeed here, then, they must show more than an interference with priorities and aspirations; they must show the infringement of a right which is included in the concept of security of the person. The proposition that women enjoy a constitutional right to have an abortion is devoid of support in the language of s. 7 of the Charter or any other section. While some human rights documents, such as the American Convention on Human Rights, 1969 (Article 4(1)), expressly address the question of abortion, the Charter is entirely silent on the point. It may be of some significance that the Charter uses specific language in dealing with other topics, such as voting rights, religion, expression and such controversial matters as mobility rights, language rights and minority rights, but remains silent on the question of abortion which, at the time the Charter was under consideration, was as much a subject of public controversy as it is today.

... Governmental action for the due governance and administration of society can rarely please everyone. It is hard to imagine a governmental policy or initiative which will not create significant stress or anxiety for some and, frequently, for many members of the community.

... To invade the s. 7 right of security of the person, there would have to be more than state-imposed stress or strain.... The mere fact of pregnancy, let alone an unwanted pregnancy, gives rise to stress.

The evidence reveals that much of the anguish associated with abortion is inherent and unavoidable and that there is really no psychologically painless way to cope with an unwanted pregnancy.

It is for these reasons I would conclude, that save for the provisions of the Criminal Code, which permit abortion where the life or health of the woman is at risk, no right of abortion can be found in Canadian law, custom or tradition, and that the Charter, including s. 7, creates no further right. Accordingly, it is my view that s. 251 of the Code does not in its terms violate s. 7 of the Charter.

... The solution to th[e abortion] question in this country must be left to Parliament. It is for Parliament to pronounce on and to direct social policy. This is not because Parliament can claim all wisdom and knowledge but simply because Parliament is elected for that purpose in a free democracy and, in addition, has the facilities — the exposure to public opinion and information — as well as the political power to make effective its decisions....

I would dismiss the appeal.

...

Wilson J.:

At the heart of this appeal is the question whether a pregnant woman can, as a constitutional matter, be compelled by law to carry the foetus to term. The legislature has proceeded on the basis that she can be so compelled.

... A consideration as to whether or not the procedural requirements for obtaining or performing an abortion comport with fundamental justice is purely academic if such requirements cannot as a constitutional matter be imposed at all. If a pregnant woman cannot, as a constitutional matter, be compelled by law to carry the foetus to term against her will, a review of the procedural requirements by which she may be compelled to do so seems pointless. Moreover, it would, in my opinion, be an exercise in futility for the legislature to expend its time and energy in attempting to remedy the defects in the procedural requirements unless it has some assurance that this process will, at the end of the day, result in the creation of a valid criminal offence. I turn, therefore, to what I believe is the central issue that must be addressed.

... I agree with the Chief Justice that we are not called upon in this case to delineate the full content of the right to life, liberty and security of the person. ... What we are asked to do ... is define the content of the right in the context of the legislation under attack. Does section 251 of the Criminal Code ... violate her right to life, liberty and security of the person within the meaning of s. 7?

Leaving aside for the moment the implications of the section for the foetus and addressing only the s. 7 right of the pregnant woman, it seems to me that we can say with a fair degree of confidence that a legislative scheme for the obtaining of an abortion which exposes the pregnant woman to a threat to her security of the person would violate her right under s. 7.

... The Charter is predicated on a particular conception of the place of the individual in society. An individual is not a totally independent entity disconnected from the society in which he or she lives. Neither, however, is the individual a mere cog in an impersonal machine in which his or her values, goals and aspirations are subordinated to those of the collectivity. The individual is a bit of both. The Charter reflects this reality by leaving a wide range of activities and decisions open to legitimate government control while at the same time placing limits on the proper scope of that control. Thus, the rights guaranteed in the Charter erect around each individual, metaphorically speaking, an invisible fence over which the state will not be allowed to trespass. The role of the courts is to map out, piece by piece, the parameters of the defence.

The Charter and the right to individual liberty guaranteed under it are inextricably tied to the concept of human dignity. ... The idea of human dignity finds expression in almost every right and freedom guaranteed in the Charter.... Thus, an aspect of the respect for human dignity on which the Charter is founded is the right to make fundamental personal decisions without interference from the state. This right is a critical component of the right to liberty.... Liberty in a free and democratic society does not require the state to approve the personal decisions made by its citizens; it does, however, require the state to respect them.

... The question then becomes whether the decision of a woman to terminate her pregnancy falls within this class of protected decisions. I have no doubt that it does. This decision is one that will have profound psychological, economic and social consequences for the pregnant woman. The circumstances giving rise to it can be complex and varied and there may be, and usually are, powerful considerations militating in opposite directions. It is a decision that deeply reflects the way the woman thinks about herself and her relationship to others and to society at large. It is not just a medical decision; it is a profound social and ethical one as well. Her response to it will be the response of the whole person.

It is probably impossible for a man to respond, even imaginatively, to such a dilemma not just because it is outside the realm of his personal experience (although this is, of course, the case) but because he can relate to it only by objectifying it, thereby eliminating the subjective elements of the female psyche which are at the heart of the dilemma.

... Given then that the right to liberty guaranteed by s. 7 of the Charter gives a woman the right to decide for herself whether or not to terminate her pregnancy, does s. 251 of the Criminal Code violate this right? Clearly it does. The purpose of the section is to take the decision away from the woman and give it to a committee. ... The fact that the decision whether a woman will be allowed to terminate her pregnancy is in the hands of a committee is just as great a violation of the woman's right to personal autonomy in decisions of an intimate and private nature as it would be if a committee were established to decide whether a woman should be allowed to continue her pregnancy. Both these arrangements violate the woman's right to liberty by deciding for her something that she has the right to decide for herself.

... I agree with my colleague ... the present legislative scheme for the obtaining of an abortion clearly subjects pregnant women to considerable emotional stress as well as to unnecessary physical risk. I believe, however, that the flaw in the present legislative scheme goes much deeper than that. In essence, what it does is assert that the woman's capacity to reproduce is not to be subject to her own control. It is to be subject to the control of the state. She may not choose whether to exercise her existing capacity or not to exercise it. This is not, in my view, just a matter of interfering with her right to liberty in the sense (already discussed) of her right to personal autonomy in decision making, it is a direct interference with her physical "person" as well. She is truly being treated as a means — a means to an end which she does not desire but over which she has no control. She is the passive recipient of a decision made by others as to whether her body is to be used to nurture a new life. Can there be anything that comports less with human dignity and self-respect? How can a woman in this position have any sense of security with respect to her person? I believe that s. 251 of the Criminal Code deprives the pregnant woman of her right to security of the person as well as her right to liberty.

... I believe, therefore, that a deprivation of the s. 7 right which has the effect of infringing a right guaranteed elsewhere in the Charter cannot be in accordance with the principles of fundamental justice.

In my view, the deprivation of the s. 7 right with which we are concerned in this case offends s. 2(a) of the Charter. I say this because I believe that the decision whether or not to terminate a pregnancy is essentially a moral decision, a matter of conscience. I do not think there is or can be any dispute about that. The question is: whose conscience? Is the conscience of the woman to be paramount or the conscience of the state? I believe, for the reasons I gave in discussing the right to liberty, that in a free and democratic society it must be the conscience of the individual. Indeed, s. 2(a) makes it clear that this freedom belongs to "everyone", i.e., to each of us individually.

... The Chief Justice sees religious belief and practice as the paradigmatic example of conscientiously held beliefs and manifestations and as such protected by the Charter. But I do not think he is saying that a personal morality which is not founded in religion is outside the protection of s. 2(a). Certainly, it would be my view that conscientious beliefs which are not religiously motivated are equally protected by freedom of conscience in s. 2(a). In so saying I am not unmindful of the fact that the Charter opens with an affirmation that "Canada is founded upon principles that recognize the supremacy of God...." But I am also mindful that the values entrenched in the Charter are those which characterize a free and democratic society.

... It seems to me ... that in a free and democratic society "freedom of conscience and religion" should be broadly construed to extend to conscientiously held beliefs, whether grounded in religion or in a secular morality. Indeed, as a matter of statutory interpretation, "conscience" and "religion" should not be treated as tautologous if capable of independent, although related, meaning. Accordingly, for the state to take sides on the issue of abortion, as it does in the impugned legislation by making it a criminal offence for the pregnant woman to exercise one of her options, is not only to endorse but also to enforce, on pain of a further loss of liberty through actual imprisonment, one conscientiously held view at the expense of another. It is to deny freedom of conscience to some, to treat them as means to an end, to deprive them ... of their "essential humanity". Can this comport with fundamental justice?

... In my view, the primary objective of the impugned legislation must be seen as the protection of the foetus. It undoubtedly has other ancillary objectives, such as the protection of the life and health of pregnant women, but I believe that the main objective advanced to justify a restriction on the pregnant woman's s. 7 right is the protection of the foetus. I think this is a perfectly valid legislative objective. ... I think s. 1 of the Charter authorizes reasonable limits to be put upon the woman's right having regard to the fact of the developing foetus within her body. The question is: at what point in the pregnancy does the protection of the foetus become such a pressing and substantial concern as to outweigh the fundamental right of the woman to decide whether or not to carry the foetus to term? At what point does the state's interest in the protection of the foetus become "compelling" and justify state intervention in what is otherwise a matter of purely personal and private concern?

... It would be my view ... that the value to be placed on the foetus as potential life is directly related to the stage of its development during gestation. The undeveloped foetus starts out as a newly fertilized ovum; the fully developed foetus emerges ultimately as an infant. A developmental progression takes place in between these two extremes and, in my opinion, this progression has a direct bearing on the value of the foetus as potential life. It is a fact of human experience that a miscarriage or spontaneous abortion of the foetus at six months is attended by far greater sorrow and sense of loss than a miscarriage or spontaneous abortion at six days or even six weeks. This is not, of course, to deny that the foetus is potential life from the moment of conception. ... It is simply to say that in balancing the state's interest in the protection of the foetus as potential life under s. 1 of the Charter against the right of the pregnant woman under s. 7, greater weight should be given to the state's interest in the later stages of pregnancy than in the earlier. The foetus should accordingly, for purposes of s. 1, be viewed in differential and developmental terms.... A developmental view of the foetus ... supports a permissive approach to abortion in the early stages of pregnancy and a restrictive approach in the later stages. In the early stages the woman's autonomy would be absolute; her decision, reached in consultation with her physician, not to carry the foetus to term would be conclusive. The state would have no business inquiring into her reasons. Her reasons for having an abor-

tion would, however, be the proper subject of inquiry at the later stages of her pregnancy when the state's compelling interest in the protection of the foetus would justify it in prescribing conditions. The precise point in the development of the foetus at which the state's interest in its protection becomes "compelling" I leave to the informed judgment of the legislature which is in a position to receive guidance on the subject from all the relevant disciplines. It seems to me, however, that it might fall somewhere in the second trimester.

... One final word. I wish to emphasize that in these reasons I have dealt with the existence of the developing foetus merely as a factor to be considered in assessing the importance of the legislative objective under s. 1 of the Charter. I have not dealt with the entirely separate question whether a foetus is covered by the word "everyone" in s. 7 so as to have an independent right to life under that section. The Crown did not argue it and it is not necessary to decide it in order to dispose of the issues on this appeal.

I would allow the appeal.

...

Appeal allowed, McIntyre and La Forest J.J. dissenting.

Abortion Through a Feminist Ethics Lens

Susan Sherwin

Abortion has long been a central issue in the arena of applied ethics, but, the distinctive analysis of feminist ethics is generally overlooked in most philosophic

discussions. Authors and readers commonly presume a familiarity with the feminist position and equate it with liberal defences of women's right to choose abortion, but, in

Earlier versions of this paper were read to the Department of Philosophy, Dalhousie University, and to the Canadian Society for Women in Philosophy in Kingston. I am very grateful for the comments received from colleagues in both forums; particular thanks go to Lorraine Code, David Braybrooke, Richmond Campbell, Sandra Taylor, Terry Tomkow and Kadri Vihvelin for their patience and advice.

fact, feminist ethics yields a different analysis of the moral questions surrounding abortion than that usually offered by the more familiar liberal defenders of abortion rights. Most feminists can agree with some of the conclusions that arise from certain non-feminist arguments on abortion, but they often disagree about the way the issues are formulated and the sorts of reasons that are invoked in the mainstream literature.

Among the many differences found between feminist and non-feminist arguments about abortion, is the fact that most non-feminist discussions of abortion consider the questions of the moral or legal permissibility of abortion in isolation from other questions, ignoring (and thereby obscuring) relevant connections to other social practices that oppress women. They are generally grounded in masculinist conceptions of freedom (e.g., privacy, individual choice, individuals' property rights in their own bodies) that do not meet the needs, interests, and intuitions of many of the women concerned. In contrast, feminists seek to couch their arguments in moral concepts that support their general campaign of overcoming injustice in all its dimensions, including those inherent in moral theory itself.[1] There is even disagreement about how best to understand the moral question at issue: non-feminist arguments focus exclusively on the morality and/or legality of performing abortions, whereas feminists insist that other questions, including ones about accessibility and delivery of abortion services must also be addressed.

Although feminists welcome the support of non-feminists in pursuing policies that will grant women control over abortion decisions, they generally envision very different sorts of policies for this purpose than those considered by non-feminist sympathizers. For example, Kathleen McDonnell (1984) urges feminists to develop an explicitly " 'feminist morality' of abortion.... At its root it would be characterized by the deep appreciations of the complexities of life, the refusal to polarize and adopt simplistic formulas" (p. 52). Here, I propose one conception of the shape such an analysis should take.

WOMEN AND ABORTION

The most obvious difference between feminist and non-feminist approaches to abortion can be seen in the relative attention each gives to the interests and experiences of women in its analysis. Feminists consider it self-evident that the pregnant woman is a subject of principal concern in abortion decisions. In most non-feminist accounts, however, not only is she not perceived as central, she is rendered virtually invisible. Non-feminist theorists, whether they support or oppose women's right to choose abortion, focus almost all their attention on the moral status of the developing embryo or the fetus.

In pursuing a distinctively feminist ethics, it is appropriate to begin with a look at the role of abortion in women's lives. Clearly, the need for abortion can be very intense; women have pursued abortions under appalling and dangerous conditions, across widely diverse cultures and historical periods. No one denies that if abortion is not made legal, safe, and accessible, women will seek out illegal and life-threatening abortions to terminate pregnancies they cannot accept. Anti-abortion activists seem willing to accept this price, but feminists judge the inevitable loss of women's lives associated with restrictive abortion policies to be a matter of fundamental concern.

Although anti-abortion campaigners imagine that women often make frivolous and irresponsible decisions about abortion, feminists recognize that women have abortions for a wide variety of reasons. Some women, for instance, find themselves seriously ill and incapacitated throughout pregnancy; they cannot continue in their jobs and may face enormous difficulties in fulfilling their responsibilities at home. Many employers and schools will not tolerate pregnancy in their employees or students, and not every woman is able to put her job, career, or studies on hold. Women of limited means may be unable to take adequate care of children they have already home and they may know that another mouth to feed will reduce their ability to provide for their existing children. Women who suffer from chronic disease, or who feel too young, or too old, or who are unable to maintain lasting relationships may recognize that they will not be able to care properly for a child at this time. Some who are homeless, or addicted to drugs, or who are diagnosed as carrying the AIDS virus may be unwilling to allow a child to enter the world under such circumstances. If the pregnancy is a result of rape or incest, the psychological pain of carrying it to term may be unbearable, and the woman may recognize that her attitude to the child after birth will always be tinged with bitterness. Some women have learned that the fetuses they carry have serious chromosomal anomalies and consider it best to prevent them from being born with a condition bound to cause suffering. Others, knowing the fathers to be brutal and violent, may be unwilling to subject a child to the beatings or incestuous attacks they anticipate; some may have no other realistic way to remove the child (or themselves) from the relationship.

Or a woman may simply believe that bearing a child is incompatible with her life plans at this time, since continuing a pregnancy is likely to have profound repercussions throughout a woman's entire life. If the woman is young, a pregnancy will very likely reduce her chances of education and hence limit her career and life opportunities: "The earlier a woman has a baby, it seems, the more likely she is to drop out of school; the less education she gets, the more

likely she is to remain poorly paid, peripheral to the labour market, or unemployed, and the more children she will have between one and three more than her working childless counterpart" (Petchesky 1984, p. 150). In many circumstances, having a child will exacerbate the social and economic forces already stacked against her by virtue of her sex (and her race, class, age, sexual orientation, or the effects of some disability, etc.). Access to abortion is a necessary option for many women if they are to escape the oppressive conditions of poverty.

Whatever the reason, most feminists believe that a pregnant woman is in the best position to judge whether abortion is the appropriate response to her circumstances. Since she is usually the only one able to weigh all the relevant factors, most feminists reject attempts to offer any general abstract rules for determining when abortion is morally justified. Women's personal deliberations about abortion include contextually defined considerations reflecting her commitment to the needs and interests of everyone concerned including herself, the fetus she carries, other members of her household, etc. Because there is no single formula available for balancing these complex factors through all possible cases, it is vital that feminists insist on protecting each woman's right to come to her own conclusions. Abortion decisions are, by their very nature, dependent on specific features of each woman's experience; theoretically dispassionate philosophers and other moralists should not expect to set the agenda for these considerations in any universal way. Women must be acknowledged as full moral agents with the responsibility for making moral decisions about their own pregnancies.[2] Although I think that it is possible for a woman to make a mistake in her moral judgment on this matter (i.e., it is possible that a woman may come to believe that she was wrong about her decision to continue or terminate a pregnancy), the intimate nature of this sort of decision makes it unlikely that anyone else is in a position to arrive at a more reliable conclusion; it is, therefore, improper to grant others the authority to interfere in women's decisions to seek abortions.

Feminist analysis regards the effects of unwanted pregnancies on the lives of women individually and collectively as a central element in the moral evaluation of abortion. Even without patriarchy, bearing a child would be a very important event in a woman's life. It involves significant physical, emotional, social, and (usually) economic changes for her. The ability to exert control over the incidence, timing, and frequency of childbearing is often tied to her ability to control most other things she values. Since we live in a patriarchal society, it is especially important to ensure that women have the authority to control their own reproduction.[3] Despite the diversity of opinion among feminists on most other matters, virtually all feminists seem to agree that women must gain full control over their own reproductive lives if they are to free themselves from male dominance.[4] Many perceive the commitment of the political right wing to opposing abortion as part of a general strategy to reassert patriarchal control over women in the face of significant feminist influence (Petchesky 1980, p. 112).

Women's freedom to choose abortion is also linked with their ability to control their own sexuality. Women's subordinate status often prevents them from refusing men sexual access to their bodies. If women cannot end the unwanted pregnancies that result from male sexual dominance, their sexual vulnerability to particular men can increase, because caring for an(other) infant involves greater financial needs and reduced economic opportunities for women.[5] As a result, pregnancy often forces women to become dependent on men. Since a woman's dependence on a man is assumed to entail that she will remain sexually loyal

to him, restriction of abortion serves to channel women's sexuality and further perpetuates the cycle of oppression.

In contrast to most non-feminist accounts, feminist analyses of abortion direct attention to the question of how women get pregnant. Those who reject abortion seem to believe that women can avoid unwanted pregnancies by avoiding sexual intercourse. Such views show little appreciation for the power of sexual politics in a culture that oppresses women. Existing patterns of sexual dominance mean that women often have little control over their sexual lives. They may be subject to rape by strangers, or by their husbands, boyfriends, colleagues, employers, customers, fathers, brothers, uncles, and dates. Often, the sexual coercion is not even recognized as such by the participants, but is the price of continued "good will" — popularity, economic survival, peace, or simple acceptance. Few women have not found themselves in circumstances where they do not feel free to refuse a man's demands for intercourse, either because he is holding a gun to her head or because he threatens to be emotionally hurt if she refuses (or both). Women are socialized to be compliant and accommodating, sensitive to the feelings of others, and frightened of physical power; men are socialized to take advantage of every opportunity to engage in sexual intercourse and to use sex to express dominance and power. Under such circumstances, it is difficult to argue that women could simply "choose" to avoid heterosexual activity if they wish to avoid pregnancy. Catherine MacKinnon neatly sums it up: "the logic by which women are supposed to consent to sex [is]: preclude the alternatives, then call the remaining option 'her choice,'" (MacKinnon 1989, p. 192).

Nor can women rely on birth control alone to avoid pregnancy. There simply is no form of reversible contraception available that is fully safe and reliable. The pill and the IUD are the most effective means offered, but both involve significant health hazards to women and are quite dangerous for some. No woman should spend the 30 to 40 years of her reproductive life on either form of birth control. Further, both have been associated with subsequent problems of involuntary infertility, so they are far from optimum for women who seek to control the timing of their pregnancies.

The safest form of birth control involves the use of barrier methods (condoms or diaphragms) in combination with spermicidal foams or jelly. But these methods also pose difficulties for women. They may be socially awkward to use: young women are discouraged from preparing for sexual activity that might never happen and are offered instead romantic models of spontaneous passion. (Few films or novels interrupt scenes of seduction for the fetching of contraceptives.) Many women find their male partners unwilling to use barrier methods of contraception and they do not have the power to insist. Further, cost is a limiting factor for many women. Condoms and spermicides are expensive and are not covered under most health care plans. There is only one contraceptive option which offers women safe and fully effective birth control: barrier methods with the back-up option of abortion.[6]

From a feminist perspective, a central moral feature of pregnancy is that it takes place in women's bodies and has profound effects on women's lives. Gender-neutral accounts of pregnancy are not available; pregnancy is explicitly a condition associated with the female body.[7] Because the need for abortion is experienced only by women, policies about abortion affect women uniquely. Thus, it is important to consider how proposed policies on abortion fit into general patterns of oppression for women. Unlike non-feminist accounts, feminist ethics demands that the effects on the oppression of women be a principal consideration when evaluating abortion policies.

THE FETUS

In contrast, most non-feminist analysts believe that the moral acceptability of abortion turns on the question of the moral status of the fetus. Even those who support women's right to choose abortion tend to accept the central premise of the anti-abortion proponents that abortion can only be tolerated if it can be proved that the fetus is lacking some criterion of full personhood.[8] Opponents of abortion have structured the debate so that it is necessary to define the status of the fetus as either valued the same as other humans (and hence entitled not to be killed) or as lacking in all value. Rather than challenging the logic of this formulation, many defenders of abortion have concentrated on showing that the fetus is indeed without significant value (Tooley 1972, Warren 1973); others, such as Wayne Sumner (1981), offer a more subtle account that reflects the gradual development of fetuses whereby there is some specific criterion that determines the degree of protection to be afforded them which is lacking in the early stages of pregnancy but present in the later stages. Thus, the debate often rages between abortion opponents who describe the fetus as an "innocent," vulnerable, morally important, separate being whose life is threatened and who must be protected at all costs, and abortion supporters who try to establish some sort of deficiency inherent to fetuses which removes them from the scope of the moral community.

The woman on whom the fetus depends for survival is considered as secondary (if she is considered at all) in these debates. The actual experiences and responsibilities of real women are not perceived as morally relevant (unless they, too, can be proved innocent by establishing that their pregnancies are a result of rape or incest). It is a common assumption of both defenders and opponents of women's right to choose abortion that many women will be irresponsible in their choices. The important question, though, is whether fetuses have the sort of status that justifies interfering in women's choices at all. In some contexts, women's role in gestation is literally reduced to that of "fetal containers"; the individual women disappear or are perceived simply as mechanical life-support systems.[9]

The current rhetoric against abortion stresses the fact that the genetic make-up of the fetus is determined at conception and the genetic code is incontestably human. Lest there be any doubt about the humanity of the fetus, we are assailed with photographs of fetuses at various stages of development demonstrating the early appearance of recognizably human characteristics, e.g., eyes, fingers, and toes. The fact that the fetus in its early stages is microscopic, virtually indistinguishable from other primate fetuses to the untrained eye, and lacking in the capacities that make human life meaningful and valuable is not deemed relevant by the self-appointed defenders of fetuses. The anti-abortion campaign is directed at evoking sympathetic attitudes towards this tiny, helpless being whose life is threatened by its own mother; it urges us to see the fetus as entangled in an adversarial relationship with the (presumably irresponsible) woman who carries it. We are encouraged to identify with the "unborn child" and not with the (selfish) woman whose life is also at issue.

Within the non-feminist literature, both defenders and opponents of women's right to choose abortion agree that the difference between a late-term fetus and a newborn infant is "merely geographical" and cannot be considered morally significant. But a fetus inhabits a woman's body and is wholly dependent on her unique contribution to its maintenance while a newborn is physically separate though still in need of a lot of care. One can only view the distinction between being in or out of a woman's womb

as morally irrelevant if one discounts the perspective of the pregnant woman; feminists seem to be alone in recognizing her perspective as morally important.[10]

Within anti-abortion arguments, fetuses are identified as individuals; in our culture which views the (abstract) individual as sacred, fetuses qua individuals should be honoured and preserved. Extraordinary claims are made to try to establish the individuality and moral agency of fetuses. At the same time, the women who carry these fetal individuals are viewed as passive hosts whose only significant role is to refrain from aborting or harming their fetuses. Since it is widely believed that the woman does not actually have to do anything to protect the life of the fetus, pregnancy is often considered (abstractly) to be a tolerable burden to protect the life of an individual so like us.[11]

Medicine has played its part in supporting these sorts of attitudes. Fetal medicine is a rapidly expanding specialty, and it is commonplace in professional medical journals to find references to pregnant women as "fetal environments." Fetal surgeons now have at their disposal a repertory of sophisticated technology that can save the lives of dangerously ill fetuses; in light of such heroic successes, it is perhaps understandable that women have disappeared from their view. These specialists see fetuses as their patients, not the women who nurture them. Doctors perceive themselves as the *active* agents in saving fetal lives and, hence, believe that they are the ones in direct relationship with the fetuses they treat.

Perhaps even more distressing than the tendency to ignore the woman's agency altogether and view her as a purely passive participant in the medically controlled events of pregnancy and childbirth is the growing practice of viewing women as genuine threats to the well-being of the fetus. Increasingly, women are viewed as irresponsible or hostile towards their fetuses, and the relationship between them is characterized as adversarial (Overall 1987, p. 60). Concern for the well-being of the fetus is taken as licence for doctors to intervene to ensure that women comply with medical "advice." Courts are called upon to enforce the doctors' orders when moral pressure alone proves inadequate, and women are being coerced into undergoing unwanted Caesarean deliveries and technologically monitored hospital births. Some states have begun to imprison women for endangering their fetuses through drug abuse and other socially unacceptable behaviours. An Australian state recently introduced a bill that makes women liable to criminal prosecution "if they are found to have smoked during pregnancy, eaten unhealthful foods, or taken any other action which can be shown to have adversely affected the development of the fetus" (Warren 1989, p. 60).

In other words, physicians have joined with anti-abortionist activists in fostering a cultural acceptance of the view that fetuses are distinct individuals, who are physically, ontologically, and socially separate from the women whose bodies they inhabit, and who have their own distinct interests. In this picture, pregnant women are either ignored altogether or are viewed as deficient in some crucial respect and hence subject to coercion for the sake of their fetuses. In the former case, the interests of the women concerned are assumed to be identical with those of the fetus; in the latter, the women's interests are irrelevant because they are perceived as immoral, unimportant, or unnatural. Focus on the fetus as an independent entity has led to presumptions which deny pregnant women their roles as active, independent, moral agents with a primary interest in what becomes of the fetuses they carry. Emphasis on the fetus's status has led to an assumed licence to interfere with women's reproductive freedom.

A FEMINIST VIEW OF THE FETUS

Because the public debate has been set up as a competition between the rights of women and those of fetuses, feminists have often felt pushed to reject claims of fetal value in order to protect women's claims. Yet, as Addelson (1987) has argued, viewing abortion in this way "tears [it] out of the context of women's lives" (p. 107). There are other accounts of fetal value in the context of women's lives that are more plausible and less oppressive to women.

On a feminist account, fetal development is examined in the context in which it occurs, within women's bodies rather than in the imagined isolation implicit in many theoretical accounts. Fetuses develop in specific pregnancies which occur in the lives of particular women. They are not individuals housed in generic female wombs, nor are they full persons at risk only because they are small and subject to the whims of women. Their very existence is relational, developing as they do within particular women's bodies, and their principal relationship is to the women who carry them.

On this view, fetuses are morally significant, but their status is relational rather than absolute. Unlike other human beings, fetuses do not have any independent existence; their existence is uniquely tied to the support of a specific other. Most non-feminist commentators have ignored the relational dimension of fetal development and have presumed that the moral status of fetuses could be resolved solely in terms of abstract metaphysical criteria of personhood. They imagine that there is some set of properties (such as genetic heritage, moral agency, self-consciousness, language use, or self-determination) which will entitle all who possess them to be granted the moral status of persons (Warren 1973, Tooley 1972). They seek some particular feature by which we can neatly divide the world into the dichotomy of moral persons (who are to be valued and protected) and others (who are not entitled to the same group privileges); it follows that it is a merely empirical question whether or not fetuses possess the relevant properties.

But this vision misinterprets what is involved in personhood and what it is that is especially valued about persons. Personhood is a social category, not an isolated state. Persons are members of a community; they develop as concrete, discrete, and specific individuals. To be a morally significant category, personhood must involve personality as well as biological integrity.[12] It is not sufficient to consider persons simply as Kantian atoms of rationality; persons are all embodied, conscious beings with particular social histories. Annette Baier (1985) has developed a concept of persons as "second persons" which helps explain the sort of social dimension that seems fundamental to any moral notion of personhood:

> A person, perhaps, is best seen as one who was long enough dependent upon other persons to acquire the essential arts of personhood. Persons essentially are *second* persons, who grow up with other persons.... The fact that a person has a life *history*, and that a people collectively have a history depends upon the humbler fact that each person has a childhood in which a cultural heritage is transmitted, ready for adolescent rejection and adult discriminating selection and contribution. Persons come after and before other persons [p. 84-85; her emphasis].

Persons, in other words, are members of a social community which shapes and values them, and personhood is a relational concept that must be defined in terms of interactions and relationships with others.

A fetus is a unique sort of being in that it cannot form relationships freely with others, nor can others readily form relationships with it. A fetus has a primary and particularly intimate relationship with the woman in whose womb it develops; any other relationship it may have is indirect, and must be mediated through the pregnant woman. The relationship that exists between a woman and her fetus is clearly asymmetrical, since she is the only party to the relationship who is capable of making a decision about whether the interaction should continue and since the fetus is wholly dependent on the woman who sustains it while she is quite capable of surviving without it.

However much some might prefer it to be otherwise, no one else can do anything to support or harm a fetus without doing something to the woman who nurtures it. Because of this inexorable biological reality, she bears a unique responsibility and privilege in determining her fetus's place in the social scheme of things. Clearly, many pregnancies occur to women who place very high value on the lives of the particular fetuses they carry, and choose to see their pregnancies through to term despite the possible risks and costs involved; hence, it would be wrong of anyone to force such a woman to terminate her pregnancy under these circumstances. Other women, or some of these same women at other times, value other things more highly (e.g., their freedom, their health, or previous responsibilities which conflict with those generated by the pregnancies), and choose not to continue their pregnancies. The value that women ascribe to individual fetuses varies dramatically from case to case. There is no absolute value that attaches to fetuses apart from their relational status determined by the context of their particular development.

Since human beings are fundamentally relational beings, it is important to remember that fetuses are characteristically limited in the relationships in which they can participate; within those relationships, they can make only the most restricted "contributions."[13] After birth, human beings are capable of a much wider range of roles in relationships with an infinite variety of partners; it is that very diversity of possibility and experience that leads us to focus on the abstraction of the individual as a constant through all her/his relationships. But until birth, no such variety is possible, and the fetus is defined as an entity within a woman who will almost certainly be principally responsible for it for many years to come.

No human, and especially no fetus, can exist apart from relationships; feminist views of what is valuable about persons must reflect the social nature of their existence. Fetal lives can neither be sustained nor destroyed without affecting the women who support them. Because of a fetus's unique physical status — *within* and dependent on a particular woman — the responsibility and privilege of determining its specific social status and value must rest with the woman carrying it. Fetuses are not persons because they have not developed sufficiently in social relationships to be persons in any morally significant sense (i.e., they are not yet second persons). Newborns, although just beginning their development into persons, are immediately subject to social relationships, for they are capable of communication and response in interaction with a variety of other persons. Thus, feminist accounts of abortion stress the importance of protecting women's right to continue as well as to terminate pregnancies as each sees fit.

FEMINIST POLITICS AND ABORTION

Feminist ethics directs us to look at abortion in the context of other issues of power and not to limit discussion to the standard questions about its moral and legal acceptability. Because coerced pregnancy has repercussions for women's oppressed status generally, it is important to ensure that abortion not only be made legal but that adequate services be made accessible to all women who seek them. This means that within Canada, where medically approved abortion is technically recognized as legal (at least for the moment), we must protest the fact that it is not made available to many of the women who have the greatest need for abortions: vast geographical areas offer no abortion services at all, but unless the women of those regions can afford to travel to urban clinics, they have no meaningful right to abortion. Because women depend on access to abortion in their pursuit of social equality, it is a matter of moral as well as political responsibility that provincial health plans should cover the cost of transport and service in the abortion facilities women choose. Ethical study of abortion involves understanding and critiquing the economic, age, and social barriers that currently restrict access to medically acceptable abortion services.[14]

Moreover, it is also important that abortion services be provided in an atmosphere that fosters women's health and well-being; hence, the care offered should be in a context that is supportive of the choices women make. Abortions should be seen as part of women's overall reproductive health and could be included within centres that deal with all matters of reproductive health in an open, patient-centred manner where effective counselling is offered for a wide range of reproductive decisions.[15] Providers need to recognize that abortion is a legitimate option so that services will be delivered with respect and concern for the physical, psychological, and emotional effects on a patient. All too frequently, hospital-based abortions are provided by practitioners who are uneasy about their role and treat the women involved with hostility and resentment. Increasingly, many anti-abortion activists have personalized their attacks and focussed their attention on harassing the women who enter and leave abortion clinics. Surely requiring a woman to pass a gauntlet of hostile protesters on her way to and from an abortion is not conducive to effective health care. Ethical exploration of abortion raises questions about how women are treated when they seek abortions[16]; achieving legal permission for women to dispose of their fetuses if they are determined enough to manage the struggle should not be accepted as the sole moral consideration.

Nonetheless, feminists must formulate their distinctive response to legislative initiatives on abortion. The tendency of Canadian politicians confronted by vocal activists on both sides of the abortion issue has been to seek "compromises" that seem to give something to each (and, thereby, also deprives each of important features sought in policy formation). Thus, the House of Commons recently passed a law (Bill C-43) that allows a woman to have an abortion only if a doctor certifies that her physical, mental, or emotional health will be otherwise threatened. Many non-feminist supporters of women's right to choose consider this a victory and urge feminists to be satisfied with it, but feminists have good reason to object. Besides their obvious objection to having abortion returned to the Criminal Code, feminists also object that this policy considers doctors and not women the best judges of a woman's need for abortion; feminists have little reason to trust doctors to appreciate the political dimension of abortion or to respond adequately to women's needs. Abortion must be a woman's decision, and not one controlled by her doctor. Further, experience shows that doctors are already reluctant to provide abortions to women;

the opportunity this law presents for criminal persecution of doctors by anti-abortion campaigners is a sufficient worry to inhibit their participation.[17] Feminists want women's decision making to be recognized as legitimate, and cannot be satisfied with a law that makes abortion a medical choice.

Feminists support abortion on demand because they know that women must have control over their reproduction. For the same reason, they actively oppose forced abortion and coerced sterilization, practices that are sometimes inflicted on the most powerless women, especially those in the Third World. Feminist ethics demands that access to voluntary, safe, effective birth control be part of any abortion discussion, so that women have access to other means of avoiding pregnancy.[18]

Feminist analysis addresses the context as well as the practice of abortion decisions. Thus, feminists also object to the conditions which lead women to abort wanted fetuses because there are not adequate financial and social supports available to care for a child. Because feminist accounts value fetuses that are wanted by the women who carry them, they oppose practices which force women to abort because of poverty or intimidation. Yet, the sorts of social changes necessary if we are to free women from having abortions out of economic necessity are vast; they include changes not only in legal and health care policy, but also in housing, child care, employment, etc. (Petchesky 1980, p. 112). Nonetheless, feminist ethics defines reproductive freedom as the condition under which women are able to make truly voluntary choices about their reproductive lives, and these many dimensions are implicit in the ideal.

Clearly, feminists are not "pro-abortion," for they are concerned to ensure the safety of each pregnancy to the greatest degree possible; wanted fetuses should not be harmed or lost. Therefore, adequate pre- and postnatal care and nutrition are also important elements of any feminist position on reproductive freedom. Where anti-abortionists direct their energies to trying to prevent women from obtaining abortions, feminists seek to protect the health of wanted fetuses. They recognize that far more could be done to protect and care for fetuses if the state directed its resources at supporting women who continue their pregnancies, rather than draining away resources in order to police women who find that they must interrupt their pregnancies. Caring for the women who carry fetuses is not only a more legitimate policy than is regulating them; it is probably also more effective at ensuring the health and well-being of more fetuses.

Feminist ethics also explores how abortion policies fit within the politics of sexual domination. Most feminists are sensitive to the fact that many men support women's right to abortion out of the belief that women will be more willing sexual partners if they believe that they can readily terminate an unwanted pregnancy. Some men coerce their partners into obtaining abortions the women may not want.[19] Feminists understand that many women oppose abortion for this very reason, being unwilling to support a practice that increases women's sexual vulnerability (Luker 1984, p. 209-15). Thus, it is important that feminists develop a coherent analysis of reproductive freedom that includes sexual freedom (as women choose to define it). That requires an analysis of sexual freedom that includes women's right to refuse sex; such a right can only be assured if women have equal power to men and are not subject to domination by virtue of their sex.[20]

In sum, then, feminist ethics demands that moral discussions of abortion be more broadly defined than they have been in most philosophic discussions. Only by reflecting on the meaning of ethical pronouncements on actual women's lives and the connections between judgments on abortion and the conditions of domination and subordination can we come to an adequate understanding of the moral status of abortion in our society. As Rosalind Petchesky (1980) argues, feminist discussion of abortion "must be moved beyond the framework of a 'woman's right to choose' and connected to a much broader revolutionary movement that addresses all the conditions of women's liberation."(p. 113).

NOTES

1. For some idea of the ways in which traditional moral theory oppresses women, see Morgan (1987) and Hoagland (1988).

2. Critics continue to want to structure the debate around the *possibility* of women making frivolous abortion decisions and hence want feminists to agree to setting boundaries on acceptable grounds for choosing abortion. Feminists ought to resist this injunction, though. There is no practical way of drawing a line fairly in the abstract; cases that may appear "frivolous" at a distance, often turn out to be substantive when the details are revealed, i.e., frivolity is in the eyes of the beholder. There is no evidence to suggest that women actually make the sorts of choices worried critics hypothesize about: e.g., a woman eight months pregnant who chooses to abort because she wants to take a trip or gets in "a tiff" with her partner. These sorts of fantasies, on which demands to distinguish between legitimate and illegitimate personal reasons for choosing abortion chiefly rest,

reflect an offensive conception of women as irresponsible; they ought not to be perpetuated. Women, seeking moral guidance in their own deliberations about choosing abortion, do not find such hypothetical discussions of much use.

3. In her monumental historical analysis of the early roots of Western patriarchy, Gerda Lerner (1986) determined that patriarchy began in the period from 3100 to 600 B.C. when men appropriated women's sexual and reproductive capacity; the earliest states entrenched patriarchy by institutionalizing the sexual and procreative subordination of women to men.

4. There are some women who claim to be feminists against choice in abortion. See, for instance, Callahan (1987), though few spell out their full feminist program. For reasons I develop in this paper, I do not think this is a consistent position.

5. There is a lot the state could do to ameliorate this condition. If it provided women with adequate financial support, removed the inequities in the labour market, and provided affordable and reliable child care, pregnancy need not so often lead to a woman's dependence on a particular man. The fact that it does not do so is evidence of the state's complicity in maintaining women's subordinate position with respect to men.

6. See Petchesky (1984), especially Chapter 5, "Considering the Alternatives: The Problems of Contraception," where she documents the risks and discomforts associated with pill use and IUDs and the increasing rate at which women are choosing the option of diaphragm or condom with the option of early legal abortions as back-up.

7. See Zillah Eisenstein (1988) for a comprehensive theory of the role of the pregnant body as the central element in the cultural subordination of women.

8. Thomson (1971) is a notable exception to this trend.

9. This seems reminiscent of Aristotle's view of women as "flower pots" where men implant the seed with all the important genetic information and the movement necessary for development and women's job is that of passive gestation, like the flower pot. For exploration of the flower pot picture of pregnancy, see Whitbeck (1973) and Lange (1983).

10. Contrast Warren (1989) with Tooley (1972).

11. The definition of pregnancy as a purely passive activity reaches its ghoulish conclusion in the increasing acceptability of sustaining brain-dead women on life support systems to continue their functions as incubators until the fetus can be safely delivered. For a discussion of this new trend, see Murphy (1989).

12. This apt phrasing is taken from Petchesky (1986), p. 342.

13. Fetuses are almost wholly individuated by the women who bear them. The fetal "contributions" to the relationship are defined by the projections and interpretations of the pregnant woman in the latter stages of pregnancy if she chooses to perceive fetal movements in purposeful ways (e.g.,"it likes classical music, wine, exercise").

14. Some feminists suggest we seek recognition of the legitimacy of non-medical abortion services. This would reduce costs and increase access dramatically,

with no apparent increase in risk, provided that services were offered by trained, responsible practitioners concerned with the well-being of their clients. It would also allow the possibility of increasing women's control over abortion. See, for example McDonnell (1984), chap. 8.

15. For a useful model of such a centre, see Wagner and Lee (1989).

16. See CARAL/Halifax (1990) for women's stories about their experiences with hospitals and free-standing abortion clinics.

17. The Canadian Medical Association has confirmed those fears. In testimony before the House of Commons committee reviewing the bill, the CMA reported that over half the doctors surveyed who now perform abortions expect to stop offering them if the legislation goes through. Since the Commons passed the bill, the threats of withdrawal of service have increased. Many doctors plan to abandon their abortion service once the law is introduced, because they are unwilling to accept the harassment they anticipate from anti-abortion zealots. Even those who believe that they will eventually win any court case that arises, fear the expense and anxiety involved as the case plays itself out.

18. Therefore, the Soviet model, where women have access to multiple abortions but where there is no other birth control available, must also be opposed.

19. See CARAL/Halifax (1990), p. 20-21, for examples of this sort of abuse.

20. It also requires that discussions of reproductive and sexual freedom not be confined to "the language of control and sexuality characteristic of a technology of sex" (Diamond and Quinby 1988, p. 197), for such language is alienating and constrains women's experiences of their own sexuality.

REFERENCES

Addelson, Kathryn Pyne. "Moral Passages." In *Women and Moral Theory*. Edited by Eva - Feder Kittay and Diana T. Meyers. Totowa, NJ: Rowman & Littlefield, 1987.

Baier, Anette. *Postures of the Mind: Essays on Minds and Morals*. Minneapolis: University of Minnesota Press, 1985.

Callahan, Sidney. "A Pro-Life Feminist Makes Her Case." *Utne Reader* (March/April 1987): 104-14.

Daly, Mary. *Beyond God the Father: Toward a Philosophy of Women's Liberation*. Boston: Beacon Press, 1973.

Diamond, Irene, and Lee Quinby. "American Feminism and the Language of Control." In *Feminism & Foucault: Reflections on Resistance*. Edited by Irene Diamond and Lee Quinby. Boston: Northeastern University Press, 1988.

Eisenstein Zillah R. *The Female Body and the Law*. Berkeley: University of California Press, 1988.

Hoagland, Sara Lucia. *Lesbian Ethics: Toward New Values*. Palo Alto, CA: Institute of Lesbian Studies, 1988.

Lange, Lynda. "Woman is Not a Rational Animal: On Aristotle's Biology of Reproduction." In *Discovering Reality: Feminist Perspectives on Epistemology, Metaphysic,*

Methodology, and Philosophy of Science. Edited by Sandra Harding and Merrill B. Hintikka. Dordrecht, Holland: D. Reidel, 1983.

Lerner, Gerda. *The Creation of Paradise*. New York: Oxford University Press, 1986.

Luker, Kristin. *Abortion and the Politics of Motherhood*. Berkeley: University of California Press, 1984.

MacKinnon, Catherine. *Toward a Feminist Theory of the State*. Cambridge, MA: Harvard University Press, 1989.

McDonnell, Kathleen. *Not an Easy Choice: A Feminist Re-examines Abortion*. Toronto: The Women's Press, 1986.

McLaren, Angus, and Arlene Tigar McLaren. *The Bedroom and the State: The Changing Practices and Politics of Contraception and Abortion in Canada, 1880-1980*. Toronto: McClelland and Stewart, 1986.

Morgan, Kathryn Pauly. "Women and Moral Madmen." In *Science, Morality and Feminist Theory*. Edited by Marsha Hanen and Kai Nielsen. *Canadian Journal of Philosophy*, Supplementary Volume 13:201-26.

Murphy, Julien S. "Should Pregnancies Be Sustained in Brain-dead Women?: A Philosophical Discussion of Postmortem Pregnancy." In *Healing Technology: Feminist Perspectives*. Edited by Kathryn Srother Ratcliff et al. Ann Arbor: The University of Michigan Press, 1987.

Overall, Christine. *Ethics and Human Reproduction: A Feminist Analysis*. Winchester, MA: Allen and Unwin, 1987.

Petchesky, Rosalind Pollack. "Reproductive Freedom: Beyond 'Woman's Right to Choose.'" In *Women: Sex and Sexuality*. Edited by Catharine R. Simpson and Ethel Spector Person. Chicago: University of Chicago Press, 1980.

———. *Abortion and Woman's Choice: The State, Sexuality, and Reproductive Freedom*. Boston: Northeastern University Press, 1984.

Sumner, L. W. *Abortion and Moral Theory*. Princeton: Princeton University Press, 1981.

Thomson, Judith Jarvis. "A Defense of Abortion." *Philosophy and Public Affairs* 1 (1971):47-66.

Tooley, Michael. "Abortion and Infanticide." *Philosophy and Public Affairs* 2:1 (Fall 1972): 37-65.

Van Wagner, Vicki, and Bob Lee. "Principles into Practice: An Activist Vision of Feminist Reproductive Health Care." In *The Future of Human Reproduction*. Edited by Christine Overall. Toronto: The Women's Press, 1989.

Warren, Mary Anne. "On the Moral and Legal Status of Abortion." *The Monist* 4: 57(1973): 43-61.

———. "On the Moral Significance of Birth." *Hypatia* 4: 2 (Summer 1989): 46-65.

Whitbeck, Carolyn. "Theories of Sex Difference." *The Philosophical Forum* 5: 1-2 (Fall/Winter 1973-74): 54-80.

Toward a Credible View of Abortion

L. W. Sumner

As little as a decade ago most moral philosophers still believed that the exercise of their craft did not include defending positions on actual moral problems. More recently they have come to their senses, one happy result being a spate of articles in the last few years on the subject of abortion.[1] These discussions have contributed much toward an understanding of the abortion issue, but for the most part they have not attempted a full analysis of the morality of abortion.[2] Such an analysis is too large a task for a single paper, but a sketch of it will be undertaken here, the details to be filled in elsewhere.[3]

The moral problem which abortion poses results from some familiar biological and social contingencies. Because *homo sapiens* is a mammal the young of the species are carried by the female during the period of initial development. The weight of reproduction itself is therefore divided unequally between the sexes. Social practice ordinarily enhances this unequal division of labour by arranging that the woman will rear the children as well as bearing them. Her fertility is therefore no small matter for a woman, affecting as it does her opportunity to plan the course of her own life. Thus in the first instance she seeks to control whether (or when) she will conceive. But once conception has occurred its normal outcome is avoidable only by terminating the pregnancy, that is to say by killing the developing fetus. Such an intentional interruption of the gestation process is an abortion. And so the issues are drawn.

Were one or another of these contingencies otherwise abortion might create no moral problem. But as matters now stand the liberty of the woman may conflict directly with the life of the fetus. Such is the stuff of the abortion issue.

The temporal boundaries of abortion are conception and birth: abortion is necessarily post-conceptive and pre-natal. Therein lies its ambiguous moral status. Contraception functions by preventing pregnancy rather than interrupting it. For this reason it does not destroy life and only a small minority persists in objecting to it (or to some particular contraceptive method) on moral grounds. At the other extreme, infanticide involves killing the newborn child. Only an even smaller minority is able to accept infanticide on moral grounds, except perhaps in some extreme cases. Contraception and infanticide are relatively clear moral cases precisely because they are located on either side of pregnancy. Abortion is a difficult case precisely because it occupies this uncertain middle ground. Pro-abortionists tend to assimilate it to contraception while anti-abortionists tend to assimilate it to infanticide. An analysis of the morality of abortion must properly locate it on this continuum between the clear cases.

To speak of the morality of abortion may obscure the fact that there are at least two distinct moral problems concerning abortion. The first requires developing and defending a moral evaluation of abortion itself. We may assume that it will answer

L.W. Sumner, "Toward a Credible View of Abortion," *Canadian Journal of Philosophy* 4 (September 1974) 163-181.

the question: When is an abortion morally permissible and when is it not? The second problem requires developing and defending a state policy on abortion. We may assume that it will answer the question: When should an abortion be legally permissible and when should it not? These questions are both moral ones, since they both ask for evaluations from the moral point of view, but they are different moral questions, since evaluating abortion is not the same as evaluating abortion policies. Once we have decided on the moral status of abortion, it is a further issue how it should be treated by the law.[4]

To be complete, positions on the morality of abortion must speak to both problems and most have done so. Two such positions are worth outlining as material for discussion. The first, which may be called the liberal position, is a defense of abortion and of a woman's right to have an abortion if she so chooses. It has at its heart the contention that abortion is a matter private to the woman because it does not substantially affect the welfare of any other person. As such, it raises no moral issues whatsoever, although it may, because of its potential hazards, raise prudential ones. As in the case of other medical procedures, we need to ensure only that the operation is carried out safely, efficiently, and with consent. Any further legal regulation of abortion is incompatible with the principle that the state has no right to interfere in the private activities of the individual. Laws which prohibit or restrict abortion constitute an illegitimate tampering with individual liberties. A woman has the right to decide for herself whether to bear children, a right which is already recognized when the state refrains from regulating contraception. The availability of abortion is simply a further guarantee of this right for cases in which an unwanted pregnancy has already occurred. Furthermore, prohibitive or restrictive abortion policies have the

defect of enforcing the moral views of some (anti-abortionists) against the rest. Indeed, in the light of the traditional Catholic position on abortion, such policies establish the moral beliefs of a particular religious sect, thus undermining the separation of church and state. A permissive policy, or no policy at all, leaves each woman free to decide the matter for herself.

What may by contrast be called the conservative position rests upon the view that abortion is not a private matter because it involves the killing of the fetus. It is generally agreed that the taking of human life is in most circumstances wrong. But the fetus is a human life and so abortion is always homicide. As such, it is morally justifiable only in very special circumstances, such as when the continuation of pregnancy would endanger the life of the woman. The welfare or liberty of one person is not in general sufficient to justify the killing of another. It is also usually agreed that protection of human life is one of the legitimate functions of the law. Prohibitive or restrictive laws are therefore not to be seen as the enforcement of private morals or as the establishment of a church but rather as a proper extension of laws forbidding homicide. While it may be true that more permissive laws would produce benefits for women, and perhaps for others as well, these benefits must always be balanced against the toll in human life which abortion necessarily exacts.

These two positions are the ones most commonly heard in discussions of the morality of abortion. Each is internally coherent, each has a venerable tradition behind it, and each is now promoted by vocal and organized pressure groups. The two positions are also diametrically opposed and between them they define the opposite poles in the abortion debate. Nevertheless, it is likely that each position commands the allegiance only of a minority among persons aware of the abortion problem. Many, perhaps most, find themselves somewhere in the middle ground between the two sides. To such persons neither position as it stands seems very credible, because each represents an extreme among available possibilities. The one focuses entirely on the rights of the woman and ignores the fate of the fetus; the other just as resolutely fastens on the welfare of the fetus and subordinates the problem of the woman. The one entirely assimilates abortion to contraception, while the other simply identifies it with infanticide. Each position attaches itself too thoroughly to one of the two ingredients whose conjunction creates the moral issue in the first place. Surely abortion is not just a private matter but is also not always a full-blown case of homicide. Surely there are less crude and less simplistic alternatives available than either of these.

So goes the view from the middle. This paper is an attempt to vindicate this view. It will argue that neither of the standard positions is acceptable because each is too extreme. It will also outline a more credible, because more moderate, alternative. The first step involves a closer look at the two given positions. Out of each can be distilled the basic argument around which the position as a whole is built.

PRIVACY ARGUMENT

P1 Actions which cause no harm are never morally wrong.

P2 The law may not legitimately prohibit actions which cause no harm.

P3 The fetus is not a human individual.

P4 Abortion is never morally wrong.

P5 The law may not legitimately prohibit abortion.

HOMICIDE ARGUMENT

H1 It is always morally wrong to kill a human individual.

H2 The law may legitimately prohibit the killing of human individuals.

H3 The fetus is a human individual.

H4 Abortion is always morally wrong.

H5 The law may legitimately prohibit abortion.

Neither of these arguments is here formulated so as to be logically tight, although the missing steps could be easily supplied, and each argument is presented in a particularly strong and unqualified form. The arguments are therefore more extreme even than the positions from which they were extracted, and it may be that few would defend them in their present form. As stated, however, they will serve as excellent reference points for discussion. Ultimately it will be clearer to what extent, and in what manner, they must be weakened in order to be acceptable.

The arguments plainly have a common structure. Each contains two conclusions which speak to the two moral questions about abortion. Analogous conclusions in the two arguments (P4 and H4, P5 and H5) are mutually incompatible. Each argument derives its conclusions from three premises, of which the first two (P1 and P2, H1 and H2) are moral principles. The third premise in each case (P3 and H3) seems to be a statement of fact about the fetus which serves as the hinge between principles and conclusions. Further, the real differences between the arguments, in virtue of which they yield incompatible conclusions, do not seem to lie in the moral principles to which they appeal. These principles form a mutually compatible set and when put in a somewhat more qualified manner might all have considerable appeal. The point of departure would appear to lie in the third premise. There the homicide argument seems to flatly affirm what the privacy argument just as flatly denies, namely that the fetus is human.

This question about 'the status of the fetus' is obviously in one way or another at the heart of the abortion debate.[5] It cannot be true that abortion is homicide unless the fetus is to be accounted a human person, and it cannot be true that abortion is a private matter unless the fetus is not to be so accounted. Doubts about abortion are above all doubts about how to classify, and therefore treat, the fetus. Sooner or later this question must be confronted. The larger part of this paper will be spent confronting it.

It will be convenient to organize the discussion as a commentary on the privacy and homicide arguments, but particularly on the latter. It is natural to begin by examining the contention that the fetus is human. The structure of the argument suggests that this is the crucial fact about the fetus whose acceptance will pave the way to acceptance of the argument's conservative conclusions. If this is so then one implication follows immediately. It cannot be that the humanity of the fetus is a matter of theological tenet or religious dogma. It is sometimes argued that an individual is human in virtue of possession of a soul, or perhaps a distinctively human soul, and thus that the fetus is human from the moment that it acquires such a soul. The history of controversy about abortion within the Catholic Church consists largely of disagreement over when to locate this moment of 'ensoulment'.[6] Whereas Aquinas seems to have believed that the event occurred sometime during the gestation period, the weight of official opinion now is that it accompanies conception. The role of this opinion within the homicide argument will be obvious. Whatever the merits of contrary positions within this theological debate, its outcome cannot affect our evaluation of the homicide argument or of abortion. The one

characteristic of the event of ensoulment which seems to be universally accepted is that, whenever it occurs, it is not observable or open to any sort of empirical test. There exists no empirical method of confirming that, or when, an individual is ensouled. But if the premise concerning the fetus is to play its role within the homicide argument it must be open to confirmation or disconfirmation. Otherwise the argument as a whole is undecidable and will carry no weight whatever for anyone who rejects the theology on which it rests. Sectarian dogmas based upon faith, revelation, or scriptural authority can have no place in public moral discussion of abortion. They may of course be used to reinforce the consciences of the faithful, but the homicide argument, if it is to carry any weight whatever for the unfaithful, must be able to stand free of theological props.

However, once we have agreed that whether an individual is human is an empirical fact about that individual, we encounter an intractable problem. The argument cannot just stipulate what it will mean by this word 'human' for that again would be to abandon its aim of widespread acceptance. It must show that in some common and ordinary sense of the word the fetus is clearly human. But therein lies the problem: there are too many such common and ordinary senses. Like all predicates the word 'human' is a tool of classification; when we use it we distinguish the category of things human from things not human. But different categories suit different purposes and different contexts, and so the word comes to be used in different senses. For example, in saying that a person is human we may mean that he is particularly warm, or gentle, or loving (as opposed to inhuman, i.e. cold, callous, unfeeling), or we may mean that he is fallible or imperfect (as opposed to superhuman or divine). As a classificatory term 'human' in this respect somewhat resembles the word 'real', which can be opposed to any of 'artificial', 'counterfeit', 'fake', 'forged', 'synthetic', 'imitation', 'illusory', and so on, depending on the sort of object being described and on the context. Like 'real', 'human' admits of a variety of meanings. No doubt there are some common threads running through these meanings, but the fact remains that deciding whether the fetus is human is rather like deciding whether the wax apple is real. It may or may not be, depending on the categories one has in mind.

The nature of the term 'human' makes things at once easy and difficult for the proponent of the homicide argument. It is easy to show that in some ordinary sense the fetus is human, but it is difficult to show either that it is human in all such senses or that one particular sense is privileged. The nature of the problem will be clearer if we restrict our attention, as proponents of the homicide argument tend to do, to senses of 'human' which are biological in nature. It is sometimes claimed that advances in biology (and especially in genetics and embryology) in the past two centuries or so have shown beyond any doubt that the fetus is human from conception.[7] Biologists and other professionals have agreed that the fetus is human, and there's an end to it. We must be wary of arguments of the form "the professionals all agree ..." For one thing the professionals seldom do all agree, and the existence of many prominent pro-abortionist biologists and obstetricians would seem to indicate that they do not all agree in this instance. But even if they did, it is surely not a matter for them to decide. They will of course be expert in a number of facts which are relevant to deciding whether a fetus is human, but these may not be the only relevant facts and anyway scientific professionals have no license to tell us how to construct our categories. It will be apparent presently how deciding that a fetus is human is not making a simple statement of fact about it but rather

drawing a particular conclusion from accepted facts or organizing these facts in a certain manner. Professionals are not notably better qualified than the rest of us to draw such conclusions or to decide how the facts are best organized.

If we explore what biology can tell us that is relevant to classifying individuals as human we find again more possible categories than we want. There are at least three distinct senses of the word 'human', each of which is derived from and therefore consonant with the biological facts. The first and simplest of these may be called the *specific* sense, because it pertains to the distinction of animal species. Certainly one thing we can mean by saying that an individual is human is that it is not a baboon or a tuna or a woodpecker. The category of human individuals which is generated by this sense of the word has the undoubted virtue of being quite sharp at the edges: it includes all and only members of the species *homo sapiens*. We would be uncertain only of hybrids or mutations, and these are rare.

This specific sense of 'human' can be used as the basis of two other, still biological, senses of the term. Each of these further senses generates a narrower category of human individuals, since it includes only a subset of the members of the species. When biologists do animal classification (taxonomy) they tend to describe the characteristics of a given species in terms of a model individual of the species which satisfies two conditions: it is structurally and functionally normal and it is mature. This procedure is a simplifying device which involves describing the model individual first and then allowing for variations displayed by members of the species which are either abnormal (runts and albinos, for example) or immature and not fully developed. Species are compared primarily in terms of the properties of their standard or model members. Thus *homo sapiens* is identified, and differentiated from other primate species, in terms of the height range, weight range, posture, skeletal and muscular structure, brain size, and so on, of the normal and mature individual.[8] What is interesting for our purpose is that normality and maturity can themselves serve as criteria which generate quite different, though overlapping, categories of human individuals.

Consider first normality. If a member of our species is abnormal enough in physiology then he is liable to be described as a freak, or a monster, or a vegetable, or an animal. Even staid medical science continues to use the term 'monster' to describe a specified set of gross abnormalities or anomalies.[9] Since fetal growth proceeds so rapidly from such a small beginning, even minor deviations from normal development early in pregnancy can produce gross malformations in the later fetus. No part of the human physiology is immune. The most extreme fetal malformations affect the central nervous system: total absence or extreme underdevelopment of the brain, nonclosure of the spinal column, and so on. Other major organ systems are however also susceptible to gross malformations. When we refer to such malformed individuals as monsters it certainly seems that we are denying that they are completely or fully human, despite the fact that they may be genetically quite normal and that they are unquestionably members of our species. They fail of being fully human because they are so abnormal, because they fall so far short of the paradigm or model member of the species. It is only at the margin, only in the extreme cases, that we are likely to describe members of the species, on physiological grounds, as monsters or to say that they are less than human. But to the extent that we do so we are employing a sense of the word 'human' other than the specific one. It is appropriate to call it the *normic* sense.

Finally, a member of the species can fail to exhibit the characteristics of the model individual not because it is abnormal but because it is immature. Thus if we follow the adult backward through the developmental process we sooner or later reach a stage when the individual is so undeveloped or immature that we begin to speak of its potential, or what it will become, rather than what it is. Thus the chicken is at the earliest stage an egg, the oak an acorn, the plant a seed. It is proper to say that the egg, acorn, or seed will grow into, develop into, or become the chicken, oak, or plant and also that they are not yet these things. Likewise, in our species, at the earliest stage of development the individual is a single cell (zygote), the result of the union of sperm and ovum. It is common and natural to say that this cell is a potential human individual, or that it will grow into, develop into, or become a human individual but that it is not yet a human individual. Again we tend to use this classification only at the margin; the child or infant is a human individual, but the zygote will become one. And again the operative consideration seems to be the degree to which the individual fails to exhibit the properties of the model member of the species. The zygote is microscopic in size, spherical in shape, and contains no organ systems whatsoever. When we react to this difference in degree by saying that the zygote is not yet a human individual we are once more employing a sense of the term other than the specific sense. Since level of development is now central it seems suitable to call this third sense of the word 'human' the *developmental* sense.

There may well be other ways in which categories of human individuals are constructed out of raw biological data, but these three will suffice for the present discussion. It seems that even the hard facts of biology generate no unique and privileged category of human individuals. In the specific sense all members of the species are human, however abnormal or undeveloped. In the normic sense only those members of the species are human who display, or will come to display, to a sufficient degree the physiological characteristics of the normal individual. In the developmental sense only those members of the species are human who have reached some minimal stage of development. It should be stressed that each of these senses of the word is quite legitimate. Each is grounded in the biological data, though each organizes these data differently. Each picks out one of the strands of meaning in the ordinary word 'human', and each of the resulting categories appears in common speech. Each is internally coherent and each enables us to distinguish tolerably well between what is human and what is not. Finally, each corresponds to analogous distinctions for other animal species.

If we bring these categories to bear on the fetus we derive divergent answers to the question whether the fetus is human. We must remember that 'the fetus' is a developmental stage in the history of the individual. Technically, the fetal stage does not occupy even all of the individual's pre-natal history, since it is preceded by the zygotal stage (first five weeks) and embryonic stage (next four weeks). If we use the term 'fetus' loosely to cover all developmental stages prior to birth, then it is clear that the class of fetuses contains individuals very different in many important ways. A newly fertilized ovum or zygote is a tiny dot barely visible to the naked eye, while the full-term fetus is usually 18-22 inches long and 5-10 pounds in weight, with almost all major bodily systems in working order. Given the sheer quantity of development in the first nine months of life, the fetal category *must* contain very different sorts of individuals. We should of course be wary of attributing to all fetuses characteristics pertaining only to a particular stage of development.

In the specific sense of the word all fetuses conceived of human parents are human, regardless of normality or developmental stage. In the normic sense most fetuses are human, gross abnormalities being rare. In the developmental sense the zygote is clearly not yet human and the full-term fetus is just as clearly human, while the fetus at some stages in between will not be easily classifiable. We will return later, from a slightly different perspective, to both the extreme and the middle cases. For the present we need only note that in the developmental sense of the word some fetuses are human while others are not and that the difference between them lies only in their level of development.

We are now back where we started. The deceptively simple question 'Is the fetus a human individual?' has no unique answer, even when only biological data are admitted. We can perhaps now see why many biologists shy away from this category of humanity. It is not itself a ground-floor biological category, but rather a way of organizing ground-floor data. Unfortunately, there are a number of alternative ways of organizing and presenting these data, none of which is privileged *so long as we consider only the facts themselves*. Even though our question certainly looks like a factual one, there seems no way to answer it satisfactorily by appeal even to a limited range of facts. The substance of premise H3 of the homicide argument is that all fetuses conceived of human parents are human. This contention is true of the specific sense of the term 'human' and only of that sense. Thus the homicide argument requires this sense of the word, but there is so far no way of showing that this sense is privileged or that it should be preferred. The status of the homicide argument is thus far undecidable. The privacy argument, however, fares less well. The substance of its premise P3 is that no fetus, regardless of stage of development, is human. We have located no common biological sense of the word 'human' in which this claim is true. Unless some viable candidate has been overlooked, which is certainly possible, we are entitled to suspect that the privacy argument rests its conclusions on a highly implausible premise.

It is an attractive strategy to consider the homicide argument piecemeal, and to begin with that premise which looks like a straightforwardly empirical one. It can now be seen why the strategy must fail. In the absence of a specific context the question of the humanity of the fetus is undecidable. But the homicide argument itself, through its first two premises, provides just such a context. Once these premises are given (and it should be remembered that each of them appears a familiar and attractive moral principle) then only one step remains to generate the argument's conclusions. In this context to concede that the fetus is human is to concede that it is to be included within the scope of the two moral principles and therefore to concede the conclusions. Conversely, if the conclusions are to be avoided, given the principles, then the humanity of the fetus must be denied. This surely is why debates about whether the fetus is human are so heated: each side knows the moral issue at stake, namely when it is morally permissible for the fetus to be killed. The assumption common to both sides is that if the fetus is human it is wrong to kill it. Against this assumption the question of the humanity of the fetus is no longer a neutral and empirical one, which is how it has so far been treated in this discussion. Now the fate of the fetus turns on the answer to this question alone. Suddenly all of the moral passion which is part of the abortion debate is infused into this supposed question of fact, and a decision on it, one way or the other, becomes itself a moral decision. It ought to be obvious that some basic and hard moral decisions must somewhere be involved in either accepting or rejecting the homicide argument. This fact is concealed when we are first asked to accept some moral principles which appear quite reasonable and then, because of the 'facts' of the matter, shown that we are thereby committed to some strong conclusions about abortion. The facts will simply not bear this weight and the underlying moral disagreement will show itself as a preference for one or another interpretation of the word 'human'. Our assessment of the homicide argument will be much more clearheaded if the moral decisions involved are clearly located and carefully identified.

The homicide argument must be evaluated as a whole and not piecemeal. It is a requirement of logic that in order for the argument to be sound it must not equivocate on this word 'human': the sense of the term which is employed in one part of the argument must be employed throughout. We have seen already that H3 requires the specific sense of the term; this sense must therefore be employed as well in the two moral principles H1 and H2. When interpreted in this manner the principles include in their scope all members of the species, including the fetus. To assent to the principles is to agree that the fetus, regardless of its level of development, is to be treated from the moral point of view in just the same manner as the child or the adult. It is now obvious just how much is being conceded in making even the first two moves in the argument, and how short the distance is from there to its conclusions. If H3 is rendered uncontroversially true by use of the specific sense of 'human' the moral issue simply shifts to the two principles. In no way can this issue be evaded: Does the fetus belong within the scope of H1 and H2? Can we devise moral principles concerning homicide which are plausible for both the fetus and the adult? Should the fetus be accorded the same treatment, and therefore the same protection of life, as the adult? This surely is the moral crux in the abortion debate: not whether the fetus is human but how it is to be treated.

The homicide argument makes the moral claim that the fetus is to be treated in the same way as the adult and it does this by including the fetus within the scope of its principles concerning homicide. These principles state that it is wrong to take human life and that human life should have legal protection. In this somewhat stark form they are probably too strong for most moral tastes; surely killing is sometimes morally justifiable and should be sometimes legally justifiable. Still, if the argument is to yield suitably conservative conclusions about abortion, such as that abortion is justifiable only to save the life of the mother, the principles must be given a strong formulation. Proponents of the homicide argument speak sometimes of human life as possessing a uniquely high or absolute value, where this seems to mean that nothing but the preservation of life can compensate the loss of life. If we incorporate this valuation into the two principles we derive the result that it is wrong to kill except to preserve life and that in all cases save this one killing must be prohibited by law. Even in this somewhat weakened form these principles are not easy to live by. They suffice to condemn killing in almost every instance, since it is only rarely that killing is necessary to preserve life. Virtually all warfare and political terrorism, along with such practices of the state as the death penalty and firing upon criminal suspects would be unjustifiable. We would also need to question such technological advances as the automobile where we trade annually many thousands of lives for an increase in convenience. It is a fairly safe guess that few among us are really willing to carry such principles to their inevitable conclusions. But if not, then we cannot pretend to accept the principles. This burden weighs heavy upon proponents of the homicide argument. It is generally their purpose to show that abortion is permissible only to save the life of the mother

and that in all other circumstances it should be proscribed by law. In order to generate these conclusions they require principles of the sort now under consideration. Once adopted, these principles must be applied to all cases and not just to that of abortion. The view that life can be sacrificed only for life is perhaps an admirable one, but it is a high ideal with radical implications. The acceptance of these implications, all of them, is the test of the anti-abortionist's sincerity.

Let us suppose, as the argument requires, that these are acceptable moral principles concerning human life. They are formulated for, and commonly applied to, post-natal life — infants, children, and adults. The question remains: Is the fetus to be included within their scope? In asking this question we place a severe strain on our moral principles. How far back in the life-history of the individual are we to take them to apply? To birth only? To conception? How different from the child or adult must the individual be before we will place him in a separate moral category? The point of the homicide argument is to extend these principles back to conception. To decide whether this extension is plausible we should look at the extreme case: the zygote, the individual at the point of conception, at the earliest stage in his life-history. If it is plausible to extend the principles to the zygote then it is plausible to extend them to all fetal stages; if it is not then the homicide argument must be rejected.

We must remember that at conception the zygote is a single cell, a tiny and barely visible entity. Consider now the following situation. Some experimental work has been done on a so-called 'morning-after' pill which is sometimes loosely referred to as a contraceptive but is in fact an abortifacient, since it causes the expulsion of the zygote should the woman conceive. What are we to think of a woman who regularly uses such a pill? She does so not knowing whether she will conceive, but knowing that if she does then the pill will cause the death of the zygote. Is she committing homicide? Her behaviour is structurally similar to that of someone who regularly leaves time bombs in randomly selected locations, set to explode at randomly selected times, not knowing whether anyone will be in the proximity when the bomb explodes, but knowing that if someone is then he will die. Is our moral attitude toward the two cases the same? Are we likely to condemn the woman, on moral grounds, as a probable killer? Would we consider her using the morning-after pill to fall into a different category from using an oral contraceptive? Would we insist that the pill be taken off the market, that all testing of it be curtailed? Would we support a law which made the use of the pill punishable with the severity usual to homicide statutes? The homicide argument requires affirmative answers to all of these questions.

There is as yet no morning-after pill in general use. But many women do now use the intrauterine device (IUD) which probably also works to expel the fertilized ovum by preventing its implantation in the wall of the uterus.[10] If so, it too is an abortifacient and all of the foregoing questions can be raised concerning it. Again the homicide argument requires that we regard women on the IUD as presumptively guilty of multiple homicide. Are we really ready to do so? Should we pass a law forbidding use of the IUD and begin arresting women who are using it? Is every such woman a public menace comparable to the setter of time bombs? If the homicide argument is correct then human life on a grand scale is at stake and innocent victims are dying every hour. But can we really accept this view of the matter?

Some laboratory experiments have united sperm and ovum in an artificial extrauterine environment. The resulting zygote does not long survive because of the absence of the sustaining uterine wall. Are experimenters who permit such conceptions murderers? Are their experiments comparable, morally speaking, to those Nazi medical experiments which cost the lives of their victims? Or consider the matter this way. Suppose that one experiment involves killing the sperm and ovum just before union while a second kills the resulting zygote immediately after union. Should we regard the two as radically different in their moral implications because conception occurred in the second but not in the first? The homicide argument requires that we do so. Finally, a large number of pregnancies end in spontaneous abortions. If the homicide argument is correct every such case costs a human life. Should we not take care that the abortion, while certainly accidental and unintended, was not in any way the result of negligence on the part of the woman? After all, we do take just such care to ensure that accidental death resulting from a highway accident was not the result of negligence on the part of the driver. A genuine desire to protect human life in the womb, however early its development, would surely require such steps. But are we really prepared to accept them?

The argument so far is simply an attempt to identify commonly shared moral intuitions. The homicide argument has certain unavoidable implications for the case of the zygote. If these implications are unacceptable then the argument must be rejected. I believe that most persons who reflect carefully on the situations described will be unable to accept these implications. I know that I cannot. Most persons, I suspect, regard the developmental stage of the individual as relevant to the morality of killing that individual. Killing the zygote does not strike us as homicide because developmentally the zygote is too primitive, too unlike the adult, child, or even the fetus in its later stages. It is precisely level of development which the homicide argument rules out as relevant. It tries to draw a firm and inflexible line at conception. Before that point no questions about homicide occur, while immediately after it the individual is to be regarded morally as the equal of a child or adult. Few will accept this hard and fast division of cases. The zygote for most will not seem to fall in a different moral category from the sperm or ovum, despite the fact that the zygote is, and the sperm and ovum are not, a genetically complete member of the species. Abortion at the earliest stage, through the agency of the morning-after pill or IUD, will be regarded by most as morally identical to contraception. At this extreme abortion is indeed assimilable to contraception for the purposes of morality.

Consider now the opposite extreme case, the full-term fetus. At term the fetus differs from the newborn (neonate) principally in its occupation of a quite different environment. Because this environment is both confined and fluid, the fetus is unable to breathe or to ingest food. Both oxygen and nourishment are received from the maternal blood supply through the medium of the placenta. All other organ systems which will be functioning just after birth are functioning just before it. The birth process transfers the individual to a new environment and severs the direct physical link between mother and child: the neonate must breathe and eat. In no other important respect does birth alter the individual. The process occupies only a few minutes and the individual is the same size, weight, and shape directly after it as before. Most of his bodily systems are unaffected by the process. In the light of these facts it seems difficult to accept the view that birth is of crucial importance from the point of view of the morality of killing. Assuming that it is wrong to kill the infant directly after birth, it would seem equally wrong, and for the same reasons, to kill it directly before birth. The differences between full-term fetus and neonate do not seem morally relevant, especially when we consider that the temporal point at which birth occurs varies widely and therefore that many full-term fetuses are older and more developed than many newborn infants. It would seem natural then to extend our moral principles concerning killing beyond the neonate to embrace the full-term fetus. At this extreme abortion is morally assimilable to infanticide. If this view of the matter is taken then the privacy argument as well cannot be accepted, since it implies that abortion at no stage of pregnancy, however late, is to be considered as an instance of homicide.

If I am right, then upon reflection most persons would be willing to include the full-term fetus, but not the zygote, within the scope of moral principles concerning homicide. They will therefore reject both the homicide argument and the privacy argument. Since attention has here been focused especially on the homicide argument, its fate should be described in detail. Its three premises must all employ the same sense of the word 'human'. The appeal to moral intuition implies that if the specific sense is chosen, so as to render H3 true, then H1 and H2 are both false. Conversely, if the developmental sense is chosen so as to render H1 and H2 true, H3 is false. There is no possible formulation of the homicide argument which preserves the truth of all three premises. In order to be acceptable, the homicide argument must be amended. There are two alternatives open:

AMENDED HOMICIDE ARGUMENT (1)

H1 It is always morally wrong to kill a human individual.

H2 The law may legitimately prohibit the killing of human individuals.

H3* Some fetuses are human individuals and some are not.

H4* Some instances of abortion are morally wrong and some are not.

H5* The law may sometimes legitimately prohibit abortion and sometimes not.

AMENDED HOMICIDE ARGUMENT (2)

H1* It is sometimes morally wrong to kill a human individual and sometimes not.

H2* The law may sometimes legitimately prohibit the killing of human individuals and sometimes not.

H3 The fetus is a human individual.

H4* Some instances of abortion are morally wrong and some are not.

H5* The law may sometimes legitimately prohibit abortion and sometimes not.

Formulation (1) employs the developmental sense of 'human' and therefore preserves H1 and H2 from the homicide argument, but not H3. Formulation (2) employs the specific sense of 'human' and so preserves H3 from the homicide argument, but not H1 and H2. It is now clear that the question of whether the fetus is human is not in itself crucial to the argument, since the same conclusions are derivable in either case. The considerations which would lead us to classify the fetus at different stages as human or not, in the developmental sense, are of course relevant since the developmental level of the fetus plays a large part in our moral decisions concerning abortion. But the ultimate questions at stake are moral ones.

The liberal and conservative positions, and the arguments on which they rest, are unacceptable because they entail conclusions which are too extreme. The case against these positions has been made entirely by appeal to commonly shared moral intuitions. It would be strengthened if these intuitions could be shown to cohere well with our considered views on moral issues other than, but related to, abortion.

It does not seem wrong to kill a zygote, even if the reason for doing so is simply that the woman does not wish to be pregnant, while it does seem wrong to kill a full-term fetus for this reason. The difference between the two cases seems to lie principally in the level of development of the fetus. This suggests a developmental approach to abortion in which the justifying conditions for an abortion will contract as the fetus develops. On this conception the fetus comes gradually to be treated as a moral person in the full sense.[11]

The question is why fetal development should be considered morally relevant in this way. As the fetus grows it changes in two main respects: globally (increase in size, alteration of shape) and systematically (acquisition of major body systems). Of these the latter seems the more important from the moral point of view. We should probably treat as moral persons individuals who were systematically identical to us, especially in the functioning of their central nervous systems, but who differed, even radically, in size, shape, or both. Even among organ systems many seem only marginally relevant. There is nothing distinctive about much of our bodies: other animals are swifter, stronger, better shielded, and keener of sense than we. In one respect alone are we pre-eminent, our brains having evolved to a point where we have the capacity for thought and the expression of thought (language). Emphasis on the development of the central nervous system is the physiological correlate of the ancient view that man is distinguished from other creatures by his rationality.

It seems plausible to suppose that we are willing to treat a fetus as a moral person only when it has come to possess a central nervous system developed at least to some minimal extent. Once this developmental view of abortion is taken it can be connected to views on cognate moral issues. A zygote and an embryo are distinguished by their relative lack of a central nervous system. A similar lack is rare, though possible, among other members of the species. An anencephalic is an individual in which the higher levels of the brain remain underdeveloped or totally absent. Such individuals rarely survive until birth and never long thereafter. In such cases abortion, or for that matter infanticide, does not seem morally objectionable. The condition is also approximated in those victims of disease or accident who have permanently lost the functioning of the higher levels of the brain but continue to live. In such cases euthanasia does not seem morally objectionable. An early abortion is therefore similar, from the moral point of view, to some cases of eugenic abortion (early or late) and to some cases of euthanasia, in that the individual who is killed lacks at the time a central nervous system functioning in more than a rudimentary manner. The cases are of course distinguished by the fact that the early fetus has not yet developed such a system while the anencephalic will never develop one and the accident victim has lost the functioning of a developed system. Thus in the former case but in neither of the latter one is preventing the evolution of an individual who otherwise would come to possess not only a highly developed central nervous system but also all of the characteristics typical of adult members of the species. But there seems nothing wrong with preventing the development of a human person (thus the moral innocuousness of contraception) while there seems much wrong with terminating the life of one which has already developed to a considerable degree. This single difference in the case of early abortion does not appear therefore to be morally relevant.

Somewhat further afield we encounter the treatment of other species. This issue is too complex to be discussed thoroughly but some broad features should be noted. Our attitudes toward other species are complicated by our need for a reliable food supply, by our love of killing for its own sake, and by our habit of keeping certain species of animals as pets. In general the protection of life we offer to other species is largely determined by our own needs: thus we may hunt mountain lions to extinction while supporting a burgeoning population of household cats and we may eliminate wolves while protecting poodles. But we do make a pervasive distinction between the value of human life and the value of the life of all other animal species, once again on the basis of what is considered distinctive in us. Thus through all the complicating factors we display a marked preference for the more intelligent and highly evolved species. The differences are, as always, most apparent at the extremes. We destroy insects when they are merely inconvenient for us while feeling a much closer kinship to those species of great apes who are our nearest living relatives. Here too we construct our moral categories in part around this most crucial of all human characteristics.

To mould these still scattered attitudes and practices into a single coherent system would require a thoroughgoing analysis of life and death and above all an account of when and why killing is wrong. This undertaking is too ambitious for the present but until it has been completed no view of abortion can be taken as firmly established. Once such an analysis is available, however, it is very likely that only a developmental view of abortion will be compatible with it.

It has thus far been left unspecified how abortion should be regarded between the extreme cases of the zygote and the full-term fetus. I will simply state my view of the matter with little supporting argument.[12] The major factors relevant to evaluating abortion are the situation and needs of the mother and the level of development of the fetus. The gradual and continuous nature of the latter renders the drawing of sharp lines out of the question. The attempt to draw such a line (whether at conception or birth) is precisely the mistake common to the liberal and conservative positions. Any such line must make an arbitrary distinction between adjacent and similar cases. The developmental view must allow for the gradual acquisition by the fetus of the status of a moral person and the accompanying right to protection of life. It is customary to divide pregnancy (calculated at 40 weeks) into trimesters of approximately 13 weeks. Even by the end of the first trimester the fetus is well advanced in the development of its central nervous system, as well as other bodily systems. It has entered a transitional or threshold stage between its early undeveloped state and its later developed state. Likewise, the end of that trimester is the latest point at which the safest abortion procedures (dilatation and curettage, vacuum aspiration) can be employed, and by that time every woman has had an adequate opportunity to decide whether she wishes to continue her pregnancy. For all these reasons, during the early weeks of pregnancy an abortion is morally permissible whatever the woman's reason for wishing it, while during the final four or five months it is permissible only in very special circumstances analogous to those which justify killing in the case of post-natal persons. Between these relatively clear cases lies the borderline threshold period occupying a few weeks around the end of the first trimester. During this stage the morality of abortion is simply unclear.

This is so far only a sketch of a position, but when it is fully elaborated and properly defended we have a developmental view of abortion which is far more plausible than either the liberal or conservative position. While it lacks the elegant simplicity of the extreme views it makes up this lack by taking into account factors which they simply ignore. The morality of abortion is a difficult question in part because the fetus itself is so different at various stages of pregnancy. Only the developmental view allows us to attend to these differences in adopting a moral stance on abortion. It is for this reason that it both matches more closely our intuitions about abortion and coheres better with our views on related moral issues than does either of the more prominent positions.

The abortion policy appropriate to this view would permit abortion at the request of the woman before some fixed time limit, and would carefully screen abortions after that limit. Since the law must operate a workable policy, it cannot tolerate borderline cases and therefore must establish a clear and definite time limit. It is reasonable to set this limit around the end of the third month of pregnancy. Such a limit lies within the threshold period, coincides with the latest stage at which the safest abortion methods can be used, allows every woman sufficient time to discover that she is pregnant and decide whether to terminate the pregnancy, and captures the majority of abortions actually performed even where there is no time limit. After the third month the law will consider abortion as homicide and will specify the grounds on which it will be permitted. We may assume that these grounds will be narrow and strictly medical in nature and that some screening apparatus will be established. Again the details of the policy and of its justification cannot be considered here.

NOTES

1. R. B. Brandt, "The Morality of Abortion," *The Monist,* LVI, No. 4 (October 1972); B. A. Brody, "Abortion and the Law," *Journal of Philosophy,* LXVIII, No. 12 (June

17, 1971), and "Thomson on Abortion," *Philosophy and Public Affairs,* I, No. 3 (Spring 1972); R. J. Gerber, "Abortion: Parameters for Decision," *Ethics,* LXXXII, No. 2 (January 1972); Judith Jarvis Thomson, "A Defense of Abortion," *Philosophy and Public Affairs,* I, No. 1 (Fall 1971); Michael Tooley, "Abortion and Infanticide," *Philosophy and Public Affairs,* II, No. 1 (Fall 1972); Mary Anne Warren, "On the Moral and Legal Status of Abortion," *The Monist,* LVII, No. 1 (January 1973); Roger Wertheimer, "Understanding the Abortion Argument," *Philosophy and Public Affairs,* I, No. 1 (Fall 1971); B. A. Brody, "Abortion and the Sanctity of Human Life," *American Philosophical Quarterly,* X, No. 2, (April 1973).

2. The exceptions are the articles by Tooley and Warren (see note 1), each of which attempts to justify what I have classified as a liberal position on abortion. The present paper was completed before I encountered these articles and thus I have not commented on their arguments. Two of my purposes, however, are to discard this liberal view and to argue for an alternative to it.

3. A more thorough treatment of the matters discussed in this paper, and others pertinent to the abortion issue, is included in a book now in progress.

4. An answer to the first question is, however, an important step toward answering the second. The close connection between a particular view of the morality of abortion and a particular sort of abortion law is stressed by Brody, *op. cit.*

5. The unavoidability of this issue is the main point of the discussion by Brody.

6. For an account of this history see John T. Noonan, Jr., "An Almost Absolute Value in History," in *The Morality of Abortion: Legal and Historical Perspectives,* ed. John T. Noonan, Jr. (Cambridge: Harvard University Press, 1970).

7. Catholic law professor Sergio Cotta, speaking for the Vatican against the 1973 U.S. Supreme Court decision on abortion: "By investigating the basic genetic structure of life, science has determined with unquestionable certainty that since the moment of conception the embryo is a living human being, entirely distinct from the parents." Reported in the *Toronto Star,* January 24, 1973.

8. For a typical taxonomical profile of our species see E. L. Cockrum, *et al., Biology* (Philadelphia: W. B. Saunders Company, 1966).

9. For a standard classification and description of fetal abnormalities see Edith L. Potter, *Pathology of the Fetus and Infant* 2nd ed. (Chicago: Year Book Medical Publishers, 1961).

10. See the discussion of the intrauterine device in Germain Grisez, *Abortion: The Myths, the Realities, and the Arguments* (New York and Cleveland: Corpus Books, 1970), 106-109.

11. For the purpose of this discussion an individual is being treated as a full moral person when the conditions generally accepted as justifying the killing of that individual are those and only those which are generally accepted as justifying killing members of the species in general. In the language of the earlier discussion, he must be included within the scope of general moral principles concerning homicide.

12. A full defense of this view is made in the book referred to in footnote 3.

FURTHER READINGS

Borowski v. Canada (Attorney General) [1989] 1 S.C.R. 342, affirming on other grounds (1987) 33 C.C.C. (3d) 402.

Engelhardt, Jr., Tristam. *The Foundations of Bioethics.* Oxford: Oxford University Press, 1986, 301-317.

Feinberg, Joel, ed. *The Problem of Abortion.* Belmont, Calif.: Wadsworth, 1973.

Foot, Philippa. "The Problem of Abortion and the Principle of Double Effect." *Oxford Review* 5.

Kluge, E.-H.W. *The Ethics of Deliberate Death.* Port Washington, N.Y.: Kennikat Press, 1981.

———. "St. Thomas, Abortion and Euthanasia." *Philosophical Research Archives*, 1981/82.

Makdur, I. "Sterilization and Abortion from the Point of View of Islam." In *Islam and Family Planning*, vol. 2 (271).

Murphy v. Dodd et al., 70 O.R. (2d) 681.

Ney, P.G. and A.R. Wickett. "Mental Health and Abortion: Review and Analysis." *Psychiatric Journal of the University of Ottawa* 14: 4 (Nov., 1989).

Overall, Christine. *Ethics and Human Reproduction: A Feminist Analysis.* Bristol: Allen and Unwin, 1987.

———. "Selective Termination of Pregnancy and Women's Reproductive Autonomy." *Hastings Center Report* 20:3 (1990) 6-11.

Sacred Congregation for the Doctrine of the Faith. *Declaration on Procured Abortion.* Rome: Vatican, 1985.

Shaw, M. and A. Doudera, eds. *Defining Human Life: Medical, Legal and Ethical Implications.* Ann Arbor: AUPHA Press, 1983.

Tooley, Michael. *Analysis of Abortion and Infanticide.* Oxford: Clarendon Press, 1983.

Tremblay v. Daigle, 62 D.L.R. (4th) 634.

CHAPTER 14
ASSISTED SUICIDE, EUTHANASIA AND CESSATION OF TREATMENT

INTRODUCTION

Historically, people used to die by accident, through a disease, or simply as a result of gradual physical deterioration and old age. Most of the time, the way the death occurred had nothing formalized about it. It just happened — expectedly or otherwise — and there was not much anyone could do. Most of the time, too (accidents excepted), it occurred at home.

Modern scientific medicine and modern health care have changed all that. Death and dying have moved into the institutionalized setting of the hospital or health care facility. Consequently, death and dying have become increasingly medicalized not only in terms of the criteria that are used to determine death, but also in the sense that dying itself has become imbued with the nimbus of medical practice, and the ethos of the medical profession has tended to determine the shape a particular dying will take.

This has raised several problems. One is that the traditional ethos of the health care professions in general, and of the medical profession in particular, is to save and/or sustain life. That makes it psychologically very difficult for these professionals to allow death to occur. Health care professionals tend to see death as a failure.

However, not everyone sees death as a failure. Sometimes death is seen as a release. Sometimes, when death seems inevitable anyway and continued living means only a meaningless prolongation of indignity and suffering, patients may want to hasten that dying — or at least not oppose or delay it. Patients who see it that way therefore do not approach death as something that the health care professionals should try to prevent at all cost. With this, there arises the issue of deliberate death.

According to the latest available public opinion poll, the majority of Canadians feel that deliberately bringing about death is quite acceptable. A July 24, 1989, Gallup poll indicated that the proportion of Canadians who believe that a physician should be allowed to end an incurably ill patient's life has gone up from 66% in 1984, to 77%, and it has remained steady at that level ever since.[1] This appears to put the ethos of the health care professions squarely into conflict with the preferences of Canadian society.

To provide a patient only with comfort measures and allow death to occur is usually called passive euthanasia; to bring about the death of a patient deliberately by active means is referred to as active euthanasia. The health care professions have usually maintained that the two are different. For instance, while the Hippocratic Oath requires physicians to refrain from deliberately bringing about death, it does not prohibit physicians from letting nature take its course if death is inevitable and the prolongation of life would only be a prolongation of suffering.[2]

On the other hand, Canadian statute law has taken a firmer stance. It maintains that taking active steps to bring about the death of a patient is murder[3]; and goes on to say that once medical treatment has been started, the professional is under a duty to continue it if failure to do so is likely to imperil the life or health of the patient.[4]

On this issue, therefore, the strength of Canadian public opinion is fundamentally at odds with the position of the health care professions and the law. This raises several important questions: Are the tradition and the law really in touch with current ethical perceptions, or do they merely reflect a privately held morality? Are active and passive euthanasia really different, as the medical profession claims? Is the law correct in condemning both? Is public opinion correct in accepting both? And if public opinion should be respected, how should this respect be translated into medical practice and law?

Some of these issues are addressed by James Rachels in his classic article on active and passive euthanasia. Rachels argues that ultimately, the distinction may be of psychological benefit but that logically and ethically it carries very little weight.

There are several recent Canadian cases of note that deal with euthanasia and assisted suicide. The *Latimer* case deals with a father who killed his daughter Tracy by carbon monoxide poisoning. Tracy's body was tragically disfigured, incurably disabled by cerebral palsy and apparently in constant pain. According to court testimony, Tracy had been born "clinically dead" and needed to be resuscitated. As a result, she suffered serious brain damage due to lack of oxygen. Shortly after her birth she developed muscle spasms — seizures — and for a while had a seizure every minute. Drug treatment reduced the frequency of her seizures, initially to one every twenty minutes and later to five or six each day. It was expected that this would continue the rest of her life. Some seizures were light, others severe to the point where her whole body shook. She had no use of her arms or legs and could never sit up on her own. She could sit up in a wheel chair. During the last five years of her life she could not roll over even as a normal baby of two or three months old can. The muscles of her body simply could not be controlled by her brain. They tightened when they should not. As a result, her body became "twisted up." To relieve the tension of certain muscles and the pain the tension produced, Tracy underwent a number of serious operations to have muscles cut: the muscles at the top of her legs (so her hips would not dislocate), her toes, her heel chords, knee muscles and so on. During one surgery, stainless steel rods were put on either side of her spine to straighten her body sufficiently to relieve the cramping of her stomach and her lungs. Tracy had great difficulty swallowing her food and it took a long time — and considerable skill — to feed her. Often she could not keep her food down and would vomit. The family kept a bucket for this purpose near her whenever they fed her. It was necessary to keep Tracy in diapers at all times since she had no control over her excretory functions. She could not focus her eyes and was always cross-eyed. Her mother assessed her physical development and her mental development as that of a two- or three-month-old baby. Although she recognized her mother, father and her siblings, she could not understand her own name. She did not know the difference between yes and no. Her only forms of communication were laughing, smiling and crying.

At trial, Mr. Latimer claimed that he had killed Tracy to end her suffering. Nevertheless, he was found guilty of murder. This judgment was upheld on appeal. However, the Supreme Court ordered a new trial when it was found that prospective jurors in the first trial had been asked whether they would be likely to convict Mr. Latimer — apparently with the aim of selecting only those jurors that would bring in a "guilty" verdict.[5] A new trial was held, and Mr. Latimer was again found guilty. However, the presiding judge accepted the defence's plea for a constitutional exemption from the mandatory twenty-five-year sentence for such a crime. The matter is currently under appeal to the Supreme Court.

The case of Tracy Latimer is one of non-voluntary euthanasia. The case of *Rodriguez v. British Columbia (Attorney General)* is fundamentally different. It involves a woman who suffered from amyotrophic lateral sclerosis (Lou Gehrig's disease) and who wished to have assistance in dying if and when, in her estimation, she could live no longer. Section 241(b) of the Criminal Code prohibits anyone from assisting someone in committing suicide. Ms. Rodriguez decided to challenge the constitutionality of this provision. She argued that since suicide is not illegal in Canada, all persons have a freedom-right to take their own lives. However — so she argued — persons with severe disabilities like herself cannot take their own lives. Consequently, so she maintained, section 241(b) of the Code discriminates against persons who suffer from a physical disability and thereby violates the principle of equality and justice which is enshrined in Section 15 of The Charter of Rights and Freedoms. The Supreme Court unanimously agreed that this was indeed the case. However, it found on a bare majority (5 to 4) that this sort of discrimination was justified because it was demonstrably necessary in a free and democratic society. *Latimer* differs from *Rodriguez* because it deals with a proxy or substitute decision-maker for an incompetent person and who, in that capacity, makes the decision that this person is better off dead (and acts on that decision). Therefore, among other things, it raises the difficult question whether the range of choices that are open to people who make decisions for others should be more limited than those that are open to everyone else.

Richard Doerflinger argues that allowing assisted suicide — or, for that matter, any form of deliberate and actively imposed death — even in special cases, constitutes the beginning of a slippery slope whose horrible consequences we have seen in Nazi Germany. The paper by Wibren van der Burg examines this notion of a slippery slope more closely. He finds that the concept of a slippery slope may not be as clear as it might seem at first glance, and that arguments based on the notion may not be quite as cogent as their proponents think.

NOTES

1. L. Bozinoff and P. MacIntosh, *Gallup*, Gallup Canada Inc., July 24, 1989. The regional distribution is as follows: 81% in Quebec, 77% in Ontario and B.C., 72% in Atlantic Canada, and 71% in the Prairie provinces. The results are considered accurate within four percentage points, nineteen times out of twenty. A more recent Gallup poll (fall of 1991) shows only a 2% variation in these figures.

2. Similar prohibitions were traditional for other health care professionals.

3. See the various provisions in the Revised Statutes of Canada 1985, c.C-46; especially Part VIII, "Offenses Against the Person."

4. See above, s. 216, 217, 219, 220 *et pass*.

5. *R. v. Latimer* [1997] 1 S.C.R. 217.

Rodriguez v. British Columbia (Attorney General)

Lamer C.J. (dissenting):
Ms. Rodriguez suffers from amyotrophic lateral sclerosis (ALS), which is widely known as Lou Gehrig's disease; her life expectancy is between 2 and 14 months but her condition is rapidly deteriorating. Very soon she will lose the ability to swallow, speak, walk and move her body without assistance. Thereafter she will lose the capacity to breathe without a respirator, to eat without a gastrotomy and will eventually become confined to a bed. ... She does

Rodriguez v. British Columbia (Attorney General) [1993] 3 S.C.R. 519.

not wish to die so long as she still has the capacity to enjoy life. However, by the time she no longer is able to enjoy life, she will be physically unable to terminate her life without assistance. Ms. Rodriguez seeks an order which will allow a qualified medical practitioner to set up technological means by which she might, by her own hand, at the time of her choosing, end her life.

...

The relevant provision of the Criminal Code is as follows:

241. Every one who

(a) counsels a person to commit suicide, or

(b) aids or abets a person to commit suicide, whether suicide ensues or not, is guilty of an indictable offence and liable to imprisonment for a term not exceeding fourteen years.

The relevant sections of the Charter are as follows:

1. The Canadian Charter of Rights and Freedoms guarantees the rights and freedoms set out in it subject only to such reasonable limits prescribed by law as can be demonstrably justified in a free and democratic society.

7. Everyone has the right to life, liberty and security of the person and the right not to be deprived thereof except in accordance with the principles of fundamental justice.

12. Everyone has the right not to be subjected to any cruel and unusual treatment or punishment.

15. (1) Every individual is equal before and under the law and has the right to the equal protection and equal benefit of the law without discrimination and, in particular, without discrimination based on race, national or ethnic origin, colour, religion, sex, age or mental or physical disability.

... In medical matters, the common law recognizes to a very large degree the right of each individual to make decisions regarding his or her own person, despite the sometimes serious consequences of such choices. ...That does not mean that these values are absolute. However, in my opinion s. 15(1) requires that limitations on these fundamental values should be distributed with a measure of equality.

In this connection, and without expressing any opinion on the moral value of suicide, I am forced to conclude that the fact that persons unable to end their own lives cannot choose suicide because they do not legally have access to assistance is — in legal terms — a disadvantage giving rise to the application of s. 15(1) of the Charter. ... I conclude that s. 241(*b*) of the Criminal Code infringes the right to equality guaranteed in s. 15(1) of the Charter. This provision has a discriminatory effect on persons who are or will become incapable of committing suicide themselves, even assuming that all the usual means are available to them, because due to an irrelevant personal characteristic such persons are subject to limitations on their ability to take fundamental decisions regarding their lives and persons that are not imposed on other members of Canadian society.

... An individual's right to control his or her own body does not cease to obtain merely because that individual has become dependent on others for the physical maintenance of that body; indeed, in such circumstances, this type of autonomy is often most critical to an individual's feeling of self-worth and dignity. ... I ... wish to stress, however, that the scope of self-determination with respect to bodily integrity in our society is never absolute. While there may be no limitations on the treatments to which a patient may refuse or discontinue, there are always limits on the treatment which a patient may demand, and to which the patient will be legally permitted to consent. ... Most important of these limits is s. 14 of the Criminal Code, which stipulates that an individual may not validly consent to have death inflicted on him or her. ...

With these limitations in mind, I conclude that the objective of s. 241(*b*) of the Code may properly be characterized as the protection of vulnerable people, whether they are consenting or not, from the intervention of others in decisions respecting the planning and commission of the act of suicide. Underlying this legislative purpose is the principle of preservation of life. ... However, I hasten to add that the repeal of the offence of attempted suicide demonstrates that Parliament will no longer preserve human life at the cost of depriving physically able individuals of their right to self-determination. ...

... There is no way, under the present legislation, to distinguish between those people whose freely chosen will it is to terminate their life, and those people who are potentially being pressured or coerced by others. Vulnerability, in a sense, is simply imposed on all people who happen to be physically unable to commit suicide independently and the right to choose suicide is therefore removed from this entire class of persons. ... The vulnerable are effectively protected under s. 241(*b*), but so ... are those who are not vulnerable, who do not wish the state's protection, but who are brought within the operation of s. 241(*b*) solely as a result of a physical disability. ...

... The principal fear is that the decriminalization of assisted suicide will increase the risk of persons with physical disabilities being manipulated by others. This "slippery slope" argument appeared to be the central justification behind the Law Reform Commission of Canada's recommendation not to repeal this provision.

... While I share a deep concern over the subtle and overt pressures that may be brought to bear on such persons if assisted suicide is decriminalized, even in limited circumstances, I do not think legislation

that deprives a disadvantaged group of the right to equality can be justified solely on such speculative grounds, no matter how well intentioned. Similar dangers to the ones outlined above have surrounded the decriminalization of attempted suicide as well. It is impossible to know the degree of pressure or intimidation a physically able person may have been under when deciding to commit suicide. The truth is that we simply do not and cannot know the range of implications that allowing some form of assisted suicide will have for persons with physical disabilities. What we do know and cannot ignore is the anguish of those in the position of Ms. Rodriguez. Respecting the consent of those in her position may necessarily imply running the risk that the consent will have been obtained improperly. The proper role of the legal system in these circumstances is to provide safeguards to ensure that the consent in question is as independent and informed as is reasonably possible.

... I agree with the importance of distinguishing between the situation where a person who is aided in his or her decision to commit suicide and the situation where the decision itself is a product of someone else's influence. However, I fail to see how preventing against abuse in one context must result in denying self-determination in another. I remain unpersuaded by the government's apparent contention that it is not possible to design legislation that is somewhere in between complete decriminalization and absolute prohibition.

In my view, there is a range of options from which Parliament may choose in seeking to safeguard the interests of the vulnerable and still ensure the equal right to self-determination of persons with physical disabilities. ... Regardless of the safeguards Parliament may wish to adopt, however, I find that an absolute prohibition that is indifferent to the individual or the circumstances in question cannot satisfy the constitutional duty on the government to impair the rights of persons with physical disabilities as little as reasonably possible. ... I find the infringement of s. 15 by this provision cannot be saved under s. 1....

I have held that s. 241(*b*) violates the equality rights of *all* persons who desire to commit suicide but are or will become physically unable to do so unassisted. Restricting the remedy to those who are terminally ill, and suffering from incurable diseases or conditions,... does not follow from the principles underlying my holding, and might well itself give rise to a violation of the equality rights of those who do not fit that description but wish to commit suicide and need assistance. ...To summarize, then, I would make a constitutional exemption available to Ms. Rodriguez, and others, on the following conditions:

1. the constitutional exemption may only be sought by way of application to a superior court;

2. the applicant must be certified by a treating physician and independent psychiatrist,... to be competent to make the decision to end her own life, and the physicians must certify that the applicant's decision has been made freely and voluntarily, and at least one of the physicians must be present with the applicant at the time the applicant commits assisted suicide;

3. the physicians must also certify:

   (i) that the applicant is or will become physically incapable of committing suicide unassisted, and (ii) that they have informed him or her, and that he or she understands, that he or she has a continuing right to change his or her mind about terminating his or her life;

4. notice and access must be given to the Regional Coroner...;

5. the applicant must be examined daily by one of the certifying physicians;

6. the constitutional exemption will expire [after a set period of time]; and

7. the act causing the death of the applicant must be that of the applicant him- or herself, and not of anyone else.

...

Sopinka J. (for the majority of the Supreme Court):

In my view, [the position outlined by Chief Justice Lamer fails on the following grounds:]

1. It recognizes a constitutional right to legally assisted suicide beyond that of any country in the western world, beyond any serious proposal for reform in the western world and beyond the claim made in this very case. The apparent reason for the expansion beyond the claim in this case is that restriction of the right to the terminally ill could not be justified under s. 15.

2. It fails to provide ... safeguards. ...

3. The conditions imposed are vague and in some respects unenforceable. ...

4. ... The conditions ... are to serve merely as guidelines, leaving it to individual judges to decide upon application whether to grant or withhold the right to commit suicide. ...

I have concluded that the conclusion of my colleagues cannot be supported under the provisions of the Charter.

...The appellant seeks a remedy which would assure her some control over the time and manner of her death. ... She fears that she will be required to live until the deterioration from her disease is such that she will die as a result of choking, suffocation or pneumonia caused by aspiration of food or secretions. She will be totally dependent upon machines to perform her bodily functions and completely dependent upon others. Throughout this time, she will remain mentally competent and able to appreciate all that is happening to her. Although palliative care may be available to ease the pain and other physical discomfort which she will experience, the appellant fears the sedating effects of such drugs and argues, in any event, that they will not prevent the psychological and emotional distress which will result from being in a situation of utter dependence and loss of dignity. That there is a right to choose how one's body will be dealt with, even in the context of beneficial medical treatment, has long been recognized by the common law. To impose medical treatment on one who refuses it constitutes battery, and our common law has recognized the right to demand that medical treatment which would extend life be withheld or withdrawn. In my view, these considerations lead to the conclusion that the prohibition in s. 241(b) deprives the appellant of autonomy over her person and causes her physical pain and psychological stress in a manner which impinges on the security of her person. The appellant's security interest (considered in the context of the life and liberty interest) is therefore engaged, and it is necessary to determine whether there has been any deprivation thereof that is not in accordance with the principles of fundamental justice....

That respect for human dignity is one of the underlying principles upon which our society is based is unquestioned. I have difficulty, however, in characterizing this in itself as a principle of fundamental justice within the meaning of s. 7. While respect for human dignity is the genesis for many principles of fundamental justice, not every law that fails to accord such respect runs afoul of these principles. To state that "respect for human dignity and autonomy" is a principle of fundamental justice, then, is essentially to state that the deprivation of the appellant's security of the person is contrary to principles of fundamental justice because it deprives her of security of the person. This interpretation would equate security of the person with a principle of fundamental justice and render the latter redundant....

Section 241(b) has as its purpose the protection of the vulnerable who might be induced in moments of weakness to commit suicide. This purpose is grounded in the state interest in protecting life and reflects the policy of the state that human life should not be depreciated by allowing life to be taken. This policy finds expression not only in the provisions of our Criminal Code which prohibit murder and other violent acts against others notwithstanding the consent of the victim, but also in the policy against capital punishment and, until its repeal, attempted suicide. This is not only a policy of the state, however, but is part of our fundamental conception of the sanctity of human life. ...

[T]he principle of sanctity of life is no longer seen to require that all human life be preserved at all costs. Rather, it has come to be understood, at least by some, as encompassing quality of life considerations, and to be subject to certain limitations and qualifications reflective of personal autonomy and dignity. An analysis of our legislative and social policy in this area is necessary in order to determine whether fundamental principles have evolved such that they conflict with the validity of the balancing of interests undertaken by Parliament.

Mr. Justice Sopinka now discusses withdrawing treatment:

The distinction between withdrawing treatment upon a patient's request ... and assisted suicide on the other has been criticized as resting on a legal fiction — that is, the distinction between active and passive forms of treatment. The criticism is based on the fact that the withdrawal of life supportive measures is done with the knowledge that death will ensue, just as is assisting suicide, and that death does in fact ensue as a result of the action taken. ... Whether or not one agrees that the active vs. passive distinction is maintainable, however, the fact remains that under our common law, the physician has no choice but to accept the patient's instructions to discontinue treatment. ...

The fact that doctors may deliver palliative care to terminally ill patients without fear of sanction, it is argued, attenuates to an even greater degree any legitimate distinction which can be drawn between assisted suicide and what are currently acceptable forms of medical treatment. The administration of drugs designed for pain control in dosages which the physician knows will hasten death constitutes active contribution to death by any standard. However, the distinction drawn here is one based upon intention — in the case of palliative care the intention is to ease pain, which has the effect of hastening death, while in the case of assisted suicide, the intention is undeniably to cause death.... In my view, distinctions based upon intent are important, and in fact form the basis of our criminal law. While factually the distinction may, at times, be difficult to draw, legally it is clear. The fact that in some cases, the third party will, under the guise of palliative care, commit euthanasia or assist in suicide and go unsanctioned due to the difficulty of proof cannot be said to render the existence of the prohibition fundamentally unjust....

I also place some significance in the fact that the official position of various medical associations is against decriminalizing assisted suicide (Canadian Medical Association, British Medical Association, Council of Ethical and Judicial Affairs of the American Medical Association, World Medical Association and the American Nurses Association). Given the concerns about abuse that have been expressed and the great difficulty in creating appropriate safeguards to prevent these, it cannot be said that the blanket prohibition on assisted suicide is arbitrary or unfair, or that it is not reflective of fundamental values at play in our society. I am thus unable to find that any principle of fundamental justice is violated by s. 241(*b*). ...

In order to come within the protection of s. 12, the appellant must demonstrate ... that she is subjected to treatment or punishment at the hands of the state, and second, that such treatment or punishment is cruel and unusual. ... In my opinion, it cannot be said that the appellant is subjected by the state to any form of punishment within the meaning of s. 12. ...

Two difficult and important issues arise with respect to this application of s. 15:

1. whether a claim by the terminally ill who cannot commit suicide without assistance can be supported on the ground that s. 241(*b*) discriminates against all disabled persons who are unable to commit suicide without assistance;

2. whether deprivation of the ability to choose suicide is a benefit or burden within the meaning of s. 15 of the Charter....

I will assume that s. 15 of the Charter is infringed and consider the application of s. 1....

Section 241(*b*) protects all individuals against the control of others over their lives. To introduce an exception to this blanket protection for certain groups would create an inequality. ...[T]his protection is grounded on a substantial consensus among western countries, medical organizations and our own Law Reform Commission that in order to effectively protect life and those who are vulnerable in society, a prohibition without exception on the giving of assistance to commit suicide is the best approach. ... There is no halfway measure that could be relied upon with assurance to fully achieve the legislation's purpose; first, because the purpose extends to the protection of the life of the terminally ill. Part of this purpose, as I have explained above, is to discourage the terminally ill from choosing death over life. Secondly, even if the latter consideration can be stripped from the legislative purpose, we have no assurance that the exception can be made to limit the taking of life to those who are terminally ill and genuinely desire death....

I conclude, therefore, that any infringement of s. 15 is clearly justified under s. 1 of the Charter....

Active and Passive Euthanasia

James Rachels

ABSTRACT

The traditional distinction between active and passive euthanasia requires critical analysis. The conventional doctrine is that there is such an important moral difference between the two that, although the latter is sometimes permissible, the former is always forbidden. This doctrine may be challenged for several reasons. First of all, active euthanasia is in many cases more humane than passive euthanasia. Secondly, the conventional doctrine leads to decisions concerning life and death on irrelevant grounds. Thirdly, the doctrine rests on a distinction between killing and letting die that itself has no moral importance. Fourthly, the most common arguments in favor of the doctrine are invalid. I therefore suggest that the American Medical Association policy statement that endorses this doctrine is unsound.

The distinction between active and passive euthanasia is thought to be crucial for medical ethics. The idea is that it is permissible, at least in some cases, to withhold treatment and allow a patient to die, but it is never permissible to take any direct action designed to kill the patient. This doctrine seems to be accepted by most doctors, and it is endorsed in a statement adopted by the House of Delegates of the American Medical Association on December 4, 1973:

> The intentional termination of the life of one human being by another — mercy killing — is contrary to that for which the medical profession stands and is contrary to the policy of the American Medical Association.

> The cessation of the employment of extraordinary means to prolong the life of the body when there is irrefutable evidence that biological death is imminent is the decision of the patient and/or his immediate family. The advice and judgment of the physician should be freely available to the patient and/or his immediate family.

However, a strong case can be made against this doctrine. In what follows I will set out some of the relevant arguments, and urge doctors to reconsider their views on this matter.

James Rachels, "Active and Passive Euthanasia," *New England Journal of Medicine* 292:2 (Jan. 9, 1975) 78-80.

To begin with a familiar type of situation, a patient who is dying of incurable cancer of the throat is in terrible pain, which can no longer be satisfactorily alleviated. He is certain to die within a few days, even if present treatment is continued, but he does not want to go on living for those days since the pain is unbearable. So he asks the doctor for an end to it, and his family joins in the request.

Suppose the doctor agrees to withhold treatment, as the conventional doctrine says he may. The justification for his doing so is that the patient is in terrible agony, and since he is going to die anyway, it would be wrong to prolong his suffering needlessly. But now notice this. If one simply withholds treatment, it may take the patient longer to die, and so he may suffer more than he would if more direct action were taken and a lethal injection given. This fact provides strong reason for thinking that, once the initial decision not to prolong his agony has been made, active euthanasia is actually preferable to passive euthanasia, rather than the reverse. To say otherwise is to endorse the option that leads to more suffering rather than less, and is contrary to the humanitarian impulse that prompts the decision not to prolong his life in the first place.

Part of my point is that the process of being "allowed to die" can be relatively slow and painful, whereas being given a lethal injection is relatively quick and painless. Let me give a different sort of example. In the United States about one in 600 babies is born with Down's syndrome. Most of these babies are otherwise healthy — that is, with only the usual pediatric care, they will proceed to an otherwise normal infancy. Some, however, are born with congenital defects such as intestinal obstructions that require operations if they are to live. Sometimes, the parents and the doctor will decide not to operate, and let the infant die. Anthony Shaw describes what happens then:

... When surgery is denied [the doctor] must try to keep the infant from suffering while natural forces sap the baby's life away. As a surgeon whose natural inclination is to use the scalpel to fight off death, standing by and watching a salvageable baby die is the most emotionally exhausting experience I know. It is easy at a conference, in a theoretical discussion, to decide that such infants should be allowed to die. It is altogether different to stand by in the nursery and watch as dehydration and infection wither a tiny being over hours and days. This is a terrible ordeal for me and the hospital staff — much more so than for the parents who never set foot in the nursery.

I can understand why some people are opposed to all euthanasia, and insist that such infants must be allowed to live. I think I can also understand why other people favor destroying these babies quickly and painlessly. But why should anyone favor letting "dehydration and infection wither a tiny being over hours and days?" The doctrine that says that a baby may be allowed to dehydrate and wither, but may not be given an injection that would end its life without suffering, seems so patently cruel as to require no further refutation. The strong language is not intended to offend, but only to put the point in the clearest possible way.

My second argument is that the conventional doctrine leads to decisions concerning life and death made on irrelevant grounds.

Consider again the case of the infants with Down's syndrome who need operations for congenital defects unrelated to the syndrome to live. Sometimes, there is no operation and the baby dies, but when there is no such defect, the baby lives on. Now, an operation such as that to remove an intestinal obstruction is not prohibitively difficult. The reason why such operations are not performed in these cases is, clearly, that the child has Down's syndrome and the parents and doctor judge that because of that fact it is better for the child to die.

But notice that this situation is absurd, no matter what view one takes of the lives and potentials of such babies. If the life of such an infant is worth preserving, what does it matter if it needs a simple operation? Or, if one thinks it better that such a baby should not live on, what difference does it make that it happens to have an unobstructed intestinal tract? In either case, the matter of life and death is being decided on irrelevant grounds. It is the Down's syndrome, and not the intestines, that is the issue. The matter should be decided, if at all, on that basis, and not be allowed to depend on the essentially irrelevant question of whether the intestinal tract is blocked.

What makes this situation possible, of course, is the idea that when there is an intestinal blockage, one can "let the baby die," but when there is no such defect there is nothing that can be done, for one must not "kill" it. The fact that this idea leads to such results as deciding life or death on irrelevant grounds is another good reason why the doctrine should be rejected.

One reason why so many people think that there is an important moral difference between active and passive euthanasia is that they think killing someone is morally worse than letting someone die. But is it? Is killing, in itself, worse than letting die? To investigate this issue, two cases may be considered that are exactly alike except that one involves killing whereas the other involves letting someone die. Then, it can be asked whether this difference makes any difference to the moral assessments. It is important that the cases be exactly alike, except for this one difference, since otherwise one cannot be confident that it is this difference and not some other that accounts for any variation

in the assessments of the two cases. So, let us consider this pair of cases:

In the first, Smith stands to gain a large inheritance if anything should happen to his six-year-old cousin. One evening while the child is taking his bath, Smith sneaks into the bathroom and drowns the child, and then arranges things so that it will look like an accident.

In the second, Jones also stands to gain if anything should happen to his six-year-old cousin. Like Smith, Jones sneaks in planning to drown the child in his bath. However, just as he enters the bathroom Jones sees the child slip and hit his head, and fall face down in the water. Jones is delighted; he stands by, ready to push the child's head back under if it is necessary, but it is not necessary. With only a little thrashing about, the child drowns all by himself, "accidentally," as Jones watches and does nothing.

Now Smith killed the child, whereas Jones "merely" let the child die. That is the only difference between them. Did either man behave better, from a moral point of view? If the difference between killing and letting die were in itself a morally important matter, one should say that Jones's behavior was less reprehensible than Smith's. But does one really want to say that? I think not. In the first place, both men acted from the same motive, personal gain, and both had exactly the same end in view when they acted. It may be inferred from Smith's conduct that he is a bad man, although that judgment may be withdrawn or modified if certain further facts are learned about him — for example, that he is mentally deranged. But would not the very same thing be inferred about Jones from his conduct? And would not the same further considerations also be relevant to any modification of this judgment? Moreover, suppose Jones pleaded, in his own defense, "After all, I didn't do anything except just stand there and watch the child drown. I didn't kill him; I only let him die."

Again, if letting die were in itself less bad than killing, this defense should have at least some weight. But it does not. Such a "defense" can only be regarded as a grotesque perversion of moral reasoning. Morally speaking, it is no defense at all.

Now, it may be pointed out, quite properly, that the cases of euthanasia with which doctors are concerned are not like this at all. They do not involve personal gain or the destruction of normal healthy children. Doctors are concerned only with cases in which the patient's life is of no further use to him, or in which the patient's life has become or will soon become a terrible burden. However, the point is the same in these cases: the bare difference between killing and letting die does not, in itself, make a moral difference. If a doctor lets a patient die, for humane reasons, he is in the same moral position as if he had given the patient a lethal injection for humane reasons. If his decision was wrong — if, for example, the patient's illness was in fact curable — the decision would be equally regrettable no matter which method was used to carry it out. And if the doctor's decision was the right one, the method used is not in itself important.

The AMA policy statement isolates the crucial issue very well; the crucial issue is "the intentional termination of the life of one human being by another." But after identifying this issue, and forbidding "mercy killing," the statement goes on to deny that the cessation of treatment is the intentional termination of a life. This is where the mistake comes in, for what is the cessation of treatment, in these circumstances, if it is not "the intentional termination of the life of one human being by another?" Of course it is exactly that, and if it were not, there would be no point to it.

Many people will find this judgment hard to accept. One reason, I think, is that it is very easy to conflate the question of whether killing is, in itself, worse than letting die, with the very different question of whether most actual cases of killing are more reprehensible than most actual cases of letting die. Most actual cases of killing are clearly terrible (think, for example, of all the murders reported in the newspapers), and one hears of such cases every day. On the other hand, one hardly ever hears of a case of letting die, except for the actions of doctors who are motivated by humanitarian reasons. So one learns to think of killing in a much worse light than of letting die. But this does not mean that there is something about killing that makes it in itself worse than letting die, for it is not the bare difference between killing and letting die that makes the difference in these cases. Rather, the other factors — the murderer's motive of personal gain, for example, contrasted with the doctor's humanitarian motivation — account for different reactions to the different cases.

I have argued that killing is not in itself any worse than letting die; if my contention is right, it follows that active euthanasia is not any worse than passive euthanasia. What arguments can be given on the other side? The most common, I believe, is the following:

> The important difference between active and passive euthanasia is that, in passive euthanasia, the doctor does not do anything to bring about the patient's death. The doctor does nothing, and the patient dies of whatever ills already afflict him. In active euthanasia, however, the doctor does something to bring about the patient's death: he kills him. The doctor who gives the patient with cancer a lethal injection has himself caused his patient's death; whereas if he merely ceases treatment, the cancer is the cause of the death.

A number of points need to be made here. The first is that it is not exactly correct to say that in passive euthanasia the doctor does nothing, for he does do one thing that is very important: he lets the patient die. "Letting someone die" is certainly different, in some respects, from other types of action — mainly in that it is a kind of action that one may perform by way of not performing certain other actions. For example, one may let a patient die by way of not giving medication, just as one may insult someone by way of not shaking his hand. But for any purpose of moral assessment, it is a type of action nonetheless. The decision to let a patient die is subject to moral appraisal in the same way that a decision to kill him would be subject to moral appraisal: it may be assessed as wise or unwise, compassionate or sadistic, right or wrong. If a doctor deliberately let a patient die who was suffering from routinely curable illness, the doctor would certainly be to blame for what he had done, just as he would be to blame had he needlessly killed the patient. Charges against him would then be appropriate. If so, it would be no defense at all for him to insist that he didn't "do anything." He would have done something very serious indeed, for he let his patient die.

Fixing the cause of death may be very important from a legal point of view, for it may determine whether criminal charges are brought against the doctor. But I do not think that this notion can be used to show a moral difference between active and passive euthanasia. The reason why it is considered bad to be the cause of someone's death is that death is regarded as a great evil — and so it is. However if it has been decided that euthanasia — even passive euthanasia — is desirable in a given case, it has also been decided that in this instance death is no greater an evil than the patient's continued existence. And if this is true the usual reason for not wanting to be the cause of someone's death simply does not apply.

Finally, doctors may think that all of this is only of academic interest — the sort of thing that philosophers may worry about but that has no practical bearing on their own work. After all, doctors must be concerned about the legal consequences of what they do, and active euthanasia is clearly forbidden by the law. But even so, doctors should also be concerned with the fact that the law is forcing upon them a moral doctrine that may well be indefensible, and has a considerable effect on their practices. Of course, most doctors are not now in the position of being coerced in this matter, for they do not regard themselves as merely going along with what the law requires. Rather, in statements such as the AMA policy statement that I have quoted, they are endorsing this doctrine as a central point of medical ethics. In that statement, active euthanasia is condemned not merely as illegal but as "contrary to that for which the medical profession stands," whereas passive euthanasia is approved. However, the preceding considerations suggest that there is really no moral difference between the two, considered in themselves (there may be important moral differences in some cases in their *consequences,* but, as I pointed out, these differences may make active euthanasia, and not passive euthanasia, the morally preferable option). So, whereas doctors may have to discriminate between active and passive euthanasia to satisfy the law, they should not do any more than that. In particular, they should not give the distinction any added authority and weight by writing it into official statements of medical ethics.

Assisted Suicide: Pro-Choice or Anti-Life?

Richard Doerflinger

The intrinsic wrongness of directly killing the innocent, even with the victim's consent, is all but axiomatic in the Jewish and Christian worldviews that have shaped the laws and mores of Western civilization and the self-concept of its medical practitioners. This norm grew out of the conviction that human life is sacred because it is created in the image and likeness of God, and called to fulfillment in love of God and neighbor.

With the pervasive secularization of Western culture, norms against euthanasia and suicide have to a great extent been cut loose from their religious roots to fend for themselves. Because these norms seem abstract and unconvincing to many, debate tends to dwell not on the wrongness of the act as such but on what may follow from its acceptance. Such arguments are often described as claims about a "slippery slope," and debate shifts to the validity of slippery slope arguments in general.

Since it is sometimes argued that acceptance of assisted suicide is an outgrowth of respect for personal autonomy, and not lack of respect for the inherent worth of human life, I will outline how autonomy-based arguments in favor of assisting suicide do entail a statement about the value of life. I will also distinguish two kinds of slippery slope argument often confused with each other, and argue that those who favor social and legal acceptance of assisted suicide have not adequately responded to the slippery slope claims of their opponents.

ASSISTED SUICIDE VERSUS RESPECT FOR LIFE

Some advocates of socially sanctioned assisted suicide admit (and a few boast) that their proposal is incompatible with the conviction that human life is of intrinsic worth. Attorney Robert Risley has said that he and his allies in the Hemlock Society are "so bold" as to seek to "overturn the sanctity of life principle" in American society. A life of suffering, "racked with pain," is "not the kind of life we cherish."[1]

Others eschew Risley's approach, perhaps recognizing that it creates a slippery slope toward practices almost universally condemned. If society is to help terminally ill patients to commit suicide because it agrees that death is objectively preferable to a life of hardship, it will be difficult to draw the line at the seriously ill or even at circumstances where the victim requests death.

Some advocates of assisted suicide therefore take a different course, arguing that it is precisely respect for the dignity of the human person that demands respect for individual freedom as the noblest feature of that person. On this rationale a decision as to when and how to die deserves the respect and even the assistance of others because it is the ultimate exercise of self-determination — "ultimate" both in the sense that it is the last decision one will ever make and in the sense that through it one takes control of one's entire self.

Richard Doerflinger, "Assisted Suicide: Pro-Choice or Anti-Life?" *Hastings Center Report* 19:1(Jan./Feb. 1989) suppl. 16-19.

What makes such decisions worthy of respect is not the fact that death is chosen over life but that it is the individual's own free decision about his or her future.

Thus Derek Humphry, director of the Hemlock Society, describes his organization as "pro-choice" on this issue. Such groups favor establishment of a constitutional "right to die" modeled on the right to abortion delineated by the U.S. Supreme Court in 1973. This would be a right to choose *whether or not* to end one's own life, free of outside government interference. In theory, recognition of such a right would betray no bias toward choosing death.

LIFE VERSUS FREEDOM

This autonomy-based approach is more appealing than the straightforward claim that some lives are not worth living, especially to Americans accustomed to valuing individual liberty above virtually all else. But the argument departs from American traditions on liberty in one fundamental respect.

When the Declaration of Independence proclaimed the inalienable human rights to be "life, liberty, and the pursuit of happiness," this ordering reflected a long-standing judgment about their relative priorities. Life, a human being's very earthly existence, is the most fundamental right because it is the necessary condition for all other worldly goods including freedom; freedom in turn makes it possible to pursue (without guaranteeing that one will attain) happiness. Safeguards against the deliberate destruction of life are thus seen as necessary to protect freedom and all other human goods. This line of thought is not explicitly religious but is endorsed by some modern religious groups:

The first right of the human person is his life. He has other goods and some are more precious, but this one is fundamental — the condition of all the others. Hence it must be protected above all others.[2]

On this view suicide is not the ultimate exercise of freedom but its ultimate self-contradiction: A free act that by destroying life, destroys all the individual's future earthly freedom. If life is more basic than freedom, society best serves freedom by discouraging rather than assisting self-destruction. Sometimes one must limit particular choices to safeguard freedom itself, as when American society chose over a century ago to prevent people from selling themselves into slavery even of their own volition.

It may be argued in objection that the person who ends his life has not truly suffered loss of freedom, because unlike the slave he need not continue to exist under the constraints of a loss of freedom. But the slave does have some freedom, including the freedom to seek various means of liberation or at least the freedom to choose what attitude to take regarding his plight. To claim that a slave is worse off than a corpse is to value a situation of limited freedom less than one of no freedom whatsoever, which seems inconsistent with the premise of the "pro-choice" position. Such a claim also seems tantamount to saying that some lives (such as those with less than absolute freedom) are objectively not worth living, a position that "pro-choice" advocates claim not to hold.

It may further be argued in objection that assistance in suicide is only being offered to those who can no longer meaningfully exercise other freedoms due to increased suffering and reduced capabilities and lifespan. To be sure, the suffering of terminally ill patients who can no longer pursue the simplest everyday tasks should call for sympathy and support from everyone in contact with them. But even these hardships do not constitute total loss of freedom of choice. If they did, one could hardly claim that the patient is in a position to make the ultimate free choice about suicide. A dying person capable of making a choice of that kind is also capable of making less monumental free choices about coping with his or her condition. This person generally faces a bewildering array of choices regarding the assessment of his or her past life and the resolution of relationships with family and friends. He or she must finally choose at this time what stance to take regarding the eternal questions about God, personal responsibility, and the prospects of a destiny after death.

In short, those who seek to maximize free choice may with consistency reject the idea of assisted suicide, instead facilitating all choices *except* that one which cuts short all choices.

In fact proponents of assisted suicide do *not* consistently place freedom of choice as their highest priority. They often defend the moderate nature of their project by stating, with Derek Humphry, that "we do not encourage suicide for any reason except to relieve unremitting suffering." It seems their highest priority is the "pursuit of happiness" (or avoidance of suffering) and not "liberty" as such. Liberty or freedom of choice loses its value if one's choices cannot relieve suffering and lead to happiness; life is of instrumental value insofar as it makes possible choices that can bring happiness.

In this value system, choice as such does not warrant unqualified respect. In difficult circumstances, as when care of a suffering and dying patient is a great burden on family and society, the individual who chooses life despite suffering will not easily be seen as rational, thus will not easily receive understanding and assistance for this choice.

In short, an unqualified "pro-choice" defense of assisted suicide lacks coherence because corpses have no choices. A particular choice, that of death, is given priority over all the other choices it makes impossible, so the value of choice as such is not central to the argument.

A restriction of this rationale to cases of terminal illness also lacks logical force. For if ending a brief life of suffering can be good, it would seem that ending a long life of suffering may be better. Surely the approach of the California "Humane and Dignified Death Act" — where consensual killing of a patient expected to die in six months is presumably good medical practice, but killing the same patient a month or two earlier is still punishable as homicide — is completely arbitrary.

SLIPPERY SLOPES, LOOSE CANNONS

Many arguments against sanctioning assisted suicide concern a different kind of "slippery slope": Contingent factors in the contemporary situation may make it virtually inevitable in practice, if not compelling at the level of abstract theory, that removal of the taboo against assisted suicide will lead to destructive expansions of the right to kill the innocent. Such factors may not be part of euthanasia advocates' own agenda; but if they exist and are beyond the control of these advocates, they must be taken into account in judging the moral and social wisdom of opening what may be a Pandora's box of social evils.

To distinguish this sociological argument from our dissection of the conceptual *logic* of the rationale for assisted suicide, we might call it a "loose cannon" argument. The basic claim is that socially accepted killing of innocent persons will interact with other social factors to threaten lives that advocates of assisted suicide would agree should be protected. These factors at present include the following:

The psychological vulnerability of elderly and dying patients. Theorists may present voluntary and involuntary euthanasia as polar opposites; in practice there are many steps on the road from dispassionate, autonomous choice to subtle coercion. Elderly and disabled patients are often invited by our achievement-oriented society to see themselves as useless burdens on younger, more vital generations. In this climate, simply offering the *option* of "self-deliverance" shifts a burden of proof, so that helpless patients must ask themselves why they are *not* availing themselves of it. Society's offer of death communicates the message to certain patients that they *may* continue to live if they wish but the rest of us have no strong interest in their survival. Indeed, once the choice of a quick and painless death is officially accepted as rational, resistance to this choice may be seen as eccentric or even selfish.[3]

The crisis in health care costs. The growing incentives for physicians, hospitals, families, and insurance companies to control the cost of health care will bring additional pressures to bear on patients. Curt Garbesi, the Hemlock Society's legal consultant, argues that autonomy-based groups like Hemlock must "control the public debate" so assisted suicide will not be seized upon by public officials as a cost-cutting device. But simply basing one's own defense of assisted suicide on individual autonomy does not solve the problem. For in the economic sphere also, offering the option of suicide would subtly shift burdens of proof.

Adequate health care is now seen by at least some policymakers as a human right, as something a society owes to all its members. Acceptance of assisted suicide as an option for those requiring expensive care would not only offer health care providers an incentive to make that option seem attractive — it would also demote all other options to the status of strictly private choices by the individual. As such they may lose their moral and legal claim to public support — in much the same way that the

U.S. Supreme Court, having protected abortion under a constitutional "right of privacy," has quite logically denied any government obligation to provide public funds for this strictly private choice. As life-extending care of the terminally ill is increasingly seen as strictly elective, society may become less willing to appropriate funds for such care, and economic pressures to choose death will grow accordingly.

Legal doctrines on "substituted judgment." American courts recognizing a fundamental right to refuse life-sustaining treatment have concluded that it is unjust to deny this right to the mentally incompetent. In such cases the right is exercised on the patient's behalf by others, who seek either to interpret what the patient's own wishes might have been or to serve his or her best interests. Once assisted suicide is established as a fundamental right, courts will almost certainly find that it is unjust not to extend this right to those unable to express their wishes. Hemlock's political arm, Americans Against Human Suffering, has underscored continuity between "passive" and "active" euthanasia by offering the Humane and Dignified Death Act as an amendment to California's "living will" law, and by including a provision for appointment of a proxy to choose the time and manner of the patient's death. By such extensions our legal system would accommodate nonvoluntary, if not involuntary, active euthanasia.

Expanded definitions of terminal illness. The Hemlock Society wishes to offer assisted suicide only to those suffering from terminal illnesses. But some Hemlock officials have in mind a rather broad definition of "terminal illness." Derek Humphry says "two and a half million people alone are dying of Alzheimer's disease."[4] At Hemlock's 1986 convention, Dutch physician Pieter Admiraal boasted that he had recently broadened the meaning of terminal illness in his country by giving a lethal injection to a young quadriplegic woman — a Dutch court found that he acted within judicial guidelines allowing euthanasia for the terminally ill, because paralyzed patients have difficulty swallowing and could die from aspirating their food at any time.

The medical and legal meaning of terminal illness has already been expanded in the United States by professional societies, legislatures, and courts in the context of so-called passive euthanasia. A Uniform Rights of the Terminally Ill Act proposed by the National Conference of Commissioners on Uniform State Laws in 1986 defines a terminal illness as one that would cause the patient's death in a relatively short time if life-preserving treatment is *not* provided — prompting critics to ask if all diabetics, for example, are "terminal" by definition. Some courts already see comatose and vegetative states as "terminal" because they involve an inability to swallow that will lead to death unless artificial feeding is instituted. In the *Hilda Peter* case, the New Jersey Supreme Court declared that the traditional state interest in "preserving life" referred only to "cognitive and sapient life" and not to mere "biological" existence, implying that unconscious patients are terminal, or perhaps as good as dead, so far as state interests are concerned. Is there any reason to think that American law would suddenly resurrect the older, narrower meaning of "terminal illness" in the context of *active* euthanasia?

Prejudice against citizens with disabilities. If definitions of terminal illness expand to encompass states of severe physical or mental disability, another social reality will increase the pressure on patients to choose death: long-standing prejudice, sometimes bordering on revulsion, against people with disabilities. While it is seldom baldly claimed that disabled people have "lives not worth living," able-bodied people often say they could not live in a severely disabled state or would prefer death. In granting Elizabeth Bouvia a right to refuse a feeding tube that preserved her life, the California Appeals Court bluntly stated that her physical handicaps led her to "consider her existence meaningless" and that "she cannot be faulted for so concluding." According to disability rights expert Paul Longmore, in a society with such attitudes toward the disabled, "talk of their 'rational' or 'voluntary' suicide is simply Orwellian newspeak."[5]

Character of the medical profession. Advocates of assisted suicide realize that most physicians will resist giving lethal injections because they are trained, in Garbesi's words, to be "enemies of death." The California Medical Association firmly opposed the Humane and Dignified Death Act, seeing it as an attack on the ethical foundation of the medical profession.

Yet California appeals judge Lynn Compton was surely correct in his concurring opinion in the *Bouvia* case, when he said that a sufficient number of willing physicians can be found once legal sanctions against assisted suicide are dropped. Judge Compton said this had clearly been the case with abortion, despite the fact that the Hippocratic Oath condemns abortion as strongly as it condemns euthanasia. Opinion polls of physicians bear out the judgment that a significant number would perform lethal injections if they were legal.

Some might think this division or ambivalence about assisted suicide in the medical profession will restrain broad expansions of the practice. But if anything, Judge Compton's analogy to our experience with abortion suggests the opposite. Most physicians still have qualms about abortion, and those who perform abortions on a full-time basis are not readily accepted by their colleagues as paragons of the healing art. Consequently they tend to form their own professional societies, bolstering each other's positive self-image and developing euphemisms to blunt the moral edge of their work.

Once physicians abandon the traditional medical self-image, which rejects direct killing of patients in all circumstances, their new substitute self-image may require ever more aggressive efforts to make this killing more widely practiced and favorably received. To allow killing by physicians in certain circumstances may create a new lobby of physicians in favor of expanding medical killing.

The human will to power. The most deeply buried yet most powerful driving force toward widespread medical killing is a fact of human nature: Human beings are tempted to enjoy exercising power over others; ending another person's life is the ultimate exercise of that power. Once the taboo against killing has been set aside, it becomes progressively easier to channel one's aggressive instincts into the destruction of life in other contexts. Or as James Burtchaell has said: "There is a sort of virginity about murder; once one has violated it, it is awkward to refuse other invitations by saying, 'But that would be murder!' "[6]

Some will say assisted suicide for the terminally ill is morally distinguishable from murder and does not logically require termination of life in other circumstances. But my point is that the skill and the instinct to kill are more easily turned to other lethal tasks once they have an opportunity to exercise themselves. Thus Robert Jay Lifton has perceived differences between the German "mercy killings" of the 1930s and the later campaign to annihilate the Jews of Europe, yet still says that "at the heart of the Nazi enterprise ... is the destruction of the boundary between healing and killing."[7] No other boundary separating these two situations was as fundamental as this one, and thus none was effective once it was crossed. As a matter of historical fact, personnel who had conducted the "mercy killing" program were quickly and readily recruited to operate the killing chambers of the death camps.[8] While the contemporary United States fortunately lacks the anti-Semitic and totalitarian attitudes that made the Holocaust possible, it has its own trends and pressures that may combine with acceptance of medical killing to produce a distinctively American catastrophe in the name of individual freedom.

These "loose cannon" arguments are not conclusive. All such arguments by their nature rest upon a reading and extrapolation of certain contingent factors in society. But their combined force provides a serious case against taking the irreversible step of sanctioning assisted suicide for any class of persons, so long as those who advocate this step fail to demonstrate why these predictions are wrong. If the strict philosophical case on behalf of "rational suicide" lacks coherence, the pragmatic claim that its acceptance would be a social benefit lacks grounding in history or common sense.

NOTES

1. Presentation at the Hemlock Society's Third National Voluntary Euthanasia Conference, "A Humane and Dignified Death," September 25-27, 1986, Washington, D.C. All quotations from Hemlock Society officials are from the proceedings of this conference unless otherwise noted.

2. Vatican Congregation for the Doctrine of the Faith, *Declaration on Procured Abortion* (1974), para. 11.

3. I am indebted for this line of argument to Dr. Eric Chevlen.

4. Denis Herbstein, "Campaigning for the Right to Die," *International Herald Tribune,* 11 September 1986.

5. Paul K. Longmore, "Elizabeth Bouvia, Assisted Suicide, and Social Prejudice," *Issues in Law & Medicine* 3:2 (1987), 168.

6. James T. Burtchaell, *Rachel Weeping and Other Essays on Abortion* (Kansas City: Andrews & McMeel, 1982), 188.

7. Robert Jay Lifton, *The Nazi Doctors: Medical Killing and the Psychology of Genocide* (New York: Basic Books, 1986), 14.

8. Yitzhak Rad, *Belzec, Sobibor, Treblinka* (Bloomington, IN: Indiana University Press, 1987), 11, 16-17.

The Slippery-Slope Argument

Wibren van der Burg

INTRODUCTION

In public debates about the introduction of new technologies or about legalization of abortion, euthanasia, or human immunodeficiency virus (HIV) tests, an ever-recurrent argument is the slippery-slope or wedge argument. It has been invoked against the legalization of abortion, euthanasia, in vitro fertilization, DNA research, and so on....

The basic structure of the argument is rather simple: if we allow *A*, *B* will necessarily or very likely follow (for *A* and *B* we can fill in certain acts or practices, like euthanasia). *B* is morally not acceptable; therefore, we must not allow *A* either. Sometimes a further requirement is added: that *A* is in itself morally neutral or even justifiable.[1]...

Usually two different versions of the argument are distinguished: the logical (or conceptual) version and the empirical (or psychological) version. The logical form of the argument holds that we are logically committed to allow *B* once we have allowed

A. The empirical form tells us that the effect of accepting *A* will be that, as a result of psychological and social processes, we sooner or later will accept *B*.... There are at least two different interpretations of the logical form, whereas the empirical version is usually stated so vaguely that it remains unclear how exactly the dreaded result would be produced.

In this article, I will try to clarify the different forms of the slippery-slope argument and identify the situations in which they might produce a valid argument. I will do this by concentrating on two central questions that have never been explicitly posed. The first question that has to be answered is: In the context of what kind of norms are we considering allowing *A*? Is it the context of law or that of morality? And if morality, is it positive morality or critical morality? Are the different versions of the slippery-slope argument equally valid in each of these contexts, or are they only valid in some of them? This is the question with which we will deal in the first half of the article. Using the distinctions made by

Wibren van der Burg, "The Slippery-Slope Argument," *The Journal of Clinical Ethics* 3:4 (Winter, 1992) 256-68.

H.L.A. Hart, I will distinguish between law, *positive morality* (the morality actually accepted and shared by a given social group or society, also to be called popular or social morality), and *critical morality* (the general moral principles used in the criticism of actual social institutions including positive morality).[2] Thus, we can identify which forms of the slippery-slope argument might apply to each of these types of norms.

The second question is: What is meant by saying, "If we allow *A*"? Who is it that allows, and what exactly constitutes "allowing"? The combination of the analysis of this question with the preceding one will bring us to the conclusion that the slippery-slope argument's greatest force is in a context of institutional norms, especially law, whereas its importance in morality proper is only marginal. In the closing section, then, I will pursue the implications this conclusion has for the role of the argument in ethical and political debates.

THE LOGICAL VERSIONS

Curiously, it has seldom been explicitly noticed that we cannot talk of *the* logical version of the slippery slope. There are at least two different reasonable interpretations. The first one — I will call it *L1* — says that there is either no relevant conceptual difference between *A* and *B* or that the justification for *A* also applies to *B*, and therefore acceptance of *A* will logically imply acceptance of *B*. "A justification offered for one sort of act that strikes us as right may have logical implications for the justification of another sort of act that strikes us as wrong." A good example of this version of the argument may be found in the debate on severely handicapped newborns. In a controversial article in the *Journal of Medical Ethics,* A.G.M. Campbell and R.S. Duff proposed a policy of selective non-treatment.[3] ...

The second version, to be named *L2* hereafter, holds that there is a difference between *A* and *B*, but that there is no such difference between *A* and *M, M* and N, ... *Y* and Z, Z and *B* and that, therefore, allowing *A* will in the end imply the acceptance of *B*.[4] There may seem to be a clear distinction between abortion of a three-month-old fetus and killing a newborn child, but this distinction collapses as soon as we realize there is no such distinction between a three-month-old fetus and a three-month-and-one-day-old fetus, and so forth. Version *L2* is usually stated in a way that makes it include *L*, by saying that there may be a difference. I will, for analytical purposes, deal with them as two mutually exclusive arguments: *L2* holds that there is a difference between *A* and *B*, whereas *L1* does not.

There are two possible interpretations of *L2*. It may be an implication within deontic logic: allowing *A* logically implies allowing *M*, and so on. But, as will become clear later, this usually, though not always, is a fallacy — namely, the fallacy of the heap. ("If one grain is not a heap and one more cannot make the difference, there can never be a heap.") The more interesting interpretation is that we must see it as a weaker kind of implication in the logic of belief. If one believes that *A* is allowed, one cannot but believe that *M* is allowed, and so on. In this interpretation, it is not so much a question of pure logic but of the criteria for justified beliefs.[5]...

In this section, I will analyze whether these two logical varieties are valid arguments in the context of norms of critical morality, positive morality, and law, respectively.

CRITICAL MORALITY

Let us begin with critical morality. Version *L1* clearly has great force there. Whether it must be regarded as derived from the principle of universalizability or as a simple consistency requirement, we can postpone for a while.[6] But universalizability and consistency are, without doubt, important criteria in critical morality. Whenever it is demonstrated that there are no relevant differences between A and B and that B is clearly morally wrong, this is a valid and conclusive reason to reject A as well.

Version $L2,$ however, is a different case. The problem is not whether there is a difference between A and B — there is — but that there is no nonarbitrary cutoff point on the continuum between them. This can be called the gray-zone problem. We know B is black and A white, but we cannot tell where A stops and B begins. This is a serious problem, but it need not trouble us as an argument against A. As an argument against accepting A in critical morality, it clearly is a fallacy.[7]

For it is essential to the gray zone that we do not have conclusive reasons for seeing it as either A or B. When we do not want it to be a category of its own, gray can be seen both as black and as white. But then every choice for a line within the gray zone, though arbitrary, is a reasonable one. It is reasonable simply because a line has to be drawn, even though there are no conclusive reasons for this special line. Of course, when dealing with particular problems, this is not very satisfactory, for it might result in an inconsistent or shifting pattern of decisions within the gray zone, and this is a good reason for trying to find less vague criteria or other ways to limit the gray zone. But no logic of moral reasoning compels us to go beyond the gray zone and to regard cases clearly belonging to B as justifiable. The conclusion is that in critical morality, we can safely dismiss $L2$ as invalid.

POSITIVE MORALITY

...We might construe the logical arguments in this context as saying something about the moral beliefs that a person or a group has. If one sincerely believes that A should be allowed, and if one has a certain intellectual integrity, one might feel logically forced to allow B as well. This is more an indirect point of logic than a direct one. It assumes that moral agents strive for a logical consistency of their moral beliefs and that, for this reason, they might feel compelled to change their attitude toward B once they have accepted A. This need not be a conscious decision; more likely, it will be a gradual process.

But the question then is whether a community can be logically forced to allow B. Positive moralities are seldom or never logically consistent, even when we take the morality of a very coherent community or of one person. Moralities usually consist of many contradictory positions. And logic tells us that from an inconsistent set of premises it is logically possible to deduce every position one wants. One thus might infer both the acceptance and the prohibition of B from the positive morality that allows A. Therefore, it seems nonsense to talk of "being logically forced."

However, ... [c]an we not say that the positive morality, even when inconsistent, at least usually points in a certain direction? Though the group, strictly speaking, may not be logically forced, it may feel so. The distinction between deontic logic and logic of belief may clarify this. Whereas deontic logic does not produce a clear conclusion here, we may say that an individual who does not want to sacrifice his intellectual integrity may feel logically forced to allow B as well (and the same can be said for the individuals composing a group). Though the individual may be aware that he holds some inconsistent beliefs, he may be convinced that, unless he has very strong reasons to stick to both of the inconsistent opinions, he should change the weaker of these opinions to make his total set of beliefs more consistent. If he strongly believes that *A* should be allowed and he only has a weak objection against *B*, he should for reasons of consistency change his opinions about *B*.

I will make two comments here. The first is that this would involve a balancing of the weights of these different positions to say which is the strongest. For it does not help to say that there are three rules in favor of *B* and only one contra, if we do not know which one is the strongest. When the rule contra is a very important one (say, for example, do not kill), and the three pros are rather insignificant ones (such as do not walk over someone's property), perhaps the smallest number of rules should prevail.[8] At least logic by itself does not clearly point in one direction.

My second point is that while logic might compel us in a discussion regarding critical morality, it need not in a positive morality. A positive morality is based on the opinions of the members of the community, and it is not impossible that while "logic" points in one direction, the community's ideas point in another one. There may be a strong logical point against slavery in a democratic society, but nevertheless the southern states of the United States before the Civil War did not accept this point. So the conclusion must be that it depends on the group that accepts the positive morality as to whether logic has any force at all. Even if the group in most cases yields to the logic of its own opinions, it may be strongly convinced that this would be wrong in this case and construe some rationalizations justifying the apparently inconsistent positions. To say it more simply: it depends upon the empirical factors that are relevant in the empirical slippery-slope argument.

The distinction Bernard Williams makes between a reasonable and an effective distinction may be helpful here.[9] A reasonable distinction is one for which there is a decent argument, while an effective distinction is one that, as a matter of social or psychological fact, can be effectively defended. A reasonable distinction need not be an effective one, and vice versa.

What the logical version says is that there are no reasonable distinctions, either between *A* and *B* (*L1*) or between the intermediate positions on the continuum between *A* and *B* (*L2*). The fact that possible distinctions are not reasonable does not imply that there are no effective distinctions. Distinctions based on prejudice, for example, may be unreasonable but highly effective. Distinctions that are reasonable may be very ineffective.

It seems to me that the distinction between HIV tests and genetic tests has had this characteristic of an unreasonable but effective distinction for some time. The fact that in the early 1980s AIDS hit almost exclusively gays, blacks, and drug users — groups that are not held in great esteem by large groups in the population — caused an extreme lack of public concern about discrimination against seropositives and AIDS patients and about the use of HIV tests. Because AIDS and HIV infection hit mainly stigmatized groups, there was a very effective barrier against those discriminatory tendencies spreading to other persons, like carriers of genetic diseases. This example shows, however, that what may seem to be an effective barrier may not remain so. As AIDS spread through the "general" population, the barrier grew ineffective, and the precedent of AIDS-related discrimination threatened to spread to other groups and fields.

We must grant, nevertheless, that in social processes the logical arguments may be important factors. The fact that a distinction is unreasonable may sometimes make it more difficult to defend it effectively. But whether the arguments do have this force clearly depends on empirical processes and should, therefore, be discussed in the context of the empirical argument. Therefore, in the context of positive morality, the logical arguments do not have an independent significance.

LAW

...With respect to proposed acts of legislation, the logical slippery slopes are not valid arguments. Legislation often dictates arbitrary limits. There is no essential distinction between thirty miles per hour and thirty-one. Yet legal logic does not lead us toward accepting thirty-one miles per hour as the speed limit. When the statute formulates clear limits, there need be no fear that we are logically committed to go down a slippery slope. So *L2* is invalid.

It may be different when the new law is vague and, while it is meant to allow only *A,* could be interpreted so that *B* is also allowed. Then there is a margin of discretion resulting from the vague text of the statute itself. Within that margin there might be a slippery-slope process in the judicial interpretation of the statute. Thus, vague statutes may give way to a slide down the slope by the judiciary.

With respect to the legislature, however, this is not a slippery-slope argument but simply an argument against vagueness of statutes, which we usually should try to avoid anyhow, as a matter of good legislation.... If the law makes it illegal to drive a car while one's driving capacities are seriously impaired as a result of alcohol abuse, this will be a constant source of controversy and slippery slopes (both uphill and downhill, for that matter). But once the legislation prohibits driving with more than 0.5 mg. alcohol per ml. blood, this problem is solved, and the risk of a slippery slope has been effectively counteracted.

The appeal to consistency or universalizability in the justification of legislation (*L1*) may have a certain force in discussions on legislation, but this depends on the political situation. Legislation usually reflects popular morality in important respects; like popular morality, its justifications may therefore be inconsistent — the more so, because law usually reflects a great many different popular moralities and compromises between them. Moreover, as statutes are usually inspired by considerations of policy and efficiency and are the result of compromises between opposing groups, distinctions that would seem trivial and irrelevant in critical morality can often be legitimate in the context of legislation. Therefore, *L1*, though in a strict sense not invalid, has almost no scope in the context of legislation.

Both logical forms have a different force in adjudication. There are three reasons for this. First, adjudication is more akin to critical moral reasoning than is legislation and less akin and responsive to popular morality than legislation. Therefore, criteria of universalizability and consistency have much greater impact. Second, according to Ronald Dworkin, adjudication should be (and is) less based upon considerations of policy and political compromise and more upon arguments of principle, and it is, in this respect, also more akin to critical morality.[10] Or, if one prefers a more positivistic view, the range in which judges have discretion is much smaller than the range in which legislatures have discretion to change laws. So there are more cases in which judges are bound to consistency with "existing law" and relatively few cases in which a judge may feel free to act as a deputy legislator. These two facts give version *L1* some force in adjudication.

The third reason is especially relevant to the *L2* argument. Adjudication deals with problems case by case. Step-by-step adjustment is a very common method of change in adjudication. Instead of bringing about a major change in the law by one bold stroke, as a legislature might do, judges often prefer to reach the same result in a great number of often almost unnoticeable steps. *A* in itself an acceptable deviation from the "existing law," might therefore be the forerunner of a series of such little steps toward an unacceptable position, *B*.

This gradual process toward the acceptance of *B* usually will not be the intention of the judge who accepts *A*. That judge may think there is a clear distinction between *A* and *B* and that the principles that justify *A* do not justify *B*. But the acceptance of *A* creates a new precedent, and therefore the legal situation for the judge deciding on *A* is no longer the same as the situation for the judge who accepted *A*. Precedent has a certain gravitational force, as Dworkin calls it.[11] The very fact of the new decision may be a reason for a similar decision concerning *M* and then concerning *N*, and so on until *B*. Moreover, during this process, not only the law concerning these specific cases is developing. Sometimes the opinions of the judges about the legal justification of *A* and *M* will change as well. Thus, the legal principles that originally justified *A* but did not justify *B* may, by the different judges deciding the cases, be continuously amended during the process, so that, in the end, *B* seems legally justifiable as well. ...

...It may be possible theoretically to distinguish between *A* and *B* upon different grounds. Different judges will hold different theories about the correct ground for the distinction. But they have to accept one another's decisions as part of the law. This may be illustrated as follows. Judge X may think that *N* and *B* are similar and that the line should be drawn between *M* and *N*, while Judge Y thinks that the line should be drawn between *N* and *B*. If Judge Y upon this basis has accepted *N*, then Judge X, respecting the precedent created by Y, will make the further step toward the acceptance of *B*. Though neither Judge X nor Judge Y would have made the step from *A* to *B* directly, their combined activity leads to the acceptance of *B*.

So while *L2* is a fallacy in critical morality and often can be effectively countered by legislation, it is a very forceful argument in adjudication. There might seem to be a parallel here with my discussion of positive morality. There I concluded that it is an empirical question whether or not the logical arguments hold some force. But here I come to a different conclusion. The reason is that consistency and universalizability requirements are institutionalized in the legislative and adjudicative processes. This is different in positive morality — a person will sometimes refuse to act consistently, simply because he "feels" there is something wrong in doing *B*.[12] In legislation and adjudication, this is not allowed: politicians and judges must be able to justify their decisions in a more rational way. There should at least be some reasonable distinction. The difference between the two is that in legislation an almost trivial distinction may be reasonable, while the criteria for reasonable distinctions in adjudication are more stringent.

THE EMPIRICAL SLIPPERY SLOPE

The empirical version argues that allowing *A*, and especially doing *A,* will ultimately cause the acceptance of *B*. The causal processes suggested vary from changes in the attitude toward killing held by doctors practicing euthanasia to a general shift in the ethos of a society. ...

...In the method of reflective equilibrium, as proposed by John Rawls and Norman Daniels, critical morality is construed as an interplay between considered judgments (intuitions) and more abstract principles.[13] It does seem quite plausible that a change in someone's moral opinions on one point (especially when leading to a change in moral practice) might, in the long run, also influence other moral opinions.

Some intuitions might change or at least be weakened, and this could result in a change in the reflective equilibrium. Consequently, in the future one perhaps will accept what seems now completely reprehensible. In that sense, there is a slippery slope indeed. This problem is an inevitable consequence of the general neo-intuitionist position. The neo-intuitionist introduces elements of positive morality into his critical morality.

But should we call this a slippery slope? The notion of a slippery slope presumes that our current opinions about the wrongness of *B* are correct. But that is exactly what a neo-intuitionist might question. Intuitions are not indubitable. The neo-intuitionist will realize that her intuitions are partly historically and socially determined, and she therefore will accept that empirical influence on her future opinions cannot be an argument against the first move in a certain direction as long as this move in itself appears to be correct.

The conclusion can be that even in a neo-intuitionist theory, the empirical slippery slope is not a valid argument against allowing *A*. Therefore, we can safely dismiss the empirical version as far as critical morality is concerned.

In positive morality, the ground for the empirical argument seems much more firm. As we already noticed in our discussion of neo-intuitionism, there is an interaction between a society's moral opinions and its social practices, such that a change in moral opinion, and especially in moral practice on one point, may result in changes in moral opinion and practice on other points. The allegation that practicing euthanasia will result in a diminished respect for human life may be understood as a hypothesis about social processes. Whether this in fact is plausible is a different, empirical question. ... For now, we can conclude that, theoretically speaking, this type of argument can be valid.

Law resembles positive morality in this respect. There is, in our type of society, a clear interaction between legal norms, moral norms, and social practice. We can understand the following hypothesis, even if we do not consider it empirically sound: "Legalization of abortion might lead to a diminished respect for life, and this in turn might lead to a more positive attitude toward killing handicapped newborns, which in the end might result in a shift in legal norms on the latter subject."[14] A change of law might indeed be the first step on the empirical slippery slope.

We should make a distinction between legislation and adjudication here as well, though only a difference in emphasis. The moral opinions of the community are usually more directly represented by the elected legislature than by the life-appointed judiciary.... Therefore, new steps on the slope are more likely to be taken by legislature than by judges. An opposite tendency, however, is that creating a statute — especially in a multiparty, coalition system — costs more time, energy, and willingness to compromise than does creating a new precedent. There is a built-in conservative bias in legislation.

Judicial reasoning has a greater affinity with moral reasoning in critical morality, and therefore it will less soon yield to pressures from public opinion when that opinion is not supported by principled arguments. But even the judiciary in the end is responsive to society (be it only by new appointments), so this is no more than a minor difference here. We may conclude that in law the empirical version may be valid, though its relevance may be greater in the context of adjudication than in the context of legislation.

INTERIM CONCLUSIONS

So far, we have dealt with the first question: What type of norms will be influenced by the decision, and which versions of the argument are relevant to these different types?... We can draw a number of preliminary conclusions.... The first ... one is that in critical morality only the logical *L1* argument is acceptable, while in positive morality only the empirical argument may be valid. The law has an intermediate position on these two versions. Because law has an orientation both toward positive and toward critical morality, it gives both arguments some standing, though the importance is less than the importance they have in the respective fields of morality.

The most striking conclusion, however, is the opposite stance for statute and precedent with respect to the second logical argument. Precedent is highly vulnerable to this argument, whereas statutes may even form an explicit and safe barrier against it. For most lawyers, this conclusion will confirm their experience. A legislator makes statutes, changing them in an all-or-nothing fashion, while a judge may try a more experimental approach, be it sometimes of the "Echternach-type procession" (three steps forward and two backward).

This conclusion has some implications for the best policy in legal reform. Sometimes, when legalization of certain activities is being considered, a certain consensus exists (at least between the relevant groups) about some relatively clear new criteria and norms. In such a situation, it is desirable to incorporate these in a statute and thus prevent a slippery slope. In other cases, there is not yet a clear consensus about the exact criteria and norms to be formulated. Then the problem can best be tackled case by case, and the judge seems better equipped to do this. Clear rules will then crystallize as the result of judicial experimentation: judges can respond to new exigencies and to the critique from the legal and the public forum on their decisions. Only after this process has resulted in clear guidelines, is it useful to lay them down in a statute.

In fact, this has been the course of events regarding euthanasia in the Netherlands for the past twenty years.[15] There was a growing consensus that the existing rules had to be changed, but no exact idea of the new limits. In response to this situation, judges have tried to decide the cases brought before them, listening to public discussion and responding by sometimes broadening previous decisions, sometimes retreating. The result has been a consistent and well-defensible law of precedent on euthanasia, which is accepted by large proportions of Dutch society. The result seems much more acceptable and, from a principled point of view, better justifiable than it would have been, had a political compromise resulted in legislation somewhere in the process.

Such a situation is not one of a slippery slope, however, but only a situation of uncertainty. It has been called by Inez de Beaufort "a winding road": one knows the first steps to go, but not whether one wants to travel the whole road, because from the position where one is now, one cannot see the full length of the road.[16] Perhaps sooner or later the road will go down steeply, but we do not know, and if it does, we can always stop in time, provided we walk carefully. To return from this metaphor back to reality: provided we act carefully, we need not refrain from allowing *A* if we now regard it justifiable, only because there is a theoretical possibility that in the future this step might, through a series of further steps we need not take, lead to *B*.

WHAT DOES IT MEAN TO ALLOW *A?*

We now come to the second part of this article. In the ethical debate so far, there has been a curiously naive use of expressions such as "if we allow *A*." Of course, other expressions are used, such as "accept," "approve of," "support," or "introduce into society a rule permitting." Sometimes the argument focuses on prohibiting an action instead of allowing it. ("If the government forbids the exhibition of Robert Mapplethorpe's photographs, we will end up forbidding the exhibition of Michelangelo's *David*.") But these differences may be ignored here, because the argument would hold for all these varieties as well. There is a relevant difference, nevertheless, between "allowing *A*" on the one hand, and "doing *A*" or "practicing *A*," on the other hand. ...

We will begin with a preliminary point. In the context of the slippery-slope arguments, "allowing *A*" must imply a change in the status quo, or otherwise it cannot be a first step on the slippery slope. This can either mean that *A* was hitherto (explicitly or implicitly) forbidden or that *A* is a new case, not yet explicitly dealt with by moral or legal norms. An example of the first type is the legal permission of abortion (until then illegal) under certain conditions; an example of the second type is the social and moral acceptance of in vitro fertilization or DNA technology.

In the context of a critical morality, it is not easy to make sense of the expression "if we allow *A*." One reason is that critical morality is linked with claims about universality in time and place, and thus the idea of amending critical morality and allowing something hitherto forbidden does sound odd. A second problem is that there is no such thing as *the* critical morality; there are only many proposals for critical moralities: Rawlsian, utilitarian, and so forth. This second problem can be tackled by defining the "we" as the forum of ethicists broadly belonging to the same tradition — for example, the forum of utilitarians or the forum of contractarian Rawlsians.... Then we could interpret the phrase as: "if our forum allows *A*."

But what can bring such a forum to allow *A?* We may presume the members do not do so because of the breakfast they ate but because of good reasons they saw for allowing *A*. I see three reasons for a forum to allow *A*. The first is that, after ample reflection and discussion, it is agreed that the current formulation of a certain rule or principle should be refined in such a way that it allows *A*, because there are no convincing reasons to forbid *A*. An example is the regulation of new technologies: the rules were not formulated with these technologies in mind and therefore must be fine-tuned to deal with the new problems. The second possibility is that, after reflection and discussion, the forum finds that until now a certain principle has not been given accurate weight, and that it should be given this weight now, which results in seeing *A* as acceptable. An example might be the allowing of (voluntary) euthanasia as a result of further reflection on the principle of autonomy. We might also think of some related types of developments in ethical theory, like the modification of central concepts, the theoretical justification of new principles hitherto unnoticed, and so on. The third reason is that the members of the forum have an intuition that *A* is acceptable that is so strong that they agree to modify the existing rule forbidding *A* (or not mentioning *A* at all), so as to allow *A* explicitly. This could happen, for instance, if they are confronted with a very convincing case of someone asking for euthanasia, which makes them modify their hitherto absolute prohibition of euthanasia.

In all three cases, the forum acts on good reasons. Being trained ethicists, the members will try to find out whether the new formulation or the new weight of the principle or rule will have other implications in cases that they do not find acceptable. They will do this for reasons of consistency and because they agree that their judgments must be universalizable. We may assume that if the thought of *B* as a counterexample presents itself to the proponent of the slippery-slope argument, it will also present itself to the minds of the forum — even if, at the time of the decision, it is yet a purely hypothetical case. Therefore, they will consider *B* as well, and either modify their theories or basic concepts so that *B* is not allowed or, perhaps reluctantly, grant that *B* must be acceptable as well because they can see no good grounds for discriminating between *A* and *B*. In none of these cases, however, can we truly speak of a slippery slope. The members of the forum clearly realize at the time they discuss *A* what the implications for *B* are. The possible acceptance of *B* is not a future, unknown, and unforeseen consequence; it is explicitly weighed in the decision.

This reflection on the implications of the most reasonable interpretation of the expression "if we allow *A*" brings us to an interesting conclusion. It is that the logical version *L1* is no slippery slope at all: it is simply a question of universalizability.[17]

The same holds for the use of the argument in law: there, it does not add anything either to the implications of universalizability and consistency requirements. As *L1* seemed to be valid only in critical morality and law, we can therefore safely dismiss it from the debate altogether. The role it played until now could be played by the requirements of universalizability and consistency, which would be better and less loaded with rhetoric.

In the context of social morality, the empirical version of the slippery-slope argument was the only one that, from a theoretical point of view, could be valid. What does "we allow *A*" mean in this context? There are two possible interpretations. The first, focusing on the normative level holds that it is the positive evaluation of *A* as such that causes the subsequent steps downward on the slippery slope. The second, focusing on the level of social practices, states that it

is the resulting practice or policy *A*, that will lead us down the slope.

In [the first] ... interpretation, it is held that allowing *A* will be the beginning and the cause of a norm erosion that will ultimately end in the acceptance of *B*. But what is this act of "allowing *A*"? It is highly unlikely that the acceptance of *A* involves a sudden conversion of the whole group. It is more plausible that it is a gradual process, in which growing numbers accept *A* and their valuation of *A* is slowly evolving from negative or neutral to more positive. So we should interpret "we allow *A*" as referring to a gradual process of growing acceptance of *A* by a social group or by society.

This acceptance of *A* or *B* is not a completely isolated process, but it will usually be part of a more complex social process and will be the resultant of many social factors. Therefore, it is often impossible to isolate the acceptance of *A* as the necessary condition for, or even as the main cause of, the acceptance of *B*. That makes conclusive proof on the empirical slippery-slope argument very difficult, if not impossible, both for the proponent and for the opponent. Nevertheless, as we shall see, in some cases there may be at least enough evidence to make it a plausible argument.

To clarify the conditions for a sound and plausible argument, it may be useful to analyze two situations in which the empirical slippery-slope argument is sometimes used, but in which it must be considered an invalid argument against the acceptance of *A*.

The first situation is when the acceptance of *A* is merely a symptom of a broad social process of which the acceptance of *B* might be the outcome. It is the result of that process, without being itself a causal factor in the process leading to the acceptance of *B*. Attacking the symptom will not stop the process then, and will result in an ineffective symbolic campaign. If we do not consider *A* to be morally wrong on other grounds, it is not a good argument against accepting *A* to say that in the end the same process will lead to accepting *B*.

The second situation in which the empirical slippery-slope argument is used is when accepting *A*, though not merely a symptom but part of the social process itself, is seen as a symbol of the process.[18] Though in itself it may appear to be morally neutral or relatively harmless, it should not be allowed because it is part of that broad process that ultimately might lead to *B*. I think this is too easy a conclusion. For we could say so only if we are sure that all the constitutive and derivative elements of this social process are wrong in themselves. When we look at social processes in history, however, we find that these are always mixtures of good and bad elements. The French Revolution resulted in much violence but also in great reforms (we need only recall the great Napoleonic codifications). The growing emphasis on autonomy, symbolized in the increasing acceptance of abortion, might lead to more than only growing tolerance of infanticide upon parental request, as some of the opponents of abortion argue. (For the sake of the argument, I am assuming with some opponents of abortion that it might do so, but I doubt whether this is an empirically sound estimation.) It might also lead to a strengthening of the norm of informed consent in medical treatment. We should not protest against the acceptance of informed consent only because it is part of the process that might lead to infanticide. The simple fact that the acceptance of *A* is part of a social process leading to *B* can, as such, never be an argument against accepting *A*.

By allowing *A* we do not step on the slippery slope; we are already on the slope.[19] We only make a further step, but this step must be evaluated as an act or a process in its own right, for we cannot say *a priori* in which direction it goes. It may be a neutral step sideward. (For example, the

acceptance of informed consent might be seen so if we use only one criterion of the direction we take: Does it lead to infanticide or not?) Or it may even be a step upward. (If we strengthen the norm of informed consent, it might even form an extra barrier against infanticide.) Therefore, we need something more than the simple fact that the acceptance of *A* is part of a process toward *B* to establish a sound slippery-slope argument.

Sometimes, however, there is some further evidence. Allowing *A* is a major factor in the process leading to the acceptance of *B,* or at least a necessary condition. The acceptance that abortion may sometimes be morally justified is a necessary condition for the acceptance of an abortion program based on eugenic purposes. The line between the status quo and *A* is a clear and effective one (for example, a general prohibition against killing or abortion), but there are no such lines between *A* and *B*. Allowing *A* will then remove a social barrier without instituting a new barrier. Factor *A* may not be the only factor, and it may not even be the main factor in the process leading to *B*. But sometimes it is the only factor we can influence, or is simply the factor that is most easily influenced.

We should recall Bernard Williams's differentiation between reasonable and effective distinctions here. The argument is not that there is no reasonable distinction. The argument is that, though there may be a reasonable distinction between *A* and *B*, it is not enough. What is missing is an effective barrier against accepting *B* in the way the existing prohibition serves as an effective barrier. The prohibition against killing is effective against involuntary euthanasia, but once we have accepted voluntary euthanasia, there will be no more barriers. The old, standard rule against killing is thus weakened, and the new rule that includes the exception for voluntary euthanasia will not be a defensible new barrier — or so the opponent of legalizing voluntary euthanasia might argue.

This is, in a sense, the empirical transformation of the logical versions. If there is not a reasonable distinction, then we have the empirical analog of *L1*. If there is a reasonable distinction that is not effective, it is the empirical analog of *L2*. Once accepting *A,* we will be driven by long strides or by unnoticeable small steps toward *B*, without any possibility to stop. The reasons that there is no such effective barrier may differ. It can be that there is no consensus about the further distinctions to be drawn.[20] It may be that the concepts used in defending *A* are so vague and ambiguous that the gray zone can easily be made to encompass *B*.[21] This version of the empirical argument cannot be dismissed *a priori*. It is obvious that it may hold, and it has some intuitive appeal. Whether in a discussion it may be considered a sound argument largely depends upon the facts, and we will come back to this aspect later.

This brings us to the second interpretation of the empirical slippery slope, which concentrates on the practice of *A*. Sometimes it is argued that it is necessary that doctors have a strong attitude against killing, and that practicing abortion and euthanasia will diminish this attitude. Then the argument holds that doing *A* has a corrupting effect on the actor. Slightly different is the version that focuses on the corrupting effect of living in a society that practices and accepts *A*. The most famous example is that in a society that tolerates voluntary euthanasia, older people will feel social pressure to ask for euthanasia, especially when they think they are a burden to their relatives and to society.

We should be careful with the first version. It may seem more plausible than it is. Dentists cause a lot of pain, daily, but I do not believe that this has resulted in a more negligent attitude toward causing pain in other situations. Of course, not every situation is like the dentist's in offering clear distinctions between causing pain in a certain role and outside that role, and between causing pain justified by the goal of preventing pain and causing pain without such a justification. Especially when the two forms of causing pain (or killing) are part of the same role, there may be a corrupting effect on the actor. It seems that much depends upon the existence of clear distinctions between different roles or between different aspects of a role. The corrupting effect may be more likely to occur when there are no clear and simple distinctions. However, in the cases of voluntary euthanasia and abortion, equally clear distinctions as those in the case of the dentist may be found.

There are better arguments for the second version. We can imagine that society's practicing *A* and openly accepting it have certain side effects — for example, fear in old people's homes of involuntary euthanasia. However, I would hold that this fear is less likely when there is an accepted practice of voluntary euthanasia than when there is an official and hypocritical rejection of euthanasia while, in fact, it is largely practiced. It is better to have a public discussion on the exact limits of a certain practice, which makes clear control possible, than to let the practice go on in secret and illegally, without possible forms of control. The latter situation is more susceptible to the slippery slope.

Whether these side effects are likely is largely an empirical question. We should, however, distinguish here between side effects and slippery-slope effects. That a certain fear of *B* results from *A* is a side effect, which certainly should be taken into account. But it is not a slippery-slope effect, for it does not say that *B* itself will result. Very often when a rhetorical appeal to the slippery slope is made, it is only an appeal to side effects. That it is a side-effects argument in disguise does not imply, of course, that it should not be taken seriously. I only want to make clear that it is not a slippery-slope argument.

We may conclude that two empirical slope arguments can be sound. One holds that the effective barrier that now exists cannot be replaced by another effective one; the other, that practicing A by a certain society, group, or person may result in a changing attitude toward B. Whether in concrete situations these arguments are sound largely depends upon the facts of the situation. James Rachels rightly remarks that this is an empirical question about which philosophers have no special inside information.[22] But we can make some general remarks on the acceptability of certain arguments.

De Beaufort formulates the following requirements for the acceptability of a slippery-slope argument: one has to make plausible that the expected short-term consequences are clear, negative, and probable, and that these follow from or directly have to do with the proposed act or policy.[23] The long-term consequences should result from the short-term consequences and be clear and negative, as well, but need not be inevitable. It is enough to make plausible that it will be difficult to prevent these consequences. It must be plausible that while we can stop now, we will not have that same possibility farther down the slope.[24] The third condition she gives is that there must be an alternative that is less susceptible to the slippery slope.

It may be clear that these requirements place a heavy burden of proof on the shoulders of the proponent of the slippery-slope argument. In fact, we have good reasons to think it will seldom be possible to meet that burden. Especially the third requirement seems difficult to meet. Usually when we discuss the slippery slope, we are already on the slope, and some practice is already going on (sometimes hidden), even though it is condemned by popular

morality and law. Secrecy has its own side effects with which we must reckon, while open discussion of a change in social norms may result in reasonable and effective new distinctions. Trying to keep the old distinctions alive might well result in the opposite: a growing secret practice that is ultimately more damaging to the fundamental norms than a partially open practice. A second reason is that we know that society is usually able to cope very well with gray-zone problems, and very often reasonable distinctions may be made effectively. Therefore, there have to be good reasons to think society will not be able to do so in this case. When there is no reasonable distinction, this is different, of course, but then the main argument simply must be that because B is immoral, A is immoral as well. The slippery slope may then only be an auxiliary argument.

My conclusion is that, though we cannot give any *a priori* arguments against the empirical version of the slippery slope, there are some factors that usually make it very implausible that the empirical burden of proof is met. Therefore, I think in practical reasoning the argument should not play the important role that it often does.

Our argument until now has been rather deconstructive. The slippery-slope argument in moral discourse appeared to be either the universalizability principle in disguise (*L1*), or simply invalid (*L2*) or only very rarely plausible (the empirical version). Fortunately, in the context of law it has a legitimate and important role, so there is yet some hope for the argument.

To begin with the empirical version: while in critical and positive morality the empirical argument largely failed as a result of our analysis of "allowing A," in law often there is a clear and separate act of allowing A. Law is an institution that makes the validity of its norms largely dependent upon whether authoritative organs accept them. So whereas it seems odd to say that at time T the critical forum did allow A (without explicitly allowing B as well), or that at time T the community suddenly allowed A, it does make sense when we say that on 1 February 1989, the Supreme Court or the state's legislature did allow A.

And not only can we distinguish a separate act by which A is allowed, but this act can also sometimes be distinguished as a causal factor in further developments. The legal abolition of slavery, or the universal suffrage for women, constituted acts which, while expressing broader social processes, have had causal effects of their own. *Roe v. Wade* changed the living conditions of many people in the United States; but, moreover, it is not unlikely that the decision (and the resulting practice) has had indirect influences on the moral and legal norms. Thus, it is easy to distinguish both the act of allowing A and the resulting practice as separate causes in a social development. And this identification of A as a separate cause was one of the main problems in the moral empirical version. Moreover, because we can make safer predictions about the effects of legalization than about the effects of such an elusive phenomenon as a gradual change in moral norms, the burden of proof in the legal version is considerably less heavy.

In law, there is also a legitimate place for the second logical version of the slippery slope ($L2$), which we considered the only logical version worthy of its name. When there is a decision of a court allowing A, then this is a new element in the body of legal norms from which courts must make their own theory of law.[25] It may make one decision in a related case much stronger in the "dimension of fit" than it would have been without this precedent, and this may tip the scales.[26] Once A has been accepted, this could mean indeed that, through a series of small and often almost unnoticeable steps, in the end we arrive at B. So

the argument that allowing A will cause norm erosion may in law be a valid and sound argument, while in positive morality it largely fails because we cannot isolate A as a simple cause.

We may conclude that both varieties of the slippery slope do have standing in the legal field. When arguing about whether the law on abortion or whatever subject needs to be changed, we should take the argument into account. But we can generalize this conclusion and say that if the system of norms is institutionalized in such a way that there are normative authorities who can make normative decisions, then the slippery slope may be a risk of which we need beware.[27] For it may hold for government decisions, for a manager's decision in a company, or for an ethics committee as well. Even a university tutor is a normative authority: allowing a student to hand in a paper a day late may set a precedent. The essential element is that allowing A is a separate act, which may be distinguished as such, and which may lead to a difference in social practice. For the existence of a separate act is necessary both to make a first step (and further steps) and to be identifiable as a separate cause and not simply as a symbol or symptom.

CONCLUSIONS

Our conclusion is that the slippery-slope arguments may have an important and legitimate place in the context of law only, and a very marginal one in the context of positive morality. Yet the argument is frequently being used in ethical debates. Why? I can see four reasons for this.

The first and most trivial one is that the argument has great rhetorical — or demagogical — power. If one wants to show that test-tube babies are a horrible development, one shows the horrors of a Brave New World. If one does not have serious arguments against voluntary euthanasia, one suggests that we will end in Nazi practices.[28] Whenever one can invoke a slippery slope, the opponent will be on the defensive. But this rhetorical value can be a causal explanation for the popularity; it is not a justification.

The second explanation is that the argument appeals to a genuine concern about certain developments, for instance, in biomedical ethics. This concern should be taken seriously, but it should not be discussed in the context of the slippery-slope argument. If, for example, recent developments in biotechnology are considered to be the consequence of an extremely instrumentalistic view of nature, we should critically discuss that view, and only in the context of that discussion should we look at the more specific developments like genetic manipulation.

The third reason that the slippery-slope argument is employed in ethical debates is the interdependence of law and the two types of morality. In this article I have, for analytical reasons, assumed that law, critical morality, and positive morality are separate norm systems. But, of course, they are not. Critical and positive morality influence each other. But more important, law and the two types of morality are interdependent. Moral and public questions are discussed within an institutionalized context. When in a Western type of society a moral philosopher discusses the morality of euthanasia, this is not only a debate on the critical level of morality. It fits in an institutional context in which a debate is going on about the question whether — and, if so, under which conditions — euthanasia should be legalized. And when the general public discusses genetic manipulation of animals, this will influence the government and the legislature.

This interdependence of law and critical and positive morality (and, we could add, politics) is most strong in those areas of law and morality that are subject to rapid changes and developments.[29] An example is the field of medical ethics and health law. Ethicists are being asked their expert opinions on many questions of public policy and law, and the ethical debate directly influences legal decisions and political debates. In the field of medical ethics, the norms of law and morals have not yet become separated but are intertwined.

In such an institutionalized context, an ethicist can legitimately use slippery-slope arguments, insofar as she discusses the question of the law's or government's intervention. But she should not do so when she discusses the morality of a new technique as such. We may carefully use the slippery-slope argument, but only with respect to legal or other institutionalized decisions.

If we want to have a truly moral slippery slope, we should look for it somewhere else than we usually do. It is to be found at the core of the professional ethics of ethicists. An ethicist must realize there are differences between law and morals, and between positive and critical morality. Too often, ethicists simply assume that a sound argument in the context of morality is also sound in the context of law, and vice versa. But there is a distinction here (undoubtedly with a broad gray zone) that really matters. The really dangerous slippery slope, therefore, is that of an ethicist too easily going from the moral field to the legal field and using the same arguments in both fields.

The fourth explanation is a psychological one. For the slippery-slope argument, especially in its empirical version, usually no conclusive proof can be given, either for or against. Both sides can point to facts that fit their positions, and therefore, whether one accepts the argument largely depends on one's fundamental outlook. Someone with a more pessimistic outlook, who believes "everything is getting worse," will interpret the facts in a negative way and will see every new technique as a further step in the wrong direction. The optimist, on the other hand, will interpret new developments as steps in the right direction; the more negative aspects will be seen as accidental and correctable.

Moreover, this pessimistic outlook is reflected in a negative attitude toward the question of whether one thinks things can be stopped. Someone who trusts in the checks and balances of a democratic society in which he lives usually will also have confidence in the possibility to correct future developments. If we can stop now, we will be able to stop in the future as well, when necessary; therefore, we need not stop here yet. If one is more critical toward the existing political and legal order, one will have less confidence in the possibility to stop future developments. (However, in that situation the argument seems self-defeating. For when one does not believe that we can stop in the future, why is it reasonable to believe that we have the possibility to do so now?)

This fundamental difference in outlook makes discussion of the slippery-slope argument often futile. The discussion is not really a rational discussion of facts and norms (though it sometimes pretends to be), because the acceptance of the arguments so strongly depends on one's basic outlook. This is one more reason to be careful with the argument in moral debate — it usually will not help us any further but, rather, will frustrate the discussion. Therefore, it seems more fruitful to analyze and discuss the fundamental questions that are hidden behind the use of the argument. This will probably be more effective in preventing the developments that are feared than the rhetorical and emotional use of the slippery-slope argument.

Acknowledgments

I am grateful to Robert Heeger, Theo van Willigenburg, Theresa Takken, Anton Vedder, Marcel Verweij, Charles Goossens, and the readers and editors of *Ethics* for their comments upon earlier drafts of this paper. My colleagues at the Centre for Bioethics and Health Law at the University of Utrecht also gave helpful criticisms. The research for this article was partly financed by the Dutch State Department of Public Health.

NOTES

1. Compare I. de Beaufort, "Op weg naar het einde?" in *Euthanasie: Knelpunten in een discussie,* ed. GA. van der Wal (Baarn, the Netherlands: Ambo, 1987), 1.

2. See H.L.A. Hart, *Law, Liberty, and Morality* (London: Oxford University Press, 1963), 20. I introduce this distinction for analytical purposes, without supposing anything like clear barriers between the different types of norms.

3. A.G.M. Campbell and R.-S. Duff, "Deciding the Care of Severely Malformed or Dying Infants," *Journal of Medical Ethics* 5 (1979): 65-67.

4. For this interpretation, see, for example, B. Williams, "Which Slopes Are Slippery?" in *Moral Dilemmas in Modern Medicine,* ed. M. Lockwood (Oxford, England: Oxford University Press, 1985), 126-37.

5. Compare V. Brummer, *Theology and Philosophical Inquiry. An Introduction* (London: MacMillan, 1981), 191-97.

6. Compare T.L. Beauchamp and J.F. Childress, *Principles of Biomedical Ethics,* 2nd ed. (New York: Oxford University Press, 1983), 120.

7. For an analogous conclusion, see J. Glover, *Causing Death and Saving Lives* (Harmondsworth, England: Penguin, 1977), 166; de Beaufort, "Op weg naar het einde?" 14.

8. An additional argument would be that reasoning in such a way assumes an extremely legalistic position: it must suppose a special, even ontological, status for moral rules. Compare J.N. Shklar, *Legalism: Law, Morals and Political Trials* (1964; reprint, Cambridge, MA: Harvard University Press, 1978) for a critique on this position.

9. B. Williams, "Which Slopes Are Slippery?" 127.

10. Compare R. Dworkin, *A Matter of Principle?* (Cambridge, MA: Harvard University Press, 1985).

11. R. Dworkin, *Taking Rights Seriously* (Cambridge, MA: Harvard University Press, 1977), 113.

12. On this difference, see S. Hampshire, "Public and Private Morality," in *Public and Private Morality*, ed. S. Hampshire (Cambridge, England: Cambridge University Press, 1980), 23-53.

13. Compare J. Rawls, *A Theory of Justice* (1972; reprint, Oxford, England: Oxford University Press, 1978); and N. Daniels, "Wide Reflective Equilibrium and Theory Acceptance in Ethics," *Journal of Philosophy* 76 (1979): 256-82.

14. I doubt whether this in our Western societies is really a plausible connection, but that does not matter here. Theoretically it is not completely implausible that such a causal chain might exist in a certain society, and that is all we need establish here. See also the discussion between Hare and Rachels in R.M. Hare, "Medical Ethics: Can the Moral Philosopher Help?" in *Philosophical Medical Ethics: Its Nature and Significance*, ed. S.F. Spicker and H.T. Engelhardt, Jr. (Dordrecht, the Netherlands: Reidel, 1977), 49-61, esp. 53; and J. Rachels, "Medical Ethics and the Rule against Killing: Comments on Professor Hare's Paper," in Spicker and Engelhardt, 63-69, esp. 65-66.

15. On this subject, see J.K.M. Gevers, "Legal Developments Concerning Active Euthanasia on Request in the Netherlands," *Bioethics* 1 (1987): 156-62.

16. de Beaufort, "Opweg naar het einde?" 30.

17. B. Williams, "Which Slopes Are Slippery?" 127, seems to make the same point, when he notes that the slippery slope is sometimes used to make one see a more fundamental point that goes beyond the slippery slope: "Not all cases in which a slippery slope comes into the discussion are genuinely slippery-slope arguments."

18. That it is a symbol explains why it is so heavily fought. The broader processes are very difficult to analyze and to fight. As a symbol it may be the focus of symbolic crusades. Compare J. F. Gusfield, *Symbolic Crusade: Status Politics and the American Temperance Movement* (Chicago: University of Illinois Press, 1963).

19. Compare Harris, *The Value of Life*, 127: "We are in fact only able to identify slippery slopes when we are already on them."

20. B. Williams, "Which Slopes Are Slippery?" 128.

21. de Beaufort, "Op weg naar het einde?" 23.

22. Rachels, *The End of Life,* 173.

23. de Beaufort, "Op weg naar het einde?" 21-22. Her requirements are largely the same as those of other authors, such as Rachels, *The End of Life,* 174, and B. Williams, "Which Slopes Are Slippery? " 132.

24. This is not an easy burden of proof. Compare B. Williams, "Which Slopes Are Slippery?" 132.

25. In law, the analogy with the false Vermeer paintings by Van Meegeren therefore does make sense, because we can evaluate the resulting development from a critical point of view, from an external perspective. In a neo-intuitionist critical morality, it is a false analogy because it assumes there is an objective reality or some Archimedian point from which to criticize developments.

26. For this idea of a dimension of fit, see Dworkin, *A Matter of Principle,* 142.

27. I use the expression "institutionalized system of norms" here not in a wide sociological sense but in a more narrow sense. J. Raz, *Practical Reason and Norms* (London: Hutchinson, 1975), 123, formulates this concept as follows: "When discussing institutionalized systems we will be concerned not with any institution created by norms but with a special type of institutions, those which are not only established by norms but whose function is to create and apply norms."

28. Despite the different pretenses, this is the way the argument is used in D. Lamb, *Down the Slippery Slope* (London: Croom Helm, 1988).

29. In the terminology of J. Habermas, medical ethics is a field in which law, morals, and politics are not yet differentiated *(ausdifferenziert).*

Joint Statement on Resuscitative Interventions
Canadian Medical Association

This joint statement is intended to provide guidance for the development of policies regarding the appropriate use of cardio-pulmonary resuscitation (CPR). This joint statement was approved by the Canadian Hospital Association, the CMA and the Catholic Health Association of Canada and was developed in cooperation with the Canadian Bar Association. The co-sponsors of this statement encourage health care facilities to develop policies for their institutions.

"Canadian Medical Association Policy Summary: Joint statement on resuscitative interventions" — Reprinted from, by permission of the publisher, *CMAJ,* 1994; 151 (8), 1176A-C. Please note that this CMA Policy Summary has been updated; Joint Statement on Resuscitative Interventions (Update 1995), *CMAJ,* 1995; 153 (11), 1652A-C.

CPR was developed as a treatment intervention for cases of sudden unexpected cardiac or respiratory arrest. However, it has come to be used as a standard intervention in virtually all cases of sudden cardiac or respiratory arrest, whether unexpected or not, unless a specific order to the contrary (do not resuscitate [DNR]) has been stipulated on the patient's health record. It is clear now, after several decades of experience and review, that there are people who benefit from this treatment and others for whom there is no benefit and potentially significant harm. In the latter situations, CPR is not only generally unsuccessful but also inappropriate, as it may serve only to increase discomfort and prolong dying. It is timely to reassess the use of CPR, to suggest when it is or is not indicated and to develop mechanisms to ensure that CPR is initiated only when appropriate.

POLICY DEVELOPMENT

General

Health care facilities are encouraged to make use of an interdisciplinary committee with access to legal and ethical consultation to develop a policy, a program for its implementation and a conflict-resolution mechanism.

The policy should identify which resuscitative interventions are available in the facility; with the conflict-resolution mechanism, it should ensure sensitivity to cultural and religious differences. The implementation program should include education of all those who will be affected by the policy, including caregivers. The policy must be in accordance with relevant federal and provincial or territorial law. It should be reviewed regularly and revised when necessary in light of the clinical, ethical and legal developments on the topic.

Since policies and guidelines cannot cover all possible situations, appropriate consultation mechanisms should be available to address specific issues in a timely manner.

Guiding Principles

The following principles are integral to the development of CPR policy:

1. Good health care requires open communication, discussion and sensitivity to cultural and religious differences among caregivers, potential recipients of care, their family members and significant others.

2. A person must be given sufficient information about the benefits, risks and likely outcomes of all treatment options to enable him or her to make informed decisions.

3. A competent person has the right to refuse, or withdraw consent to, any clinically indicated treatment including life-saving or life-sustaining treatment.

4. When a person is incompetent, treatment decisions must be based on his or her wishes, if these are known.

5. When an incompetent person's wishes are not known, treatment decisions must be based on the person's best interests, taking into account:

   (a) the person's known values and preferences,

   (b) information received from those who are significant in the person's life and who could help in determining his or her best interests,

   (c) aspects of the person's culture and religion that would influence a treatment decision, and

   (d) the person's diagnosis and prognosis.

6. There is no obligation to offer a person futile or nonbeneficial treatment.

CPR As a Treatment Option

The efficacy of CPR in restoring cardiac and respiratory functioning varies from nil to very high, depending on a number of factors. On the basis of research studies of such outcomes four general categories can be distinguished.

1. People who are likely to benefit from CPR.
2. People for whom benefit is uncertain.
3. People for whom benefit is unlikely.
4. People who almost certainly will not benefit.

These categories can be adapted to the particular circumstances of the care setting and are compatible with policies that establish levels of care or intervention.

Competence

Determination of competence is made by the attending physician in consultation with other caregivers. If the person for whom resuscitation is being considered is incompetent, decisions should be made on his or her behalf as indicated earlier (guiding principles 4 and 5). If the person's incompetence is uncertain or intermittent, efforts should be made to facilitate the regaining of competence.

Treatment Decision

Decisions about resuscitative interventions should be considered before the need for intervention arises or a crisis occurs. The decision should be made within the context of discussions concerning the plan of treatment and on the basis of the person's medical condition and his or her wishes.

1. People who are likely to benefit from CPR: There is a good chance that CPR will restore cardiac and respiratory function and that the restored function will be maintained. The likelihood of the person's returning to his or her pre-arrest condition is high.

2. People for whom benefit is uncertain: The person's condition or prognosis or both may not have been assessed before the loss of cardiac and respiratory function. It is unknown or uncertain whether CPR will restore functioning. The subsequent prognosis or the likelihood of adverse consequences are also unknown or uncertain.

3. People for whom benefit is unlikely: There is little chance that CPR will restore cardiac and respiratory function; even if the function is restored, it is unlikely to be maintained. The likelihood of the patient's returning to his or her pre-arrest condition is low.

4. People who almost certainly will not benefit: There is almost certainly no chance that the person will benefit from CPR, either because the underlying illness or disease makes recovery from arrest virtually unprecedented or because the person will be permanently unable to experience any benefit.

Communication

1. Health care recipients

(a) People who are likely to benefit from CPR and people for whom benefit is uncertain will normally be made aware that emergency life-saving measures will be instituted if the need arises. This information should be presented during discussion about the plan of treatment so as not to alarm the person.

(b) People for whom benefit from CPR is unlikely should be made fully aware of the limitations of CPR, and their life goals, values and preferences should be discussed before or shortly after admission to a health care facility, before the need for intervention arises.

(c) People who almost certainly will not benefit from CPR are not candidates for CPR, and it should not be presented as a treatment option. Whether this is discussed with the person is a matter of judgement based on the circumstances of the case and the principles specified earlier.

2. Health care providers

   Decisions concerning whether CPR is an appropriate treatment option should be clearly noted on the person's health record along with the outcome of any discussions with the person so that all health care providers involved in his or her care are aware of the decision.

3. Family members and significant others

   A person should be encouraged to advise family members, significant others and potential proxy decision-makers of his or her decision about CPR.

Implementation of the Decision

1. Situations in which CPR should be performed.

   People likely to benefit from CPR should be given this treatment if the need arises, unless they have specifically rejected it.

   People for whom the benefit of CPR is uncertain or unlikely should be given this treatment if the need arises unless they have specifically rejected it. CPR should be initiated until the patient's condition has been assessed, following which an appropriate order can be made.

2. Situations in which CPR should not be performed.

   People who have rejected CPR and those who almost certainly will not benefit from it should not be given this treatment if an arrest occurs.

Review of Decisions

Appropriate intervals for review of decisions concerning CPR should be determined. The review should follow the same guidelines as the original decision regarding resuscitation.

In the following circumstances review of decisions should be undertaken immediately:

1. If a competent person (or proxy) changes his or her decision about resuscitation.

2. If there is a significant unexpected change in a person's condition.

PALLIATIVE CARE AND OTHER TREATMENTS

A decision not to initiate CPR does not imply the withholding or withdrawing of any other treatment or intervention.

A person who does not receive CPR should receive all other appropriate treatments, including palliative care, for his or her physical, mental and spiritual comfort.

FURTHER READINGS

Ashley, B.A. and K.D. O'Rourke. *Health Care Ethics: A Theological Analysis.* The Catholic Health Association of the United States: St. Louis, 1982.

Beauchamp, T.L. "A Reply to Rachels on Active and Passive Euthanasia." In Beauchamp and Perlin, *Ethical Issues in Death and Dying.* Englewood Cliffs, N.J.: Prentice Hall, 1978.

Engelhardt, Jr., H.T. "Euthanasia and Children: The Injury of Continued Existence." *Journal of Paediatrics* 83:170 (1073).

Foot, P. "Euthanasia." *Philosophy and Public Affairs* 6: 2 (Winter 1977).

Gould, J. and L. Craigmyle. *Your Death Warrant: The Implications of Euthanasia.* London: Chapman, 1971.

Kamisar, Yale. "Some Non-Religious Objections Against Proposed Mercy-Killing Legislation." *Minnesota Law Review* 42 (May 1958) 969–1042.

Kluge, E.-H.W. *The Practice of Death.* New Haven: Yale University Press, 1975.

Law Reform Commission of Canada. Report 20, *Euthanasia, Aiding Suicide and Cessation of Treatment.* Ottawa: Minister of Supply and Services, 1983.

———. Working Paper 46, *Omission, Negligence and Endangering.* Ottawa: Law Reform Commission, 1985.

Macklin, R. *Mortal Choices.* N.Y.: Pantheon Books, 1987.

Magnet, J.E. and E.-H.W. Kluge. *Withholding Treatment from Defective Newborn Children.* Cowansville: Brown Legal Publications, 1985.

Pope Pius XII. "Prolongation of Life: Allocution to an International Congress of Anesthesiologists," Nov. 24, 1957. *Osservatore Romano* 4 (1957).

Rachels, James. *The End of Life: Euthanasia and Morality.* Oxford: Oxford University Press, 1986.

Ramsey, P. "On (Only) Caring for the Dying." In *The Patient As Person.* New Haven and London: Yale University Press, 1970, 120–123.

Rosner, F. *Modern Medicine and Jewish Law.* New York: Yeshiva University, 1972.

Sade, R.M. and A.B. Redfern. "Euthanasia." *New England Journal of Medicine* 292: 16 (April 17, 1975), 96 ff.

Society for the Right to Die. *Handbook of Living Will Laws.* New York: Society for the Right to Die, 1987.

Vaux, K., ed. *Who Shall Live? Medicine, Technology, Ethics.* Philadelphia: Fortress Press, 1970.

Veatch, R. *Death, Dying, and the Biological Revolution: Our Last Quest for Responsibility.* New Haven and London: Yale University Press, 1970.

CHAPTER 15
THE RIGHT TO HAVE CHILDREN

INTRODUCTION

Advances in knowledge never take place in isolation. They occur in a social setting that lays the conceptual foundations for their development and provides
the technical basis for their realization. The social setting also furnishes the
economic base for their application, and in that sense provides them with pragmatic significance. The social context therefore has tremendous influence on
their development and, in the end, is what makes them possible.

However, the influence of the social context goes further. It also surrounds
our knowledge with value-associations that colour how it is perceived. The development of knowledge is therefore never value-neutral.

This is especially true in the area of reproductive technology. That this
should be so is not surprising. Reproduction is the normal way in which societies
regenerate their membership. Therefore, societies have an inherent interest in
ensuring that the reproductive practices that exist within their domain harmonize with the values that are characteristic of the societies themselves. To this
end, reproduction is usually surrounded by a series of taboos and more or less
formalized rituals, whose function is to define and control what is socially sanctioned. Consequently, it is not unexpected that developments in the domain of
reproduction should immediately engage societal values that are fundamental
to the world-views of the societies themselves. Therefore, unless these developments can somehow be integrated into or coordinated with the existing societal
value-framework, their introduction will be resisted.

Reproduction is also a fundamental aspect of individual biological existence.
As people mature sexually, they undergo profound biological changes that affect
how they relate to others as sexual beings. At the same time, as people grow up,

they tend to internalize the value-system that characterizes the society in which they live, and to adopt it as their own. As a result, the societal values associated with reproduction tend to become an integral part of the value-system that the individual acquires in developing as a social being, and play an important role in defining the self-image of the individual person. And, just as developments that require a change in these areas may easily evoke a negative reaction from society as a whole if they are perceived as threatening to its fundamental values, so, too, such developments may be experienced as extremely threatening on the level of the individual and evoke strong personal reactions.

The last few decades have seen profound developments in reproductive technology. Methods have been developed that allow many persons who would otherwise be childless to become biological progenitors; techniques have been invented that permit the identification and detection of congenital abnormalities while the foetus is still *in utero*; and procedures have been devised that allow us to interfere with the very genetic make-up of humanity. Even methods of reproduction that have been around for millennia, such as surrogacy, are being approached in an entirely novel fashion.

Many of these developments lie outside of the traditional realm of reproductive knowledge and practice. Consequently, they tend to challenge the traditional conceptual framework in which reproduction used to be approached, and put traditional values to the test. The government of Canada, struck by the tremendous implications of these technologies and their potential for social upheaval, has recently followed the example of several provinces[1] and other countries[2] and has struck a Royal Commission to consider the variety of ethical, social, legal and administrative issues raised by the development and use of the technologies themselves. Some of its findings and recommendations will be presented in the next chapter. The selections in this chapter deal with a rather limited, but at the same time an exceedingly important, question: Is there a right to have children? The issue has become important because it is generally assumed that there is a right to have children, and this right is often interpreted as a right to biological parenthood. Support for this assumption is often sought in the Universal Declaration of Human Rights, which states that

> Men and women of full age, without any limitation to race, nationality or religion, have the right to marry and found a family.

The development and application of much of the new reproductive technologies has therefore been presented as a means of ensuring that those who cannot otherwise have biological offspring will not be deprived of this right.

However, is this notion of a right to biological offspring of one's own really correct? Is there really a right in that sense? Of course, if there is such a right, it could then be argued that if society does not make reproductive technologies available to its citizens as a matter of principle, it will be treating those who cannot have children unfairly.

On the other hand, if there is no such right, does this mean that development of and access to the technologies should be a matter of private choice? Would it be entirely a matter of individual decision?

Finally, even if there is a right to have biological offspring of one's own, and even if that did entail a right of access to reproductive technologies as a matter of social policy, there would still be the fact that all rights have limits. What would be the limits in this case?

The selection by the Canadian Medical Association is part of the position it developed when trying to come to grips with the new reproductive technologies. It was part of its presentation to the Royal Commission on New Reproductive Technologies in 1991. The case of *Eve* is included because the Supreme Court, in trying to settle the question whether it is legally acceptable to sterilize a mentally severely disabled young woman, addressed the question whether there is a right to have children in a juridical sense. The Court rejected the notion. However, it did insist that — for a woman at least — there is a "fundamental privilege" to have a child. Christine Overall considers the right to have children in general as well as in the context of the new reproductive technologies. She reasons from a feminist perspective and considers the question in general as well as with respect to *in vitro* fertilization. Eike-Henner Kluge and Raanan Gillon examine whether, under certain circumstances, sterilization — and hence interference with this "fundamental privilege" — is ethically mandated. They reach distinct and different conclusions.

NOTES

1. Alberta, British Columbia, Manitoba, Ontario and Quebec.

2. Australia, New Zealand, Great Britain, France, Germany, etc.

The Right to Have Children

Canadian Medical Association

THE MEANING OF THE PHRASE

Once these questions are asked, they entrain a series of still more fundamental questions: What does the notion of a right to have children amount to? Does it mean that everyone has the right to biological offspring of their own? That everyone has the right to be a parent? A combination of

The Canadian Medical Association, "The right to have children" — Reprinted from *The New Reproductive Technologies: A Preliminary Perspective of the Canadian Medical Association*, by permission of the publisher, Canadian Medical Association, 1991; 42-49.

these? Or is there something else entirely that is here at stake? These are not questions of mere lexicography. Depending how the notion of a right to have children is understood, different consequences follow.

The Right to Parent

If it is understood as the right to be a parent, then nothing in principle would bar society from interfering in the reproductive capabilities of its citizens. So long as people were provided with children to parent, their right would be fulfilled. Involuntary sterilization for reasons unrelated to the health of the individual person would, therefore, not be ruled out. The capacity to parent would not thereby be affected. Furthermore, as long as society provided anyone who wanted it with the opportunity to parent, society would not have an obligation to investigate and correct the causes of infertility.

For medicine, this would mean that investigations into infertility would not have to rank high on any list of research priorities. Although infertility might well be a health issue and might be of interest to physicians from a scientific perspective, this would not necessarily be the case. Nor would physicians' obligation to their patient, whether that be understood in an individual or in a global sense, include the duty to assist in the fulfilment of parental aspirations.

The Right to Have Biological Offspring of One's Own

On the other hand, if the right to have children were to be understood as the right to have biological offspring of one's own, the situation would be entirely different. Then society would have an obligation to try to prevent or, failing prevention, to cure infertility. It would also have a *prima facie* obligation to fund those areas of research that

are directed toward improving the chances of biological parenthood.

However, by the same token, it would not follow that society had an obligation to assist or even encourage biological parents to keep their offspring. In other words, it would be gratuitous to assume that biological progenitors had an automatic right to parent the children that carried their genetic heritage. This would become particularly important in the contemporary context, where surrogate motherhood has become a reality.[94]

For medicine, this interpretation would entail an obligation to assist those who are unable to have biological offspring of their own. That obligation, in turn, would affect the orientation that the profession would have to adopt in this matter. Among other things, it would mean that investigations into the causes of infertility from a preventive perspective would become as much a priority item for the profession as would investigations into other preventable health problems, and research projects aimed at ways of curing infertility and infertility-associated problems would be mandated. The profession might even be faced with an obligation to develop new techniques of reproduction for those who are inherently incapable of having children. Furthermore, because equity and justice would demand that the right to have children could not be confined only to women, research into such things as artificial placentas, male pregnancies, etc., would become entirely appropriate.

The Right to Reproduce and to Parent

Finally, if the right to have children is understood to include both the right to have biological offspring of one's own and the right to be a parent to them, the picture would shift once again. Not only would society have an obligation to fund research aimed at eradicating or curing infertility, it would also have an obligation to help everyone in their efforts to function as parents — even if they have difficulties doing so.

This would assume considerable significance in the case of mentally or otherwise handicapped people. A whole domain of social support services would be implicated. It should also be clear that the orientation of these services could not be directed solely toward the prospective parents. It would be coloured by an admixture of the obligation that the state has toward children independent of any other duty.[95] The difficulties inherent in reconciling the two duties might well create a difficult situation.

Not only would the medical profession have an obligation to assist patients in their efforts to have biological offspring of their own, it would also have an obligation to delve into the psychology of parenting, to provide psychiatric assistance to those who need it to realize their right to parent. In other words, the profession would have to address and deal with medically based social implications of and requirements for parenting.

A Modified Social Notion

The Association suggests that there is a fourth way to understand the notion: a way that combines some of the features of the interpretations just canvassed. The right to have children should be seen as the right to take advantage of the opportunity to function in parental capacity, where it is an underlying assumption of this notion that in the normal course of events, this opportunity will arise because of the exercise of normal biological functions.

The Argument   The Association favours this interpretation for several reasons. First, it places the right firmly where it belongs: into the overall social context. It thereby recognizes that this right is not absolute. It is subject to those concerns and considerations that motivate society when dealing with any other right. It may be overruled when it conflicts with a more fundamental right or with a deeper social obligation. Furthermore, it means that like any right, the right to have children has certain preconditions. In the present case, these preconditions would centre in the capability of individuals to make reasoned choices and to function in a parental role.[96]

Second, it means that considerations of equity can be grounded in an appeal to equal opportunity. It therefore requires society to act whenever there is an inequity of opportunity, whether that be for people in general or for specific groups. This is particularly important for handicapped people who have the capacity to parent, but who may exercise that capacity only with societal assistance.

Third, it recognizes that society has a *prima facie* obligation to try to alleviate any impediments to the exercise of the reproductive biological functions that are normally found in human beings. Therefore, society would have a *prima facie* obligation to fund research into the causes of and cures for non-voluntary infertility and to make the results of that research available on an equitable basis.

Fourth, it would cast the medical and associated health care professions in an appropriate role in this matter: as providing assistance with the fulfilment of this right to have children, but not as judges of who should and who should not have that right. In other words, it would deny control in this matter to all but the individuals themselves.

Supporting Arguments   This interpretation finds support in arguments that are intended to show that there is a right to have children. The Association hastens to add that it does not support all such arguments.

The Association does not support the argument that is based on the biological nature of the human species. This argument begins with the observation that unless human beings reproduce, the species will disappear. From this it deduces that the right to reproduce — that is, the right to have children — is grounded in the biological nature of humanity itself.[97]

Although the Association is conscious that the biological facts referred to are beyond doubt, it contends that they do not support the conclusion. The fact that a species will disappear unless its members reproduce entails neither a right nor a duty to reproduce. Any such inference would require the premise that the species should continue to exist in the first place. However, the very biological facts that form the underpinning of this reasoning cast doubt on the tenability of such a premise.

More important, the Association wishes to dissociate itself from this sort of approach for another reason: it would have pernicious consequences. It would mean that not every person has the right to reproduce. It would follow that all and only those people who could reasonably be expected to contribute to the survival of the species would have that right. That, however, would exclude all who carry identifiable dominant lethal genes or who carry genes that would not be advantageous in a changing global environment. In fact, it would deny the right to everyone whose reproduction would in any way compromise the survival of the species as a whole. Instead of grounding a universal right to have children, the argument would entail a right governed by the most rigorous eugenic and evolutionary standards. The Association cannot support such a position.

Another argument for the right to have children that the Association cannot accept derives from the contention that most people want to have children. Using this as a premise, the argument then concludes that people do have a *prima facie* right. Although the argument admits that this right may be overruled on certain occasions, it contends that it could never be overruled as a matter of social whim.[98]

Although the Association applauds some aspects of this argument — in particular the thesis that the right to have children should not be overruled as a matter of societal whim — it cannot attach itself to the reasoning as a whole. The Association believes that the premise on which the argument is based is ethically unacceptable. More specifically, the Association rejects the premise that the desire to have children creates a *prima facie* right. The Association contends that, to accept that premise, it would have to accept the more general thesis that the existence of a desire in itself creates a right. In the eyes of the Association, a desire does not secure a right — not even a *prima facie* right. If it were otherwise, pathological murderers would have a *prima facie* right to their victims simply because they desire to kill them, kleptomaniacs would have a *prima facie* right to the goods of others, and so on.

The Association also notes with alarm that acceptance of the underlying premise would spell disaster for health care funding. It would mean that as soon as any member of society desired to be treated in a certain fashion, or to have access to a certain treatment modality, society had a *prima facie* obligation to provide it.

The entire practice of medicine would also be hamstrung by such an assumption. It would put the practising physician into the position of having to justify the refusal of a medically inappropriate treatment against the *prima facie* right of the patient. Although the wishes and desires of members of society are relevant when considering the extent of health care services, and although they are of central importance in the physician-patient relationship, they cannot be seen as determining.

A third argument is based on the fact that human beings have the potential to grow as persons in the context of a family. It is this context that provides an opportunity to develop qualities like empathy and compassion. It is here, also, that they can develop as nurturers, providers of security and so on. Without children, however, these potentials will never be fulfilled.[99]

The Association is sympathetic toward the sentiment expressed in this argument. It accepts the thesis that the realization of human potential may be a good in itself, and that its development might appropriately be encouraged. However, the Association cannot accept in its unconditioned form the premise that is associated with this sentiment. On a pragmatic level, in some instances the insistence on the realization of such a potential may predictably lead to dysfunctional families. Furthermore, the realization of a potential is ethically acceptable only for those potentials whose realization should be encouraged. Not all potentials fall into this category. The potential for psychotic dysfunctions falls under this rubric. Finally, and in any case, the Association would argue that the right to realize a potential is a *prima facie* right at best. The considerations that were alluded to in the previous discussion of the argument from desire are here apropos as well.

Another argument centres in the thesis that society offers its members the opportunity to have biological offspring as a matter of general and socially sanctioned expectation through an expression of their sexuality in a socially acceptable fashion. This expectation is so fundamental and so universal that it amounts to a right.

It strikes the Association that this line of reasoning is persuasive. At the same time, the Association is conscious that this line of reasoning does not stand alone. If it is accepted, its consequences would be as immediate as they would be powerful. They would include the conclusion that the right to have children is fundamental to membership in society itself, and that it may be limited or conditioned only by the circumstances in which a society may find itself and by the competing rights of others.

This would have important consequences for how the right to have children would manifest itself in practice, as well as for the obligations that it would impose on society in general and the profession of medicine in particular.

Societal implications would include society's perception of normalcy with respect to the exercise of a given right. For example, it is a normal expectation of society that people will not unnecessarily and irresponsibly expose others to harm. Therefore, the right to freedom of reproduction would be limited by this expectation.

This in turn would mean that society would have the right, and indeed the duty, to interfere with those expressions of sexuality that put other members of society at risk. The duty to control the spread of sexually transmitted diseases would here be implicated.

It would also mean that society would not be derelict in its duty if it did not develop and provide techniques of reproductive technology that went beyond ameliorating inequities of opportunity in this regard. In other words, this perspective would allow society to exercise its discretion in funding those techniques of reproductive technology whose primary function is personal convenience.

For the profession of medicine, it would mean that the refusal of individual physicians to provide what thus could be called elective reproductive services would not stand in contravention of their ethical mandate.

These implications notwithstanding, the Canadian Medical Association is inclined to accept this perspective. The Association is of the opinion that the right to have children is indeed a socially guaranteed right that finds its basis in the fact of social membership itself. However, the Association also believes that for that very reason, this right is not absolute. It is subject to the limiting conditions that affect all other socially grounded rights. The conditions that normally attend the expectation of opportunity for sexual expression and the opportunity for having children are here crucial. They may shift as the resources and abilities of society change. However, the fact remains that the right is conditioned.

SOME CONSEQUENCES

As has already been indicated, the perception of the right to have children, and the reasoning in support of it, have certain important consequences. One of these consequences centres in the expectation of normalcy referred to above. The predominant expectation of people who want children is that the children they have will meet the social norm in terms of natures and abilities. People may be aware that there is a statistical possibility that this expectation may not be met, that is, their biological offspring may suffer from some congenital disease or condition.[100] This awareness is sometimes expressed in terms of the fears that they might not have children that will be normal and healthy. Nevertheless, because people's expectations tend to be shaped by the norm of experience, their usual expectations are that their children will be normal.

The expectation in Canadian society, therefore, as a matter of perceived right, is not simply for a child as such. It also contains as a strong undercurrent the expectation that the child will be normal and healthy. This undercurrent forms part of the overall framework in which the notion of the right to have a child is at home. That in turn leads to the expectation — again as a matter of right — that if either the expectation of having a child in the first instance, or of having a normal child in the second, is unlikely to be met, then society has an obligation to assist those who cannot share in these expectations.

If this inference is granted, then the assistance that society may legitimately be expected to provide may take various forms, depending on the reason why the initial expectation is unlikely to be met. If the reason lies in infertility, then society may be seen to have an obligation to try to overcome it. The various medical techniques of assisted reproduction would then be implicated.

If the reason lies in a defect in the genetic endowment of the parents, society may be expected to try to remedy the relevant defects, or at least to ameliorate their impact. Techniques of genetic screening for carrier status and the development of techniques of germ line therapy would here have their place. So would programs designed to assist the parents of children suffering from congenital anomalies, and to assist the children themselves.

Finally, if the reason lies in the conditions that contribute to the offspring's development *in utero,* then it would seem appropriate to say that society should address the situation. The development and funding of intra-uterine screening technology, methods of intra-uterine therapy, gene therapy, etc., would here become relevant. So would efforts to provide a salubrious environment for the possibility of conception and for the gestational development of a fetus.[101]

There are only two conditions under which society would be freed from an obligation in these matters: when the reason for action is the convenience of members of society; and when it would be impossible to provide a remedy. In the former case, social actions would be at the discretion of the general will and would be subject to the availability of resources. In the second case, society would have a *prima facie* obligation to attempt to provide a remedy in some other fashion. For instance, by developing appropriately structured adoption laws, or by exploring other approaches to child bearing. Surrogate motherhood would provide a recent, albeit controversial, example.

However, the Association wishes to emphasize that in its opinion, if the reason why certain people cannot have children is by its nature irremediable, then society cannot be expected to attempt to provide a remedy. The law has an expression that applies in this context: "Equity does not require the impossible." Ethics accepts a similar principle.

A second consequence that would seem to follow is: if, under the circumstances, and despite society's best efforts, prospective parents carry such a severe and irremediable genetic load that the quality of life of any children they might have would be irremediably impaired, then these prospective parents should be counselled to exercise responsibility and not to have children. The reason lies not so much in the burden that such children would impose on society, but in the fact that the children themselves would be the recipients of harm.[102]

To reiterate, if there is a right to have children, and if that right is derivable from the fact of social existence and the expectations that normally are legitimated by such existence, then such a right is neither absolute nor unconditioned. It is conditioned by the competing rights of others. If others have rights that are more basic or more fundamental, then these rights will overrule the right to have children.

On this assumption, the right to have children is conditioned and not absolute. It presupposes that certain requirements are met. For example, it presupposes that society is materially capable of providing the opportunity for sexual expression and for supporting the children that foreseeably will result from it. It also presupposes that the other members of society are willing to subordinate their relevant and competing rights if and when the need arises. Finally, it presupposes that those who claim the right are themselves able to treat as persons the children that might result from their sexual activities.

The last point is crucial: the right to have children is not like the right to have an object or an animal. Children are persons and must be treated as persons. The right to have children is, therefore, better understood as the right to take advantage of opportunities that are open to everyone as a matter of course. When those opportunities are not present, then society has an obligation to assist those who lack the opportunities. When such a lack can be remedied by the development or application of reproductive technologies, then society has a *prima facie* obligation to develop and apply them. However, any societal action in this regard must always be with an eye to the fact that children are persons.

NOTES

94. For a discussion of surrogate motherhood, see *infra*.

95. For a fuller discussion of this from a legal perspective, see the discussion of parens patriae powers of the courts by Supreme Court Justice La Forest in *Eve*.

96. Compare *Re B (a minor),* [1987] All E R 206, 219, at 213; Lord Halsham:

> ... whilst I find La Forest J.'s history of the *parens patriae* jurisdiction of the Crown... extremely helpful, I find, with great respect, his conclusion... that the procedure of sterilization "should *never*[sic] be authorised for non-therapeutic purposes" totally unconvincing and in startling contradiction to the welfare principle.... To talk of the "basic right" to reproduce of an individual who is not capable of knowing the causal con-

nection between intercourse and childbirth, the nature of pregnancy, what is involved in delivery, unable to form maternal instincts or to care for a child appears to me wholly to part company with reality.

Lord Oliver's position, although focused on the ability to make a choice, was essentially similar:

[In the case of D], Heilbron J. declined to sanction an operation which involved depriving [D] of the right to reproduce. That, if I may say so respectfully, was plainly a right decision. But the right to reproduce is of value only if accompanied by the ability to make a choice.

For a similar position, see Alberta Institute of Law Research and Reform: *Competence and Human Reproduction,* Report no. 52, Edmonton, Alberta, 1989: 13:

6(1) In addition to the matters referred to in section 5, before determining whether an order authorizing the performance of an elective sterilization would be in the best interests of the person in respect of whom the order is sought, the judge shall consider (j) the ability of the person to care for a child at the time of application and any likely changes in that ability.

97. For a discussion of this, see Vaux K: *Birth Ethics: Religious and Cultural Values in the Genesis of Life* (Crossroads, New York, N.Y., 1989), Chapter 3, "Biologic ethics of attraction and affection."

98. This current is reflected in *re Eve* as well as most other Canadian and U.K. cases dealing with non-consensual sterilization of incompetents.

99. See *re Eve* for judicial recognition of this strand.

100. The awareness of such a possibility may be the result of a family history, genetic screening, etc. Huntington's chorea, thalassaemia, Tay-Sachs, etc., are here implicated. At present, the list of diseases or conditions extends to well over 200.

101. For discussion of research funding, see also Québec, Ministère de la Santé et des Services sociaux: *Rapport du Comité de Travail sur les Nouvelles Technologies de Reproduction Humaine,* Quebec, 1988: 92.

102. For a discussion of this position, see Purdy L.M.: Genetic diseases: can having children be immoral? In Buckley J.J. ed., *Genetics Now: Ethical Issues in Genetic Research,* Univ Press of America, Washington, D.C., 1978.

Eve v. Mrs. E.

Lamer, Wilson, Le Dain and La Forest J.J.

LA FOREST J. — These proceedings began with an application by a mother for permission to consent to the sterilization of her mentally retarded daughter who also suffered from a condition that makes it extremely difficult for her to communicate

---

[1987], 3 D.L.R. (4th) S.C.C., [1987] 2 S.C.R. 388 (S.C.C.).

with others. The application was heard by McQuaid J. of the Supreme Court of Prince Edward Island — Family Division. In the interests of privacy, he called the daughter "Eve", and her mother "Mrs. E".

BACKGROUND

... [Mr. Justice McQuaid, the trial judge, on the basis of the evidence before him, found that the following description summed up Eve's situation:]

> The evidence established that Eve is 24 years of age, and suffers what is described as extreme expressive aphasia. She is unquestionably at least mildly to moderately retarded. She has some learning skills, but only to a limited level. She is described as being a pleasant and affectionate person who, physically, is an adult person, quite capable of being attracted to, as well as attractive to, the opposite sex. While she might be able to carry out the mechanical duties of a mother, under supervision, she is incapable of being a mother in any other sense. Apart from being able to recognize the fact of a family unit, as consisting of a father, a mother, and children residing in the same home, she would have no concept of the idea of marriage, or indeed, the consequential relationship between intercourse, pregnancy and birth. Expressive aphasia was described as a condition in which the patient is unable to communicate outwardly thoughts or concepts which she might have perceived. Particularly in the case of a person suffering from any degree of retardation, the result is that even an expert such as a psychiatrist is unable to determine with any degree of certainty if, in fact, those thoughts or concepts have actually been per-

ceived, or whether understanding of them does exist. Little appears to be known of the cause of this condition, and even less of its remedy. In the case of Eve, this condition has been diagnosed as extreme.

From the evidence, he [Mr. Justice McQuaid] further concluded:

> [t]hat Eve is not capable of informed consent, that her moderate retardation is generally stable, that her condition is probably non-inheritable, that she is incapable of effective alternative means of contraception, that the psychological or emotional effect of the proposed operation would probably be minimal, and that the probable incidence of pregnancy is impossible to predict.

Mrs. E. wanted to be sure she had a right to consent to the sterilization of Eve, so she applied ... for the following remedies:

(a) that Eve be declared a mentally incompetent pursuant to the provisions of the Mental Health Act;

(b) that Mrs. E. be appointed the committee of the person of Eve;

(c) that Mrs. E. be authorized to consent to a tubal ligation operation being performed on Eve.

... Having reviewed the Canadian and English case law and found no governing authorities, McQuaid J. considered whether the court should, in the exercise of its parens patriae jurisdiction, intervene on behalf of Eve. He had no doubt that the court could authorize a surgical procedure necessary to health even though a side-effect might be sterilization, and he postulated that it could also do so where the public interest clearly required it, though he found it difficult to come up with an example. However, McQuaid J. was of the view that Eve, like other individuals, was entitled to the inviolability of her person, a right that superseded her right to be protected from pregnancy. That this might result in inconvenience and even hardship to others was irrelevant. The law must protect those who are unable to protect themselves; it must ensure the protection of the higher right. He, therefore, concluded that the court had no authority or jurisdiction to authorize a surgical procedure on a mentally retarded person, the intent and purpose of which was solely contraceptive. It followed that, except for clinically therapeutic reasons, parents or others similarly situated could not give a valid consent to such a surgical procedure either, at least in the absence of clear and unequivocal statutory authority. He, therefore, denied the application.

An appeal to the Supreme Court of Prince Edward Island, in banco, was launched, and an order was then made appointing the Official Trustee as Guardian ad litem for Eve. The appeal was allowed. The general view of the court is set forth in an addendum to its notes of judgment as follows:

> In rendering judgment in this matter, we are unanimously of the opinion that the Court has, in proper circumstances, the authority and jurisdiction to authorize the sterilization of a mentally incompetent person for non-therapeutic reasons. The jurisdiction of the Court originates from its parens patriae powers towards individuals who are unable to look after themselves and gives the Court authority to make the individual a ward of the Court.

The court, however, differed on the evidence. A majority (Large and Campbell J.J.) was of the view, MacDonald J. dissenting, that there was sufficient evidence to warrant the sterilization of Eve. The court therefore ordered that:

(a) "Eve" be appointed a ward of the Court pursuant to the parens patriae juris-

diction for the sole purpose of facilitating and authorizing her sterilization;

(b) the Court authorizes the sterilization of "Eve" by a competent medical practitioner;

(c) the Court reserves its approval of the method of sterilization to be followed pending further submissions of counsel as to the medically preferred surgical procedure.

... Leave to appeal to this Court was then granted to Eve's Guardian ad litem by the Prince Edward Island Supreme Court, Appeal Division. The major issues raised in this appeal are substantially as follows:

1. Is there relevant provincial legislation that gives a court jurisdiction to appoint a committee vested with the power to consent to or authorize surgical procedures for contraceptive purposes on an adult who is mentally incompetent?

2. In the absence of statutory authority, does the court's parens patriae jurisdiction allow the court to consent to the sterilization of an adult who is mentally incompetent?

3. What is the appropriate standard of proof to be applied in a case where an application is made to the court for its substituted consent to a non-therapeutic procedure on behalf of a mentally incompetent adult? Upon whom is the onus of proof?

4. If the court has jurisdiction to provide substituted consent for a non-therapeutic procedure on behalf of a mentally incompetent adult, did the Supreme Court of Prince Edward Island, in banco, properly exercise its jurisdiction in granting an order authorizing the sterilization of Eve?

5. Does the Canadian Charter of Rights and Freedoms protect an individual against sterilization without that individual's consent?

6. If the Charter provides such protection, when will it permit the non-therapeutic

sterilization of a mentally incompetent who is incapable of giving consent?

7. Does the Charter give an individual the right to choose not to procreate, and if so does the court have jurisdiction to make that choice on behalf of an individual who is unable to do so?

GENERAL CONSIDERATIONS

Before entering into a consideration of the specific issues before this Court, it may be useful to restate the general issue briefly. The Court is asked to consent, on behalf of Eve, to sterilization since she, though an adult, is unable to do so herself. Sterilization by means of a tubal ligation is usually irreversible. And hysterectomy, the operation authorized by the Appeal Division, is not only irreversible; it is major surgery. Eve's sterilization is not being sought to treat any medical condition. Its purposes are admittedly non-therapeutic. One such purpose is to deprive Eve of the capacity to become pregnant so as to save her from the possible trauma of giving birth and from the resultant obligations of a parent, a task the evidence indicates she is not capable of fulfilling. As to this, it should be noted that there is no evidence that giving birth would be more difficult for Eve than for any other woman.

A second purpose of the sterilization is to relieve Mrs. E. of anxiety about the possibility of Eve's becoming pregnant and of having to care for any child Eve might bear.

... *[Mr. Justice La Forest then discusses the history and rationale of proxy decision making in the U.K. and the role of the courts. He then turns to the U.S. and discusses two approaches to proxy decision making that have been used there.]*

... While many state courts have, in recent cases, been prepared to recognize an inherent power in courts of general jurisdiction to authorize sterilization of mentally incompetent persons, they differ on the standard of review. Two distinct approaches have emerged: the "best interests" approach and the "substituted judgment" approach. In five of the nine states in which equitable jurisdiction to authorize the non-consensual sterilization of a mentally incompetent person is recognized, that jurisdiction is based on the inherent equitable power of the courts to act in the best interests of the mentally incompetent person.... The test necessarily leads to uncertainties... and in an effort to minimize abuses, American courts have developed guidelines to assist in determining whether the best interests of the affected person would be furthered through sterilization....

... As noted, these facts indicate that the courts of the United States in acting under the best interests test have a very wide discretion.

The second approach, the substituted judgment test, raises Charter implications.

... The primary purpose of the substituted judgment test is to attempt to determine what decision the mental incompetent would make, if she were reviewing her situation as a competent person, but taking account of her mental incapacity as one factor in her decision. It allows the court to consider a number of factors bearing directly upon the condition of the mental incompetent. Thus the court may consider such issues as the values of the incompetent, any religious beliefs held by her, and her societal views as expressed by her family. In essence, an attempt is made to determine the actual interests and preferences of the mental incompetent. This, it is thought, recognizes her moral dignity and right to free choice. Since the incompetent cannot exercise that choice herself, the court does so on her behalf. The fact that a mental incompetent is, either because of age or mental disability, unable to provide any aid to the court in its decision does not preclude the use of the substituted judgment test.

The respondent submitted that this test should be adopted in this country. As in the case of the best interests test, various guidelines have been developed by the courts in the United States to ensure the proper use of this test.

... [I]t is easy to understand the natural feelings of a parent's heart. ...[However] a court ... must exercise great caution to avoid being misled by this all too human mixture of emotions and motives. So we are left to consider whether the purposes underlying the operation are necessarily for Eve's benefit and protection.

The justifications advanced are the ones commonly proposed in support of non-therapeutic sterilization.... Many are demonstrably weak. The [Law Reform] Commission dismisses the argument about the trauma of birth by observing at p. 60:

> For this argument to be held valid would require that it could be demonstrated that the stress of delivery was greater in the case of mentally handicapped persons than it is for others. Considering the generally known wide range of post-partum response would likely render this a difficult case to prove.

The argument relating to fitness as a parent involves many value-loaded questions. Studies conclude that mentally incompetent parents show as much fondness and concern for their children as other people; see *Sterilization*, supra, p. 33 et seq., 63-64. Many, it is true, may have difficulty in coping, particularly with the financial burdens involved. But this issue does not relate to the benefit of the incompetent; it is a social problem, and one, moreover, that is not limited to incompetents. Above all it is not an issue that comes within the limited powers of the courts, under the parens patriae juris-diction, to do what is necessary for the benefit of persons who are unable to care for themselves. Indeed, there are human rights considerations that should make a court extremely hesitant about attempting to solve a social problem like this by this means. It is worth noting that in dealing with such issues, provincial sterilization boards have revealed serious differences in their attitudes as between men and women, the poor and the rich, and people of different ethnic backgrounds.

As far as the hygienic problems are concerned, the following view of the Law Reform Commission ([*Sterilization*] at p. 34) is obviously sound:

> ... if a person requires a great deal of assistance in managing their own menstruation, they are also likely to require assistance with urinary and fecal control, problems which are much more troublesome in terms of personal hygiene.

Apart from this, the drastic measure of subjecting a person to a hysterectomy for this purpose is clearly excessive.

The grave intrusion on a person's rights and the certain physical damage that ensues from non-therapeutic sterilization without consent, when compared to the highly questionable advantages that can result from it, have persuaded me that it can never safely be determined that such a procedure is for the benefit of that person. Accordingly, the procedure should never be authorized for non-therapeutic purposes under the parens patriae jurisdiction.

To begin with, it is difficult to imagine a case in which non-therapeutic sterilization could possibly be of benefit to the person on behalf of whom a court purports to act, let alone one in which that procedure is necessary in his or her best interest. And how are we to weigh the best interests of a person in this troublesome area, keeping in mind that an error is irreversible? Unlike other cases involving the use of the parens patriae jurisdiction, an error cannot be corrected by the subsequent exercise of judicial discretion. That being so, one need only recall Lord Eldon's remark, supra, that "it has always been the principle of this Court, not to risk damage to children which it cannot repair" to conclude that non-therapeutic sterilization may not be authorized in the exercise of the parens patriae jurisdiction. McQuaid J. was, therefore, right in concluding that he had no authority or jurisdiction to grant the application.

Nature or the advances of science may, at least in a measure, free Eve of the incapacity from which she suffers. Such a possibility should give the courts pause in extending their power to care for individuals to such irreversible action as we are called upon to take here. The irreversible and serious intrusion on the basic rights of the individual is simply too great to allow a court to act on the basis of possible advantages which, from the standpoint of the individual, are highly debatable. Judges are generally ill-informed about many of the factors relevant to a wise decision in this difficult area. They generally know little of mental illness, of techniques of contraception or their efficacy. And, however well presented a case may be, it can only partially inform. If sterilization of the mentally incompetent is to be adopted as desirable for general social purposes, the legislature is the appropriate body to do so. It is in a position to inform itself and it is attuned to the feelings of the public in making policy in this sensitive area. The actions of the legislature will then, of course, be subject to the scrutiny of the courts under the Canadian Charter of Rights and Freedoms and otherwise.

... The foregoing, of course, leaves out of consideration therapeutic sterilization and where the line is to be drawn between therapeutic and non-therapeutic sterilization. On this issue, I simply repeat that the utmost caution must be exercised commensurate with the seriousness of the procedure. Marginal justifications must be weighed against what is in every case a grave intrusion on the physical and mental integrity of the person.

... I cannot agree that a court can deprive a woman of that privilege for purely social or other non-therapeutic purposes without her consent. The fact that others may suffer inconvenience or hardship from failure to do so cannot be taken into account. The Crown's parens patriae jurisdiction exists for the benefit of those who cannot help themselves, not to relieve those who may have the burden of caring for them.

I should perhaps add ... that sterilization may, on occasion, be necessary as an adjunct to treatment of a serious malady, but I would underline that this, of course, does not allow for subterfuge or for treatment of some marginal medical problem.

The foregoing remarks dispose of the arguments based on the traditional view of the parens patriae jurisdiction as exercised in this country. Counsel for the respondent strongly contended, however, that the Court should adopt the substituted judgment test recently developed by a number of state courts in the United States. That test, he submitted, is to be preferred to the best interests test because it places a higher value on the individuality of the mentally incompetent person. It affords that person the same right, he contended, as a competent person to choose whether to procreate or not.

There is an obvious logical lapse in this argument. I do not doubt that a person has a right to decide to be sterilized. That is his or her free choice. But choice presupposes that a person has the mental competence to make it. It may be a matter of debate whether a court should have the power to make the decision if that person lacks the mental capacity to do so. But it is obviously fiction to suggest that a decision so made is that of the mental incompetent, however much the court may try to put itself in her place. What the incompetent would do if she or he could make the choice is simply a matter of speculation. The sophistry embodied in the argument favouring substituted judgment has been fully revealed in *Eberhardy* ....where... the court stated:

> The fault we find in the New Jersey case is the ratio decidendi of first concluding, correctly we believe, that the right to sterilization is a personal choice, but then equating a decision made by others with the choice of the person to be sterilized. It clearly is not a personal choice, and no amount of legal legerdemain can make it so.
>
> ...
>
> We conclude that the question is not choice because it is sophistry to refer to it as such, but rather the question is whether there is a method by which others, acting in behalf of the person's best interests and in the interests, such as they may be, of the state, can exercise the decision. Any governmentally sanctioned (or ordered) procedure to sterilize a person who is incapable of giving consent must be denominated for what it is, that is, the state's intrusion into the determination of whether or not a person who makes no choice shall be allowed to procreate.

Counsel for the respondent... argued that there is what he called a fundamental right to free procreative choice. Not only, he asserted, is there a fundamental right to bear children; there is as well a fundamental right to choose not to have children and to implement that choice by means of contraception.... [H]e appears to base this argument on s. 7 of the Charter. But assuming for the moment that liberty as used in s. 7 protects rights of this kind (a matter I refrain from entering into), counsel's contention seems to me to go beyond the kind of protection s. 7 was intended to afford. All s. 7 does is to give a remedy to protect individuals against laws or other state action that deprive them of liberty. It has no application here.

Another Charter related argument must be considered. In response to the appellant's argument that a court-ordered sterilization of a mentally incompetent person, by depriving that person of the right to procreate, would constitute an infringement of that person's rights to liberty and security of the person under s. 7 of the Canadian Charter of Rights and Freedoms, counsel for the respondent countered by relying on that person's right to equality under s. 15(1) of the Charter, saying "that the most appropriate method of ensuring the mentally incompetent their right to equal protection under s. 15(1) is to provide the mentally incompetent with a means to obtain non-therapeutic sterilizations, which adequately protects their interests through appropriate judicial safeguards." A somewhat more explicit argument along the same lines was made by counsel for the Public Trustee of Manitoba. His position was stated as follows:

> It is submitted that in the case of a mentally incompetent adult, denial of the right to have his or her case presented by a guardian ad litem to a Court possessing jurisdiction to give or refuse substituted consent to a non-therapeutic procedure such as sterilization, would be tantamount to a denial to that person of equal protection and equal benefit of the law. Such a denial would constitute discrimination on the basis of mental disability, which discrimination is prohibited by Section 15 of The Canadian Charter of Rights and Freedoms.

Section 15 of the Charter was not in force when these proceedings commenced but, this aside, these arguments appear flawed. They raise in different form an issue already dealt with, i.e. that the decision made by a court on an application to consent to the sterilization of an incompetent is somehow that of the incompetent. More troubling is that the issue is, of course, not raised by the incompetent, but by a third party. The court undoubtedly has the right and duty to protect those who are unable to take care of themselves, and in doing so it has a wide discretion to do what it considers to be in their best interests. But this function must not, in my view, be transformed so as to create a duty obliging the court, at the behest of a third party, to make a choice between the two alleged constitutional rights — the right to procreate or not to procreate — simply because the individual is unable to make that choice. All the more so since, in the case of non-therapeutic sterilization as we saw, the choice is one the courts cannot safely exercise.

... Since, barring emergency situations, a surgical procedure without consent ordinarily constitutes battery, it will be obvious that the onus of proving the need for the procedure is on those who seek to have it performed. And that burden, though a civil one, must be commensurate with the seriousness of the measure proposed. In conducting these procedures, it is obvious that a court must proceed with extreme caution; otherwise...it would open the way for abuse of the mentally incompetent....I would allow the appeal and restore the decision of the judge who heard the application.

Access to In Vitro Fertilization: Costs, Care and Consent

Christine Overall

What would be a genuinely caring approach to the provision of procedures of so-called artificial reproduction such as in vitro fertilization (IVF)? What are appropriate and justified social policies with respect to attempting to enable infertile persons to have offspring? These urgent questions have provoked significant disagreements among theologians, sociologists, health care providers, philosophers and even — or especially — among feminists. In the existing literature and in developing social policy, three different kinds of answers can be dis-cerned: (1) Some have suggested that access to IVF should be provided as a matter of right. (2) Some existing social policies and practices imply that access to IVF is a privilege. (3) Some theorists have argued that, because of its alleged violation of family values and marital security, or because of its risks, costs, and low success rate, IVF should not be available at all. After evaluating each of these views, I shall offer a feminist alternative, describing what I think would constitute the caring provision of in vitro fertilization.

Christine Overall, "Access to In Vitro Fertilization: Costs, Care and Consent," *Dialogue* XXX (1991), 383-97.

1. THE RIGHT TO REPRODUCE AND THE RIGHT NOT TO REPRODUCE

Is there a moral *right* of access to in vitro fertilization? To answer that question requires consideration of the idea of a reproductive right. Some feminists are remarkably suspicious of any use of rights talk by a feminist, particularly in the context of reproductive technology.[1] While talk of rights does not exhaust feminist moral and political discourse about reproduction, and while appeals to rights can sometimes be used against women (for example, the appeal to the supposed "right" to be a "surrogate" or contract mother), surely the history of feminist activism with respect to abortion provides some indication that use of rights claims is not yet nugatory or outdated, and that claims about reproductive rights need clarification, not abandonment.

It is necessary, first, to distinguish between the right to reproduce and the right *not* to reproduce.[2] The two are sometimes unnecessarily conflated as, for example, when Justice Bertha Wilson referred in her Supreme Court decision on the Morgentaler case to "[t]he right to reproduce or not to reproduce which is in issue in this case."[3] The right not to reproduce means the entitlement not to be compelled to beget or bear children against one's will; the alternative to recognition of such a right is the acceptance of forced reproductive labour, or procreative slavery. To say that women have a right not to reproduce implies that there is no obligation of women to reproduce. The right not to reproduce is the entitlement not to be compelled to donate gametes or embryos against one's will, and the entitlement not to have to engage in forced reproductive labour. This right mandates access to contraception and abortion.

The right not to reproduce is distinct from the right to reproduce; that is, the right not to reproduce neither implies a right to reproduce nor follows from a right to reproduce. In my view, access to artificial reproduction cannot be defended by extension of the right not to reproduce.

The right to reproduce has two senses, the weak sense and the strong sense. The weak sense of the right to reproduce is a negative or liberty right: it is the entitlement not to be interfered with in reproduction, or prevented from reproducing. It would imply an obligation on the state not to inhibit or limit reproductive liberty, for example, through racist marriage laws, fornication laws,[4] forced sterilization, forced abortion, or coercive birth control programs. (In both the United States and Canada there is a sorry history of forced sterilization of people of colour and native people.)

In its strong sense, however, the right to reproduce as a positive or "welfare" right would be the right to receive all necessary assistance to reproduce. It would imply entitlement of access to any and all available forms of reproductive products, technologies and labour, including the gametes of other women and men, the gestational services of women and the full range of procreative techniques including in vitro fertilization, gamete intrafallopian transfer, uterine lavage, embryo freezing and sex preselection.

Liberal writers such as American legal theorist John A. Robertson defend the right to reproduce in the strong sense by claiming that it is just an extension of the right to reproduce in the weak sense. As he puts it, "the right of the married couple to reproduce noncoitally" and "the right to reproduce noncoitally with the assistance of donors and surrogates" both follow from "constitutional acceptance of a married couple's right to reproduce coitally."[5] Robertson believes that these rights entitle married couples certainly, and possibly single persons, to "create, store, transfer, donate and possibly even manipulate extra-corporeal embryos," and "to contract for eggs, sperm, embryos, or surrogates." They would also, he thinks, justify compelling a contract mother to hand over a child to its purchasers, even against her will.[6]

In addition, American attorney Lori B. Andrews argues that the right to reproduce in the strong sense is probably founded upon the right to marital privacy.[7]

Nevertheless, there is good reason to challenge the legitimacy and justification of this right to reproduce in the strong sense. Recognizing it would shift the burden of proof on to those who have moral doubts about the morality of technologies such as IVF and practices such as contract motherhood, for it suggests that a child is somehow owed to each of us, as individuals or as members of a couple, and that it is indefensible for society to fail to provide all possible means for obtaining one. Recognition of the right to reproduce in the strong sense would create an active right of access to women's bodies and in particular to their reproductive labour and products. Thus, it might be used, as Robertson advocates, to imply an entitlement to obtain other women's eggs, and to make use of donor insemination and uterine lavage of another woman, all in order to maximize the chances of reproducing.[8] It would guarantee the entitlement to hire a contract mother, and force contract mothers to surrender their infants after birth. This would constitute a type of slave trade in infants, and commit women to a modern form of indentured servitude. Finally, the right to reproduce in the strong sense might be used to found a claim to certain kinds of children — for example, children of a desired sex, appearance, or intelligence.

Exercise of the alleged right to reproduce in this strong sense could potentially require violation of some women's right not to reproduce. There is already good evidence, in both the United States and Great Britain, that eggs and ovarian tissue have been taken from some women without their knowledge, let alone their informed consent.[9] It is not difficult to imagine that recognizing a strong right to reproduce could require either a similar theft of eggs or embryos from some women, if none can be found to offer them willingly, or a commercial inducement to sell these products. It could be used as a basis for requiring fertile people to "donate" gametes and embryos. Even on a more ordinary level, recognition of a right to reproduce in the strong sense would seem to give men questionable rights over the reproductive products and labour of their female partners. Because of these implications — particularly the obligations that recognition of such a right would incur — I conclude that there is no right to reproduce in the strong sense. Even if some people willingly donate gametes, there is no *right* or entitlement on the part of the infertile that they should do so.

2. ACCESS TO ARTIFICIAL REPRODUCTION AS A PRIVILEGE

Access to methods of artificial reproduction such as in vitro fertilization cannot be justified by reference to an alleged right to reproduce in the strong sense. But while I am arguing that there is no right in the strong sense to IVF, such a claim does not of course imply that all use of IVF is thereby unjustified.

However, if appeal to such a right is abandoned, then it may seem that we are committed to holding that having children by means of artificial reproduction is necessarily a *privilege* that must be earned through the possession of certain personal, social, sexual, and/or financial characteristics. The provision of reproductive technology then appears to become a luxury service, access to which can be controlled by means of criteria used to screen potential candidates.[10] Such limitations appear to be the price of sacrificing a right to reproduce in the strong sense.

And indeed, in actual practice, for processes such as IVF the criteria of eligibility have included such characteristics as sexual orientation — only heterosexuals need apply; marital status — single women are not usually eligible (unless they are part of an ongoing marriage-like relationship);[11] and consent of the spouse. Because IVF is costly, economic status and geographical location have also become, at least indirectly, criteria of eligibility. We can speculate that these are likely to lead to de facto discrimination against working-class women and women of colour.[12] Further criteria have also been used — for example, reproductive age, the absence of physical disabilities and characteristics such as "stability" and parenting capacities.[13] Some have also suggested or implied that infertility which is the result of the patient's own choices (for example, tubal ligation) should render the patient ineligible for IVF.

Should access to IVF be treated as a matter of privilege rather than right? Three arguments tell against this approach. First, persons who do not have fertility problems are not compelled to undergo any evaluation of their eligibility for parenthood. Moreover, some medical responses to infertility — for example, the surgical repair of damaged fallopian tubes — are undertaken without any inquiry into the patient's marital status, sexual orientation, or fitness for parenthood. If in vitro fertilization is classed as a medical procedure in the way that tubal repair is a medical procedure, then discrimination in access for the former and not for the latter is unjustified. The case of IVF seems to present an instance of discrimination on the basis of social criteria against

people with infertility — and only certain kinds of infertility at that.

A second argument is the general difficulty of assessing the presence of some of the characteristics which have been assumed to be relevant for access to IVF. For example, for some women sexual orientation is a fluid and changing personal characteristic.[14] In addition, it is difficult to see how "stability" or aptitude for parenthood can be adequately measured, and there is likely to be a lot of disagreement about the appropriateness of criteria for evaluating these characteristics. One could also challenge the justification of allotting the assessment of these characteristics to IVF clinicians, who are not likely to have any better expertise than the rest of the population for making such evaluations.

Finally, it is essential to challenge the moral legitimacy of discrimination on the basis of characteristics such as sexual orientation and marital status.

Such discrimination is founded upon false assumptions about the nature and abilities of single and lesbian women, and about the kind of mothering they can provide. While promoting good parenting practices is indisputably a worthwhile social goal, there is no evidence to suggest either that marriage and heterosexuality necessarily make women better mothers, or that the presence of a father is indispensable to childhood developmental processes. Nor do any research findings suggest that the ability to pay the enormous financial costs of IVF increases one's capacity to be a good parent.

Thus, many purveyors of IVF (at least in Canada) seem to be guilty of an inconsistency. Medical practice is not usually premised on the assumption that only some patients deserve treatment, and IVF clinicians themselves see their role as relieving a disability or responding to an "illness" in infertile women.[15] Yet they are only willing to treat infertile women with social characteristics that they judge acceptable, and they disregard the experiences and needs of other infertile women who fail to conform to their criteria. There is no adequate justification for making access to procedures such as in vitro fertilization a privilege for which it is legitimate to erect social barriers that discriminate on arbitrary and unfair grounds—grounds such as marital status, sexual orientation, putative stability or parenting potential, or economic level. Moreover, given that IVF is, as I shall argue later, an experimental procedure rather than an established medical practice, it is particularly unjust to exact money from those women whose bodies function as experimental material.

Acceptance of these social barriers to accessibility is not the only alternative to claiming a right of access to IVF. Instead, it is important to critically evaluate screening processes for IVF, and to resist and reject practices of unjustified discrimination in access.

3. CALLING A HALT TO ARTIFICIAL REPRODUCTION: RELIGIOUS CONSERVATIVES

Some critics of artificial reproduction regard access as neither a right nor a privilege; instead they condemn research in IVF and call for an end to IVF services. There are two very different reasons for this perspective.

On the one hand, it is claimed by some writers, particularly those influenced by the teachings of the Roman Catholic Church,[16] that in vitro fertilization threatens marital relationships, sexual interactions and the integrity of the nuclear family. One representative of this approach is Canadian philosopher Donald DeMarco, who states:

IVF demands sundering flesh from spirit in an area where the integrity of parenthood demands they be one, and sundering [sic; probably "surrendering" is intended] that flesh to the manipulation of technicians. Inevitably, something important, though unseen, stands to be harmed in the process. And what stands to be harmed is human parenthood.[17]

As a mother myself, I have seldom found that human parenthood is "unseen." However, DeMarco explains further:

By removing the child from the personal context of conjugal love, as IVF does, a decisive step is taken which necessarily depreciates that love.... And to weaken this love which is the essential bonding act of the family ... is to weaken the family. And since the family is the basic unit of society, what weakens the family also weakens the society.[18]

But this set of claims is highly implausible. There is no evidence of an appreciable debilitation of the nuclear family attributable to the use of IVF. If anything, as many feminists have pointed out, the use of IVF strengthens the traditional nuclear family,[19] since it is usually provided only or primarily to persons who are part of heterosexual, married couples, and it does not challenge the traditional belief that a family is not a real family without one or more genetically related children. Moreover, the legitimacy and value of adoptive relationships is implicitly and unjustifiably called into question by DeMarco's argument, since adopted children are not linked to their social parents through "the personal context of conjugal love." Finally, there is in DeMarco's claims a peculiar reification of married heterosexual relationships, a reification which has an especially sinister aspect when DeMarco assures his readers elsewhere that "[h]usband and wife do have a *right to* engage in intercourse with each other."[20] DeMarco's belief that IVF "degrad[es] the two-in-one flesh unity of parents by deflating the importance of the flesh as a vehicle of love in the formation of new life"[21] suggests that heterosexual intercourse has an extraordinary vulnerability most of us would never have imagined. After all, nothing in the provision of IVF prevents heterosexual married couples from continuing to have sexual intercourse. DeMarco's claims also implicitly condemn any and all intercourse (such as that which involves contraception, or that between two persons one of whom is not fertile) that lacks the potential to result in conception. For all these reasons, DeMarco's reservations about IVF are not persuasive, and the call by religious conservatives for a ban on IVF lacks justification.

4. CALLING A HALT TO ARTIFICIAL REPRODUCTION: FEMINISTS

At the other end of the spectrum of general opposition to IVF, however, are criticisms expressed by some feminist scholars, scientists, and activists, criticisms that carry considerable empirical weight. For example, Canadian journalist Ann Pappert has investigated the sorry success record — perhaps more appropriately called a failure record — of IVF in Canada and the United States. She states: "Of the more than 150 IVF clinics in the United States, half have never had a birth, and only a handful have recorded more than five. Fifty per cent of all U.S. IVF babies come from three clinics."[22] The success rate at the best IVF clinic in Canada is 13 percent; the majority of Canada's twelve IVF clinics have success rates of 8 percent or lower.[23]

The stressful and debilitating nature of the IVF experience for women has been powerfully documented by Canadian sociologist Linda Williams[24]: IVF's psychological costs include depression, anxiety and low self-esteem. But the physical suffering and health costs are even worse. They include the adverse effects of hormones such as Clomid, which are usually taken in large, concentrated doses to stimulate hyperovulation; repeated anaesthesia and surgery to extract eggs; the heightened risk of ectopic pregnancy; the development of ovarian cysts and of menstrual difficulties; and the early onset of menopause and an increased risk of some forms of cancer.

Moreover, while it is often said that the children "produced" through IVF are healthy, some recent studies in Australia dispute that claim. Rates of multiple pregnancy, spontaneous abortion, preterm delivery, perinatal death, birth defects and low birth weight are higher in IVF pregnancies than in other pregnancies.[25]

Because IVF represents an ongoing medical experiment on women and children, an experiment whose first success, Louise Joy Brown, is not yet fourteen years old, its long-term effects and risks are not known. Anita Direcks, a DES daughter from Holland, has written movingly about the parallels between the use of the synthetic hormone diethylstilbestrol (DES) allegedly to prevent miscarriage during the 1940s, 1950s and 1960s, and the use of in vitro fertilization, allegedly to alleviate infertility, during the 1970s and 1980s. Direcks writes:

> IVF is delivered by the same men who brought us DES, dangerous contraceptives, and other fertility-destroying technologies. One of the most important concerns I have in regard to IVF is the concern about the long-term effects of an IVF-treatment for mother and child: the consequences of the hormonal treatment,

the medium, and so on.... IVF is an experiment on healthy women.[26]

Indeed, the parallels between the development and use of DES and the development and use of IVF are alarming. DES was not adequately tested before being used on thousands of women; IVF was not adequately tested (not even on animals!) before being used on thousands of women. The long-term effects of DES were not widely known or were ignored when the drug was first being prescribed; the long-term effects of IVF are still not known. DES has intergenerational effects; there is a possibility that IVF may have intergenerational effects, especially in view of the extensive use of hormones in the generation of test-tube babies. DES was not effective in its alleged purpose, preventing miscarriages, but this was not made known to the public; IVF has a very low success rate, but this is almost systematically hidden from public awareness. Women using DES were not adequately informed about it; women undergoing IVF are not adequately informed about it. DES was recommended for routine use in all pregnancies, supposedly to produce "better babies"; similarly, some of the promoters and defenders of IVF have claimed that the process produces more intelligent infants. Thus, the potential uses for DES were gradually and needlessly expanded, just as the potential uses for IVF are being gradually, and perhaps needlessly, expanded, including its use in cases of male infertility.

Second, there are significant similarities in the ideological underpinnings of DES development and the development of IVF. These include the idea of the inadequacy of women's bodies; the goal of improving women's reproductive functioning; the emphasis upon science and scientists as the white knights coming to rescue women from their underfunctioning reproductive systems; the emphasis upon doing everything possible in the attempt to produce a baby, genetically related to oneself, the eugenic emphasis on having the perfect baby; and the ongoing focus on fertility and reproduction as central to, and perhaps definitive of, women and womanhood.

As a result of considerations such as these, some feminists have called for a ban on further IVF research and practice. For example, Renate Klein and Robyn Rowland state, "IVF — in all its forms — must be ... abandoned. It is a failed and dangerous technology. And it produces a vulnerable population,[27] of women on which to continue experimentation." FINRRAGE, the Feminist International Network of Resistance to Reproductive and Genetic Engineering, calls for resistance to "the development and application of genetic and reproductive engineering" and to "the takeover of our bodies for male use, for profit making, population control, medical experimentation and misogynous science."[28]

Feminists who would ban IVF depict those women who use it in a way entirely opposite to the picture painted by liberals who identify IVF access as a right. Far from being free and equal contractors in the reproductive marketplace, women are depicted as victims who are the incomprehending dupes of the scientific and medical systems. Whereas the rights advocates regard IVF as inevitably serving women's reproductive autonomy, advocates of a ban on IVF regard IVF as inevitably destroying it. Whereas the rights advocates claim, "Women want IVF," advocates of a ban on IVF claim, "Women do not (really) want IVF," or, "Women's want for IVF is artificial."

Does not this obsessive craving to have a child of one's own in many cases stem from an individual's sense of private property or the desire to have somebody around over whom one has substantial control for some years at least? Let us also face the questions that (a) is not this craving more created than natural and (b) does not the social pressure to fit to the image of "motherhood" put women in a more vulnerable position?[29]

But while many feminists have rightly stressed both the social construction of the desire for motherhood and the dangers and ineffectiveness of in vitro fertilization,[30] not all of them have been willing simply to attribute women's desire for IVF to false consciousness. Margarete Sandelowski suggests that:

> Feminists critical of the new conceptive technology and certain surrogacy and adoption arrangements suggest misguided volition on the part of infertile women, a failure of will associated not with causing infertility but with seeking solutions for it deemed hazardous to other women. ... Beyond being politically useful as evidence for women's oppressive socialization to become mothers and their continued subservience to institutionalized medicine, infertile women occupy no more empathic place in many current feminist discussions than in the medical and ethical debates on reproductive technology feminists criticize.[31]

Sandelowski argues that some feminist theorists "equate women's desire for children with their oppression as women, viewing this desire and the anguish women feel when it remains unfulfilled as socially constructed rather than authentically experienced."[32] Thus, women's desires are discounted and their autonomy denied through the designation of socialization as the shaper and molder of female selves. Similarly, Christine St. Peters argues,

> The appeal to resist [the social imperative that women achieve personhood only through motherhood], an appeal that is heavily pedagogic in tone, is a staple of virtually all the feminist discussions of female infertility, which generally argue that the desire for motherhood is socially construct-

ed and therefore susceptible to revision. Of course this is demonstrably true, although to what extent we cannot prove, since we cannot definitively demonstrate where nature and culture are separable. But the limitations of the message are particularly obvious at a strategic level where we must respond to infertile women's suffering; here the often homiletic tone probably alienates many women, especially as we have not yet changed the social contexts in which the desire for children takes the shape of desiring genetically related offspring.[33]

In fact, women's motives for seeking IVF are complex,[34] and it is important not to deny or underestimate the needs and experiences of infertile women.[35] It is, surely, inappropriate for feminists to claim to understand better than infertile women themselves the origins and significance of their desire for children. Even if the longing felt by infertile women is socially produced, it is nevertheless real longing. Furthermore, that longing cannot be assumed to extinguish women's autonomy. Women who are "trying everything" in order to obtain a baby are not necessarily less autonomous, less free from social conditioning, than women who gestate and deliver without technological intervention, nor less free than the feminists who call into question infertile women's motivations.

Sociologist Judith Lorber claims that consent to IVF is not a freely chosen act unless the woman is "an equal or dominant in the situation."[36] But if that is the criterion for freedom of choice, then almost no women make free choices, ever. I find philosopher Mary Anne Warren more plausible when she claims, "Freedom is not an all or nothing affair. We can rarely be completely free of unjust or inappropriate social and economic pressures, but we can sometimes make sound and appropriate decisions, in the light of our own circumstances."[37]

Radical feminist Janice G. Raymond has poured scorn on the kind of approach I advocate here, which she dismissively labels the "nuanced" approach to evaluating reproductive technologies.[38] This approach, she says, seeks to "limit the abuse [of women by reproductive technologies] by gaining control of some of these technologies, and by ensuring equal access for all women who need/desire them." The error here, she suggests, is in conflating need with desire, and then claiming that to oppose such needs/desires is to "limit women's reproductive liberty, options, and choices." In fact, however, "women as a class have a stake in reclaiming the female body — not as female nature — and not just by taking the body seriously — but by refusing to yield control of it to men, to the fetus, to the State...."[39]

My view, however, is that as feminists we can be extremely critical of the easy equation of need and desire, and of the social processes that create women's alleged "need" for babies and that require that that "need" be fulfilled through a biologically related infant acquired in any way possible. We can also reject the facile claim that access to any and all reproductive services, products and labour, is indispensable to reproductive freedom. But it does not follow that feminists should protect women from these social processes and from acting on their own desires. We need not take women's desires as an unanalyzable and unrejectable given. But neither can we ignore or belittle what women say they feel. We can attack the manipulation of women's desires by current medical/scientific reproductive practices. But we can also resist the too-simple depiction of infertile women as nothing but dupes or victims.

Raymond claims that when radical feminists expose the victimization of women by men, they, the radical feminists, are then inappropriately "blamed for creating" that victimization.[40] Obviously, feminists did not create the harm of IVF to which they have called attention. What I am suggesting is that feminists can expose the harm of IVF to the women themselves most likely to be affected by it, and then let them make the decision about whether to seek access nevertheless.

The demand for an end to all use of IVF is an expression of a kind of feminist maternalism,[41] which seeks to protect the best interests of the women affected by IVF. I cannot agree with those who wish to ban IVF to protect women from the dangers of coercive IVF, any more than I can agree with so-called "pro-life feminists" who wish to ban abortion to protect women from the dangers of coercive abortions. It is not the role of feminist research and action to protect women from what is interpreted to be their own false consciousness. If, as Judith Lorber claims, women seeking IVF make "a patriarchal bargain" rather than a free choice,[42] then those women must be given the information and support they need in order to genuinely choose.

At this time, while women candidates are told something about the mechanical procedures for IVF, so far there is not much evidence that they are fully informed about the low success rates and the suffering and risks associated with IVF. The solution to the making of ideologically coerced choices is not always and necessarily the banning of the choices themselves, but education about that which is chosen.

Therefore, while I cannot support and endorse highly ineffective, costly and painful procedures such as IVF, until infertile women themselves, by the thousands, and especially those who seek and have sought IVF, call for the banning of artificial reproduction, I am uneasy about endorsing such a call by some feminists, any more than I would endorse a call for a ban on all interventionist hospital births in low-risk deliveries. I assume that when women are provided with complete information, real choices and full support with regard to artificial reproduction, they will be empowered to make reproductive decisions that will genuinely benefit themselves and their children. Based on my subjective impressions, from talking to women who have already rejected IVF, and to women who now have serious criticisms of IVF after trying it, it may well turn out that, when fully informed, women will reject in vitro fertilization at a much higher rate than they do now.

5. A FEMINIST ALTERNATIVE

Or they may not. It is therefore necessary to consider what a caring, feminist approach to the provision of in vitro fertilization would look like — an approach which is founded upon women's experiences, values and beliefs, which acknowledges the political elements of reproductive choices and practices, which seeks to minimize harm to women and children, and which recognizes and fosters women's dignity and self-determination. The caring provision of artificial reproduction services requires (a) truly informed choice and consent; (b) equal and fair access, unbiased by geographic, economic, or social criteria; (c) adequate record keeping, follow-up and research; and (d) appropriate support systems for all participants. All of these services could be provided in free-standing women's reproductive health clinics, run on feminist principles, where the health care providers are primarily both responsible and responsive to their women clients.[43]

First, then, it is necessary to ensure that women—as individuals, not as part of a couple — entering and participating in infertility treatment programs make a genuinely informed choice and consent.

Counselling should not be provided by the clinic itself, but by third parties who have no personal investment in persuading clients to use the clinic's services.

The notion of informed choice involves not merely telling women of the possible risks of the procedure, but discussion of the alternatives to in vitro fertilization.[44] It would also require open acknowledgment of the experimental status of the procedure. This point has recently been emphasized by Marsden Wagner, Director of Maternal and Child Health, European Regional Office of the World Health Organization. Wagner says, "There has not been one single prospective, randomized controlled trial of the efficacy and safety of [IVF].... IVF is clearly an experimental procedure by all criteria. It should not be included in the health *care* budget, but in the health *research* budget."[45] Prospective patients must therefore be informed of IVF's unknowns, the short- and long-term risks, the possible benefits, the chances of success and failure, alternative approaches and treatments and pronatalist social pressures to procreate and other ways of responding to them. In particular, women who are offered in vitro fertilization for infertility in their male partners should clearly understand that they could become pregnant much more easily, safely and with lower risks if they made use of donor insemination.[46]

Second, it is essential to critically examine the artificial criteria, such as marital status, sexual orientation and ability to pay, that get in the way of women's fair access to reproductive technologies, with a view to dismantling those barriers that discriminate unjustifiably. If IVF is a valuable medical service (and, given its high risks and low success rate, that assumption is and will remain debatable) then it deserves to be made available, like other medical services, through medicare, as it is now in Ontario.

Third, an adequate system of record keeping should be established, to track the long-term effects of IVF on women and their offspring, and to ensure that any women who provide eggs for the program have genuinely chosen to do so, so that "egg-snatching" is eliminated. Moreover, donors should really be donors, not vendors; the commodification of reproductive products and services is morally unjustified. It is essential to resist the commercialization of reproduction and the spread of reproductive entrepreneurialism, the primary targets of which are likely to be poor women and women of colour. It would also be important to ensure thorough screening and long-term follow-up of donors of eggs and sperm, and to avoid too-frequent use of the same donors. The issue of control over and decision making about so-called "spare" embryos, including those that are subject to cryopreservation, must also be faced. In addition, offspring of artificial reproduction need certain protections, in particular, access to information about their origins and the health status of their biological parents (if they were conceived using donor gametes), and knowledge of the lifelong questions about and implications of IVF for their own health prospects.

Finally, participants and potential participants in IVF programs should be provided with support systems to enable them to evaluate fully their own reasons and goals for being in the program, and to provide assistance throughout the emotionally and physically demanding aspects of the treatment. It would be important that all counselling and group support not just function as a means of ensuring the patients' continued acquiescence, or eliminating those without the stamina to endure the ordeal,[47] but that it facilitate their active involvement and participation in their treatment.

I have tried to indicate what I think is a fair and caring approach to the justification of and access to in vitro fertilization. The approach that I have just sketched avoids, on the one hand, claiming access to artificial reproduction as a right in the strong sense, and on the other hand, making reproductive technology a privilege to be earned through the possession of certain personal, social, sexual and/or financial characteristics. Sweeping generalizations about the moral justification of all forms of artificial reproduction are on very uncertain ground: processes of artificial reproduction need to be evaluated individually, on their own merits, to determine which ones, if any, are genuinely valuable and worth supporting.

For the sake of brevity, this discussion has set aside some crucial macro-allocation questions about the relative importance of IVF in comparison to other health care services, particularly infertility prevention, prenatal care, research on acquired immunodeficiency syndrome (AIDS) and sex education. I do not assume that IVF inevitably ranks equal in importance with these other measures, or that IVF could not legitimately be limited perhaps by confining it to those who do not have any children already, or by eliminating IVF as a so-called "treatment" for male infertility for the sake of research in and access to other more pressing health services. Over the long term, certainly, the caring provision of artificial reproduction should also be coupled with research into the incidence and causes of and cures for infertility, and the elimination of iatrogenic and environmental sources of infertility, so that the apparent need for artificial reproduction is reduced. Ultimately, the genuinely caring provision of artificial reproduction will require a feminist reevaluation and reconstruction of all reproductive values, technologies and practices.

NOTES

1. For example, see Janice G. Raymond, "Reproductive Technologies, Radical Feminism, and Socialist Liberalism," *Reproductive and Genetic Engineering: Journal of International Feminist Analysis,* 2, 2 (1989): 141.

2. Christine Overall, *Ethics and Human Reproduction: A Feminist Analysis* (Boston: Allen & Unwin, 1987), 166-96.

3. *Morgentaler, Smolling and Scott v. A. G. Canada,* Supreme Court of Canada, January 28, 1988. Judgment by Justice Wilson, 15.

4. Ethics Committee of the American Fertility Society, "The Constitutional Aspects of Procreative Liberty," in *Ethical Issues in the New Reproductive Technologies,* edited by Richard T. Hull (Belmont, CA: Wadsworth, 1990), 9.

5. John A. Robertson, "Procreative Liberty, Embryos, and Collaborative Reproduction: A Legal Perspective," in *Embryos, Ethics and Women's Rights: Exploring the New Reproductive Technologies,* edited by Elaine Hoffman Baruch, Amadeo F. D'Adamo, Jr., and Joni Seager (New York: Haworth Press, 1988), 180. Cf. Lori B. Andrews, "Alternative Modes of Reproduction," in *Reproductive Laws for the 1990s,* edited by Sherrill Cohen and Nadine Taub (Clifton, NJ: Humana Press, 1989), 364. Robertson's heterosexist bias is not much mitigated by his later concession that there is "a very strong argument for unmarried persons, either single or as couples, also having a positive right to reproduce" (Robertson, "Procreative Liberty," 181).

6. Robertson, "Procreative Liberty," 180, 186 and 190.

7. Uri B. Andrews, *New Conceptions: A Consumer's Guide to the Newest Infertility Treatments* (New York: Ballantyne Books, 1985), 138.

8. From this point of view, then, IVF with donor gametes could be more problematic than IVF in which a woman and a man make use of their own eggs and sperm.

9. Genoveffa Corea, "Egg Snatchers," in *Test-Tube Women: What Future for Motherhood,* edited by Rita Arditti, Renate Duelli Klein and Shelley Minden (London: Pandora Press, 1984), p. 37-51.

10. Andrews, "Alternative Modes of Reproduction," 374-77.

11. Gena Corea and Susan Ince report that in the United States in 1985, 42 out of the 54 clinics accepted only married couples. See their "Report of a Survey of IVF Clinics in the U.S.," in *Made to Order: The Myth of Reproductive and Genetic Progress,* edited by Patricia Spallone and Deborah Lynn Steinberg (Oxford: Pergamon Press, 1987), 140.

12. Judith Lorber, "In Vitro Fertilization and Gender Politics," in Baruch et al., *Embryos, Ethics and Women's Rights,* 118-19.

13. There are comparable barriers to access to donor insemination. See, e.g., Deborah Lynn Steinberg, "Selective Breeding and Social Engineering: Discriminatory Policies of Access to Artificial Insemination by Donor in Great Britain," in Spallone et al., *Made to Order,* 184-89.

14. See Rebecca Shuster, "Sexuality as a Continuum: The Bisexual Identity," in

Lesbian Psychologies: Explorations and Challenges, edited by the Boston Lesbian Psychologies Collective (Urbana, IL: University of Illinois Press, 1987), 56-71.

15. See Thomas A. Shannon, "In Vitro Fertilization: Ethical Issues," in Baruch et al., *Embryos, Ethics, and Women's Rights,* 156-57.

16. See Congregation for the Doctrine of the Faith, "Instruction on Respect for Human Life in Its Origin and on the Dignity of Procreation: Replies to Certain Questions of the Day" (Vatican City, 1987). This document, of course, also expresses many concerns about the treatment and destruction of embryos, arguments which are not evaluated here.

17. Donald DeMarco, *In My Mother's Womb: The Catholic Church's Defense of Natural Life* (Manassas, VA: Trinity Communications, 1987), 156-57.

18. Ibid., 157; cf. Ronald D. Lawler, "Moral Reflections on the New Technologies: A Catholic Analysis," in Baruch et al., *Embryos, Ethics, and Women's Rights,* 167-77.

19. Janice G. Raymond, "Fetalists and Feminists: They Are Not the Same," in Spallone et *al., Made to Order,* 63.

20. DeMarco, *In My Mother's Womb,* 147; my emphasis.

21. Ibid., 159.

22. Ann Pappert, "In Vitro in Trouble, Critics Warn," *Globe and Mail,* February 6, 1988, A l. For a comparable discussion of IVF success rates in France, see Francoise Laborie, "Looking for Mothers You Only Find Fetuses," in Spallone et al., *Made to Order,* 49-50.

23. Pappert, " In Vitro in Trouble, " A 14.

24. Linda S. Williams, "No Relief Until the End: The Physical and Emotional Costs of In Vitro Fertilization," in *The Future of Human Reproduction,* edited by Christine Overall (Toronto: Women's Press, 1989), 120-38.

25. "What You Should Know About In Vitro Fertilization," in *Our Bodies... Our Babies? Women Look at the New Reproductive Technologies* (Ottawa: Canadian Research Institute for the Advancement of Women, 1989); "Current Developments and Issues: A Summary," *Reproductive and Genetic Engineering,* 2, 3 (1989): 253.

26. Anita Direcks, "Has the Lesson Been Learned?: The DES Story and IVF," in Spallone et al., *Made to Order,* 163. For a discussion of the harmful effects of one hormone used in IVF, clomiphene citrate, see Renate Klein and Robyn Rowland, "Women As Test-Sites for Fertility Drugs: Clomiphene Citrate and Hormonal Cocktails," *Reproductive and Genetic Engineering: Journal of International Feminist Analysis,* 1, 3 (1988): 251-73.

27. Klein and Rowland, "Women As Test-Sites," 270.

28. "Resolution from the FINRRAGE Conference, July 3-8, 1985, Vallinge, Sweden," in Spallone et al., *Made to Order,* 211.

29. Sultana Kamal, "Seizure of Reproductive Rights? A Discussion on Population Control in the Third World and the Emergence of the New Reproductive Technologies in the West," in Spallone et al., *Made to Order,* 153.

30. See, e.g., Susan Sherwin, "Feminist Ethics and In Vitro Fertilization," in *Science*

Morality and Feminist Theory, edited by Marsha Hanen and Kai Nielsen (Calgary: University of Calgary Press, 1987), 265-84.

31. Margarete Sandelowski, "Failures of Volition: An Historical Perspective on Female Agency and the Cause of Infertility," *Signs: Journal of Women in Culture and Society,* 15, 3 (Spring 1990): 498.

32. Ibid.

33. Christine St. Peters, "Feminist Discourse, Infertility and the New Reproductive Technologies," *National Women's Studies Association Journal* 1, 3 (Spring 1989): 359.

34. Christine Crowe, "'Women Want It': In Vitro Fertilization and Women's Motivations for Participation," in Spallone et al., *Made to Order,* 84-93.

35. See Alison Solomon, "Integrating Infertility Crisis Counseling into Feminist Practice," *Reproductive and Genetic Engineering,* 1, 1 (1988): 41-49; and Naomi Pfeffer, "Artificial Insemination, In-Vitro Fertilization and the Stigma of Infertility," in *Reproductive Technologies: Gender, Motherhood and Medicine,* edited by Michelle Stanworth (Minneapolis: University of Minnesota Press, 1987), 81-97.

36. Judith Lorber, "Choice, Gift, or Patriarchal Bargain?" *Hypatia,* 4 (Fall 1989): 30.

37. Mary Anne Warren, "IVF and Women's Interests: An Analysis of Feminist Concerns, *Bioethics,* 2, 1 (1988): 40-41.

38. Raymond, "Reproductive Technologies," 133-42.

39. Ibid., 135.

40. Ibid., 137.

41. Deborah Poff, "Reproductive Technology and Social Policy in Canada," in Overall, *The Future of Human Reproduction,* 223.

42. Lorber, "Choice, Gift, or Patriarchal Bargain?" 24.

43. Vicki Van Wagner and Bob Lee, "Principles into Practice: An Activist Vision of Feminist Reproductive Health Care," in Overall, *The Future of Human Reproduction,* 238-58.

44. Nikki Colodny, "The Politics of Birth Control in a Reproductive Rights Context," in Overall, *The Future of Human Reproduction,* 43.

45. "Current Developments and Issues: A Summary," *Reproductive and Genetic Engineering,* 2, 3 (1989): 253, Wagner's emphasis.

46. Lorber, "Choice, Gift, or Patriarchal Bargain?" 23-26.

47. Annette Burfoot, "Exploitation Redefined: An Interview with an IVF Practitioner," *Resources for Feminist Research/Documentation sur la recherche feminists,* 18:2 (June 1989): 27.

Sterilisation of the Mentally Severely Handicapped: A Violation of the Right to Have Children?

Eike-Henner W. Kluge

INTRODUCTION

The Universal Declaration of Human Rights (1948) stated, and the Declaration of Teheran (1968) reiterated, that every person 'of full age' has the right to have children and 'found a family'. The right thus enunciated is usually interpreted as being universal, inalienable and indefeasible: and it is at least in part on this basis that many jurisdictions have rejected the non-consensual sterilisation of the mentally severely handicapped as being both discriminatory and unethical when performed for reasons other than to safeguard the health and welfare of the handicapped person. It is on this basis also that most commentators have rejected such sterilisation.

However, both the general thesis, as well as its application to the mentally severely handicapped, may be challenged. The general claim may be challenged on three grounds: the nature of the right claimed, as well as its legitimacy, is extremely dubious; the grounding of the alleged right presents severe ontological problems; and the claim that such a right is indefeasible ignores the contextual nature of all rights. As to the particular claim as advanced for the mentally severely handicapped, three further arguments may be raised against it: the mentally severely handicapped cannot meet the basic precondition for such a right; insistence on such a right would violate the rights of children; and, finally, it would also violate the rights of other people.

While none of these considerations, even if successful, entail that the mentally severely handicapped should be sterilised as a matter of course, they do entail that under circumstances where conception and procreation of the mentally severely handicapped can reasonably be prevented only in this fashion, sterilisation is ethically permissible.

THE NATURE OF THE CLAIM

To begin with the nature of the claim itself: what precisely does the alleged right to have children amount to? Several possibilities come to mind, but one is generally taken to be central: the right to have biological progeny of one's own. In the interest of clarity, however, it should be noted that such an interpretation is rather simplistic. In the first place, one cannot have a right to what it is impossible to provide. Many persons are irremediably sterile and cannot have biological progeny. In their case, therefore, the alleged right would fail for want of its logical precondition. Whence it would follow that, contrary to the initial claim, the alleged right would not be universal (unless, of course, it were to be argued that the right is universal after all, and that in cases such as these, society has an obligation to develop and employ techniques of artificial reproduction that would overcome this problem. We shall not pursue the issue here.)

E.-H.W. Kluge, "Sterilisation of the Mentally Severely Handicapped: A Violation of the Right to Have Children?" *Ethical Problems in Reproductive Medicine* 1989; 1:1, 12-15.

Second, the right, no matter how construed, centrally involves children. Children, however, are not objects. They are persons. Therefore it follows that if there is a right to have progeny at all, it could not ethically be interpreted in a proprietary or dispositionary fashion. It would have to be understood in some other way. But how?

Finally, the right to have biological progeny of one's own would not ordinarily be considered to be satisfied by the mere existence of such progeny without any contact and association on part of the progenitor. A direct and personal interaction of an ongoing and formative sort is also taken to be implicated. An acceptable interpretation of the right claim, therefore, must include this associative parameter.

How to combine all this into a reasonable whole? The Universal Declaration of Human Rights, in its insistence on the right to 'found a family', points the way. Whatever its cultural idiosyncracies of constitution, the family context is one of nurturing, of education, and of raising children. In short, insofar as the person context is concerned, it is one of parenting. Therefore in keeping with the preceding considerations we suggest that the claim of a universal right to have children amounts to this: everyone has the right to (attempt to) have biological progeny and parent without undue state interference.

GROUNDING THE RIGHT

If we assume that this is an appropriate interpretation, the next question is, 'How could such a right be grounded?' The literature, and indeed pure reasoning itself, suggest several possibilities: in the biological survival needs of the human species, the fact of individual desire, the requirements for the realisation of a truly human potential, and the fact of social policy. We shall not here examine these possibilities in detail but merely sketch some consideration.

No purely material fact, and *a fortiori* no fact of biology, can establish an ethical right. That requires an ethical premise, which is here not given. Less abstractly, it is one thing to say that the human species will not survive unless its members reproduce; but is another to say that it ought to reproduce, or that it has the right to do so. Furthermore, even if the right were granted, it would not follow that every member of the species therefore had a right to progeny. Logically, such an inference would commit the fallacy of division because materially, the facts of biology would deny it. At best, what would follow from this basis would be that all and only those whose progeny could reasonably be expected to advance species survival would have such a right. The biological argument, therefore, would only allow for a limited right conditioned by evolutionary considerations.

The argument from individual desire fares no better. To put it bluntly, the connection between desire and right must be shown. It cannot merely be assumed. Otherwise it begs the question. As to the argument from the realisation of personal potential, it faces the same problem. The existence of a fact, in this case, personal potential, does not establish a right. As it stands, the argument assumes that the connection between the fact (desire) and the right is established independently, in some other fashion; but that is not the case. The argument requires that children be considered as objects, as entities whose function it is to assist in the development of others. That, however, is ethically anathema. What one can argue is that *if* there is a particular potential and *if* there is a child, then *ceteris paribus* whoever has that potential has a *prima facie* right to use the child's existence to realise the potential. But *only if* the child will not be treated as an object. That, however, is quite different from the right claimed in the first instance. It is not the right to bring about a child for that purpose.

The argument from social existence has two versions, one legally oriented, the other ethical. The former focuses in the law extant in a given society. We shall not deal with it here. The latter is based on the thesis that society, whether it recognises this explicitly in its laws or not, *de facto* guarantees each of its members certain fundamental rights as a condition of membership, and that the right to procreation and to parenting is one of these. However, while we may grant that society does indeed guarantee certain fundamental rights to its members, this does not establish that the right in question is one of them.

Furthermore, even if we did allow that there was such a right and that it was grounded in the fact of social existence, this would not show that it was absolute and unconditioned. The very fact that it was grounded in the social context would entail that like all other rights thus grounded, it would be subject to conditioning constraints. For one thing, it would be conditioned by the competing rights of others. Therefore if the exercise of this right interfered with the exercise of another person's more fundamental right e.g., the right to life, then the right would become ineffective. For another, it would be conditioned from the perspective of society as a whole. That is to say children, both as persons and as biological organisms, have needs. Providing for these, however, is not simply a parental function. No matter how wealthy, well-endowed or positioned, no set of parents can meet these conditions alone. Directly or indirectly, meeting them involves whole social institutions such as health, education and welfare which no one is wholly able to defray. The coming-into-being of a child, therefore, is a social affair; and society, by allowing someone to claim the right to have a child, acquires the obligation to provide for its needs if, when and as it becomes necessary. Justice, however, entails that no one can have an obligation unilaterally thrust upon

him or her. There must be some ethically acceptable way for the individual to escape the obligation. This means that it must be possible for society to avoid being locked into the relevant obligations vis-à-vis the new child. This would be possible only by preventing the child from coming into existence in the first place. It therefore follows that although there may be a socially guaranteed right to have children, that right is not absolute but defeasible from the side of society itself.

Finally, the right also is defeasible from the side of the child. That is to say, there are situations in which the conditions governing the genesis of a child are the beginning of a causal chain which predictably will eventuate in such a qualitative state for the child that, were it imposed *de novo* upon a person who is already present, it would constitute the infliction of harm. To procreate under such circumstances would be tantamount to a temporally protracted infliction of harm. Therefore while the act of procreation *per se* may be morally blameless, the act *under such circumstances* would be blameworthy and constitute an injury. Under such circumstances, therefore, the right to have a child fails.

THE MENTALLY SEVERELY HANDICAPPED

The right to have a child, therefore, even if it is granted, is neither universal, absolute nor unconditioned. So far, we have only argued this for persons in general. How does it apply to the mentally severely handicapped?

To avoid confusion, we shall define a mentally severely handicapped person as someone who is congenitally so severely impaired that he or she cannot look after his or her needs as an independent and autonomous being but requires continuous supervision and assistance in order to allow him or her to survive and function; and furthermore as someone who cannot grasp the nature of a child as a person, and who fails to comprehend the requirements inherent in providing for a child. Does such an individual have a right to have a child, in the sense discussed above? And is there a right on the part of society to sterilise such an individual in order to prevent him or her from having children?

If our preceding analysis is correct, then the answer to the first question is negative. There are two reasons for this: one logical, the other ethical. *Ex hypothesi,* the mentally severely handicapped cannot perceive, relate to or otherwise treat children as persons. Consequently, they cannot fulfil the requirements of a parenting role. Since the ability to fulfil such a role is a precondition of the right to have children, it follows that the right itself fails from a purely logical perspective. As to the ethical reason for its failure, the very nature of the handicap entails that a child born into such a situation would play the role of an object of personal development and self-gratification for the severely handicapped. However, as we said before, no right can involve the use of persons purely as objects in an instrumental fashion. The right, therefore, fails once again.

It might be argued that while the inabilities of the handicapped to parent and to see children as persons may be admitted, this does not entail that they do not have a right to have children. Instead, it entails that society has an obligation to provide for the services of someone who will take over those areas of parenting which the severely handicapped are constitutionally unable to provide: to act, as it were, *in loco parentis* towards the children. The inability of the handicapped thus being made up, their right is preserved and they will be able to benefit from and enjoy the remainder of the parenting experience.

But such an argument would fail. The central precondition ineluctably associated with the right to have a child is that the individual who claims the right must be able to experience, relate to and otherwise interact with the child as a person. The proposal at hand would not allow the mentally severely handicapped to meet this precondition. It would be the parent-proxy, the individual who is provided by society to act *in loco parentis,* who would relate to the children in the requisite manner. Short of changing his or her nature, nothing can be done for or to the mentally severely handicapped that would allow him or her to meet this condition. For him or her, the children will still remain objects. In more formal terms, if a's having quality ϕ is a necessary precondition of having right $R,$ then the fact that b has quality ϕ does not establish that therefore a has R after all. The only way in which a can acquire R is for a to acquire ϕ. In this case it would mean that the mentally severely handicapped would have to cease being mentally severely handicapped. If that were possible, there would be no ethical problem. As it stands, however, it is not the case.

STERILISATION

If the foregoing is correct, then the mentally severely handicapped do not have a right to have children in the sense we have developed. Society has both a right and a duty to step in. But in what fashion? Surely sterilisation is too restrictive? Surely contraception and even abortion are less permanent, less irreversible and less intrusive alternatives?

As to abortion, it is almost as intrusive as tubal ligation and since it does not prevent future conceptions, it is a potentially repetitive procedure. Given that it does have an intrusive nature, it follows on the last count that any advantage it might have over sterilisation would have to be sought in the fact that it did not bring about an irreversible condition. That, however, prompts the following question: Under what circumstances would reversibility be a relevant consideration? The answer is only in those cases where the factor that mandated interference in the first place, the severe mental handicap, was not a permanent characteristic of the individual in question. However, instead of telling against sterilisation *per se,* this surely means that sterilisation is unacceptable *in those cases.* It does not mean that in cases where the severe mental handicap is permanent, sterilisation should also be withheld, in the expectation of a miracle, as it were.

Turning to contraception, since it is the least permanent and least intrusive alternative, it appears to be the method of choice. However, those methods of contraception which under the circumstances would be the most appropriate, subcutaneous implants, IUDs, etc., while they are indeed least intrusive in a mechano/physiological sense, emerge as quite intrusive when it is considered that they are biochemically active on the person as a whole. In any case they do have quantifiable risks of morbidity and mortality that exceed those of sterilisation. Their attractiveness on this count, therefore, wanes. As to their lack of permanence and irreversibility, not only do they also have long-term effects in that direction, but relevance of the criterion of reversibility should also be re-examined.

We suggest, therefore, that there are cases in which sterilisation is appropriate. All and only those, namely, where according to all appropriate standards of medical certitude the severe mental handicap is a permanent feature of the individual.

However, a fundamental question remains: Does the state have the right to breach the principle of inviolability and commit trespass to the person in the pursuit of its right and in order to prevent perceived harm to future persons?

There must be a proportion between a right/duty that is claimed and the method used to pursue it. And here the following consideration seems germane. Sterilisation by vasectomy or tubal ligation is currently being used by competent people on a voluntary basis to control their own fertility. Nor is sterilisation deemed ethically inappropriate or indefensible in this context. The method itself, therefore, is ethically acceptable *per se.* The only reason an objection might arise is that in the case of the mentally severely handicapped it would be imposed in a nonconsensual manner. Here, however, we should like to suggest the following as a particularisation of the principle of equality. If a particular method or procedure is unobjectionable when employed by a competent individual on a voluntary basis in order to control a particular activity or bodily function, then the fact that it is employed by a proxy decision-maker for an incompetent individual for reasons that are ethically defensible in their own right, does not render it ethically objectionable. If this principle is false, then nothing that a proxy decision-maker decides on the basis of comparison with normal situations will ever be ethically defensible. On the other hand if, as we have suggested, it is correct, then in many cases sterilisation will be an ethically appropriate way to proceed.

On Sterilising the Mentally Handicapped

Raanan Gillon

At the time of writing, the House of Lords in England had not ruled in the case of Jeanette — a seventeen-year-old with allegedly the skills of at most a five- or six-year-old whose mother and gynaecologist wished to perform probably irreversible sterilisation by an operation to tie her fallopian tubes.[1] Whatever the legal decision, the ethical issues underlying decisions of this kind deserve analysis.

In the normal case the matter is settled by the decision of the woman and her gynaecologist — if she wishes to be sterilised, for example for the purposes of contraception, and a gynaecologist agrees to her request that is the end of the matter so far as the law in England is concerned.[2] The underlying ethical argument may presumably be simply but perhaps not inaccurately summarised along the lines that such sterilisation is an operation of sufficient potential benefit and sufficiently small likely harm to be justified if a patient understandingly and autonomously chooses it, and that there are no generally overriding considerations of justice, either in terms of people's rights or in terms of distribution of resources, to prevent such operations.

What changes the ethical argument in the case of a severely mentally handicapped person is of course the absence of sufficient autonomy in the potential patient to make possible her understanding and autonomous choice either to have or not to have the operation. We have developed, however, several apparently justifiable systems for dealing with cases of inadequate autonomy. In general the preferred approach is to try to approximate as closely as possible to what would be the autonomous decision of the person concerned (for instance by reference to earlier expressed autonomous preferences and decisions). That route is blocked however in the case of those people who have never developed sufficient autonomy, such as those who have been severely mentally handicapped from birth or early childhood. The second route is that commonly adopted in the case of children, where autonomous decisions are exercised by proxy on the child's behalf. The normally acceptable proxies are the parents (and there is argument as to whether they should exercise their proxy autonomy in the child's best interests or merely in the child's interests). The assumption that the parents are the appropriate proxies is however defeasible, certainly when there is reason to believe that they are unjustifiably acting against their child's interests and arguably even if they are failing to act in their child's *best* interests.[3] What reasons are there to reject such an approach to proxy consent in the case of sterilisation of severely mentally handicapped people?

Three arguments are plausible candidates. The first is that it can never be in a mentally handicapped person's interests, let alone in his or her best interests, to be sterilised. The second is that it violates the rights of a mentally handicapped person to sterilise him or her without the person's understanding and autonomous consent. The third is that it is against the interests

Raanan Gillon, "On Sterilising the Mentally Handicapped," *Journal of Medical Ethics* 13 (2) 1987; 59-61.

of society to permit it, either because of anticipated harm and/or because of some other anticipated injustice to others.

So far as the first argument is concerned it is hard to see why it can *never* be in the best interests of a severely mentally handicapped person to be sterilised if it is accepted that it can sometimes be in the best interests of a mentally normal woman to be sterilised. The main benefit in the normal case is usually the virtually certain avoidance of pregnancy. Now of course there is a widespread countervailing presumption that pregnancy is a good thing. Doubtless this presumption is based on the evident truths that for many women pregnancy and the consequent nurturing of children are goods, fundamental to their flourishing, and moreover that the undergoing of pregnancy by at least *some* women is a necessary condition of the continued flourishing of humankind. But neither of those truths is sufficient for a conclusion that it is *never* in the best interests of a normal woman to be sterilised. If, as is widely accepted, it may for some women, whose beliefs permit such a choice, be beneficial, in their best interests and morally acceptable to be sterilised, why may not the same be true of some severely mentally handicapped women?

It could hardly be argued that the benefits of pregnancy justify such a ban for it is widely accepted even by those who absolutely oppose sterilisation of severely mentally handicapped women that great care should be taken to try to ensure that such women do not become pregnant. Nor can the argument that women flourish through the rearing and nurturing of their children be applied in such cases for almost inevitably severely mentally handicapped mothers will be unable to rear and nurture their children who will therefore be taken from them and placed elsewhere.

If the question of such women's best interests is pursued it becomes less and less clear that sterilisation is necessarily against

their best interests. Given for example the pervasive assumption that pregnancy must if at all possible be avoided, women in such circumstances are likely to be subjected to considerably more repressive control over their contacts with men, and especially mentally handicapped men, in the hospitals, hostels and day centres where severely mentally handicapped people often spend much of their time. Indeed, only total sexual segregation can guarantee the avoidance of pregnancy. On the other hand if the possibility of pregnancy is eliminated by some effective means of contraception then ordinary mixed social intercourse becomes a much easier option.

Here people divide about the desirability of any form of contraception for the severely mentally handicapped. But suppose it is accepted that (a) ordinary social life, including the mixing of the sexes, is desirable for severely mentally handicapped too, and (b) that in the nature of mixed sex social life it is impossible to eliminate the possibility that sexually developed members of such a group will from time to time have sexual intercourse (some would argue that provided such intercourse was mutually desired and not exploitative it should not be prevented[4]) and (c) that it is important to ensure that no pregnancy results from any such intercourse, then the desirability of some form of effective contraception follows. However, even if contraception is accepted as desirable it may still be argued that other reversible and less dangerous forms of contraception are preferable to sterilisation which is usually irreversible and involves a surgical operation.

So far as the irreversibility is concerned this only seems to be important if there is some realistic chance that the severely mentally handicapped person will develop sufficiently to become capable of parenting and being allowed to parent a child. For it is surely the denial of possible parenthood and of the fulfilment that accompanies it which underlies such concern about the irreversibility of sterilisation. Where there is some realistic chance of such development then it does indeed seem in the best interests of the woman not to have an irreversible sterilisation. However, in many cases no such realistic chance of maturation to a state compatible with parenthood exists — and then the irreversibility of the operation seems to be irrelevant.

Undoubtedly other methods of contraception exist. Condoms and pills would probably be unsuitable for severely mentally handicapped people but intrauterine devices and long-acting injectable contraceptives could be suitable alternatives. Both, however, carry their own risks of harms (for example abdominal cramps, contraceptive failure, ectopic pregnancy, heavy and or irregular vaginal bleeding) and in particular cases may be unacceptable. Certainly sterilisation involves a surgical operation and probably a general anaesthetic — but such risks are regularly taken by the mentally normal in their own interests — again it is difficult to see how acceptance of such risks in preference to those of other methods of contraception could *never* be in the best interests of a mentally handicapped person.

The second type of argument favouring an absolute ban on sterilisation of severely mentally handicapped people is that it transgresses their rights. Such arguments must be taken very seriously but also need careful dissection. Precisely *which* rights are being protected? Preferred candidates seem to be a right to reproduce, a right not to be stopped from reproducing, a right to have sexual intercourse, a right not to be stopped from having sexual intercourse with a willing partner, and a right not to be surgically assaulted. The normal case again allows us to see these more clearly. Obviously there is no general right to reproduce — but there is a general *prima facie* right not to be stopped from reproducing and certainly in the normal case

sterilisation without the person's understanding consent would be considered an outrageous transgression of his or her right not to be stopped from reproducing and his or her right not to be surgically assaulted. But again in the normal case these rights can be waived when it is in the interests of the person to waive them. One might even say that in the normal case people have a right to waive these rights.

As indicated above, we generally accept that where autonomous consent is unavailable (as is the case with severely mentally handicapped people) then the right not to have surgical intervention without consent can in some cases properly be waived, proxy autonomous consent for surgery be justifiably given and the surgery properly considered not to be an assault. So far as the right not to be stopped from reproduction is concerned we have seen that this is in general denied to severely mentally handicapped people; if this right were to justify a ban on sterilisation then it would equally require us not to prevent in other ways severely mentally handicapped people from reproducing. So far as the right not to be stopped from having sexual intercourse is concerned, sterilisation in no way infringes any such right, as the normal case makes clear. On the contrary, reliable contraception makes its implementation easier, though there are few, apart from those actually working on behalf of mentally handicapped people, who show any concern to accommodate their sexual desires, and the law, while complicated, tends to diminish any such sexual rights (though it by no means excludes them[4]).

Thus no absolute rights of the severely mentally handicapped are recognised either not to have surgery without consent or to be allowed to reproduce, and any right to have sexual intercourse would not be transgressed by sterilisation (on the contrary). Thus these rights-based arguments do not seem to justify an absolute ban on the possibility of proxy consent to sterilisation of a severely mentally handicapped person. The criterion for such consent would still have to be agreed — the weakest acceptable criterion presumably being that the action would not be against the person's interests, the next strongest being that it would be in his or her interests, and the strongest of all being that it would be in his or her best interests. Even with the last and strongest of these criteria (itself open to major objection for excluding any consideration of the interests of others) there seems no reason to assume that sterilisation could never be in such a person's best interests.

The third argument against sterilisation of a severely mentally handicapped person is that it would be against the interests of society to permit it, either because of harm to others or because of some other injustice to society or its members. In this context we have the appalling example of Hitler's reich in which mass sterilisation of the mentally incompetent was commonplace, by a variety of disgusting methods,[5] and which is one of 'the ghosts that haunt the Jeanette file'.[6] Certainly if there were reason to believe that permitting of sterilisation in the interests of a mentally handicapped person would lead to the crimes of the third reich that would justify laws to ban it absolutely. This argument is an instance of the slippery slope argument, of which there are two types, the logical and the empirical. There is no logical slippery slope here if, unlike the case of the third reich, it is ensured that sterilisation is only permitted when it is not against the interests of the individual concerned (with mechanisms established to defend those interests). The problem with the second sort of slippery slope argument, the empirical, is that it can be used against *any* proposal that is capable of misuse. *Of course* if there were any realistic probability that sterilisation of the severely mentally handicapped when this was not against their own interests would lead to harm to others in society,

let alone to the sort of repugnant society that characterised the third reich, then it should be prohibited. But there seems no reason to predict such developments if each case of proposed sterilisation of a mentally handicapped person is (a) not against the person's interests (and it might be safer to specify that it must be positively in his or her interests) and (b) decided in a way which explicitly protects that person's interests.

Given the worries involved, and given the peculiar vulnerability of the mentally handicapped, and given also the obvious conflicts between self-interest and the interests of the mentally handicapped which carers, parents and health care professionals alike, are likely to face, and given the irreversibility of sterilisation, it does seem wise to introduce a procedure for approval of proposed sterilisations which can be seen to defend the interests of the mentally handicapped person. One such procedure would be for all cases to obtain the approval of a court. Another might be to set up a committee to approve such proposals, of people with different backgrounds and independent of the mentally handicapped person's care, who would provide a backstop for protecting his or her interests, a system somewhat analogous to the approval now required under the Mental Health Act for certain sorts of irreversible treatments such as psychosurgery.[7]

Our attitudes to proposals for the sterilisation of mentally handicapped people are subject to powerful emotions — emotions that influence our responses to sexuality in general, emotions that influence our responses to mental handicap in general, and emotions that are heightened by our attitudes to a society whose morality functions as a dread warning of the depths to which human behaviour can sink. In such circumstances we must be even more than usually meticulous about subjecting our 'gut responses' to the searchlight of critical moral reasoning.

NOTES

1. Brahams D. Medicine and the law. *Lancet* 1987; vol. 1, 857-858.

2. Mason J.K., McCall Smith R.A. *Law and medical ethics.* London: Butterworths, 1983, 48.

3. Kennedy I., Dworkin G. Children and the law. In: Nicholson R.H., ed. *Medical research with children: ethics, law and practice.* Oxford, New York, Tokyo: Oxford University Press, 1986, 125-139.

4. Dixon H., Gunn M. *Sex and the law — a brief guide for staff working in the mental handicap field (England and Wales only).* London: Family Planning Association Education Unit, 1985.

5. Ivy A.C. Nazi war crimes of a medical nature. In: Reiser S.J., Dyck A.J., Curran W.J. *Ethics in medicine — historical perspectives and contemporary concerns.* Cambridge Mass, London: MIT press, 1977: 267-272.

6. Acherson N. Ghosts that haunt the Jeanette file. *The Observer* 1987 Mar 22: 9.

7. Mental Health Act, 1983, s 57, 58, and regulations.

FURTHER READINGS

Alberta Institute of Law Research and Reform. *Report for Discussion No. 6,* "Sterilization Decisions: Minors and Mentally Incompetent Adults." Edmonton, Alta, 1988.

Alberta Institute of Law Research and Reform. *Report No. 52,* "Competence and Human Reproduction." Edmonton, Alta, 1989.

Arras, J.D. "HIV and Childbearing," *Milbank Memorial Quarterly* 68:3 (1990) 353-382.

Bayles, Michael D. *Reproductive Ethics.* Englewood Cliffs, N.J.: Prentice Hall, 1984.

Chambers, D. "The Right to the Least Restrictive Alternative," in M. Kindred et al, eds. *The Mentally Retarded Citizen and the Law.* New York: Free Press, 1976.

Finch-Noyes, C.A.P. "Sterilization of the Mentally Retarded Minor: the Re K. Case." *Canadian Journal of Family Law* 5:1 (1986) 277-99.

Great Britain, Department of Health and Social Services. *Report of the Committee of Enquiry into Human Sterilization and Embryology,* ed. by M. Warnock. London: HM Stationer's Office, 1984: "The Warnock Report."

Grubb, A. and D. Pearl. "Sterilization and the Courts." *Cambridge Law Journal* 46:3 (1987) 439-64.

Law Reform Commission of Canada. Working Paper 24, *Sterilization: Implications for Mentally Retarded and Mentally Ill Persons.* Ottawa: Minister of Supply and Services, 1978.

McLaren, Angus. "The Creation of a Haven for 'Human Thoroughbreds': Sterilization of the Feebleminded and the Mentally Ill in British Columbia." *Canadian Historical Review* 67:2 (1986) 127-50.

McLean, S. "The Right to Reproduce," in T. Campbell et al, eds., *Human Rights: From Rhetoric to Reality.* New York: Basil Blackwell, 1986.

Ryan, M.A. "The Argument for Unlimited Reproductive Liberty: A Feminist Critique." *Hastings Center Report* 20:4 (1990) 6-12.

Stefan, S. "Whose Right Is It Anyway? Reproductive Rights of Incarcerated, Institutionalized and Incompetent Women." *Nova Law Review* 13:2 (1989) 405-456.

CHAPTER 16
THE NEW REPRODUCTIVE TECHNOLOGIES

INTRODUCTION

In the last few decades, medical research has come a long way. Nowhere is this more true than in the area of reproduction. The advances that have been made in reproductive technology now make it possible for many people who traditionally had been considered infertile and incapable of having children to have biological offspring of their own.

However, as in some many cases, the development of the technologies, and indeed the technologies' use of the technologies themselves, are not without ethical problems. In the first selection, the Royal Commission on New Reproductive Technologies identifies some of these problems. The selections are taken from the Commission's final Report to Parliament, which appropriately enough is entitled *Proceed With Care.*[1] The Commission's mandate was to "inquire into and report upon the current and potential medical and scientific developments related to new reproductive technologies, considering in particular their social, ethical, health, research, legal and economic implications and the public interest, recommending what policies and safeguards should be applied."[2] The selection includes excerpts from the Commission's deliberations and recommendations about such issues as *in vitro* fertilization, collection and use of human ova, embryo donation and harvesting, etc. The recommendations were the basis of an attempt by the government to pass legislation regulating the use of the reproductive technologies in clinical practice. The attempt failed when Parliament prorogued in the fall of 1997. The Bill that contained many of the recommendations of the Royal Commission died on the order papers. It is expected that a new attempt to legislate in these areas will be made within the near future. Until then, Canada is essentially without any law that regulates the use of the technologies. Should the use of the technologies be regulated? Is the Commission correct in its concerns?

The second selection in this chapter deals not with the new reproductive technologies as such but with a modern use of the technologies in an old practice: surrogate motherhood. The selection presents the position that the Canadian Medical Association adopted as its formal policy and which it presented to the Royal Commission on New Reproductive Technologies. It is the perspective of "organized medicine." It might be interesting to ask whether this position of health care processionals differs from that of ordinary people.

The final selection is an article by Nancy Jecker. It deals with a problem that has recently arisen with the advent of reproductive technologies and screening techniques: Should parents be allowed to conceive a child in order to harvest biological parts of this new child—say, bone marrow—to save the life of another one of their children? Is it ethical to conceive a child to save a child?

NOTES

1. Royal Commission on New Reproductive Technologies, *Proceed With Care: Final Report of the Royal Commission on New Reproductive Technologies* (Ottawa: Minister of Supply and Services, 1993) 2 vols.

2. Ibid., vol. 1, Letter of Submission to His Excellency, the Governor General in Council.

Infertility Treatments: In Vitro Fertilization

In the Commission's estimation, policies and guidelines should not be arbitrary, they should be applied to everyone equally, and they should not be misused in a discriminatory way to deny services. Lack of a partner, sexual orientation, or disability should not be reasons in and of themselves to deny access, as ... they clearly are in some clinics.

If a woman is diagnosed as having bilateral tubal blockage, we have recommended that she have access to IVF to treat it. As with any other medical service provided through the publicly funded health care system, this would be available whether she is married or single, heterosexual or homosexual. However, as the diagnosis of tubal blockage is usually made following a failure to conceive by natural means, it is likely that very few women not in heterosexual relationships would be aware that they have

Royal Commission on New Reproductive Technologies, *Proceed With Care: Final Report of the Royal Commission on New Reproductive Technologies* (Ottawa: Minister of Supply and Services, 1993) 2 vols., vol. 1, 553-54.

this problem. It is theoretically possible that a woman would find out, for instance, following failure to conceive using donor insemination, and in such a case there are no grounds for denying a single woman or a lesbian access to IVF using donor sperm as a medical treatment available to any woman with this diagnosis.

The second category of potential obstacles consists of factors in the health care delivery system that make gaining access to infertility services more difficult. For example, Canadians whose first language is neither English nor French may be reluctant to approach an infertility treatment program, or less likely to be able to make fully informed decisions if they do, if services are not designed with the pluralistic nature of Canadian society in mind. Similarly, level of education influences income, awareness, empowerment, and other attitudes and characteristics. These characteristics are significant factors in allowing people to negotiate the complex and unclear route to new reproductive technology services and therefore in gaining access to them.

Workplace policies can also influence access to services depending on whether paid sick leave or vacation leave is available and whether sick leave can be used when undergoing infertility treatment; the degree of flexibility in work schedules and the amount of time off that can be taken, when it can be taken, and how much notice is required; and the existence or nature of employer-sponsored supplementary health insurance (to cover services and drugs not included under public health insurance).

Admission policies are set by IVF clinic directors and treatment teams, and individual cases are usually decided upon by the attending physician and the rest of the treatment team. Our review of current practices showed admission policies set by clinics do present barriers to treatment and they vary from clinic to clinic. We found that speed of access to IVF also varies wide-

ly across Canada; private clinics and four of the five non-teaching hospitals had no waiting list at all. Patients at most (16 of 20) teaching hospitals, however, could expect to wait at least a week for an appointment, and five hospitals reported waiting lists of 30 weeks or more for treatment. Close to half the programs (7 of 16) told the Commission, however, that they turned away fewer than 5 percent of applicants in 1991. Only one clinic reported that more than 10 percent of applicants were turned away. Most programs told applicants who were refused treatment about other clinics — referral to U.S. clinics was almost as common as referral to other Canadian programs. Six clinics said they did not refer to other programs.

Clinics told us that they accepted patients who had been infertile for varying lengths of time. Couples with a clear diagnosis of the cause of their infertility were accepted right away, but for couples with no clear diagnosis (about 20 percent of IVF patients have "unexplained" infertility), some clinics would allow admission after one year of infertility, while others accepted patients only after three years of infertility. Although most programs considered previous fertility treatment (fertility drug treatment or assisted insemination using the partner's sperm) before deciding to admit a patient to the IVF program, there were few fixed criteria in this regard. If there was no clear diagnosis — and if drugs or insemination with the partner's sperm had not worked — some clinics offered IVF as a method that might enable the couple to have a child related to them both.

Many groups and individuals told the Commission that upper middle class, well-educated, married couples are more likely than other people to use IVF treatment. The Commission's survey of patients based on voluntary return of questionnaires confirmed this. Of the 750 IVF patients surveyed by the Commission, 66 percent were employed full-time, 41 percent had professional occupations (compared with 31 percent of the general population), and 80 percent had annual family incomes over $50 000 (compared to 33.3 percent of the general population).

The Commission believes that no medical treatment offered through the publicly funded health care system should be limited to a select group of people. Although physicians may encounter instances where non-medical factors mean it is appropriate to refuse access, these instances should be rare, and the use of discriminatory criteria such as marital status, income, or sexual orientation in and of themselves to deny access violates fundamental constitutional and human rights guarantees. If the situation is one into which any child born would clearly be harmed, then a physician may in conscience refuse to provide access, but decisions about who is "worthy" of treatment should not be made in an ad hoc way using such discriminatory criteria by practitioners. The Commission therefore recommends that

121. Access to IVF treatment be determined on the basis of legitimate medical criteria, without discrimination on the basis of factors such as marital status, sexual orientation, or economic status.

The Retrieval and Use of Human Ova

Commission ... recommends that

166. Eggs for donation be obtained only from women already undergoing surgical procedures or egg retrieval as part of their own treatment. Egg retrieval exclusively for purposes of donation should not be permissible.

DESIGNATED EGG DONATION

Designated egg donation refers to the situation where a known donor, often a sister or close friend of the recipient, donates an egg for use in IVF. Seven of the eight Canadian programs offering IVF with donated eggs permit designated donations, and two have reported live births from sister-donated eggs. Some clinics encourage women to find their own donors because of the scarcity of anonymously donated eggs. One hospital-based clinic, however, explicitly forbids designated donations in its program.

There appears to be somewhat greater acceptance of designated egg donation than designated sperm donations. Surveys have shown, for example, that couples are more comfortable with the idea of the sister of a woman who is infertile providing an egg for IVF than with the notion of the brother of a man who is infertile providing sperm for use in donor insemination. The former is usually depicted as a "gift," while donor insemination still carries some of the cultural connotations and psychological implications associated with adultery.

Royal Commission on New Reproductive Technologies, *Proceed With Care: Final Report of the Royal Commission on New Reproductive Technologies* (Ottawa: Minister of Supply and Services, 1993) 2 vols., vol.1, 592-94.

Advocates of designated egg donation cite advantages: there is firsthand knowledge of the donor's physical, psychological, family, and social history; no third party or "broker" has to be involved; and relationships between the parties can be discussed and clearly defined before the donation takes place.

But the practice also raises serious concerns. The potential for coercion of the women involved exists, especially between family members, who may feel it is their "duty" to supply eggs. The potential donor may be subject to overt or covert pressure from the recipient or from other family members. Most important, donation would require her to undergo the risks, discomfort, and inconvenience of medical procedures that will be of no benefit to her and may even cause her harm.

The most troubling aspect of such arrangements is the potential for harm to the eventual child. Although egg donation is relatively new, and we therefore have little knowledge on which to base an assessment of the likely effects on children, there is reason to believe this could cause considerable difficulties in relationships between the child and its parents, the child and its genetic mother, and the social parents and the egg donor.

The Commission believes that the potential for coercion and exploitation of the donor, as well as the potential adverse effects on the resulting child, are too great to justify designated egg donation. Therefore, the Commission recommends that

167. Designated donation of eggs to a named recipient not be permissible.

PAYMENT FOR EGG DONATION

Although the Commission is not aware of any Canadian cases of payment for egg donation, U.S. clinics regularly advertise for egg donors and pay them a fee. There are also cases where U.S. clinics have offered free medical care to women who want a tubal ligation, provided they agree to undergo ovulation induction and egg retrieval. As we have recommended with respect to sperm donation, payment for human gametes is inappropriate, as it would constitute commercialization of human reproductive material, a situation that the Commission considers ethically unacceptable.

The Commission considers payment for eggs unacceptable on other grounds as well; multiple egg induction and retrieval are accompanied by medical risks, pain, and the possibility of long-term health effects. As already established with respect to organ and tissue donation, it is unethical to allow people to risk their health to sell parts of their bodies. The potential for exploitation is simply too great to justify this practice. Thus, the Commission concludes that payment in connection with egg donation is never acceptable. Only women who would be having invasive procedures anyway (egg retrieval during IVF procedures; surgery for other reasons) would be in a position to consent to donate eggs. The Commission therefore recommends that

168. Payment for egg donation not be permissible.

POTENTIAL USE OF EGGS FROM FETUSES

We would object strongly to fertilization of eggs obtained from female fetuses, even if it becomes technically feasible to retrieve and mature them. We find this suggestion deeply offensive to all notions of human dignity and have recommended that it be among the activities prohibited outright in the Criminal Code of Canada ....

HANDLING OF EGGS AND EMBRYOS

Recommendations

Egg and Embryo Donation

The Commission recommends that

172. Designated donation of eggs and zygotes to a named recipient is not permissible.

173. Women who have experienced menopause at the usual age should not be candidates to receive donated eggs or zygotes.

174. Eggs and zygotes for donation or research should be obtained only from women already undergoing surgical procedures or egg retrieval as part of their own treatment. Egg retrieval solely for purposes of donation is not permissible. Any woman asked to donate (whether in the context of IVF or a surgical procedure) should be subject to protocols regarding counselling, informed consent, donor testing, and record keeping established by the Assisted Conception Sub-Committee of the National Commission.

175. (a) Full and informed consent to any egg or embryo donation should be obtained under circumstances that make it clear that a decision not to donate will in no way affect the patient's current or future care or access to treatment.

(b) Counselling and informed consent of potential embryo donors must include the fact that donors will be tested for HIV antibodies at the time of donation and six months later and that their embryos will be quarantined for six months to allow for this testing.

176. (a) In the case of eggs and zygotes for donation, identifying information, including the donor's full name, address, and date and place of birth, should be collected from the donors as soon as they consent to donation under specified conditions (for example, in the event of their deaths). Immediately upon collection of the identifying information, a donor identification code number should be attributed to it.

(b) Non-identifying information about the donor's medical and genetic history, age, and physical and social attributes, including race and ethnicity, should be collected in a standardized form once consent to donation has been obtained. Non-identifying donor information, all test results, and the donated eggs and zygotes should then be identified only by the donor identification code number. Appropriate record storage procedures should be in place to preserve confidentiality.

(c) Where a child is born as a result of a donation, identifying information about the donor, the donor's identification code number, the name of the egg or zygote recipient, and information about the child born as a result of the donation should be forwarded to the National Reproductive Technologies Commission, for storage under secure conditions for a minimum period of 100 years.

177. All necessary steps for testing donors of eggs and zygotes for infectious diseases or other conditions that could potentially affect the health of the woman receiving the donated egg, of the zygote, or of the resulting child should be strictly followed.

178. Testing for HIV 1 and 2 should include a zygote quarantine period of at least six months, with retesting of the

donor's blood for antibodies to HIV at the expiry of that period.

and that

179. Egg and embryo donors should not be compensated in any way.

Disposition of Unused Eggs and Zygotes

The Commission recommends that

180. Zygotes should be disposed of in accordance with the wishes of the gamete donor(s), expressed in writing before gamete retrieval. Zygotes should not, however, be stored for more than five years from the date they are frozen.

Zygotes stored for a couple's own use should be stored only up to the death of either partner.

181. Surplus eggs should not be fertilized or used without the express permission of the egg and sperm donors.

and that

182. Adherence to these requirements, set by the Assisted Conception Sub-Committee of the National Reproductive Technologies Commission, with respect to the handling of eggs and embryos would be a condition of licence to offer assisted conception services. Failure to comply would result in loss of licence.

Preconception Arrangements

THE COMMISSION'S ASSESSMENT

As the preceding sections make clear, preconception arrangements raise ethical and legal issues that are neither straightforward nor easy to deal with. As Commissioners listened to the continuing debate about this practice, one conclusion became evident: proponents and opponents are not likely to change each other's minds about the ethical and social dimensions of preconception arrangements. Views on preconception arrangements are based on fundamentally different convictions about human nature and about how the world works or ought to work; therefore assessments of the actual or potential implications of preconcep-

tion arrangements for women, for children, for couples, and for our evolution as a society also differ.

COMMERCIAL ARRANGEMENTS

Using our ethical framework and standards, the Commission finds commercial preconception arrangements offensive on several grounds.

First, they offend human dignity by commodifying women's reproductive capacities and commodifying children; they contradict the principle that human reproduction should not be commercialized in any way. Second, we see actual and potential harms

---

Royal Commission on New Reproductive Technologies, *Proceed With Care: Final Report of the Royal Commission on New Reproductive Technologies* (Ottawa: Minister of Supply and Services, 1993) 2 vols., vol. 2, 683-84.

for families, for individual women and children, and for specific groups within society. Finally, we believe that public policy that condones or supports the establishment of adversarial relationships is fundamentally flawed; public policy should seek instead to support and encourage humane, non-conflictual family and social relationships. Any attempt to legitimize or support commercial preconception arrangements through public policy would represent the antithesis of this goal.

Commodification of Children and Reproduction

The fundamentally repugnant aspect of preconception arrangements is that they instrumentalize human beings through the deliberate act of creating a child for the express purpose of giving it up, usually in exchange for money. The premise of commercial preconception contracts is that a child is a product that can be bought and sold on the market. The moral point of view requires that people be treated as ends in themselves, not as means to the ends of others. We must therefore uphold the value of children in and of themselves. Children are not a commodity, nor are they instruments to be used to serve the purposes of others. The commodification of children entailed by preconception arrangements ignores these essential values.

Moreover, commercial preconception arrangements commodify women's reproductive functions and place women in the situation of alienating aspects of themselves that should be inherently inalienable. A preconception contract obliges the gestational mother to sell an intimate aspect of her human functioning to provide someone else with a genetic, related child; the capacity to become pregnant and bear a child is reduced to a marketable service. We do not allow people to give up their freedom and become slaves, even if they make a choice to do so, because of our collective conviction that this would negate the value we attach to human dignity and the inalienability of the person. Similarly, assigning commercial value to the human function of reproduction would result eventually in a new and, in our view, undesirable social understanding of the value and dignity of women, their reproductive capacity, and their bodily integrity.

Commercial preconception contracts by their nature — the exchange of money for a child — contradict one of the fundamental tenets of the Commission's ethical framework. On these grounds alone, we could recommend prohibition of such arrangements, since we believe that all public policy in this field should be based on the principle of non-commercialization of reproduction.

The evidence is clear that in commercial preconception contracts the principal motivation of both the broker and the gestational woman is money. Far from being the idyllic situation portrayed by brokers — gestational woman as "altruistic angel" giving the gift of a child to a couple who is happy but infertile — commercial preconception contracts are business transactions. The child is a product being sold by one party and bought by the other.

Surrogate and Gestational Motherhood

Canadian Medical Association

The terms "surrogate" and "gestational" motherhood refer to the practice where a woman volunteers to bear a child on the explicit understanding that once the child is born, she will relinquish her rights and responsibilities with respect to the rearing of that child to a second party, where that second party then assumes the status of legal parent to the child. This arrangement may be informal or it may be formalized in terms of a contractual agreement. In some instances, payment is made to the gestator for the services rendered; in other cases, no payment or consideration is involved.

As was noted before, there are several ways in which the phrase "surrogate mother" can be understood. In the most simple case, the so-called surrogate mother is artificially inseminated with the sperm of the male partner of the couple with whom the woman has struck the arrangement, and the ovum involved is her own. Variations include the fertilization of the woman's ovum in vitro with the sperm of the male partner of the couple or of a donor, and placement of the fertilized ovum into her uterus. ZIFT [Zygote Intrafallopian Transfer] and TET [Tubal Embryo Transfer] are still further variations.[168]

On the other hand, a woman may agree to bear a child for another person or group of people, but the ovum involved may not be that of the woman herself. Here again, several variations are possible. For example, the ovum may be that of the woman who has arranged to raise the child. Alternatively, the ovum may be one that has been donated. Of course the various methods of ovum/zygote recovery and transfer referred to a moment ago may also be involved, as may ZIFT, TET and similar techniques.[169] Finally, in vivo fertilization in the woman who will ultimately be the social mother of the child, followed by lavage and implantation in the gestational mother, is also a possibility.

Both the concept of surrogacy and the concept of gestational motherhood have been criticized from several perspectives. One concern centres around the claim that when financial considerations are introduced into the notion of child-bearing for others, the practice amounts to a modern version of commerce in human beings.[170] Another concern is that both undertakings represent a threat to the nuclear family, which is the backbone of Western culture.[171] Some commentators have maintained that the consequences of these practices for women and women's relationship to their corporal autonomy, maternity and children is devastating,[172] and they have portrayed the practices as demeaning to women by turning them into walking incubators. The possibility has even been raised that surrogacy and gestational motherhood, if allowed, would prey on socioeconomically underprivileged women and lead to the development of two female classes: those who bear children, and those who can afford to raise them.[173]

Almost all jurisdictions in the world have begun to examine the issue. British Columbia, Ontario and Quebec have con-

The Canadian Medical Association, "Surrogate and gestational motherhood." — Reprinted from *The New Reproductive Technologies: A Preliminary Perspective of the Canadian Medical Association*, by permission of the publisher, Canadian Medical Association, 1991.

sidered it already, as have several professional organizations.[174] Not all of the bodies who have considered the matter have agreed. In Canada, the Ontario Law Reform Commission has recommended acceptance and legal recognition of surrogate motherhood arrangements, subject to certain conditions[175]; the Quebec Bar Association has suggested that surrogacy agreements should be banned altogether[176]; the British Columbia Bar Association has recommended that they should be permitted, but regulated.[177] In Great Britain, the Warnock Commission recommended rejection.[178] The Glover Report of the European Commission recommends acceptance, but control.[179] The American College of Obstetricians and Gynaecologists has expressed "significant reservations about this approach to parenthood," but has left its members free to decide whether to participate in such arrangements.[180] The American Medical Association has rejected it,[181] the Society of Obstetricians and Gynaecologists of Canada allows it at least in a research context under strictly monitored guidelines.[182]

The fact that there are a variety of opinions is not surprising. Surrogate motherhood presents many social, legal and ethical questions. Implicated are issues of legitimacy and economic coercion, the relationship between genetic parents and their offspring, autonomy, children as objects and so on. Given the differences in professional, legal and cultural perspective from which the issue has been approached, it would be surprising if there were unanimity, or even general agreement.

The Association cannot mention, let alone deal with, all of the issues that are raised by the topic. It has raised the issue because surrogate motherhood brings together several fundamental questions that are central to having children. One question is that of autonomy. All other things being equal, does a woman have the right to do with her body as she pleases? Equality and

autonomy here move into the forefront. At first glance, at least, to interdict either surrogate or gestational motherhood would seem to limit a woman's personal autonomy severely. Both ethics and law recognize that autonomy may be curtailed under certain circumstances. However, before such a decision to curtail is made, the ethical and legal factors that outweigh the right to autonomy would have to be clearly spelled out and considered. In the eyes of the Canadian Medical Association, the case against a woman's autonomy in this matter has not been made.

Another argument against legitimizing surrogate and gestational motherhood is based on the contention that the way in which children would be brought into the world, and the reason for which they would be engendered, would constitute an ethical affront to these children as people.

In its deliberations on these and other issues, the Canadian Medical Association considered, among other things, the argument that, because of the affinity that a woman who bears a child may develop for that child, her custodial rights should be considered to be greater than the rights of any person other than herself even if the gametes of those other persons have been the genetic origin of the child. According to this line of reasoning, the claims of the birth mother should always take priority in cases of conflict. This would mean that exceptions would obtain only if the child could be shown to be in need of protection under the normal social service mechanisms. In such cases — so this reasoning has it — the courts should determine who should have custodial rights and obligations.

The Association can understand the thrust of these various positions. However, it is not convinced that all of them are valid. So far as the Association can see, all techniques of assisted reproduction are liable to this critique. In all of these instances, there is a deliberateness about the process, and there is someone who stands to gain materially from it. However, the Association does not believe that this should be seen as somehow degrading to the child that is born.

More specifically, the Association believes that the ethical status of a child has nothing to do with who engendered it or how it was brought about. Instead, the Association believes that its ethical status lies in the fact that it is a person. Nothing can take away from that fact. Furthermore, the Association would characterize any argument to the contrary as committing the fallacy of genesis; it confuses the origin or way that someone came about with the ethical status of the individual as a person.

The Association also believes that deliberately gestating a child to hand it to someone else need not constitute commerce in human beings. That would be true if some value or consideration were exchanged for the child that was handed over. However, the Association does not believe that this would be a correct way of characterizing either surrogate or gestational motherhood. Without holding any brief as to whether payment or consideration should change hands in the first instance, the Association believes that such an exchange might just as legitimately be described as an exchange of considerations for services rendered: namely the gestational service itself.

This last train of reasoning may be accepted in the case of gestational motherhood. However, it is possible to argue that it would not hold in the case of surrogate motherhood. Here, since the ovum involved is that of the surrogate mother, the latter is not merely a gestational parent, but a biological parent as well. That — so the argument goes — makes all the difference.

Although such an argument may be possible, the Association does not believe that it would establish the point at issue. The reason lies in the fact that ovum donation is accepted as an ethically praiseworthy act. It seems to the Association that surrogate motherhood may well be construed as an act of donation where what is donated — the ovum — does not leave the body of the donor. On that understanding, adding to the act of donation the service of a gestator does not turn the donation into the sale of a human being.

Finally, the issue of surrogate motherhood brings to a head one of the most fundamental issues that underlies all of the reproductive technologies: what should be the primary consideration in childbearing in general and in the use of reproductive technologies in particular? Should it be the welfare of the child, the position of the gestating woman, the feelings of prospective parents, or the expectations of society? The Association is in no position to give a definitive answer. However, it is always reminded that although the progenitors of children always have at least a modicum of choice in the matter, limited though it may be, the children that will result from that choice have none. Yet they are people.

After careful deliberation, the preceding considerations notwithstanding, the Association has come to the conclusion that, aside from medical problems of the sort already canvassed in the preceding discussion of AI, IVF and associated technologies, the issue of surrogate or gestational motherhood is not inherently medical in nature. It is ethical and legal. The Association looks forward to seeing an ultimate resolution of the question in social terms. However, it would like to offer the following observations.

First, the Association believes that the bond of biological or of gestational parenthood is not an indissoluble one. The generally accepted practice of adoption indicates how this is the case. It also points the way in which the bond of parenthood, as and where it exists, may be dissolved. Society accepts that it may be dissolved at the discretion of the parents and for reasons that are good and sufficient in the eyes of society itself.[183] If the Association understands the matter correctly, this process of dissolution attempts to balance the rights of the parents against the rights of the child. The Association believes that such a balancing approach is not only ethically sound, but may also lead to a resolution of the issues surrounding surrogate and gestational motherhood.

Second, as far as the Association is concerned, there is nothing inherently unethical about a woman exercising her autonomy by volunteering to act as gestational mother, even though she may have no intention to act as social mother as well. The Association, therefore, endorses the notion of surrogacy. Consequently it rejects the claim that either surrogate or gestational motherhood amounts to "baby selling." Irrespective of whether they involve a transfer of financial or other considerations, the Association believes that to categorize them in that fashion is to misrepresent their nature as undertakings that allow others the privilege of becoming partners. This does not mean that the Association is blind to the emotional and personal implications of this procedure. It merely means that as far as the Association is concerned, to categorize the practice as "baby selling" is to introduce an emotional bias into the debate that falsifies the whole nature of the issue.

Third, the Association believes that informed consent is a necessary condition of such an undertaking. In the eyes of the Association, to fully understand the nature of the undertaking requires that the woman in question should have had the experience of motherhood. In no other way will she be able to estimate with anything approaching a reasonable degree of confidence, whether she will be able to carry through with the undertaking and give the child to the social parents. The Association, therefore, recommends that only women who have already had a child be allowed to volunteer as surrogate or gestational mothers.

Fourth, the Association is concerned that surrogate arrangements should oper-ate according to certain guidelines, so as to avoid the possibility of coercion of the prospective surrogate or gestational mother or the introduction of other socially undesirable consequences. The Association, therefore, recommends that surrogacy arrangements be subject to prior legal screening, as was suggested by the Law Reform Commission of Ontario.[184] The Association is aware that this would mean judicial involvement in the process. However, it is convinced that such a review could be handled by appropriate adjustments to current adoption mechanisms. Such mechanisms include appropriate screening provisions for prospective adoptive parents. The Canadian Medical Association believes that the same criteria should be operative in the case of prospective social parents.

The Association is not prepared to go further than that at the present time. However, the Association recognizes that many issues of implementation remain unresolved. Consequently, it calls on this Commission to clarify the following issues:

- whether surrogacy and gestational arrangements should be enforceable against the surrogate or gestational mother;

- whether surrogate or gestational mothers should have the same amount of time to consider their decision to relinquish custody as they would have in normal adoption cases;

- whether in case of conflict between the surrogate or gestational mother and other parties (party) to the arrangement, the claims of the former should take priority over those of the latter; and

- whether, if the surrogate or gestational mother chooses to keep the child, contrary to the surrogacy agreement, the prospective social parents should have any rights of access to the child, or whether the surrogate or gestational mother, or the child, should have any claim on the prospective social parents.

The Association can also envision situations where the child is appropriately adopted by the social parents, but these turn out to be unsuitable as parents according to current adoption standards. The Association believes that currently existing mechanisms embodied in child welfare legislation are sufficient to cover these cases.

As to the matter of payment to the surrogate mother, the Association believes that in itself, this would not be objectionable. It would be payment for an act, not payment for the child itself. The Association is aware that this opinion is not shared universally. Furthermore, the Association believes that to prevent any form of payment to surrogate or gestational mothers would be to treat them according to a standard whose stringency would exceed even that which is deemed appropriate in the case of gamete donation. Consequently the Association recommends that surrogate or gestational mothers be entitled to receive remuneration calculated to defray their gestation-related expenses and opportunity costs.

NOTES

168. The Ontario Law Reform Commission (*Report on Human Artificial Reproduction and Related Matters,* 2 vols, Ministry of the Attorney General, Toronto, 1985, vol 2, 218-219) explains the notion of surrogate motherhood as follows: "A surrogate motherhood arrangement involves an agreement between the woman who is to bear the child and the persons who are to receive it to raise as their own. While a variety of terms may be agreed upon by the parties, the heart of any arrangement is a promise on the part of the surrogate mother to undergo the medical procedure necessary to achieve a pregnancy and to surrender custody of the child irrevocably upon birth, and a reciprocal promise on part of the other party or parties to accept the child." It will be clear that some refinements in the notion of surrogacy have occurred since the time of the Commission's writing.

169. For a somewhat similar discussion of the various possibilities, albeit one that does not include the more recent variations, see Ontario Law Reform Commission (*supra,* note 168), 218.

170. This view seems to underlie Brodribb S. (*Women and Reproductive Technologies,* Status of Women Canada, Ottawa: May 1988, note 148): "The impact on the child of selling the child for money and on other children in the contract mother's family should also be studied," 48.

171. Combined Ethics Committee of the Canadian Fertility and Andrology Society and the Society of Obstetricians and Gynaecologists of Canada: *Ethical Considerations of the New Reproductive Technologies,* Final Draft Copy, 1989, note 108) 27.

172. Brodribb (*supra,* note 148), 44.

173. Ibid., 44 and 46 for such a suggestion.

174. The British Columbia Bar Association, the Society of Obstetricians and Gynaecologists of Canada, the Christian Dental Association of Canada, etc.

175. Ontario Law Reform Commission: *Report on Human Artificial Reproduction* (note 168), 41-45.

176. Barreau de Quebec: *Les Enjeux Ethique et Juridique des Nouvelles Technologies de Reproduction,* Quebec, April 1988: 33-34.

177. Canadian Bar Association, British Columbia Branch: *Report of the Special Task Force Committee on Reproductive Technology,* Vancouver, June 1989.

178. See Warnock M., ed., *Report of the Committee of Enquiry into Human Sterilization and Embryology,* Her Majesty's Stationer's Office, London, GB, 1984.

179. Glover J. et al., *Ethics of New Reproductive Technologies: the Glover Report to the European Commission,* Northern Illinois Univ Press, DeKalb, IL, 1989.

180. American College of Obstetricians and Gynecologists: *Ethical Issues in Surrogate Motherhood.* ACOG Statement of Policy, May 1983.

181. American Medical Association, Judicial Council report I-83 (1983). *Current Opinions* 1989; 2 (18).

182. Combined Ethics Committee (*supra,* note 108), Ethical Issue no. 7, Surrogacy.

183. The Association is aware that such a dissolution may also take place for socially sanctioned legal reasons. However, that does not alter the thrust of the present considerations.

184. See *supra,* note 168, vol. 2, chapter 6, section 5: Proposals relating to surrogate motherhood.

Conceiving a Child to Save a Child: Reproductive and Filial Ethics

Nancy S. Jecker

INTRODUCTION

Reproductive and filial ethics raise moral questions that touch our most intimate relationships with other persons. Often relationships within the family are infused with strong emotions that seem to defy rational argument. Many philosophers even doubt that ethical concepts, such as justice, apply at all in the context of filial relationships. Aristotle, for example, wrote that justice does not pertain to relationships between parents and offspring, because young children are an extension or part of their parents and "the just and the unjust always involve more than one person."[1] More recently, Ferdinand Schoeman has argued that "traditional moral boundaries, which give rigid shape to the self," do not apply in the context of intimate relationships, and that "talk about rights of others, respect for others, and even welfare of others is to a certain extent irrelevant."[2] Other philosophers direct little attention to filial ethics because they regard the family itself as legitimate. Plato reckoned that in a just

Nancy S. Jecker, "Conceiving a Child to Save a Child: Reproductive and Filial Ethics," *The Journal of Clinical Ethics* 1:2 (Summer 1990), 99-107.

state wives and children must be held in common by guardians in order to prevent "whatever tears [the city] apart into many communities instead of one."[3] In our own day, Rawls has characterized the family as violating a principle of fair equality of opportunity and considered the possibility that the family should be abolished![4]

One reason that contemporary moral philosophy may lend little assistance to persons wrestling with questions about filial ethics is that it tends to frame ethical questions against a backdrop of impersonal relationships. Kant, for example, concentrates on the moral law that holds for rational beings as such, not for rational beings as members of special groups and alliances, such as a family. Likewise, utilitarian ethics originally was developed to justify reforms in the British legal system and to craft a more humane system of punishment. Contemporary versions of utilitarianism focus on the effect actions have on the welfare of society at large and treat individual members as replaceable by other persons.

Contemporary ethical theory itself reflects the modern age. As Bernard Williams notes, inhabitants of the modern world achieve an immense amount through impersonal relations: "We do a great deal by relying on egoistic micro-motivations, and it is a remarkable achievement of the modern world to have brought this about. Indeed, it is obvious beyond a certain level of social size and complexity that we must rely a lot on such motivations...."[5] Yet the presence of personal relationships in our lives is highly valued, even if seldom acknowledged. These relationships shape the very persons we become, and a life wholly void of personal relationships would hardly be worth living. We cannot hold personal relationships immune from ethical reflection then, nor can we afford to neglect thinking about our ethical responsibilities in personal relationships without paying a high price. Not considering personal rela-

tionships in ethical terms may make us less sensitive to close associates in situations where we find spontaneous support difficult to muster. It also may make it possible for the status quo to persist in personal relationships where it falls far short of ethical standards and ideals.

How should we begin, then, to view personal relationships in an ethical light? Although impartial theories may define, in broad brush, the contours of an ethics for personal relationships,[6] they cannot begin to complete a rich and finished picture. In this essay, I will examine some of the broad ethical guides that govern personal relationships generally, and filial relationships in particular. I focus this task by describing a specific case that raises ethical questions about reproduction and parenting.

THE CASE

In July 1989, a middle-aged couple from a Los Angeles suburb conceived a child to save the life of their teenage daughter who is dying of cancer. The couple, Abe and Mary Ayala, had learned two years prior that their daughter, Anissa, was suffering from leukemia and needed a bone marrow transplant to survive. Neither Anissa's parents nor her brother, Airon, have compatible bone marrow. A search for a non-related donor has been fruitless to date.

When the Ayalas first decided to conceive a child their chance of success was slim.[7] Abe, forty-four years old, had to undergo an operation to reverse a vasectomy performed sixteen years earlier. The chance of vasectomy reversal leading to pregnancy is 50 percent. Mary, at the age of forty-two, had a 73 percent chance of becoming pregnant. Finally, the likelihood that any offspring Abe and Mary conceived would qualify as a bone marrow match for Anissa was 25 percent. Overall, the odds of Anissa's being cured of leukemia by her parents' effort to conceive a child to save her was 6.4 percent.

To date, many of these obstacles have been overcome. On April 3, 1990, Mary delivered a baby girl, Marissa, who is a suitable donor for her sister. While it was not possible to collect stem cells from Marissa's umbilical cord during delivery, doctors predict that once the baby grows enough bone marrow, surgery to obtain bone marrow from Marissa's hip will have a 70 to 80 percent chance of success. Family members apparently are delighted about their youngest member. "She's my baby sister," Anissa declares, "and we're going to love her for who she is not for what she can give me."[8] Mary adds, "Our baby is going to have more love than she can put up with."[9] Abe reflects that even if Anissa didn't survive, "we'd have another child in the house to help us with our sense of loss."[10]

Outside the family, the Ayalas' success is greeted with mixed emotions. Some argue that conceiving persons to benefit others insinuates the norms of production and commodification into the parent-child relationship. For example, George Annas asserts that "children aren't medicine" manufactured for other people.[11]Alternatively, it could be claimed that conceiving children to benefit others violates a principle that should guide ethical decision making regarding becoming a parent; namely, doing what will be best from the potential child's point of view.[12] It also could be contended that Marissa is likely to suffer psychological harm as a result of being conceived for the purpose of benefitting her sister. For example, she might be prone in the future to regard her worth as conditional on the benefits she can provide others. She might harbor resentment toward her parents for choosing to conceive her for this purpose, or toward her sister for reaping benefits from her conception. These feelings could present formidable obstacles to loving relationships within the family, and thereby handicap Marissa in the future. Family relationships profoundly shape our relationships with persons outside the family circle, and they influence the kind of person we strive to become. Finally, some have voiced the concern that conceiving a child for the purpose of saving another violates a principle of respect for persons, because it involves using a child as a means to another's end. "One of the fundamental precepts of ethics," Alexander Capron states, "is that each person is an end in himself or herself and is never to be used solely as a means to another person's ends without the agreement of the person being used."[13]

THE ETHICAL ANALYSIS

Depersonalizing Personal Relationships

Let us first consider whether conceiving children to benefit another family member is harmful to persons or to relationships within the family. One way harm might occur is that conceiving a child in this way imputes the norms of production into the parent-child relationship. It might be said, on the one hand, that producing Marissa in order to make bone marrow for her sister degrades Marissa, because it implies treating her body as a good to be manufactured and used. On the other hand, it could be argued that Mary's and Abe's procreative labor is itself degraded, because its primary function becomes making an object for use, rather than a child to love. If either of these objections is valid, then Marissa's conception may violate an important principle governing personal relationships: actions should not depersonalize personal relationships, for doing so does violence to what these relationships are and to the intentions, desires, and hopes persons have in becoming involved in them.[14]

In response, it might be argued that prior to Marissa's conception, she did not stand in a personal relationship to her future parents; therefore, the decision to beget her does not depersonalize a personal relationship. After all, even if we may feel personally related to nonextant persons (for example, dead family members), the parties in personal relationships must be particular and non-substitutable individuals. For example, if I stand in a personal relationship to someone, then I must be the object of that person's attention. Prospective parents cannot possibly be personally involved with still-to-be-conceived offspring, since there is no particular future person that could be the object of this involvement. Even after Marissa's conception and birth it could be maintained that the parent-child relationship does not yet qualify as personal. To have a personal relationship with someone might be thought to imply "mutuality of meaning — either verbal or sign — because shared meanings are necessary for the mutual agreement on meaning that form the basis of the relationship."[15]

Initiating Personal Relationships

Yet perhaps the ethics that apply to personal relationships also govern relationships that are likely to be personal in the future. For example, initiating a personal relationship with ulterior objectives is ethically suspect, because this may harm a future personal relationship. One reason harm might occur is that the touchstone of having a personal relationship is that the motive for being in it and continuing it is that we value it for its own sake. For example, friends simply want to give and receive from one another because of the joy and value inherent in doing so.[16] In the case of the Ayalas, the relationship between

Marissa and her sister, Anissa, could be harmed because Anissa comes to it in dire need. As John Hardwig states,

> If I see myself primarily as a being in need, I will be too focused on myself and my needs. I will then tend to depersonalize you as someone who can meet my needs. And I will also be generally unable to freely and joyously give.... Characteristically and normatively, the appropriate motive for action in personal relationships is simply that we want to do these things.[17]

Likewise, the future intimacy between Marissa and her parents could be endangered because Mary and Abe established this relationship to aid their other child. In some respects, this would be analogous to a person learning that a man had shown romantic attention or initiated a sexual relationship in order to benefit someone else; for example, to benefit himself by making a former girlfriend jealous. In this case, the desire to initiate a personal relationship is born of some motive other than the desire to be in a personal relationship. Similarly, Marissa is conceived not because she is wanted, but because she can be useful. Hence, upon learning the reason for her conception, Marissa might feel betrayed.

Although these points initially may appear troublesome, upon reflection they are much less so. First, it is reasonable to suppose that intimacy and harmony already will have developed by the time Marissa is able to comprehend the circumstances of her conception. This intimate basis will make it more likely that harmony and good relationships can be restored if they are suspended or strained, because in once intimate associations the pain of disaffection and the desire for union offer strong motives for reconciliations.[18] Similarly, if the woman betrayed by the man who displays affection finds out about his initial motives after many years of intimacy, there would be good reason to think that intimacy between the two would not wither. Of course, reparations may not restore harmony automatically, or entirely eliminate bad feelings. For example, these feelings can continue to operate at an unconscious level. But even if there can be no guarantee that strong family relations can be sustained, intimate associations always involve the risk of dissolution.

A second redeeming point is that, unlike other actions that can render personal relationships hurtful, the decision to conceive Marissa is not intended to hurt Marissa. For example, neither Abe, Mary, nor Anissa is motivated by spite or by a desire to harm Marissa. Quite the contrary, they say that they intend to love her. By contrast, someone who bestows romantic attention or sexual favors to make a former partner jealous does not intend to love the object of his favors (even if he later does).

In addition, it is far from clear that the act of conceiving Marissa for the purpose of benefitting Anissa could cause any tangible harm to Marissa. The argument here is that Marissa is better off having been conceived and living the life that she does, despite its added tensions, than she would be if she had never been conceived at all.[19] Presumably, Marissa will prefer to endure certain hardships so long as the hardships in question are necessary for her coming into existence.

Honesty in Personal Relationships

One way that her conception could impose a clear harm to Marissa is if she were not told about the facts surrounding it. Once an intimate relationship is formed, parties to it should establish honest and open relations. This is partly owing to the fact that the more time people spend together, the less likely it is that they can keep up a dishonest front.[20] Each can maintain an arti-

ficial posture for only so long. Another consideration about honesty that applies in the context of close relationships is that intimates have more reason to reveal important details of their lives because such revelations create and sustain their intimacy. By contrast, withholding important facts can bar intimacy or create the false appearance of intimacy where genuine intimacy is absent. False intimacy exists to varying degrees in personal relationships. It develops, for example, when we encourage distortions in another's view of us, or when we deny another's shortcomings. Shakespeare called these processes "love's best habit,"[21] and noted the costs associated with lovers' efforts to know each other. In the case of parent-child relationships, false intimacy would be created if, for example, Marissa's parents and sister concealed, altered, or denied the facts surrounding her conception. Yet, there is no reason to expect that this will occur. Marissa's family does not express shame about their decision or view it as something to hide. As one commentator puts it, "By all appearances the Ayalas are not an exploitive family. To them the ethical questions that swirl around them are airy abstractions, not the terrifying reality they daily confront."[22]

Privacy in Personal Relationships

In addition, the Ayalas' decision can be defended on the grounds that a sphere of privacy surrounds families and protects their decisions about whether and when to procreate. Family privacy might be elaborated in terms of a "family privacy right," which is a right to be free from surveillance and interference within the internal workings of the family.[23] This right implies that Mary and Abe should be left alone in making decisions about whether to conceive a child. It implies more generally that we should reject the position that the state is the proper authority for making reproductive choices, a position which Plato states in stark terms: "If a man still of begetting years unites with a woman of child-bearing age without the sanction of the rulers ... we shall say that he brings into the city an unauthorized and unhallowed bastard ... born in darkness."[24]

Even if the state's interests did override a family's privacy right, it is unlikely that the state could bar couples from conceiving children where they are able to conceive on their own. Unlike conception that is carried out through new reproductive technologies and relies upon the assistance of others, reproductive acts between two consenting persons are far more difficult to control. Mary and Abe's sexual and procreative acts are as antithetical to regulation as are present efforts to prohibit consensual sodomy or homosexuality.

Respect for Individuals in Personal Relationships

Let us next turn to examine the question of whether conceiving a child to benefit another fails to accord proper respect to the child-to-be. One objection to Mary and Abe's decision was that respecting persons calls for treating persons as ends in themselves. According to this objection, by conceiving and bearing Marissa as a means to save their daughter's life, Mary and Abe treat Marissa as a means to their own end.

Yet this way of stating the objection glosses over important distinctions. First, parents have multiple reasons for conceiving, and it is not unethical if some of these involve using their child. For example, it is not unethical if a royal couple conceives to have an heir, or if a couple produces a second offspring to give their first a sibling, or if two people have a child to enrich their

own lives. Second, reasons for reproducing reveal a lack of respect only if prospective parents do not also want and love their children. The point here is that there is nothing blatantly unethical about treating persons as means to our own ends. Using persons as means is unethical only when we regard persons as nothing but means. Respect for offspring requires recognizing, as Kant said, "that man, and in general every rational being exists as an end-in-himself, not merely as a means for arbitrary use by this or that will," and that a person "must, in all his actions, whether they are directed to himself or to other rational beings, always be viewed at the same time as an end."[25]

Understood in this way, Abe and Mary's decision to conceive Marissa fails to show respect toward her only if their sole reason for conceiving is to use Marissa for example, as a means to save their other daughter's life, or to keep the house from feeling empty if their other daughter dies. But their statements and actions indicate that they intend to love Marissa for who she is, quite apart from what she can give. Thus, the Ayalas' action is morally different from a situation where a couple intends to conceive a child to serve as a bone marrow donor and abort the child if it is not medically useful. It also is morally distinct from a situation where a woman becomes pregnant with the sole intention of providing fetal tissue to a parent with Parkinson's disease, and then terminates her pregnancy. In these cases the desire to create a child is disassociated from any intention to raise a child and value it for its own sake. Thus, in these instances prospective parents truly fail to respect the individual they call to life.

Now it might be argued that the injunction to treat rational beings always as ends does not even apply to Marissa, because she is not even minimally rational. Arguably, she will not be rational for some time to come. Her cerebral cortex did not form until late in the second trimester, and even well after birth she will not have developed her full rational powers. Kant states in *The Groundwork* that "every rational being exists as an end-in-himself." This suggests that being rational is sufficient for being valuable as an end in oneself. He also states that "nothing but the idea of the law in itself, which ... is present only in rational beings ... can constitute that preeminent good which we call moral." This last passage suggests that being rational is necessary for possessing moral value within oneself. Are Abe and Mary absolved of the responsibility to treat Marissa as an end on the grounds that Marissa is not yet a person?

To answer this question, let us consider next what form respect should take in the context of personal relationships. One way of elaborating the requirement of respect in close relationships is that Marissa should be treated always as an end by persons who stand in a special relationship to her, regardless of whether she possesses the intrinsic moral qualities that confer strict moral status. Unlike animals of similar cognitive functioning, Marissa is Mary and Abe's daughter, and she is Anissa and Airon's sibling. Thus Mary, Abe, Anissa, and Airon are not entitled to treat Marissa as they would treat any being of similar cognitive functioning. Even if Marissa were never to develop rationality or consciousness, she merits respect by virtue of her position in a family.[26] Regardless of whether Marissa is a person in the Kantian sense, she is nonetheless a person in the social sense.[27]

Sacrifices in Personal Relationships

Should the above remarks quiet the concern that Marissa is not being fully or adequately respected, and that she deserves to be? One answer to this question is that treating persons as ends implies obtaining their consent before making them the subject of medical procedures.

Since Marissa obviously cannot give consent, perhaps it is disrespectful to harvest her marrow for transplant. Ordinarily, Mary and Abe would be vested with the ethical authority to make this decision,[28] but it could be argued that their obvious stake in the situation biases their ability to dispassionately weigh the pros and cons of the decision.

However, the ethical requirement of respect takes different shape when placed against a backdrop of personal relationships. Where an antecedent tie or bond exists between the person who makes some sacrifice and the person who benefits, the requirements of respect subtly shift. Relationships vary in the degree to which they are personal, and the closer and more personal a relationship is, the stronger the claims it can make ethically on our allegiance. This is not to say that persons can legitimately exploit those with whom they are most intimate. Rather, it establishes that family members are governed by stronger ethical responsibilities than strangers, and we expect them to serve each other's welfare to a greater extent.

The ethical quandary with which Mary and Abe are left is where to draw the line. How much can they ask of one daughter on behalf of another? The operation Marissa may undergo to extract marrow from her hipbone involves slight pain and minimal risks. Thus, it is considerably less than asking Marissa to give a kidney or other organ. It would have involved still less sacrifice if Marissa's marrow could have been taken from her umbilical cord at birth. In either case, I would argue that the demands placed upon Marissa do not exceed the ordinary sacrifices family members make and expect from one another. Marissa's sacrifice differs only in that it requires her to give a tangible product. Ordinarily, the benefits we bestow upon family members are more intangible, such as time and energy, or love and affection. What we give up is often less tangible as well; for example, other ways of using that time and attention.

It might be said, in response, that parents are required to do far more for offspring than offspring are required to do for siblings. After all, we choose whether to conceive, bear, and rear children, but children do not choose to be siblings. Yet, even so, we still owe far more to siblings than to strangers because of the presence of a close relationship. However, it might be argued that families are not always a locus of intimacy and closeness. Thus, if filial duties are founded on intimacy, then merely being someone's sibling does not show that one is required to make special sacrifices. In reply, it should be noted that families in fact are a common locus of intimacy, because we live in a family for an extended period during early formative years. The Ayala family's rallying around Anissa to save her life attests to the strength of their love. There is no reason to think that this love will not permeate Marissa's relationship with her sister.

Summary

I conclude that Mary and Abe's decision to conceive a child to save a child does not impose harm on persons or on relationships in the family. Nor does it evince a lack of respect for the child they have conceived. The ethical guidelines that support this con-clusion can now be summarized. First, actions should not depersonalize or otherwise endanger personal relationships. Second, although ideally personal relationships are initiated and continued for their own sake, after a personal relationship has been established and sustained, the motives for establishing it recede in importance. Third, the requirement of honesty looms especially large in the context of personal relationships. Fourth, privacy protects personal relationships in the family from intrusion by the state. Fifth, even if those with whom we stand in personal relationships are not fully rational or self-conscious, we should treat them with respect. Finally, persons often are called upon to make greater sacrifices in personal relationships. These principles represent only the barest beginnings of an ethics for filial relationships. Nonetheless, they mark progress in the direction of developing a more complete account. We should not suppose that ethics in the family always will be spontaneous or "natural."[29] Over a century ago, Mill warned that nature and natural are "one of the most copious sources of false taste, false philosophy, false morality, and even bad law."[30] Especially in the wake of medical advances, such as recombinant DNA and new reproductive technologies, the complexity of filial ethics will only increase. The demographics of an aging society will add further complexity to filial contexts.[31] We can hardly afford to cling tenaciously to the idea that ethical conduct in the family will issue forth in a spontaneous fashion.

NOTES

1. *Aristotle, Nicomachean Ethics,* trans. W.D. Ross (Oxford: Clarendon Press, 1966), see especially 1138a19.

2. F. Schoeman, "Rights of Children, Rights of Parents and the Moral Basis of the Family," *Ethics* 91 (1980): 6-19.

3. Plato, *Republic,* trans. G.M.A. Grube (Indianapolis: Hackett Publishing Company, 1974), 123.

4. J. Rawls, *A Theory of Justice* (Cambridge: Harvard University Press, 1971), 511.

5. B. Williams, "Formal Structure and Social Reality," *Trust: Making and Breaking Cooperative Relations,* ed. D. Gambetta (Oxford: Basil Blackwell Press, 1989), 3-13.

6. N.S. Jecker, "Impartiality and Special Relationships," *Kindred Matters: Rethinking the Philosophy of the Family,* ed. D. Meyers, K. Knipnis, and N. Murphy (Ithaca, NY: Cornell University Press), in press.

7. A. Toufexis, "Creating a Child to Save Another," *Time,* March 15, 1990, 56.

8. Ibid.

9. "(2) Having a Baby To Save Daughter," *New York Times,* February 17, 1990.

10. Toufexis, "Creating a Child to Save Another."

11. Quoted in Toufexis, "Creating a Child to Save Another."

12. Although this principle is stated in another context, it pertains in obvious ways to the case at hand. S. Callahan, "An Ethical Analysis of Responsible Parenthood," *Genetic Counseling: Facts, Values, and Norms,* ed. A.M. Capron (New York: Alan R. Liss, Inc., 1979), 217-38.

13. "(2) Having a Baby To Save Daughter."

14. J. Hardwig, "In Search of an Ethics of Personal Relationships," *Person to Person*, ed. G. Graham and H. LaFollette (Philadelphia: Temple University Press, 1989), 63-81.

15. S.J. Mills, "Conceptualizing Personal Relationships," *Generations* 10 (1986):6-9.

16. Ibid.

17. Ibid.

18. J. Deigh, "Morality and Personal Relations," *Person to Person*, ed. G. Graham and H. LaFollette (Philadelphia: Temple University Press, 1989), 106-23.

19. N.S. Jecker, "Reproductive Risk Taking and the Nonidentity Problem," *Social Theory and Practice* 13 (1987):219-35; D. Parfit, *Reasons and Persons* (Oxford: Clarendon Press, 1984), chapter 16.

20. G. Graham and H. LaFollette, "Honesty and Intimacy," *Person to Person*, ed. G. Graham and H. LaFollette (Philadelphia: Temple University Press, 1989), 167-81.

21. W. Shakespeare, Sonnet 138, in *Complete Works,* ed. W.J. Craig (London: Oxford University Press, 1980).

22. Toufexis, "Creating a Child to Save Another."

23. F. Schoeman, "Adolescent Confidentiality and Family Privacy," *Person to Person*, ed. G. Graham and H. LaFollette (Philadelphia: Temple University Press, 1989).

24. Plato, *Republic*, 122.

25. I. Kant, *Groundwork of the Metaphysic of Morals,* transl. H.J. Paton (New York: Harper and Row Publishers, 1964).

26. N.S. Jecker, "Anencephalic Infants and Special Relationships," *Theoretical Medicine*, 11 (1990):333-42.

27. N.S. Jecker, "The Moral Status of Patients Who Are Not Strict Persons," *The Journal of Clinical Ethics*, 1 (1990):35-8.

28. N.S. Jecker, "The Role of Intimate Others in Medical Decision Making," *The Gerontologist* 30 (1990):65-71.

29. S.M. Okin, *Justice, Gender, and the Family* (New York: Basic Books, 1989); especially 33 ff.

30. J.S. Mill, "Nature," *Essential Works of John Stuart Mill,* ed. M. Lerner (New York: Bantam Books, 1961), 367-401.

31. N.S. Jecker, "Are Filial Duties Unfounded?" *American Philosophical Quarterly* 26 (1989):73-80.

FURTHER READINGS

Alberta Institute of Law Research and Reform. *Status of Children*. Report No. 20, 1976.

Anderson, E.S. "Is Women's Labour a Commodity?" *Philosophy and Public Affairs* 19:1 (Winter, 1990) 71-92.

Arras, J.D. "HIV and Childbearing." *Milbank Memorial Quarterly* 68:3 (1990) 353-382.

Australia, Queensland. *Report of the Special Committee Appointed by the Queensland Government to Enquire into the Laws Relating to Artificial Insemination, In Vitro Fertilization and Other Related Matters.* Brisbane, 1984.

Australia, Victoria, Committee to Consider Social, Ethical and Legal Issues Arising from In Vitro Fertilization. *Report on the Disposition of Embryos Produced by In Vitro Fertilization.* Melbourne.

Bartels, D.M., et al., eds. *Beyond Baby M: Ethical Issues in New Reproductive Techniques.* Clifton, NJ: Humana Press, 1990.

Bayles, Michael D. *Reproductive Ethics.* Englewood Cliffs, N.J.: Prentice Hall, 1984.

British Columbia Royal Commission on Family and Children's Law. *Ninth Report of the Royal Commission on Family and Children's Law: Artificial Insemination.* Victoria: 1975.

Brodrib, S. *Women and Reproductive Technologies.* Ottawa: Status of Women Canada, May 1989.

Bryant, Heather. *The Infertility Dilemma: Reproductive Technologies and Prevention.* Calgary: Canadian Advisory Council on the Status of Women, February, 1990, 4.

Cahill, Lisa Sowle. "Moral Tradition, Ethical Language, and Reproductive Technologies." *The Journal of Medicine and Philosophy* 14: 5 (October, 1989) 497-522.

Corea, G. *The Mother Machine: Reproductive Technologies from Artificial Insemination to Artificial Wombs.* New York: Harper and Row, 1986, 6.

Ethical Considerations of the New Reproductive Technologies. A Report of the Combined Ethics Committee of the Canadian Fertility and Andrology Society and the Society of Obstetricians and Gynecologists of Canada (1990).

Field, M.A. *Surrogate Motherhood.* Cambridge and London: Harvard University Press, 1988.

Gostin, L., ed. *Surrogate Motherhood: Politics and Privacy*. Bloomington: Indiana University Press, 1990.

Gouvernement du Québec, Conseil du Statu de la Femme. *General Opinion of the Conseil du Statu de la Femme in Regard to New Reproductive Technologies*. Quebec City, 1989.

Health and Welfare Canada. *Report of the Advisory Committee on the Storage and Utilization of Human Sperm*. Ottawa: HWC, 1981.

Holmes, H., B. Hoskins and M. Gross. *The Custom-Made Child: Woman-Centered Perspectives*. Clifton, NJ: Humana Press, 1981.

Lauritzen, Paul. "What Price Parenthood?" *Hastings Center Report* 20: 2 (March/April 1990) 38–46.

Law Reform Commission of Ontario. "The Propriety of Artificial Conception Technologies." *Report on Artificial Human Reproduction,* Ministry of the Attorney General, 1985, vol. 2, 140-149.

Law Reform Commission of Saskatchewan. *Tentative Proposals for a Human Artificial Insemination Act*. Regina, 1981.

Lenow, J.L. "The Foetus As Patient: Emerging Rights As a Person?" *American Journal of Law and Medicine*, 9: 1 (Spring 1983), at 1-29.

Macklin, Ruth. "Artificial Means of Reproduction and Our Understanding of the Family." *Hastings Center Report* 21:1 (1991) 5-11.

Merrick, J. "Selling Reproductive Rights: Policy Issues in Surrogate Motherhood." *Politics and the Life Sciences* 8:2 (1990) 161-172.

Ontario Law Reform Commission. *Report on Human Artificial Reproduction and Related Matters*. Toronto: Ministry of the Attorney General, 1985.

Raymond, J.C. "Reproductive Gifts and Gift Giving: The Altruistic Woman." *Hastings Center Report* 20:6 (Nov/Dec 1990) 7-11.

Report of the Commission of Enquiry of the German Bundestag, Prospects and Risks of Genetic Engineering, Parts I and II. Deutscher Bundestag, 10. Wahlperiode: Bonn 1987; the so-called *Inquiry Commission*.

Rich, A. *Of Woman Born: Motherhood As Experiment and Institution*. New York, W.W. Norton and Co., 1976.

Shalev, C. *Birth Power: The Case for Surrogacy*. New Haven and London: Yale University Press, 1989.

Silver, L.M. "New Reproductive Technologies in the Treatment of Human Infertility and Genetic Disease." *Theoretical Medicine* 11:2 (1990) 103-110.

Somerville, M. "Weaving 'Birth' Technology into the Value and Policy 'Web' of Medicine, Ethics and Law: Should Policies on 'Conception' Be Considered?" *Nova Law Review* 13:2 (1989) 515-608.

South Australia. *Report of the Working Party on In Vitro Fertilization and Artificial Insemination by Donor* (1984).

The British Columbia Bar Association. *Report of the Special Task Force Committee on Reproductive Technology of the British Columbia Branch, The Canadian Bar Association*. Vancouver: June 1989.

U.K., Department of Health and Social Security. *Report of the Committee of Inquiry into Human Fertilization and Embryology*. Cmnd. 9314, 1984.

CHAPTER 17
GENETIC KNOWLEDGE

INTRODUCTION

Since time immemorial, people have known that the nature of living things depends not only on environmental influences, but also on the characteristics of the parents. People have put this knowledge to use in breeding livestock, developing food-crops and the like. They knew *that* selective breeding worked, but they did not know *why*.

Around the turn of the century, building on the pioneering work of Gregor Mendel, scientists began to unravel the mysteries of inheritance. With the discovery of the DNA molecule, the understanding of the nature of inheritance took a quantum leap forward. Subsequent decades saw the discovery of techniques for manipulating DNA by slicing it here and splicing there. With this, humanity acquired the ability to manipulate directly the blueprint of life.

Initially, this knowledge was applied only to animals and plants. However, right from the very start, some people argued that this knowledge should be applied not only to the breeding of animals and plants, but also to humans. After all, so they maintained, humans are also animals, and therefore are governed by the same laws of inheritance. Furthermore, if we take the trouble to improve animal and plant stocks — to remove hereditary diseases and provide them with beneficial characteristics — why shouldn't we take the same care for human beings? Surely human beings deserve the same amount of attention and care!

On the other side of the debate stand those who see this reasoning as specious. They contend that human beings have a dignity that transcends the merely material. They maintain that to treat human biological failings as defects that should be corrected by scientific means is to objectify human beings. They also see a danger in the fact that we do not know what the long-term effects of "correcting" so-called genetic defects would be. In fact, they maintain that what counts as a defect is very much a function of the conceptual framework we employ and the values by which we operate. In other words, it is culture-relative. Consequently, we cannot even define the notion of a genetic defect in any usable sense.

Finally, those who are opposed to the application of genetic technology and knowledge to the human sphere argue that humanity has worked for millennia to achieve a plateau of moral development that includes values like compassion, equality and the like. These values allow us to see beyond the handicap of the human body to the dignity of the human person. To apply the various genetic techniques to human beings is to erase this progress. Furthermore, applying this knowledge will result in an uncaring, callous and materialistic world. It will foster the attitude that it is appropriate to deal only with the material problem of a handicap, rather than trying to accommodate the handicap in agreement with the fundamental ethical principle of respect for persons and equality and justice.

The genetic knowledge we have gained and the mastery of techniques that we have acquired in order to find out something about the genetic predispositions of human persons, all have important ethical implications. The Royal Commission on New Reproductive Technologies addressed some of these in its report *Proceed With Care*. Some of the major considerations and recommendations of the Commission are reproduced below.

David DeGrazia and L.M. Purdy deal with a somewhat different issue: What do you do with genetic knowledge when you have it? As the biblical story of Adam and Eve illustrates, knowledge is not without its dangers. Genetic knowledge also has ethical implications. DeGrazia explores the question, To what degree should the genetic counsellor provide information to those who carry a defective gene and who will be stricken later on in life by the disease that is associated with it? May the counsellor act paternalistically and withhold information? For the good of the patient? Especially when nothing can be done for the person who carries the defective gene and there is at present no treatment that will help her or him? DeGrazia focuses on Huntington's disease, and in the course of his discussion develops a theory of paternalism that in many ways builds on concepts already familiar from the discussions of the health care professional relationship in chapter 5.

Purdy addresses the other side of this issue: Once we have found out that we carry a defective gene, can we, ethically, ignore the implications of such knowledge? In particular, she asks the question whether we can ethically go ahead and have children when we know that they are likely to inherit characteristics that many would consider a curse. Like DeGrazia, she frames her discussion in terms of Huntington's disease. However, the implications of what she says potentially extend to any genetically determined debilitating condition.

Prenatal Diagnosis, Genetic Disease and Genetic Alteration

PATIENT INFORMATION, CONSENT, AND COUNSELLING

The Commission recommends that

243. Prenatal diagnosis services should be provided in a manner that protects the patient's privacy and safeguards patient records from unauthorized access by third parties. Standard procedures and safeguards for ensuring the privacy and confidentiality of patient and medical records should be developed by the National Reproductive Technologies Commission.

244. Standard information materials and consent forms should be developed by the Prenatal Diagnosis and Genetics Sub-Committee of the National Reproductive Technologies Commission and should be distributed to all patients contemplating the use of prenatal diagnosis services.

245. Information materials should be in accessible language and format.

246. Consent forms should fully identify the specific procedures being consented to. Patients should be given ample time to discuss and fully comprehend consent forms, and consent forms should be signed by the patient before any procedure is initiated.

247. The decision about whether to terminate a pregnancy should remain entirely with the woman; prior willingness or unwillingness to terminate a pregnancy should never operate as a precondition for prenatal diagnosis.

248. Genetics counselling should be an integral part of prenatal diagnosis services and should be provided by counsellors with appropriate training and expertise. For this reason, among others, we recommend that prior accreditation of a facility by the Canadian College of Medical Geneticists, which is equipped to assess this, be required.

249. Materials for patients about counselling and procedures should be developed by the Prenatal Diagnosis and Genetics Sub-Committee of the National Reproductive Technologies Commission. These should be designed to ensure that patients are fully informed of the probability, nature, burden, and possible variability of the disorder for which diagnosis or treatment is being provided, and that they are helped to reach a decision that best meets their particular situation and needs.

250. Counselling prior to and following termination of pregnancy, including grief counselling, should also be available, either on site or by referral.

Royal Commission on New Reproductive Technologies, *Proceed With Care: Final Report of the Royal Commission on New Reproductive Technologies* (Ottawa: Minister of Supply and Services, 1993) 2 vols., vol. 2, 836-38.

REPORTING, LICENCE RENEWAL, AND REVOCATION OF LICENCES

In addition to the specific conditions of licence outlined above, the Commission recommends that

251. Prenatal diagnosis services follow record-keeping, data collection, and data-reporting requirements established by the Prenatal Diagnosis and Genetics Sub-Committee of the National Reproductive Technologies Commission.

252. Licensed prenatal diagnosis services report to the National Reproductive Technologies Commission on their activities, in a standard form, annually or in the event of any change substantially affecting the conditions of licence.

253. Prenatal diagnosis services be required to apply to the National Commission for licence renewal every five years.

and that

254. Licences to provide prenatal diagnosis services be revocable by the National Reproductive Technologies Commission at any time for breach of conditions of licence.

These measures would ensure that services provided at the core of the PND [Prenatal Diagnosis] system are consistent across the country and are monitored to ensure that they are provided in a safe and ethical manner.

PRENATAL DIAGNOSIS (PND) FOR CONGENITAL ANOMALIES AND GENETIC DISEASES

If we are to ensure that PND services are provided in a way that is both beneficial to individuals and couples and consistent with social values, certain changes are required. The reforms we have proposed would promote the autonomy of patients and the appropriate use of resources, while also protecting vulnerable interests of individuals and society and ensuring only ethical uses. In general, and in line with our ethic of care, one goal of our recommendations is to foster a spirit of cooperation among all participants.

In the system we envisage, some regional differences in the use of services would remain — reflecting levels of demand and budgetary resources — but we should see far less variation in referrals to genetics centres. Although there will still be differences between practitioners on various aspects of PND, there would be far less variation in adherence to clinical, counselling, and other standards of practice. There will be mechanisms for public input and public accountability with regard to the evolution of the system. Finally, there will be far fewer opportunities to introduce new diagnostic tests without appropriate assessment and monitoring, as well as far more in the way of disciplined across-Canada assessment and use of new technologies. These reforms will ensure that at-risk women and couples have equal access to a wide range of proven beneficial services.

Ibid., 843-46.

Is this vision feasible? We believe that Canada has a unique capacity to put in place a structure for the provision of PND services that will serve Canadians now and adapt to the coming changes in technology and demand. The necessary factors are in place: we have a strong history of voluntary cooperation by the genetics centres and the CCMG[1] in the disciplined introduction of new PND technologies; there is good will among referring practitioners who have the interests of their patients at heart; we have a single-payer system of health care, which allows for control over the proliferation of new technologies; and we have strong incentives for cooperation on the part of provincial/territorial ministries of health, which are very cognizant of the need to manage the health care system more efficiently and of the need for better data on which to base planning and resource allocation decisions.

The reforms we propose offer the potential to manage more efficiently within existing resources and even to save resources. Although additional resources will be required to establish this structure and work through the first round of facility accreditation and quality assurance activities, there will be significant savings over time. This is because new technologies that do not work or do not provide benefit will not become part of the system. Thus, there are not only ethical but financial reasons for supporting the approach we propose. Canada has a unique opportunity to make this area of clinical practice a vibrant example of evidence-based medicine. PND in the framework we envisage would exemplify how the health care system should strive to work to the benefit of those who use and provide its services.

The track record of the medical genetics community has been impressive in terms of determining the efficacy and safety of the various prenatal diagnostic techniques before they are introduced widely. For example, the randomized across-Canada collaborative clinical trials of amniocentesis and chorionic villus sampling are models that other areas of medicine could do well to follow. Seldom have health care providers done as well in collaborating and limiting new technology until it is assessed — that is, in providing evidence-based services. Yet the public and various interest groups are relatively unaware of this.

At our public hearings and in submissions to the Commission, we noted a high level of suspicion and mistrust of services provided by the genetics community from some members of the public. We heard perceptions that prenatal diagnosis is being used as a "search and destroy" mission to "weed out defective fetuses"; we heard that prenatal diagnosis counselling is biased and predicated on the assumption that it is better to abort a fetus found to have an anomaly than to consider raising a child with a disability; we heard statements that some of the newer developments in this area are being used for eugenic purposes and that women were coerced into terminating pregnancies. These themes were raised by vocal and well-organized groups representing women, people with disabilities, and the pro-life movement, as well as some concerned individuals.

It has become evident that the genetics community needs to find better ways of communicating about how it carries out its work and needs to listen closely to what women are saying about their treatment experience. Not enough attention has been given to how patients view the experience or how the public perceives genetics services. There is a great deal of misinformation and a need for accurate, unbiased, and accessible information about genetics and about what services are actually provided, and in what ways, across the country. The referral network of the physicians in particular needs to realize more clearly the need for providing full information and for respecting the autonomy and decision making of women.

The system we propose should make knowledge about activities in genetic medicine more open and accessible to the general public. Lack of knowledge leads to concerns about what "might be going on." Clear, open information is a much better basis for decisions about use of genetic knowledge, use in which the values of Canadians have an influence.

NOTE

1. Canadian Council on Medical Genetics (ed. note).

The Ethical Justification for Minimal Paternalism in the Use of Predictive Tests for Huntington's Disease

David DeGrazia

INTRODUCTION

Huntington's disease (HD) is a hereditary, neurological disorder that typically results in cognitive impairment, choreic movements, and various sorts of behavioral changes. Presently, it is incurable. It is transmitted as an autosomal, dominant trait, so that a child of a parent with Huntington's has a 50 percent chance of inheriting the gene. HD is 100 percent penetrant, meaning that anyone who inherits the disease gene will develop the disease if he or she lives long enough.

Since the discovery in 1983 of a DNA-restriction-fragment-length polymorphism (RFLP) genetically linked to the disease gene's locus, a test has been developed that identifies this DNA marker (D4S10). (The disease gene itself has not yet been identified.) This test permits identification of individuals who almost certainly carry the gene, in advance of clinical symptoms. In order to produce an informative test result, it is necessary to examine the segregation of the DNA marker among affected and unaffected family members; this unfortunately requires the cooperation of many relatives, since the RFLP pattern may differ in different families. Because the precise location of the gene is estimated and not known, an informative test can establish the probability of one's having it as usually much higher or much lower than 50 percent, without allowing perfect certainty.[1] Recently, several new markers have been discovered, some of which are much closer to the HD gene than is D4S10. Now, with enough information from family members, the test can reach about 99 percent accuracy.[2]

This predictive test for detection of the HD gene in individuals and fetuses of at-risk individuals was originally offered at various research centers in the United States and Canada. Aware of the risks of adverse

---

David DeGrazia, "The Ethical Justification for Minimal Paternalism in the Use of Predictive Tests for Huntington's Disease," *Journal of Clinical Ethics* 2:4 (1991) 219-28.

psychological reactions and other consequences, including suicide, for individuals receiving positive test results, these centers' research protocols excluded from the testing program individuals thought to be especially likely to have adverse reactions. The protocols also required extensive counseling and other forms of psychological support for those admitted into the programs.

Predictive testing for HD is no longer in the research phase, and it is now employed in wider clinical practice in some fourteen testing centers in the United States (and several more in other countries).[3] Now that testing is more widely available, certain ethical and policy questions must be addressed. First, is it ever justified to exclude individuals from this test, thereby paternalistically overriding their desire to gain very significant, obtainable information about themselves? If so, what selection criteria are justified? Second, for those persons entering testing programs, what degree of counseling, if any, is justifiably required? Because the recently published *Guidelines for Predictive Testing for Huntington's Disease* by the Huntington's Disease Society of America (HDSA)[4] has served as a standard for public policy, I will specifically evaluate its recommendations concerning screening and mandatory counseling. (In this article, the word "screening" is used to refer to the clinical evaluation of persons who request appraisal for their suitability for HD testing.)

PREDICTIVE TESTING FOR HD: RISKS AND PRELIMINARY EXPERIENCES

Before the predictive test for HD was developed, results of several surveys alarmed the medical community; some of the individuals who stated that they would take the test if it were available also stated that they anticipated psychologically devastating consequences in the event of positive test results. One survey found that 11 percent mentioned suicide as a possible response and 5 percent stated they would commit suicide if they received positive results.[5] Another survey found that 20.8 percent acknowledged that they would, or probably would, be at risk of suicide.[6]

It is easy to see how the test might pose such risks. HD entails gradual, irreversible, neurological deterioration, which causes grotesque bodily movements and facial expressions, cognitive impairment, and eventually death. A positive test result might cause great anxiety or depression in the affected individual.[7] At-risk individuals might already have affected offspring by the time they learn of their own carrier status, or a positive result might complicate reproductive plans. Those with the gene, and their families, are likely to watch intensively for the onset of symptoms, and they may (rightly or wrongly) interpret clumsiness, memory lapses, or emotional outbursts as early indications of HD.[8] Studies have suggested that the suicide rate for persons already symptomatic for HD might be seven times higher than the national rate.[9] Another study shows that the rate of suicide among those recently diagnosed or suspected of having HD is four to fourteen times the rate of the general population.[10] Actual use of the test, however, has not painted such an alarming picture[11] — though this may be largely due to various factors that weed out many of the most vulnerable prospective test-takers (see below). Let us look at the clinical experiences of the two centers that pioneered testing in this country.

At Massachusetts General Hospital, whose protocol allows for the exclusion of subjects on the basis of psychological frailty,[12] participants are encouraged to bring loved ones to accompany them during testing, and are given at least four hours of counseling and eight hours of psychological evaluation. During the research stage, one-third of those requesting the test quit before receiving results. Since then, far more than one-third have quit — possibly reflecting the fact that the test is no longer provided free of charge. Although roughly one-half of those receiving positive results have reported experiencing severe depression, and the same proportion have reported experiencing moderate depression, their depression has almost never been debilitating. No one has attempted suicide or, as far as is known, experienced suicidal ideation; and, with only one exception, no one has been hospitalized or given medication for depression. Everyone who was employed has continued working (although, for the one individual treated for depression, at a reduced level), and (with the same possible exception) participants have not expressed regret for taking the test.[13] (As of June 1991, thirty persons had received informative test results, and fourteen of the outcomes were positive.[14])

The experiences at Johns Hopkins University have been similar. Subjects receive about ten hours of preparation and counseling prior to disclosure and they may contact a therapist if they desire. The protocol excludes those incapable of giving informed consent and those who express a current willingness to commit suicide. Of the individuals tested, extremely few, if any, of the subjects have expressed suicidal thoughts, no one has attempted suicide, and only one has expressed regret for having taken the test. Those with jobs have continued to work, although those who have received positive results have had a higher frequency of being laid off or demoted. (All who were laid off were later able to find work.) Thus far there has been only one case of depression serious enough to warrant psychiatric care (two weeks of hospitalization). As of 31 December 1990, seventy-four persons had received informative results, with twenty testing positive.[15]

The data from the testing centers at Massachusetts General Hospital and Johns Hopkins University suggest (at least *prima facie*) that with adequate preparation, counseling, and availability of psychiatric care, at-risk individuals who come voluntarily for testing are generally not likely to be psychologically devastated. They have thus far not attempted suicide and have shown great resilience, continuing to lead productive lives. However, exclusion of certain subjects has been part of the centers' protocols, raising this question: if predictive testing for HD were unrestricted, would the prospective test-takers who are psychologically most vulnerable run a significant risk of suicide or debilitating depression? This has to remain an open question, given the absence of relevant data.

Interestingly, the directors of these two programs have indicated that virtually all exclusion has been self-exclusion; subjects frequently decide to discontinue their participation during the course of counseling.[16] Apparently, counseling and psychiatric support can not only mitigate the effects of depression on those who receive positive results, but also educate those who are less psychologically robust and would be endangered by a positive result, such that they can come to realize that testing may not be in their interests.

Because the pioneer testing centers have cautiously excluded certain subjects and provided significant counseling and support for test-takers, the testing centers' experiences might not be at odds with the alarming results of the earlier surveys. The surveys may have accurately reflected the dispositions of a significant proportion of individuals to harm themselves if they test positive. Some of those so inclined may have been directly persuaded not to take the test. Others may have found the lengthy testing process — which requires family participation, extensive travel for some, and (since the end of the research phase) funds or the right kind of insurance — unworthy of the potential benefits. Thus, what these data tell us about the risk of suicide is not entirely clear. In any event, with this background on the development and use of the test, let us turn to the HDSA *Guidelines*.

HDSA'S GUIDELINES: ARE THEY JUSTIFIED?

Because the HDSA *Guidelines* (published in November 1989) serve as a standard for public policy — as a set of recommendations for American testing sites — these recommendations merit careful ethical scrutiny. Like the protocols at Johns Hopkins and Massachusetts General, the *Guidelines'* recommendations include the paternalistic policies of mandatory counseling and of excluding certain individuals who wish to take the test. The *Guidelines* state that the criteria for inclusion "are based on the assumption that the test-taker has made an informed choice."[17] Individuals deemed unable to fulfill this requirement would include those with a current diagnosis of schizophrenia, manic depression, retardation, alcoholism, or other disorders which can alter judgment.[18] Additionally, a thorough evaluation of current suicidal risk should be undertaken for test applicants with a previous history of a suicide attempt.[19] The *Guidelines* also recommend a total of four to seven hours of counseling and evaluation (more, if needed) over three visits prior to disclosure of test results and continued support in follow-up visits.

To address the issue of whether these paternalistic recommendations are justified, we must examine paternalism itself. In the next section, I analyze this concept, offer a working principle that justifies certain paternalistic actions (and omissions), and vindicate this principle by appeal to three kinds of ethical theory.

ETHICAL ANALYSIS

Paternalism

The issue of whether paternalism[20] is ethically justified arises because of a clash between the principles of respect for autonomy and beneficence or non-maleficence. Sometimes respecting a person's autonomy seems likely to allow or to cause considerable harm to that person. By way of definition, an act (or omission) is paternalistic if it overrides — for a person's own good — her known or probable preferences concerning her actions or decision making.[21] *Paternalism* refers both to paternalistic practices and to the view that such overriding is sometimes justified.

In saying that issues involving paternalism arise because respecting a person's autonomy might lead to considerable harm, I do not mean that paternalism occurs only with the overriding of perfectly autonomous wishes — wishes formed in an atmosphere of perfect freedom from external influences and pressures. Paternalism occurs when a person's wishes — whether they are reached perfectly autonomously or they express a not fully autonomous intention—are overridden for that person's own good.[22] Thus, if a father overrules his son's desire to borrow the car because the boy is upset and has drunk two beers, the father acts paternalistically although his son's decision making is not entirely free from external influences (distress and mild intoxication).

Critical in this discussion is the distinction between weak and strong paternalism. *Weak paternalism* holds that it is sometimes right to interfere with a person's less-than-substantially autonomous decision making for his own good. *Strong paternalism* is the view that it is sometimes right to interfere with a person's substantially autonomous decision making for his own good.

Virtually everyone is a weak paternalist. Suppose an eighteen-year-old schizophrenic is experiencing an acute psychotic episode. Tormented by voices that tell her to jump off the roof, she prepares to do so when a parent prevents her and, in spite of her protests, takes her to a hospital for examination. If weak paternalism is unjustified, such an intervention — assuming it is done for the sake of the girl — is impermissible. But this is extremely counterintuitive. Weak paternalism is not really controversial because it constitutes no major threat to the integrity of the principle of respect for autonomy; those whose wishes are overridden are acting with less than substantial autonomy. The trick is to separate justified from unjustified cases of weak paternalism. On the border might be an attempt to place in a nursing home an elderly man with early-phase Alzheimer's disease (whose ability to care for himself is questionable), although he insists on being allowed to live alone in his apartment.

The issue of real controversy is strong paternalism. Suppose a normally happy man has become depressed upon his wife's leaving him, and he reveals to a psychiatrist his intention to commit suicide. The psychiatrist believes that the man is reasoning clearly enough for his decision making to be what we would call *substantially autonomous*. But the psychiatrist thinks there is an excellent chance that, with therapy and a little time, the man would find enough joy in life to want to continue living. (He notes, among other things, that the man has never experienced the termination of a romantic relationship.) The psychiatrist arranges for involuntary commitment to determine whether the patient could improve with inpatient psychiatric care. While I would probably support this strongly paternalistic intervention, I think that justified cases of strong paternalism are very rare.

A WORKING PRINCIPLE FOR APPLICATION TO PREDICTIVE TESTING FOR HD

Now I will articulate and defend a working principle that gives a more determinate shape to our analysis and allows application to issues raised by HDSA's recommendations concerning exclusion criteria and mandatory counseling. I assert this principle, which I call the *principle of minimal paternalism* (PMP), only for medical and public policy contexts and only when significant restrictions of liberty are involved. My examples will reveal that I think PMP does, in fact, reach beyond medicine and public policy, but broadening its scope would require more qualifications than I can specify here. For example, paternalism in family contexts may be justified much more often than PMP would allow. As for restrictions of liberty, there may be trivial restrictions of liberty, even in the specified contexts, that are justified though they are not necessary to prevent extremely grave danger (a condition of PMP). Think of a nurse requiring a hospitalized child to go to bed earlier than he wishes. PMP is as follows:

1. Do not override a person's substantially autonomous decision making for that person's benefit, unless (a) there is substantial evidence that otherwise he or she will be in extremely grave danger, (b) such overriding offers a reasonable prospect of success (that is, of bringing about a net benefit to the person),[23] and (c) such overriding is the least restrictive known way to achieve the desired protection.[24]

2. Do not override a person's less-than-substantially autonomous decision making for that person's benefit, unless (a) there is evidence, whose strength is proportionate to that (diminished) level of autonomy, that otherwise he

or she will be in extremely grave danger, and (b) and (c) as above.

A few clarifications are in order. The idea behind part 2(a) is that the less autonomous a person's choices are, the less evidence there needs to be that not restricting that person's liberty will gravely endanger him, in order to justify overriding his wishes for his own good. That (b) and (c) are necessary conditions is fairly straightforward. Interference with someone's decision making is a *prima facie* evil, requiring justification. If no benefits were likely from such interference, or benefits were likely but could be achieved by less restrictive means (such as outpatient therapy rather than involuntary commitment for a non-dangerous psychiatric patient), the interference would not be justified. A further point concerns how high a probability there must be that great harm will otherwise result, to justify a paternalistic act or omission.[25] No easy answer is possible, and assigning a numerical value would be arbitrary. Let me simply say that the probability must be considerable. As an example, I believe that it would be right to prevent an autonomous, risk-enjoying person from playing Russian roulette, even if we knew he would fire only one shot (so that the likelihood of death would be one chance in six).[26] On the other hand, I think it would be unjustified to outlaw skydiving just because a nonzero percentage of skydivers dive to their deaths.

PMP is defensible from a variety of theoretical viewpoints, suggesting its plausibility. I will attempt to show how it can be vindicated from the perspectives of rule-utilitarianism, Kantian universalizability, and a rights approach.

Rule Utilitarianism

Utilitarianism is the theory that the right action or policy is that which maximizes good (over evil) consequences. For various reasons, I favor the variant called *rule utilitarian* action is right if and only if it is in accordance with a rule or set of rules with which general compliance will maximize good consequences in the long run.[27]

The trick is to show that PMP is a plausible candidate for a utility-maximizing rule. Let us contrast PMP with a completely anti-paternalistic rule: do not (ever) override a person's substantially autonomous decision making for her own benefit. The reasoning in support of this rule would be that each person able to make autonomous choices is the best judge of her own good; interventions by others often cause more harm than good and tend to create resentment.

I would argue, however, that sometimes a policy or action that respects a person's autonomous decisions is likely to result in harms that outweigh the usual benefits of respecting her decision making. The example of the depressed man whose wife left him is a possible candidate. Consider also the case of a competent adult who wishes to use the drug crack. Due to its formidable addictive power and its typically devastating effect on the user's life, there is good reason to think that preventing people from taking this substance would maximize benefits over harms.[28] Thus, unlike a perfectly anti-paternalistic rule, a rule that allows occasional paternalistic interventions, when there exists substantial evidence that not intervening will gravely endanger the agent, is likely to lead to the best overall consequences. This rule is essentially part 1(a).

Part 2(a) is vindicated as follows. Not paternalistically interfering with people's autonomous choices usually maximizes good consequences, precisely because the persons in question can make autonomous choices and can, therefore, generally know what is in their interests. By the same logic, the presumption that a person knows what is in his own interests becomes less secure the less autonomous his decision making is. Accordingly, 2(a) would seem part of a utility-maximizing rule, because someone to whom it applies acts with substantially reduced autonomy. Since the presumption that he knows his own best interests is not very strong, we need comparatively little evidence to justify a paternalistic act that attempts to prevent great harm.

Parts (b) and (c) of PMP state two common-sensical conditions — that paternalistic actions offer a reasonable prospect of bringing about the intended benefit and that they minimize the interference with decision making. Good outcomes cannot be maximized if the prospects for success are too low. And since restrictions of liberty may be regarded as harmful, evil consequences cannot be minimized unless the least invasive or restrictive way of pursuing the desired benefits is taken. Thus, it appears that PMP is a plausible candidate for a rule in rule-utilitarianism.

The Kantian Categorical Imperative (Universalizability)

Kant argued that reason dictates a principle or law of action that applies to any rational being. This *categorical imperative* has several formulations, but we will consider just this one:

> Act only according to that maxim [principle of action] whereby you can at the same time will that it should become a universal law.[29]

Kant is famous for arguing that to act according to a maxim whose universal adoption one would be unable to will involves a kind of contradiction and therefore a violation of reason. While various aspects of Kant's moral philosophy have been extensively criticized, the idea that one must be able to accept the universal adoption of one's principles of action has been developed by some of the leading moral philosophers of our day.[30]

Is PMP universalizable? First, let us contrast it with the rule that results if part 1(a) of PMP is replaced with this: "Do not override a person's substantially autonomous decisions for her own good unless there is some evidence that otherwise she would be endangered." Few people are likely to accept a policy whereby their autonomous wishes can be interfered with whenever there is some evidence that they would otherwise be in some danger. There is very often such evidence. For example, this standard would entail the prohibition of most or all sports. Nor — given the value of autonomy to us — would it be sufficient to require either (1) substantial evidence of (some) danger or (2) (some) evidence of extremely grave danger. Note that the following actions could probably be justified by appeal to one or both of these requirements: the prohibition of contact sports, cigarettes, alcohol, flying in airplanes, and even driving cars — as well as the involuntary commitment of large classes of psychiatric patients (such as paranoid schizophrenics) regardless of whether their recent behavior suggests a present danger of self-harm.

PMP, on the other hand, seems to survive the test of universalizability. It allows most of the space for decision making that perfect liberty would allow (up to the point of harming others), thereby securing a sense of respect for us as autonomous decision-makers. But PMP saves us if our decisions appear to be clearly and strongly against our interests. It seems rational to want and give prior consent to such occasional interference. Admittedly, there will be some especially risk-loving and fiercely independent individuals who will resist even this minor intrusion into their liberty; indeed, probably no rule is universalizable by all persons. So I conclude only that Kantianism broadly vindicates PMP.

The Rights Approach

A third major kind of ethical theory gives prominence to the concept of moral rights. Such rights may be thought of as moral protections of an individual's most fundamental interests against intrusions that can result from promoting the common good. I believe that a plausible rights view is consistent with PMP.

How, on a rights view, would the relevant right be articulated? It would probably be claimed that there is a right to autonomy or liberty, meaning that, so long as one does not harm others, one has a right to live one's life as one sees fit (essentially, Mill's "harm principle"[31]). But rights theorists generally do not (at least when pressed) claim that rights are absolute; there will always be some cases where a given right may justifiably be overridden. Ronald Dworkin, one of the most important contemporary philosophers in the rights tradition, holds that a right may be overridden or limited (1) when necessary to protect another right from infringement, (2) when the value protected by the right (for example, freedom of expression) is not or is only negligibly at stake (as in the case of being free to shout "fire" in a crowded movie theatre), or (3) when granting the right is likely to result in extremely damaging consequences.[32]

Recognizing that rights, at least the right to autonomy, could plausibly allow for some exceptions, I suggest that the exceptions stated in parts l(a) and 2(a) of PMP would be reasonable grounds for limiting a right to autonomy. In fact, the justification provided for limiting this right in accord with part l(a) (though rights language was not used) is very much like Dworkin's third reason: the grave danger or likelihood of damaging consequences if liberty is not restricted. And the justification for limiting a right to autonomy by way of part 2(a) shares in the spirit of rights theories generally, all of which allow certain paternalistic interventions in the case of minors, the mentally ill, and others with diminished competence. On the other hand, parts (b) and (c) may themselves be thought of as plausible rights claims, limiting paternalistic interference to cases in which there is reasonable prospect of benefit and the least restrictive measures are taken.

Thus, it appears that PMP can be justified by a plausible rights theory, by rule utilitarianism, and (at least broadly) by appeal to universalizability. Because it enjoys this grounding in three leading kinds of ethical theory, I assume PMP's reasonableness in addressing issues of screening and mandatory counseling for the use of the predictive test for HD.

IMPLICATIONS FOR THE CLINICAL SETTING

What implications does PMP have for the recommendations contained in HDSA's *Guidelines* concerning screening and mandatory counseling in the clinical use of the predictive test for HD? Let us begin with the recommendations for psychological screening of those who request testing. Is this paternalistic practice ever ethically justified? If so, are the exclusion criteria that are recommended in the *Guidelines* themselves justified, or are they unreasonably restrictive or too permissive? As mentioned above, the *Guidelines* base their inclusion criteria on the assumption that the prospective test-taker can make an informed choice.[33] Persons thereby excluded include those with a current diagnosis of schizophrenia, manic depression, retardation, alcoholism, or other disorders which can alter judgment.[34] In addition, a thorough evaluation of current suicidal risk should be undertaken for test applicants with a previous history of a suicide attempt.[35]

In evaluating these criteria, the first point to note is that different considerations come into play for differing degrees of autonomous decision making on the part of the individuals who request testing. Consider first the purest case, that of persons who have the capacity, at the relevant time, for substantially autonomous decision making and action; I call such persons *autonomous persons*. To warrant excluding an autonomous, at-risk person from testing would require substantial evidence that admitting her would put her in extremely grave danger (condition l(a) of PMP). The danger that seems to meet this description is that of trauma so devastating that it leads to suicide.[36] (By focusing on suicide, I have, in theory, ignored another outcome at least as bad: namely, an action so self-destructive that it results in a life not worth living from the point of view of the patient. Examples might include impulsively blinding oneself, severing a limb, or paralyzing oneself by gunshot. But I cannot see how it could be determined that one is at risk for these sorts of actions — unless one is also believed to be at risk for suicide.) What we need, then, to justify paternalistic interference with an autonomous test-seeker is substantial evidence that testing her would create a considerable likelihood of suicide — because of the test result.[37]

But I believe that only strong evidence of a current disposition to commit suicide would count as "substantial" evidence of such grave danger. Such a disposition might be revealed by a patient's stating in pretest counseling that there is a significant chance that he would commit suicide if he tested positive; however, less direct statements and other actions might be equally strong forms of evidence to a psychiatrist. In any event, if one is now (apparently) disposed to suicide, there is not perfect or definite, but substantial, reason to believe that one is in grave danger of suicide if allowed to undergo testing.[38] But the fact that a person was previously suicidal, yet is not currently so disposed, does not constitute such evidence.

Conditions (b) and (c) of PMP are also satisfied. Condition (b), which requires that the paternalistic act have a reasonable prospect of success, is satisfied to the extent that exclusion in appropriate circumstances removes a feared stimulus of suicidal behavior. Doing so should substantially reduce the likelihood of suicide unless the patient is disposed to commit suicide no matter what (and not just in the event of a positive result). In this case, the patient should not only be excluded from testing, but also committed to a psychiatric institution or otherwise treated; he is now a "danger to self" and therefore satisfies legal (and, I think, ethical) criteria for involuntary commitment. Condition (c) is satisfied to the extent that the patient's liberty is not restricted more than necessary for obtaining the desired protections (a point developed in the discussion of counseling immediately below).

Thus, I conclude the following regarding the *Guidelines'* implied policies on the screening of autonomous individuals: (1) the general practice of screening is justified; (2) mandatory evaluation of persons with a history of suicide is justified, but such persons should be excluded from testing only if determined to be currently disposed to suicide; (3) the implication that persons "with a current diagnosis of schizophrenia, manic depression, retardation, alcoholism, or other disorders which can alter judgment" are not substantially autonomous is reasonable, as long as "other disorders" is restricted in interpretation to disorders comparable in severity to those listed.

It may seem oversimplified to assume that persons with the disorders mentioned above are less than substantially autonomous. After all, what is important is one's degree of autonomy or capacity with respect to a given decision or action, and persons with these disorders can manifest different degrees of capacity at different times. For example, many alcoholics, during sober hours, demonstrate ordinary decision-making capacities. However, in the context of testing for HD, one must consider decision-making capacity over lengthy periods of time. An alcoholic who makes reasoned decisions about commencing testing might go on a self-destructive binge later, after receiving test results. Analogous points could be made about members of the other groups listed above.

The role of counseling in the selection process is all-important and must not be overlooked. Researchers and testing personnel at Johns Hopkins and Massachusetts General have found that those persons thought unfit for testing were able, after counseling and discussion, to decide for themselves that they did not believe entering the program was desirable at the time — leaving open the possibility of entering later.[39] The possibility of trying again later is important in ensuring that the restriction of liberty is the least restrictive alternative consistent with the goal of adequate protection. Moreover, it appears that the most satisfying outcome is usually possible: the testers and the at-risk person come to agree that the latter should not be tested at a given time, so that autonomy is respected while harm is avoided, obviating paternalism. This is the realization of the medical ethical goal of shared decision making.

The promise of counseling is also important in another way. While I suggest that, among autonomous persons, only persons currently disposed to suicide should be mandatorily excluded, persons not fitting this description who nevertheless seriously concern testers, for whatever reason, may be given the recommendation that they postpone their decision. As long as the "recommendation" is not so heavy-handed that its pressure is coercive, autonomy is, in this case, also duly respected. The possibility of respectful recommendation exists for both autonomous persons and those with reduced autonomy. Let us turn to the second group.

This group I describe as having *moderately reduced autonomy*. It includes, for example, alcoholics, and those currently diagnosed as schizophrenic or manic depressive, who nevertheless retain considerable capacity for decision making in spite of being less-than-substantially autonomous. For these people, I think PMP recommends the following standard: if a person has ever been suicidal and there are any reasonable doubts about his current desire to live should he receive a positive test result, he may be deferred until such doubts are removed. Resources permitting, periodic psychological reexamination of such a person would be appropriate if he continues his interest in the testing program. We have just seen that the *Guidelines* exclude those with the clinical conditions just mentioned; categorical exclusion in accordance with these criteria seems overly paternalistic.

I describe the third group of possible subjects as having *greatly reduced autonomy*. Here the impediment to fuller autonomy might be mild retardation or the presence of psychoses where there remains only partial functioning and significantly reduced decision-making ability. Paternalism in this case is far more easily justified than in the case of an autonomous person. Any significant amount of depression or emotional instability would seem to warrant deferral until grounds for uneasiness about testing are removed. Of course, some victims of psychosis and many retarded persons will never obtain a condition of sufficient stability and mental capacity to warrant bringing them into a testing program, but all persons should be free to request evaluation to determine their suitability for testing. Therefore, again, I think that categorical exclusion of members of the groups identified above is too paternalistic.

It might be worth mentioning a fourth group, comprised of individuals in whom autonomy is simply absent, for example, the extremely retarded or autistic. It is not obvious that it makes sense to think of such individuals as requesting testing. In such a case, a request for testing should be made by a parent or legally appointed guardian. Such a request should be granted only if some weighty reason, consistent with the interests of the at-risk individual, exists for obtaining test results. Such a reason might be to plan for the individual's future, in the event that she is likely to develop HD.[40]

To sum up these remarks concerning HDSA's recommendations for screening, I think that the general thrust is reasonable, being (in rough outline) supportable by PMP and, therefore, by leading ethical theories. But I also think the exclusion criteria are a bit too rigid and bluntly categorizing, masking morally relevant facts like actual degree of autonomy or decision-making capacity with somewhat oversimplified characterizations.

Let us turn to the question of whether and how much counseling should be required in a testing program. This issue is not trivial; to require several visits and numerous hours of counseling and discussion is a substantial imposition on one's time (especially if one lives far from the testing center) and, possibly, one's emotional energy if counseling is upsetting or anxiety-provoking. Still, I think some amount is justifiably required. When not adequately informed with respect to a particular decision, one does not make the decision or act on it substantially autonomously (or with the greatest degree of autonomy that one is capable). Even if one is an autonomous person — so that one has the capacity for substantially autonomous action — one does not actualize this capacity in the absence of vital information.[41] While there may be persons who come for the first time to the testing center already extremely well informed, aware of all the relevant facts, and sensitive to their own psychological characteristics, practical considerations favor using the same standard for them. Doing so would add a considerable measure of safety for bor-

derline cases and would spare testers the trouble of carefully determining in individual cases whether the person may be exempted — a process that might take as long as counseling would! HDSA's *Guidelines* recommend a total of four to seven hours of counseling and evaluation (more, if needed) over three visits prior to disclosure of test results, and continued support in follow-up visits. This recommendation seems reasonable and is supported by the success of counseling requirements at the pioneer centers during the research stage (since test-takers fared very well psychologically). Because all persons entering a program have survived screening, their status in terms of autonomy may — at that point, for all practical purposes — be considered equal. Therefore, applying the same number of hours of mandatory counseling to everyone is perfectly sensible.

One issue of paramount practical importance is how minors fit into our categories, if at all. HDSA's *Guidelines* recommend excluding persons under the age of eighteen with possible exceptions for pregnant minors and potential fathers.[42] Even with these exceptions, the nearly categorical exclusion of minors seems too restrictive. The ethical considerations of this paper support extending access to the test to at least some minors not falling under these exceptions. It seems fairly clear that the decision making of some sixteen- and seventeen-year-olds is substantially autonomous. Additionally, some minors whose decision making is less than substantially autonomous would not be excluded by the criteria discussed above. Autonomy is a matter of decision-making capacity, not of age *per se*.

HD test results constitute a profound piece of information for the individual; accordingly, centers must be very cautious in making results available to minors. I cannot imagine that it would be appropriate to give such information to twelve- or thirteen-year-olds, although I am not prepared to specify a precise minimum age requirement. Testers will have to use a great deal of discretion in deciding which individuals closer to eighteen may take the test, and there is nothing wrong with this. But it would probably be wise to err on the side of caution, remembering that (normal) minors may always take the test at a later age if they are excluded at a given time. Counseling may bring the minor to agree with an uncertain tester that deferral is the most desirable course. Also, if a minor's desire for testing is opposed by the wishes of his parents, a great deal of caution must be used and due consideration given to the potential for damaging family relations. If there is a standoff between minor and parents, unless the minor is very independent, it would probably be reasonable to defer the minor until he or she reaches the age of eighteen. Under no circumstances should testers allow minors to be forced by their parents to be tested.[43]

CONCLUSION

Humankind finds itself at the dawn of an age of previously unimagined genetic understanding. As we increase our knowledge of the genetic causes of many of the diseases that afflict us, we cannot evade ethical issues concerning how to proceed in the light of such knowledge. This is true not only in the case of Huntington's disease, but also in the case of cystic fibrosis, Alzheimer's disease, the major psychiatric disorders, and others.

Down the road a bit, genetic engineering holds some promise for greatly reducing, or even eliminating, some genetic diseases.

But whatever the future holds for us, we must not lose sight of our present situation. There are, and for the foreseeable future there will be, many persons at risk for HD and other genetic diseases — persons who, like everyone else, form life plans and may wish to plan with maximum information about their prospects of being afflicted with a particular disease. For those at risk for developing HD, I have attempted to develop a rational approach, grounded in ethical theory (but also with due appreciation of clinical realities), for establishing exclusion criteria and counseling requirements. I believe the HDSA has responded reasonably to these issues in its *Guidelines,* although I have disagreed on various specific points regarding their exclusion criteria. It is my hope that the analysis developed here will be applicable to questions of pretest screening and mandatory counseling for predictive tests for other genetic diseases, for paternalism is likely to be at the heart of ethical issues surrounding all of them.

Acknowledgments

I am greatly indebted to Charles R. MacKay, PhD, who stimulated my thinking on these issues and enhanced my understanding of them in many illuminating discussions. I would also like to thank two very insightful anonymous reviewers for their comments.

NOTES

1. G.J. Meissen, R.H. Myers, C.A. Mastromauro, *et al,* "Predictive Testing for Huntington's Disease with Use of a Linked DNA Marker," *New England Journal of Medicine* 318 (3 March 1988): 535-42.

2. J. Brandt, K.A. Quaid, S.E. Folstein, *et al.,* "Presymptomatic Diagnosis of Delayed-Onset Disease with Linked DNA Markers: The Experience in Huntington's Disease," *Journal of the American Medical Association* 261 (2 June

1989): 3108-14; personal communication from J. Brandt, PhD, director of testing program, Johns Hopkins University, 7 June 1991.

3. Of course, what I am calling "the research stage" included the clinical use of the test to provide informative results to particular individuals. "Research" is meant to convey that access to the test was tightly controlled and the results carefully studied, in order to pave the way for broader clinical use.

4. Huntington's Disease Society of America, *Guidelines for Predictive Testing for Huntington's Disease* (New York: HDSA, November 1989).

5. S. Kessler, T. Field, L. Worth, and H. Mosbarger, "Attitudes of Persons at Risk for Huntington's Disease Toward Predictive Testing," *American Journal of Medical Genetics* 26 (February 1987): 259-70.

6. C. Mastromauro, R.H. Myers, and B. Berkman, "Attitudes Toward Presymptomatic Testing in Huntington's Disease," *American Journal of Medical Genetics* 26 (February 1987): 271-82.

7. S. Kessler, "Psychiatric Implications of Pre-symptomatic Testing for Huntington's Disease," *American Journal of Orthopsychiatry* 57 (April 1987): 212-19. Kessler concludes his study by stating:

   Persons at risk for HD are also at risk for major affective disorders and other psychiatric dysfunctions and are more likely to be hospitalized for psychiatric reasons than individuals in the general *population, particularly when the former are faced by the stresses imposed by positive predictive test outcomes* [emphasis added].

8. S.J. Bird, "Presymptomatic Testing for Huntington's Disease," *Journal of the American Medical Association* 253 (14 June 1985): 3286-91.

9. See, for example, Commission for the Control of Huntington's Disease and Its Consequences, *Report,* vol. 1: Overview, DHEW Pub. No. (NIH) 78-1501 (Washington, D.C.: Government Printing Office, 1977). It has also been reported that about 5.7 percent of HD patients known to the National HD Roster committed suicide and that 27.6 percent had attempted suicide at least once. See L.A. Farrer, "Suicide and Attempted Suicide in Huntington's Disease: Implications for Preclinical Testing of Persons at Risk," *American Journal of Medical Genetics* 24 (June 1986): 305-11.

10. M. Shoenfeld, R-H. Myers, L.A. Cupples, *et al.*, "Increased Rate of Suicide among Patients with Huntington's Disease," *Journal of Neurology, Neurosurgery, and Psychiatry* 47 (December 1984): 1283-87.

11. Surveys that asked whether at-risk persons would take the test if available differed in their results, but the lowest proportion was 56 percent; see S.M. Swavely, W.H. Silverman, and A. Falek, "Psychological Impact of the Development of a Presymptomatic Test for Huntington's Disease," *Health Psycholog* 6, no. 2 (1987): 149-57. The highest was 78.8 percent; see Kessler, Field, Worth, and Mosbarger, "Attitudes of Persons at Risk." When the test became available, a much lower proportion was willing to go through the testing process; K.A. Quaid, J. Brandt, and S.E. Folstein, "The Decision to be Tested for Huntington's Disease" (letter), *Journal of the American Medical Association* 257 (26 June 1987): 3362.

12. More exactly, they exclude applicants if they have had a serious diagnosed mental illness, such as schizophrenia or manic-depression, if they have attempted sui-

cide in the previous ten years, or if they have stated they would commit suicide if they received a positive result. If applicants have had a history of substance abuse or an episode of serious depression, they are referred to further evaluation. Like the other testing centers, Massachusetts General also requires that each test-taker be at least eighteen; personal communication from R. Myers, PhD, clinical director of the testing program, 12 October 1989.

13. Meissen, Myers, Mastromauro, *et al.,* "Predictive Testing"; confirmation of this information in personal communication from R. Myers, 7 June 1991.

14. Personal communication from R. Myers, 12 June 1991.

15. Personal communication from J.Brandt, 10 June 1991.

16. Personal communication from R. Myers, 7 June 1991; personal communication from J. Brandt, 10 June 1991.

17. Huntington's Disease Society of America, *Guidelines*, 6.

18. Ibid.

19. Ibid.

20. The *Oxford English Dictionary* dates the term to the 1880s, though the essential idea behind the term may be much older. A classic discussion of paternalism is offered by John Stuart Mill in *On Liberty,* where he defends this anti-paternalistic "harm principle":

    The only purpose for which power can be rightfully exercised over any member of a civilized community, against his will, is to prevent harm to others. His own good, either physical or moral, is not a sufficient warrant.

    Cited in *Essential Works of John Stuart Mill* (New York: Bantam Books, 1961), 263.

21. The idea of overriding someone's preferences regarding her own decision making is meant broadly enough to include paternalistic cases of deception (for example, a psychiatrist's prescribing a placebo when the patient clearly expects an active drug). This is in keeping with the common subsumption of veracity under respect for autonomy in bioethics texts; see, T.L. Beauchamp and J.F. Childress, *Principles of Biomedical Ethics,* 3rd ed. (New York: Oxford University Press, 1989), 85-99. That deception can be paternalistic is argued clearly in B. Gert and C.M. Culver, "Paternalistic Behavior," in *Medicine and Moral Philosophy,* ed. M. Cohen, T. Nagel, and T. Scanlon (Princeton, N.J.: Princeton University Press, 1981).

22. Beauchamp and Childress, *Principles*, 214.

23. C. MacKay pointed out to me the need for such a condition.

24. Now widely recognized, this condition is included, for example, in the analysis of J.C. Callahan, "Liberty, Beneficence, and Involuntary Confinement," *Journal of Medicine & Philosophy* 9 (August 1984): 261-93. Callahan's analysis is intended to apply to all paternalistic interventions (whereas mine is, again, restricted to significant limitations of liberty in medical and public policy contexts).

25. This issue was brought to my attention by C. MacKay.

26. C.M. Culver and B. Gert make a similar point in "The Morality of Involuntary Hospitalization," in *The Law-Medicine Relation: A Philosophical Exploration,* ed. S.F. Spicker, J.M. Healey, Jr., and H.T. Engelhardt (Boston: D. Reidel, 1978), 164.

Though, unlike me, they appeal to the concept of rationality in identifying justifying conditions for paternalistic acts:

> Suppose a man had just suffered a heart attack and it was known that his risk of death was essentially zero if he remained in bed for one to three days (whether he liked it or not) but was 16 percent if he insisted, without any adequate reason, on being up and about. We believe that nearly everyone would view it as irrational if he did insist on being up, even though we knew that by universally recommending bedrest we were needlessly confining five people for every one person for whom it would be appropriate.

> Suppose the figure were 10 percent. We believe that the large majority of people would still view it as irrational not to choose to be confined for a few days. How low the percentage would have to go before a significant number of people would think it rational to get out of bed we do not know.

27. Perhaps the most serious objections against act-utilitarianism (the major variant of the theory to whose problems rule-utilitarianism is a response) stem from some of our strongest convictions regarding justice. Potent criticisms have been leveled against utilitarianism, especially act-utilitarianism, by J. Rawls, *A Theory of Justice* (Cambridge: Harvard University Press, 1971); A. Donagan, *The Theory of Morality* (Chicago: University of Chicago Press, 1977), 192-96; and R. Dworkin, *Taking Rights Seriously* (Cambridge: Harvard University Press, 1977), 94-100, 232-38.

28. This claim is controversial, however. If compelling evidence emerges that suggests that legalization would maximize good over evil consequences, utilitarianism will be committed to legalization.

29. I. Kant, *Grounding for the Metaphysics of Morals*, in *Ethical Philosophy*, trans. James W. Ellington (Indianapolis: Hackett, 1983), 30.

30. See for example, R.M. Hare, *The Language of Morals* (Oxford, England: Clarendon Press, 1952); M.G. Singer, *Generalization in Ethics* (New York: Knopf Press, 1961); Donagan, *The Theory of Morality;* A. Gewirth, *Reason and Morality* (Chicago: University of Chicago Press, 1978); and B. Gert, *Morality: A New Justification of the Moral Rules* (New York: Oxford University Press, 1988).

31. Mill, *On Liberty*.

32. R. Dworkin, "Taking Rights Seriously," ch. 7 in *Taking Rights Seriously*.

33. Huntington's Disease Society of America, *Guidelines*, 6.

34. Ibid.

35. Ibid.

36. For the purposes of this essay I make the simplifying assumption that suicide is not in a patient's best interests. I think, however, that there are rare and very unfortunate cases in which suicide is not an irrational option. But in the present public policy context, I think it is wisest to assume that suicide is to be prevented, or at least is not to be contributed to (with devastating news or otherwise).

37. Most persons who request testing have an affected parent and therefore a 50 percent chance of having the defective gene; some know only that they have an affected grandparent and therefore have a 25 percent chance. I assume that, in either case, if there is a substantial possibility that a patient will commit

suicide in the event of a positive test result, the chance of extremely grave harm is great enough to warrant paternalistic restrictions—as suggested by the judgment above concerning Russian roulette and in note 26.

38. Then again, a suicidal person may benefit greatly from receiving the result that she does not have the defective gene. Is exclusion of suicidal persons therefore unfair in denying them the possibility of a very substantial benefit? Maybe PMP is inapplicable whenever a paternalistic intervention would deny the possibility of a major benefit.

    I think the following considerations neutralize this concern. The dictum *primum non nocere* is relevant here. While it is morally important to benefit persons, it seems even more important not to harm them — even in the health care professions, in which the moral importance of benefitting is universally acknowledged. Various considerations could be adduced to support this claim. As an intuitive appeal, it is surely unethical, in the absence of very special circumstances, to kill one person simply to save another. And I find it suggestive that there is an ethical theory (libertarianism) that argues for duties not to harm but none to benefit, but there is no ethical theory that argues for duties to benefit while denying any duty not to harm. For developed defenses of this position, see W.K. Frankena, *Ethics*, 2nd ed. (Englewood Cliffs, N.J.: Prentice-Hall, 1973), 45-48; and Gert, *Morality*, 47-61.

    Psychological considerations also go some distance to address this theoretical concern. A prospective test-taker who is currently suicidal may be suicidal for any number of reasons, reasons that may have little or nothing to do with her ignorance or concerns about having the HD gene. It is very uncertain, at best, that receiving good news would lift such a person out of a suicidal state. However, there is a very immediate danger that a suicidal person who received the crushing news of having the HD gene would "go over the edge."

39. Personal communication from R. Myers, 12 October 1989; personal communication from J. Brandt, 10 June 1989.

40. One might wonder why the *Guidelines* did not mention conditions such as autism, which can eventuate in a lack of autonomy, as further exclusion criteria. Perhaps it was because such persons simply do not request testing.

41. This is a large part of the point of informed consent.

42. Huntington's Disease Society of America, *Guidelines*, 6.

43. Allowing minors access to certain kinds of very important information without parental permission has some basis in law. Minors may take the human immunodeficiency virus antibody test at anonymous testing centers and may have pregnancy tests, without permission of their parents. While not involving access to information, the legal right to have an abortion and to get a prescription for birth control, without parental permission, is also extended to minors. While each is only partly analogous to presymptomatic testing for HD, these examples provide some support for a policy of not excluding all minors from testing.

    Space precludes my taking up numerous important ethical issues (not all of which concern paternalism). First, there are various further issues concerning family relations. For example, what if a mature minor wishes to be tested, but his identical twin, who is likely to learn of test results, is horrified at the prospect of receiving test results? Or, what if one cannot get an informative test result without the testing of a reluctant relative? While it is obvious that testing centers must make every effort to avoid psychological harm and the damaging of family relations, specific guidelines would be useful here. A second untouched area of ethical concern is the confidentiality of test results, a topic discussed in the HDSA *Guidelines.* Third, many thorny issues arise when we consider testing fetuses for HD. Unlike (many) minors, of course, fetuses cannot consent to testing. Even to comment responsibly on issues concerning the testing of fetuses would take me beyond the scope of this paper. Fourth, I have said little about how the guidelines I suggest could best be implemented. The HDSA *Guidelines* suggest that institutions considering a testing program establish an institutional review board (IRB) for guidance (Huntington's Disease Society of America, *Guidelines,* Preface). A thorough discussion of ethical issues concerning presymptomatic testing for HD would enter into specifics about IRBs and other facets of implementation.

Genetic Diseases:
Can Having Children Be Immoral?
L. M. Purdy

I. INTRODUCTION

Suppose you know that there is a fifty percent chance you have Huntington's chorea, even though you are still free of symptoms, and that if you do have it, each of your children has a fifty percent chance of having it also. Should you now have children?

There is always some possibility that a pregnancy will result in a diseased or handicapped child. But certain persons run a higher than average risk of producing such a child. Genetic counselors are increasingly able to calculate the probability that certain problems will occur; this means that more people can find out whether they are in danger of creating unhealthy offspring *before* the birth of a child.

Since this kind of knowledge is available, we ought to use it wisely. I want in this paper to defend the thesis that it is wrong to reproduce when we know there is a high risk of transmitting a serious disease or defect. My argument for this claim is in three parts. The first is that we should try to provide every child with a normal opportunity for health; the second is that in the course of doing this it is not wrong to prevent possible children from existing. The third is that this duty may require us to refrain from childbearing.[1]

One methodological point must be made. I am investigating a problem in biomedical ethics: this is a philosophical enterprise. But the conclusion has practical importance since individuals do face the

L.M. Purdy, "Genetic Diseases: Can Having Children Be Immoral?" in *Genetics Now: Ethical Issues in Genetic Research,* ed. by J.J. Buckley, Jr. (Washington, D.C.: University Press of America, 1978).

choice I examine. This raises a question: what relation ought the outcome of this inquiry bear to social policy?[2] It may be held that a person's reproductive life should not be interfered with. Perhaps this is a reasonable position, but it does not follow from it that it is never wrong for an individual to have children or that we should not try to determine when this is the case. All that does follow is that we may not coerce persons with regard to childbearing. Evaluation of this last claim is a separate issue which cannot be handled here.

I want to deal with this issue concretely. The reason for this is that, otherwise, discussion is apt to be vague and inconclusive. An additional reason is that it will serve to make us appreciate the magnitude of the difficulties faced by diseased or handicapped individuals. Thus it will be helpful to consider a specific disease. For this purpose I have chosen Huntington's chorea.[3]

II. HUNTINGTON'S CHOREA: COURSE AND RISK

Let us now look at Huntington's chorea. First we will consider the course of the disease, then its inheritance pattern.

> The symptoms of Huntington's chorea usually begin between the ages of thirty and fifty, but young children can also be affected. It happens this way:

> Onset is insidious. Personality changes (obstinacy, moodiness, lack of initiative) frequently antedate or accompany the involuntary choreic movements. These usually appear first in the face, neck, and arms, and are jerky, irregular, and stretching in character. Contractions of the facial muscles result in grimaces; those of the respiratory muscles, lips, and tongue lead to hesitating, explo-

sive speech. Irregular movements of the trunk are present; the gait is shuffling and dancing. Tendon reflexes are increased .... Some patients display a fatuous euphoria; others are spiteful, irascible, destructive, and violent. Paranoid reactions are common. Poverty of thought and impairment of attention, memory, and judgment occur. As the disease progresses, walking becomes impossible, swallowing difficult, and dementia profound. Suicide is not uncommon.[4]

The illness lasts about fifteen years, terminating in death.

Who gets Huntington's chorea? It is an autosomal dominant disease; this means it is caused by a single mutant gene located on a non-sex chromosome. It is passed from one generation to the next via affected individuals. When one has the disease, whether one has symptoms and thus knows one has it or not, there is a 50% chance that each child will have it also. If one has escaped it then there is no risk to one's children.[5]

How serious is this risk? For geneticists, a ten percent risk is high.[6] But not every high risk is unacceptable: this depends on what is at stake.

There are two separate evaluations in any judgment about a given risk. The first measures the gravity of the worst possible result; the second perceives a given risk as great or small. As for the first, in medicine as elsewhere, people may regard the same result quite differently:

> ... The subjective attitude to the disease or lesion itself may be quite at variance with what informed medical opinion may regard as a realistic appraisal. Relatively minor limb defects with cosmetic overtones are examples here. On the other hand, some patients regard with equanimity genetic lesions which are of major medical importance.[7]

For devastating diseases like Huntington's chorea, this part of the judgment should be unproblematic: no one could want a loved one to suffer so.

There may be considerable disagreement, however, about whether a given probability is big or little. Individuals vary a good deal in their attitude toward this aspect of risk.[8] This suggests that it would be difficult to define the "right" attitude to a particular risk in many circumstances. Nevertheless, there are good grounds for arguing in favor of a conservative approach here. For it is reasonable to take special precautions to avoid very bad consequences, even if the risk is small. But the possible consequences here *are* very bad: a child who may inherit Huntington's chorea is a child with a much larger than average chance of being subjected to severe and prolonged suffering. Even if the child does not have the disease, it may anticipate and fear it, and anticipating an evil, as we all know, may be worse than experiencing it. In addition, if a parent loses the gamble, his child will suffer the consequences. But it is one thing to take a high risk for oneself; to submit someone else to it without his consent is another.

I think that these points indicate that the morality of procreation in situations like this demands further study. I propose to do this by looking first at the position of the possible child, then at that of the potential parent.[9]

III. REPRODUCTION: THE POSSIBLE CHILD'S POSITION

The first task in treating the problem from the child's point of view is to find a way of referring to possible future offspring without seeming to confer some sort of morally significant existence upon them. I will call children who might be born in the future but who are not now conceived "possible" children, offspring, individuals, or persons. I stipulate that this term implies nothing about their moral standing.

The second task is to decide what claims about children or possible children are relevant to the morality of childbearing in the circumstances being considered. There are, I think, two such claims. One is that we ought to provide every child with at least a normal opportunity for a good life. The other is that we do not harm possible children if we prevent them from existing. Let us consider both these matters in turn.

A. Opportunity for a Good Life

Accepting the claim that we ought to try to provide for every child a normal opportunity for a good life involves two basic problems: justification and practical application.

Justification of the claim could be derived fairly straightforwardly from either utilitarian or contractarian theories of justice, I think, although a proper discussion would be too lengthy to include here. Of prime importance in any such discussion would be the judgment that to neglect this duty would be to create unnecessary unhappiness or unfair disadvantage for some persons.

The attempt to apply the claim that we should try to provide a normal opportunity for a good life leads to a couple of difficulties. One is knowing what it requires of us. Another is defining "normal opportunity." Let us tackle the latter problem first.

Conceptions of "normal opportunity" vary among societies and also within them: *de rigueur* in some circles are private music lessons and trips to Europe, while in others providing eight years of schooling is a major sacrifice. But there is no need to consider this complication since we are here concerned only with health as a prerequisite for normal opportunity. Thus we can retreat to the more limited claim that every parent should try to ensure normal health for his child. It might be thought that even this moderate claim is unsatisfactory since in some places debilitating conditions are the norm. One could circumvent this objection by saying that parents ought to try to provide for their children health normal for that culture, even though it may be inadequate if measured by some outside standard. This conservative position would still justify efforts to avoid the birth of children at risk for Huntington's chorea and other serious genetic diseases.

But then what does this stand require of us: is sacrifice entailed by the duty to try to provide normal health for our children? The most plausible answer seems to be that as the danger of serious disability increases, the greater the sacrifice demanded of the potential parent. This means it would be more justifiable to recommend that an individual refrain from childbearing if he risks passing on spina bifida than if he risks passing on webbed feet. Working out all the details of such a schema would clearly be a difficult matter; I do not think it would be impossible to set up workable guidelines, though.

Assuming a rough theoretical framework of this sort, the next question we must ask is whether Huntington's chorea substantially impairs an individual's opportunity for a good life.

People appear to have different opinions about the plight of such persons. Optimists argue that a child born into a family afflicted with Huntington's chorea has a reasonable chance of living a satisfactory life. After all, there is a fifty percent chance it will escape the disease even if a parent has already manifested it, and a still greater chance if this is not so. Even if it does have the illness, it will probably enjoy thirty years of healthy life before symptoms appear; and, perhaps, it may not find the disease destructive. Optimists can list diseased or handicapped persons who have lived fruitful lives. They can also find

individuals who seem genuinely glad to be alive. One is Rick Donohue, a sufferer from the Joseph family disease: "You know, if my mom hadn't had me, I wouldn't be here for the life I have had. So there is a good possibility I will have children."[10] Optimists therefore conclude that it would be a shame if these persons had not lived.

Pessimists concede these truths, but they take a less sanguine view of them. They think a fifty percent risk of serious disease like Huntington's chorea appallingly high. They suspect that a child born into an afflicted family is liable to spend its youth in dreadful anticipation and fear of the disease. They expect that the disease, if it appears, will be perceived as a tragic and painful end to a blighted life. They point out that Rick Donohue is still young and has not yet experienced the full horror of his sickness.

Empirical research is clearly needed to resolve this dispute: we need much more information about the psychology and life history of sufferers and potential sufferers. Until we have it we cannot know whether the optimist or the pessimist has a better case; definitive judgment must therefore be suspended. In the meantime, however, common sense suggests that the pessimist has the edge.

If some diseased persons do turn out to have a worse than average life there appears to be a case against further childbearing in afflicted families. To support this claim two more judgments are necessary, however. The first is that it is not wrong to refrain from childbearing. The second is that asking individuals to so refrain is less of a sacrifice than might be thought.[11] I will examine each of these judgments.

B. The Morality of Preventing the Birth of Possible Persons

Before going on to look at reasons why it would not be wrong to prevent the birth of possible persons, let me try to clarify the picture a bit. To understand the claim it must be kept in mind that we are considering a prospective situation here, not a retrospective one: we are trying to rank the desirability of various alternative future states of affairs. One possible future state is this: a world where nobody is at risk for Huntington's chorea except as a result of random mutation. This state has been achieved by sons and daughters of persons afflicted with Huntington's chorea ceasing to reproduce. This means that an indeterminate number of children who might have been born were not born. These possible children can be divided into two categories: those who would have been miserable and those who would have lived good lives. To prevent the existence of members of the first category it was necessary to prevent the existence of all. Whether or not this is a good state of affairs depends on the morality of the means and the end. The end, preventing the existence of miserable beings, is surely good; I will argue that preventing the birth of possible persons is not intrinsically wrong. Hence this state of affairs is a morally good one.

Why then is it not in itself wrong to prevent the birth of possible persons? It is not wrong because there seems to be no reason to believe that possible individuals are either deprived or injured if they do not exist. They are not deprived because to be deprived in a morally significant sense one must be able to have experiences. But possible persons do not exist. Since they do not exist, they cannot have experiences. Another way to make this point is to say that each of us might not have been born, although most of us are glad we were. But this does not mean that it makes sense to say that we would have been deprived of something had we not been born. For if we had not been born, we would not exist, and there would be nobody to be deprived of anything. To assert the contrary is to imagine that we are looking at a world in which

we do not exist. But this is not the way it would be: there would be nobody to look.

The contention that it is wrong to prevent possible persons from existing because they have a right to exist appears to be equally baseless. The most fundamental objection to this view is that there is no reason to ascribe rights to entities which do not exist. It is one thing to say that as-yet-nonexistent persons will have certain rights if and when they exist: this claim is plausible if made with an eye toward preserving social and environmental goods.[12] But what justification could there be for the claim that nonexistent beings have a right to exist?

Even if one conceded that there was a presumption in favor of letting some nonexistent beings exist, stronger claims could surely override it.[13] For one thing, it would be unfair not to recognize the prior claim of already existing children who are not being properly cared for. One might also argue that it is simply wrong to prevent persons who might have existed from doing so. But this implies that contraception and population control are also wrong.

It is therefore reasonable to maintain that because possible persons have no right to exist, they are not injured if not created. Even if they had that right, it could rather easily be overridden by counterclaims. Hence, since possible persons are neither deprived nor injured if not conceived, it is not wrong to prevent their existence.

C. Conclusion of Part III

At the beginning of Part III I said that two claims are relevant to the morality of childbearing in the circumstances being considered. The first is that we ought to provide every child with at least a normal opportunity for a good life. The second is that we do not deprive or injure possible persons if we prevent their existence.

I suggested that the first claim could be derived from currently accepted theories of justice: a healthy body is generally necessary for happiness and it is also a prerequisite for a fair chance at a good life in our competitive world. Thus it is right to try to ensure that each child is healthy.

I argued, with regard to the second claim, that we do not deprive or injure possible persons if we fail to create them. They cannot be deprived of anything because they do not exist and hence cannot have experiences. They cannot be injured because only an entity with a right to exist could be injured if prevented from existing; but there are no good grounds for believing that they are such entities.

From the conjunction of these two claims I conclude that it is right to try to ensure that a child is healthy even if by doing so we preclude the existence of certain possible persons. Thus it is right for individuals to prevent the birth of children at risk for Huntington's chorea by avoiding parenthood. The next question is whether it is seriously wrong *not* to avoid parenthood.

IV. REPRODUCTION: THE POTENTIAL PARENT'S SITUATION

I have so far argued that if choreics live substantially worse lives than average, then it is right for afflicted families to cease reproduction. But this conflicts with the generally recognized freedom to procreate and so it does not automatically follow that family members ought not to have children. How can we decide whether the duty to try to provide normal health for one's child should take precedence over the right to reproduce?

This is essentially the same question I asked earlier: how much must one sacrifice to try to ensure that one's offspring is healthy? In answer to this I suggested that

the greater the danger of serious disability, the more justifiable considerable sacrifice is.

Now asking someone who wants a child to refrain from procreation seems to be asking for a large sacrifice. It may, in fact, appear to be too large to demand of anyone. Yet I think it can be shown that it is not as great as it initially seems.

Why do people want children? There are probably many reasons, but I suspect that the following include some of the most common. One set of reasons has to do with the gratification to be derived from a happy family life — love, companionship, watching a child grow, helping mold it into a good person, sharing its pains and triumphs. Another set of reasons centers about the parents as individuals — validation of their place within a genetically continuous family line, the conception of children as a source of immortality, being surrounded by replicas of themselves.

Are there alternative ways of satisfying these desires? Adoption or technological means provide ways to satisfy most of the desires pertaining to family life without passing on specific genetic defects. Artificial insemination by donor is already available; implantation of donor ova is likely within a few years. Still another option will exist if cloning becomes a reality. In the meantime, we might permit women to conceive and bear babies for those who do not want to do so themselves.[14] But the desire to extend the genetic line, the desire for immortality, and the desire for children that physically resemble one cannot be met by these methods.

Many individuals probably feel these latter desires strongly. This creates a genuine conflict for persons at risk for transmitting serious genetic diseases like Huntington's chorea. The situation seems especially unfair because, unlike normal people, through no fault of their own, doing something they badly want to do may greatly harm others.

But if my common sense assumption that they are in grave danger of harming others is true, then it is imperative to scrutinize their options carefully. On the one hand, they can have children: they satisfy their desires but risk eventual crippling illness and death for their offspring. On the other, they can remain childless or seek nonstandard ways of creating a family: they have some unfulfilled desires, but they avoid risking harm to their children.

I think it is clear which of these two alternatives is best. For the desires which must remain unsatisfied if they forgo normal procreation are less than admirable. To see the genetic line continued entails a sinister legacy of illness and death; the desire for immortality cannot really be satisfied by reproduction anyway; and the desire for children that physically resemble one is narcissistic and its fulfillment cannot be guaranteed even by normal reproduction. Hence the only defence of these desires is that people do in fact feel them.

Now, I am inclined to accept William James' dictum regarding desires: "Take any demand, however slight, which any creature, however weak, may make. Ought it not, for its own sole sake be satisfied? If not, prove why not."[15] Thus I judge a world where more desires are satisfied to be better than one in which fewer are. But not all desires should be regarded as legitimate, since, as James suggests, there may be good reasons why these ought to be disregarded. The fact that their fulfillment will seriously harm others is surely such a reason. And I believe that the circumstances I have described are a clear example of the sort of case where a desire must be judged illegitimate, at least until it can be shown that sufferers from serious genetic diseases like Huntington's chorea do not live considerably worse than average lives. Therefore, I think it is wrong for individuals in this predicament to reproduce.

V. CONCLUSION

Let me recapitulate. At the beginning of this paper I asked whether it is wrong for those who risk transmitting severe genetic disease like Huntington's chorea to have "blood" children. Some despair of reaching an answer to this question.[16] But I think such pessimism is not wholly warranted, and that if generally accepted would lead to much unnecessary harm. It is true that in many cases it is difficult to know what ought to be done. But this does not mean that we should throw up our hands and espouse a completely laissez-faire approach: philosophers can help by probing the central issues and trying to find guidelines for action.

Naturally there is no way to derive an answer to this kind of problem by deductive argument from self-evident premises, for it must depend on a complicated interplay of facts and moral judgments. My preliminary exploration of Huntington's chorea is of this nature. In the course of the discussion I suggested that, if it is true that sufferers live substantially worse lives than do normal persons, those who might transmit it should not have children. This conclusion is supported by the judgments that we ought to try to provide for every child a normal opportunity for a good life, that possible individuals are not harmed if not conceived, and that it is sometimes less justifiable for persons to exercise their right to procreate than one might think.

I want to stress, in conclusion, that my argument is incomplete. To investigate fully even a single disease, like Huntington's chorea, empirical research on the lives of members of afflicted families is necessary. Then, after developing further the themes touched upon here, evaluation of the probable consequences of different policies on society and on future generations is needed. Until the results of a complete study are available, my argument could serve best as a reason for persons at risk for transmitting Huntington's chorea and similar diseases to put off having children. Perhaps this paper will stimulate such inquiry.

NOTES

1. There are a series of cases ranging from low risk of mild disease or handicap to high risk of serious disease or handicap. It would be difficult to decide where the duty to refrain from procreation becomes compelling. My point here is that there are some clear cases.

    I'd like to thank Lawrence Davis and Sidney Siskin for their helpful comments on an earlier version of this paper.

2. This issue is one which must be faced most urgently by genetic counselors. The proper role of the genetic counselor with regard to such decisions has been the subject of much debate. The dominant view seems to be that espoused by Lytt Gardner who maintains that it is unethical for a counselor to make ethical judgments about what his clients ought to do. ("Counseling in Genetics," *Early Diagnosis of Human Genetic Defects: Scientific & Ethical Considerations,* ed. Maureen Harris [H.E.W. Publication No. (NIH) 72-25; Fogarty Center Proceedings No. 6]; 192.) Typically this view is unsupported by an argument. For other views see Bentley Glass "Human Heredity and Ethical Problems," *Perspectives in Biology & Medicine,* Vol. 15 (winter '72) 237-53, esp. 242-52; Marc Lappé, "The Genetic Counselor Responsible to Whom?" *Hastings Center Report,* Vol. 1, No. 2 (Sept. '71) 6-8; E. C. Fraser, "Genetic Counseling" *Am. J. of Human Genetics* 26: 636-659, 1974.

3. I have chosen Huntington's chorea because it seems to me to be one of the clearest cases of high risk serious genetic disease known to the public, despite the fact that it does not usually manifest itself until the prime of life. The latter entails two further facts. First an individual of reproductive age may not know whether he has the disease; he therefore does not know the risk of passing on the disease. Secondly, an affected person may have a substantial number of years of healthy life before it shows itself. I do not think that this factor materially changes my case, however. Even if an individual does not in fact risk passing the disease to his children, *he cannot know that this is true.* And even thirty years of healthy life may well be seriously shadowed by anticipation and fear of the disease. Thus the fact that the disease develops late does not diminish its horror. If it could be shown that these factors could be adequately circumvented, my claim that there is a *class* of genetic disease of such severity that it would be wrong to risk passing them on would not be undermined.

    It might also be thought that Huntington's chorea is insufficiently common to merit such attention. But, depending on reproductive patterns, the disease could become a good deal more widespread. Consider the fact that in 1916 nine hundred and sixty-two cases could be traced from six seventeenth-century arrivals in America. (Gordon Rattray Taylor, *The Biological Time Bomb* [New York, 1968], 176.) But more importantly, even if the disease did not spread, it would still be seriously wrong, I think, to inflict it unnecessarily on *any* members of new generations. Finally, it should be kept in mind that I am using Huntington's chorea as an example of the sort of disease we should try to eradicate. Thus the arguments presented here would be relevant to a wide range of genetic diseases.

4. *The Merck Manual* (Rahway, N.J.: Merck, 1972), 1346.

5. Hymie Gordon, "Genetic Counseling," *JAMA,* Vol. 217 No. 9 (August 30, 1971), 1217.

6. Charles Smith, Susan Holloway, and Alan E. H. Emery, "Individuals at Risk in Families — Genetic Disease," *J. of Medical Genetics,* 8 (1971), 453. See also Townes in *Genetic Counseling* ed. Daniel Bergsma, *Birth Defects Original Article Series,* Vol. VI, No. 1 (May 1970).

7. J. H. Pearn, "Patients' Subjective Interpretation of Risks Offered in Genetic Counseling," *Journal of Medical Genetics,* 10 (1973) 131.

8. Ibid., 132.

9. There are many important and interesting points that might be raised with respect to future generations and present society. There is no space to deal with them here, although I strongly suspect that conclusions regarding them would support my judgment that it is wrong for those who risk transmitting certain diseases to reproduce — for some discussion of future generations, see Gerald Leach, *The Biocrats* (Middlesex, England: Penguin Books, 1972), 150; M. P. Golding, "Obligations to Future Generations," *Monist* 56 (Jan. 1972) 84-99; Gordon Rattray Taylor, *The Biological Time Bomb* (New York, 1968), esp. 176. For some discussions of society, see Daniel Callahan, "The Meaning and Significance of Genetic Disease: Philosophical Perspectives," *Ethical Issues in Human Genetics,* ed. Bruce Hilton et al. (New York, 1973), 87 ff.; John Fletcher, "The Brink: The Parent-Child Bond in the Genetic Revolution," *Theological Studies* 33 (Sept. '72) 457-485; Glass (supra 2ᵃ); Marc Lappé, "Human Genetics," Annals of the *New York Academy of Sciences,* Vol. 26 (May 18, 1973) 152-59; Marc Lappé, "Moral Obligations and the Fallacies of 'Genetic Control,'" *Theological Studies* Vol. 33, No. 3 (Sept. '72) 411-427; Martin P. Golding, "Ethical Issues in Biological Engineering," *UCLA Law Review* Vol. 15: 267 (1968) 443-479; L. C. Dunn, *Heredity and Evolution in Human Populations* (Cambridge, Mass., 1959), 145; Robert S. Morison in *Ethical Issues in Human Genetics,* ed. Bruce Hilton et. al. (New York, 1973), 208.

10. *The New York Times,* September 30, 1975, p. 1. col. 6. The Joseph family disease is similar to Huntington's chorea except that symptoms start appearing in the twenties. Rick Donohue is in his early twenties.

11. There may be a price for the individuals who refrain from having children. We will be looking at the situation from their point of view shortly.

12. This is in fact the basis for certain parental duties. An example is the maternal duty to obtain proper nutrition before and during pregnancy, for this is necessary if the child is to have normal health when it is born.

13. One might argue that as many persons as possible should exist so that they may enjoy life.

14. Some thinkers have qualms about the use of some or all of these methods. They have so far failed to show why they are immoral, although, naturally, much

careful study will be required before they could be unqualifiedly recommended. See, for example, Richard Hull, "Genetic Engineering: Comment on Headings," *The Humanist,* Vol. 32 (Sept./Oct. 1972), 13.

15. *Essays in Pragmatism,* ed. A. Castell (New York, 1948), 73.

16. For example, see Leach, 138. One of the ways the dilemma described by Leach could be lessened would be if society emphasized those aspects of family life not dependent on "blood" relationships and downplayed those that are.

FURTHER READINGS

Adams, J. "Confidentiality and Huntington's Chorea." *Journal of Medical Ethics* 16:4 (1990) 196-99.

Annas, George. "Righting the Wrong of 'Wrongful Life.' " *Hastings Center Report* 11: 1 (Feb. 1981).

Bayles, Michael D. "Harm to the Unconceived." *Philosophy and Public Affairs* 5:3 (1976).

Benkendorf, J., and K. Fitzgerald. "Genetic Counselling for Addicted Obstetric Patients." *Journal of Clinical Ethics* 1:2 (1990) 156-57.

Bergsma, D., ed. *Ethical, Social and Legal Dimensions of Screening for Human Genetic Disease.* Birth Defect Series, vol. 10. New York: Stratton-Intercontinental.

Brown, J. "Prenatal Screening in Jewish Law." *Journal of Medical Ethics* 16:2 (1990) 75-80.

Chadwick, D., et al., eds. *Human Genetic Information: Science, Law, Ethics.* New York: Wiley, 1990.

Clark, J.T.R. "Screening for Carriers of Tay-Sachs Disease: Two Approaches." *Canadian Medical Association Journal,* 119 (1978), 450.

Fletcher, J., et al. "The Price of Silence." *Hastings Center Report* 20:3 (1990) 31-35.

Goodman, M.J., and L.E. Goodman. "The Overselling of Genetic Anxiety." *Hastings Center Report* 12:5 (1982) 20-27.

Hicks, E.K. and J.M. Berg, eds. *The Genetics of Mental Retardation: Biomedical, Psychosocial and Ethical Issues.* Boston: Kluwer, 1988.

Kenen, R.H. and R.M. Schmidt. "Stigmatization of Carrier Status: Social Implications of Heterozygote Genetic Screening Programs." *American Journal of Public Health,* 68 (1978), 116-120.

Knoppers, B.M. *Human Dignity and Genetic Heritage.* Study Paper for the Law Reform Commission of Canada. Ottawa: Law Reform Commission of Canada, 1991.

Murray, R.F. "Problems Behind the Promise: Ethical Issues in Mass Genetic Screening." *Hastings Center Report* 2 (April 1979), 46-7.

Nelkin, D. and L. Tancredi. *Dangerous Diagnostics: The Social Power of Biological Information.* New York: Basic Books, 1989.

Overall, C. *Ethics and Human Reproduction: A Feminist Analysis.* Boston: Allen and Unwin, 1987.

Powledge, Tabitha, and Joseph Fletcher. "Guidelines for the Ethical, Social, and Legal Issues in Prenatal Diagnosis." *New England Journal of Medicine* 300: 4 (1979) 168-172.

CHAPTER 18
GENETIC ENGINEERING

INTRODUCTION

In the eyes of many people, the ultimate aim of developing genetics is not merely to be able to tell whether we carry deleterious genes, but to "fix" these genes. This fixing is usually called genetic engineering. It involves excising the relevant sections from the genes of a particular person and replacing them with appropriate others. The technology already exists; the question is, should we do it?

Not surprisingly, there are several reactions. One is entirely negative: we should leave well enough alone, because we cannot foresee the ultimate consequences, or because we would be "playing God," etc.

Another approach is cautious acceptance, but only for defects that are coded on a single gene and that can be corrected by a simple substitution — and above all, only if this substitution occurs in somatic cells: cells that are not involved in human reproduction. In that way, the defect would be corrected in the individual who is affected, but the corrected trait would not be passed on.

Still another view is that not only this sort of limited somatic-cell manipulation should be permitted, but also research on reproductive, or germ line, cells. The reason is that genetic manipulation is a mode of therapy, and therefore should be developed like all others: cautiously, but developed nevertheless. Not to do this would be to deprive those who will be seriously affected by defective genes of something that could have prevented their suffering.

The selection from the Medical Research Council of Canada reflects current Canadian thinking in this area, from the standpoint of a regulatory body. It is narrowly focused on somatic-cell gene therapy.

The second selection, taken from the Royal Commission on New Reproductive Technologies' final report to Parliament, entitled *Proceed With Care*, presents the

500

view that was recommended by the Commission as the basis of legislation in this extemely important and sensitive area. It should perhaps be noted that neither the position of the Medical Research Council nor that advocated by the Royal Commission is entirely uncontroversial. In particular, the position adopted by the Royal Commission has been criticized by some. They have argued that germ-line genetic therapy should not be banned in the case of single locus diseases—diseases that are caused by a flaw in a single place of the genetic code. Not only is such a ban said to be economically inefficient since the flaw would have to be corrected every single time someone inherits the disease, but the reasons which supposedly justify a ban on multi-locus therapy do not apply in this case: There will be no unforeseen consequences as a result of interfering with the genetic heritage because only a single, precisely identifiable flaw is corrected. It might be interesting to investigate how the Commission's position can be defended against this response. In this connection, a draft of a universal declaration on the human genome and human rights, which was adopted on 25 July 1997 by the United Nations Educational, Scientific and Cultural Organization, states in Article 5 that "Research, treatment or diagnosis affecting an individual's genome shall be undertaken only after rigorous and prior assessment of the potential risks and benefits pertaining thereto and in accordance with any other requirement of national law." Is this at variance with the Royal Commission's proposed ban on germ-line therapy? If so, who is right?

Guidelines for Research on Somatic Cell Gene Therapy in Humans

Medical Research Council of Canada

2. ETHICAL ISSUES

A physician should only undertake therapy outside standard medical practice when the outlook for the patient otherwise is dismal, and when the scientific team and the physician are able to master all the aspects of the proposed therapy. Research on somatic cell gene therapy demands a team of highly specialized scientists, preferably including the patient's physician. Since many of the questions and concerns in this complex new area demand research, the Working Group believes that the use of gene transfer techniques in humans should be viewed as research at this time, and that any proposal to use gene transfer techniques in a human subject be considered for ethical acceptability as a research proposal before being implemented.

Medical Research Council of Canada, *Guidelines for Research on Somatic Cell Gene Therapy in Humans*, Chapter 2, "Ethical Issues" (Ottawa: Minister of Supply and Services, 1990), 24-33.

Change to the genome of treated individuals has implications that need to be carefully weighed and there is a clear need for the information obtained to be scientifically valid. It is therefore the view of the Committee that all gene transfer techniques used in human subjects fall within the context of clinical research, and thus require approval of the Research Ethics Board (REB) as defined in the *MRC Guidelines on Research Involving Human Subjects* (1987).

The Committee also hopes that provincial Colleges of Physicians and Surgeons and other local levels of medical authority will take the same view if approached by physicians who wish to treat desperately ill patients under the rubric of innovative therapy.

2.2.1 Background

While it is true that some genetic diseases do not express themselves to the same degree and at the same age in each individual, the diseases which meet the criteria for suitable candidates for research on somatic cell gene therapy afflict patients in very similar ways. The damage caused is often progressive, cumulative, and fatal at an early age. This leads to a dilemma. On the one hand it seems appropriate to treat individuals as soon as they have been diagnosed to maximize the potential for therapeutic benefit if gene transfer is successful; the risks of performing gene transfer will not be reduced by waiting, and delay will almost certainly cause greater harm to the patients through irreversible accumulation of the effects of the disease. On the other hand, the younger the subjects, the less able they are to consent. A basic principle of the ethics of research is that competent subjects should be chosen if possible; however, patients with some candidate genetic diseases do not attain the age of consent, or even meaningful assent.

2.2.2 The Elements of Informed Consent

It is a fundamental principle that human beings can only be involved as research subjects if they have freely consented after fully understanding the research to be undertaken and their role in that research. This principle and the difficulties of implementing it when the patient is a child are fully described in the 1987 MRC Guidelines. Briefly, and at the very least, a potential research subject, or the person (proxy) who is to give consent on behalf of the subject, must understand:

(i) the reason(s) he or she has been selected to participate in the proposed study;

(ii) the nature and objective(s) of the research;

(iii) the harms and benefits associated with participating or refusing to participate in the research;

(iv) the available alternatives and the harms and benefits associated with these;

(v) the probability that any of the potential harms or benefits will manifest themselves;

(vi) the qualifications/experience of the researcher(s) involved; and

(vii) that the consent to participate can be withdrawn at any time with no adverse effects to ongoing medical care.

2.2.3 Consent with Special Populations

a) Research Involving Children

The elements of informed consent by the subject outlined above may not be completely met in the case of research on gene therapy, for several reasons. First, the most suitable candidate diseases are usually lethal, or cause mental retardation, at an early age; proxy consent is therefore essential. Since clinical trials on severe early onset disease necessarily involve very young children, there is an ethical dilemma; restricting research on gene therapy to those subjects able to consent will exclude the most severely affected patients in whom there is early onset of the disease and rapid deterioration. These have been identified above as probably the most suitable candidates. The greatest potential benefit of research on gene therapy is before deterioration is irrevocable. However, these are the subjects least able to consent for themselves. The Working Group is very conscious of the problem this dilemma poses. Within the context of research, it is clear that there is the potential of gaining the most knowledge in these diseases if trials are carried out on the earliest diagnosed patients even though these are just the individuals who are least able to give consent or even assent. The potential benefit to the individual child is also greatest before irreparable damage from the disease has occurred.

A unique aspect of research on human gene therapy concerns the option of withdrawing. The insertion of genetically modified cells cannot be undone; the gene transfer is irrevocable, so for some aspects a consent cannot be withdrawn. Further, long-term monitoring is important to assess potential harm to the patient or to third parties. By withdrawing, the patient will not only lose the benefit from early recognition of harms to himself which might only manifest themselves later on, but will also deny any future subjects the benefits of the information to be derived from long-term monitoring for harmful effects, and will make it difficult to assess the hazards to the community.

While the rights of the individual prohibit enforced compliance, it seems appropriate that, at the least, the prospective research subject, or the person giving a proxy consent, understand the potential long-term risks prior to consenting to increase compliance after the initial intervention. Proxies must understand that they may not have the right to withdraw a child from those portions of a protocol to which they have committed the child and which are therapeutically indicated. The situation could then be subject to the common law duties of a parent to provide medical necessities to the child. If remaining in the trial is in an incompetent subject's best interest, then this might be upheld in court. Since there are possible harms to others, it is appropriate to persuade the subjects to continue in long-term follow-up. In the absence of settled law on this point, what would happen if a person nevertheless withdraws is open to question. In cases where there is possible harm to others, public policy might well overcome the individual's right to withdraw.

Full disclosure of risks is required for the subject to provide a valid informed consent to research. The risk of a harm should not only be quantified as accurately as possible but the harm itself described; the patient's or proxy's perceptions of potential harms may differ markedly from those of the physician, and a high risk of trivial harm may be acceptable, whereas a low risk of a very serious harm may not.

As children cannot provide a legally or ethically valid consent to research, consent must be sought from the parents or guardians. The decision by a parent or guardian to permit a child to participate in research on somatic cell gene therapy must be based on the same information which would be given to competent prospective research subjects. Because the proposed genetic intervention may be the child's last hope, parents and guardians may be willing to ignore the risks and to focus instead on the possible good; they may therefore be too eager to consent to their child's participation in the research. Their hope must be tempered by an adequate understanding of the risks involved. Feelings of guilt about transmitting a genetic disease may influence some parents to downgrade the risks of gene transfer. On the other hand some parents may inadvertently become over-protective and thus over-rate the risks. Provision should therefore be made in the protocol to ensure the availability of in-depth counselling to ensure full understanding by the subject or legal guardian of what is proposed in the protocol.

Though parental consent is necessary for research on children, it is not binding. A child may express a desire not to participate and this expressed wish should be respected. The *MRC Guidelines on Research Involving Human Subjects* stipulate that "parental consent may be a necessary condition of engaging the child in research, but it is not necessarily a sufficient condition; the child's negative preferences in such cases should be respected" (p. 29). Given this, children should be encouraged to participate in the consent process to the extent to which they are capable. Unfortunately, this proviso may not be relevant to the children suffering from diseases suitable for research. For example, research with possible therapeutic benefit for ADA deficiency must be started with infants or young children; the severe mental retardation often present in those patients with recessive diseases who will be candidates for gene transfer may make it impossible for the child to register either assent or dissent. In addition, some provinces have particular rules with regard to the consent process regarding adolescents and minors.

b) *Research Involving Human Fetuses*

In the future, if somatic cell gene therapy is shown to be effective and safe, it may become an appropriate strategy for diseases which result in irreversible damage by the time of birth. In this situation, the proposed genetic intervention would have to take place early enough to benefit the patient, but late enough to ensure that the germ cells would not be affected (i.e. the gonads had already fully formed.)

In the view of this Working Group, research in somatic cell gene therapy for the conceptus *in utero* should not be done at this time; it would be irresponsible to incur the added risks to the mother involved in prenatal therapy without convincing evidence that somatic cell gene transfer can be effective in individuals after birth.

The 1987 *MRC Guidelines on Research Involving Human Subjects* clearly stipulate that the foreseen benefits must outweigh the foreseen risks in order for any research proposal to be approved. Accordingly, the probable safety and effectiveness of a proposed research project will have to be carefully evaluated with particular attention given to the potential risks for both the individual and society at large before approval is given. This is a difficult area in which to make judgments, as not only do risks and benefits to an individual and to society have to be weighed, but the balances of benefits to society and risks to individuals, and vice versa, need consideration.

2.3.1 Risks for the Individual

Gene transfer using somatic cells, in humans, though potentially beneficial, has important potential risks:

— Viral vectors used to deliver the gene of interest to the host cells may recombine with undetected viruses and regain their infectious properties or perhaps affect endogenous DNA sequences and produce malignancy. Thus, information addressing these risks is needed. The risk of malignancy as a result of treatment is not confined to this new approach; it also is a consideration in radiation therapy for cancer, immunosuppressive therapy used in transplantation, and the use of drugs with the risk of causing cancer, such as the antibiotic chloramphenicol.

— There is the possibility that a functioning host gene may be interrupted by the random integration of a foreign DNA sequence, and thus have negative consequences for the patient.

— The presence of bacterial contaminants in the DNA inserted into the patient's cells could cause unwanted side effects.

— The use of strategies designed to help the engineered cells establish themselves in the patient may have hazards which will need to be considered in the assessment of risks.

— There is a possibility that the inserted gene might inadvertently become transferred to their germ cells and might affect their offspring in an unanticipated way.

— If insufficient gene product is produced by the genetically modified cells, the genetic disorder may be only partially corrected so that the lethal genetic disease could be converted to one where the individual survives but suffers greatly.

2.3.2 Risks for Society

The risk of viral vectors again becoming infectious during somatic cell gene transfer must also be considered from a community perspective. These viruses might then be transmitted inadvertently to persons with whom the patient is in contact, for example, relatives, friends or health care personnel.

The possible impact on the composition of the human gene pool must also be considered. If individuals with rare lethal genetic disorders are successfully treated by means of somatic cell gene transfer, they may choose to reproduce. As discussed in the previous chapter, this would increase the number of abnormal genes in the gene pool since they may pass on the abnormal genes to their progeny. However, as noted, since human gene transfer is likely to focus on recessive disorders, the population impact would be extremely small. It could also be argued that any medical treatment of genetic disorders, including prenatal diagnosis, has some impact on the human gene pool. In fact, somatic cell transfer could be expected to have less of an impact on the gene pool than many other medical interventions.

The most serious risk for society concerns the possibility that the new genetic information will inadvertently be transferred from somatic to germ cells, and thus to the next generation. In the short term this could mean that an individual's offspring would be adversely affected by some unintended mutation. In the long term, the consequences are unknown. The impact is likely to be very small since only children of the small number of treated individuals could contribute to the gene pool. The human gene pool could be altered but the increase judged in the context of the total numbers of mutations that are constantly occurring would be infinitesimal. It is not appropriate to approve any protocol where the germ line is foreseen to be altered, even though this is not the primary intention of transfer.

2.3.3 Minimization of Risk — Maximization of Benefit

a) Safety and Efficacy

Before a proposed trial for somatic cell gene transfer involving humans is approved, the likelihood of benefit to the research subject must be well documented. This means that both the safety and the efficacy of the proposed genetic intervention must have been carefully assessed. The proposal should show that cells with the transferred gene have obtained and are capable of producing an active gene product. Data with regard to efficiency and appropriate expression in target cells *in vitro* and *in vivo* are needed. Whenever possible, a human gene should be used. However, in some circumstances it may be acceptable to propose a non-human DNA sequence for transfer. As noted under 3.3.2, if this is the case, then the reasons why a human gene is not appropriate should be clearly documented. In this case it is important to remember that the objective is therapy to return toward normal function.

Both technical and animal data must be provided showing that every possible precaution has been taken to assess and to minimize the risks. For example, to reduce the risk of infection and/or malignancy, all vectors used must have been shown to have been disabled so that they cannot replicate themselves. Information regarding the risk of unintended transfer of the vector to the germ line must be available.

b) Animal Models

Ideally, the safety of any proposed research protocol involving humans should be assessed on the basis of animal trials designed to study both the short-term and long-term impact. One important study will be to assess the risk of infection and malignancy by assessing whether the foreign DNA remains and functions in the host cells without harming them or other cells; another will be to observe treated laboratory animals throughout their life span to address the risk of cancer; it will also be important to study the offspring of these research animals to determine possible effects on subsequent generations and if there has been any transfer to germ cells. However, safety demonstrated in studies on

animals does not guarantee lack of harm when used in humans. Ideally these trials should be conducted not only on mice and other small animals but also on primates, from which the findings may be more relevant when extrapolated to humans. There should be demonstration of correction of the disease if appropriate animal models exist.

There are no known animal models for the enzyme deficiency diseases which are likely to be early candidates for trials of somatic cell gene transfer in humans. For example, mice carrying the gene defect responsible for Lesch-Nyhan syndrome seem to function quite normally. Consequently, the potential for success may have to be assessed as far as possible on the basis of tissue cultures and research with animals. For other genetic disorders, however, it may be possible to assess efficacy on the basis of animal trials. As a minimum requirement prior to clinical studies, research with animals would have to show that:

1) new curative genes can be directed to specific cells and remain there long enough to be effective;

2) the inserted genes can express their product in the target cells at an appropriate level; and

3) no harm results to the treated cells, to the test animal or to its offspring.

Researchers should therefore provide the Research Ethics Board (REB) with detailed information about the precautions taken to minimize the various risks, and provide animal and cellular data relevant to whether the proposed research would benefit the patient.

c) Selection of Candidate Genetic Diseases

Obviously, research involving human subjects should only be undertaken if the anticipated benefits are expected to outweigh the possible harms. This means that initial trials for somatic cell gene transfer should only be considered for persons afflicted with serious genetic disorders (i.e. severely debilitating and/or rapidly lethal diseases) for whom there is no effective conventional treatment. Only if the burden imposed by the inherited disease on the afflicted individual is great and no satisfactory therapy is available, or the available therapy entails greater risks and less benefits, might clinical trials for somatic cell gene transfer be justified. There should be demonstration of accessible and appropriate target cells and of the possibility of amelioration if a functioning gene could be inserted into these cells. If the clinical trials for devastating diseases prove to be effective and safe, then research on somatic cell gene therapy might be considered in the future for less burdensome diseases such as haemophilia or PKU for which there are alternative treatments. It is clear that in the foreseeable future, research on somatic cell gene therapy should be limited to serious and untreatable genetic disorders for which there is no effective alternative treatment.

d) Selection of Research Subjects

The selection of research subjects must take into consideration the numbers of individuals to be treated in the first trials, and whether treatment should be restricted initially to one candidate disease. Experience has shown that it is very rarely possible to predict the success or failure of a new therapy on the basis of one or two cases. Beneficial approaches might not succeed in the first few subjects, or might even show harm; conversely an actually unacceptable method may be highly successful in its first few attempts. The arguments are essentially statistical; throwing heads three times in a row does not allow the prediction that the next 97 times will also be heads. For such rea-

sons, a decision to start research on gene transfer in patients must recognize the intent in principle to treat a number of individuals, even though there can be no doubt that each patient must be studied very carefully to discover unexpected outcomes or to apply what can be learned from this experience to the next patient.

It has also been suggested that studies should be undertaken initially only on treatment for one genetic disease meeting the criteria outlined above. The Working Group rejects this view with one opinion to the contrary. Most committee members felt that, because these diseases are different, the genes added to human somatic cells to treat different diseases cannot be expected to behave in similar ways. However, experience with one means of therapy may provide useful information about risks associated, for example, with the method of inserting the new gene into the cells, and this information should be taken into consideration in later decisions.

One member believes it is contradictory to say that important information about risks of gene insertion can be learned from an experiment about one disease and applied to other diseases, while saying that each study protocol should be treated independently of protocols on other diseases. In that member's view, ethical requirements that the risks of research be minimized and scientific value and validity be maximized require that, in the initial stages of somatic cell genetic manipulation in humans, the early results of each approved protocol be reviewed and analyzed by an independent team before any further protocols are approved.

Since the genetic diseases for which research on somatic cell gene therapy may be suggested are rare (1/15,000-1/100,000) it is possible that research groups may be in competition to attract prospective subjects to their particular research centre. Alternatively, since centres trying the new methods are also likely to be few, it is possible that there will be more affected individuals than can properly be incorporated into trials of a new therapy. Hence, equitable criteria for selecting research subjects are important.

In summary, the selecting criteria should be clearly documented and submitted to the REB for approval.

e) Selection of Genetic Sequence

The Working Group is of the opinion that the DNA sequence to be transferred should preferably be of human origin. The ethical concern regarding a non-human sequence arises with respect to those sequences designed to be integrated as a functional portion of the subject's genome, the so-called 'target gene', or 'gene of interest', as opposed to those sequences, commonly derived from viruses, employed as a delivery system into the genome. The use of permanently functioning non-human genetic sequence in somatic cell manipulation differs from other therapeutic uses of non-human materials, (e.g. animal-derived insulin) in its irreversible alteration of the subject at the most fundamental genetic level. Most important, while the restriction of gene alteration to normal human sequences would confine such manipulation to therapeutic use, allowing the insertion of a non-human sequence would blur the crucial ethical distinction between ther-

apy and enhancement. Therefore, the review body should apply an enhanced requirement of scientific justification to protocols intending the insertion of a non-human genetic sequence as the functional target gene. However, circumstances can be envisaged under which it may be appropriate to approve research protocols in which the gene to be transferred is from a non-human source. It might be desirable, for example, to use additional bacterial DNA sequences that would convey resistance to certain drugs and hence facilitate selection of cells in which gene transfer has occurred. Also expression of transferred genes might require, or be better controlled by, use of non-human regulatory sequences. If a non-human sequence is to be used, the reasons why this is proposed and why human sequence is not as likely to be of benefit must be fully documented, and the above concerns taken into consideration.

f) Long-Term Monitoring

With this research, there is a potential for harm to third parties, to the subjects themselves after many years (e.g. late development of cancer), and to the offspring of the subject. The proposal should address the issue of long-term monitoring of the research subjects and the outcome of their reproduction. Details on how long monitoring will be carried out, how adverse outcome will be evaluated and what strategies will be followed to handle it should be given.

Regulating Germ-Line Genetic Alteration

Royal Commission on New Reproductive Technologies

It is clear that germ-line genetic alteration is inconsistent with the Commission's guiding principles. There are many risks and potential harms, without any clear benefit to any individual. It is not an appropriate use of resources, and it jeopardizes, rather than protects, those who are vulnerable. Since any foreseeable germ-line genetic alteration would involve embryo research, it would be covered by the legislative and licensing mechanisms we propose in Chapter 22. However, we believe it is important to emphasize the unacceptability of germ-line genetic alteration by including it in the licensing conditions for fertility clinics, which in practice would be the source of human zygotes (or eggs) in Canada. The Commission recommends that

269. No research involving human zygotes be permitted or funded in Canada. This prohibition would be monitored and enforced by the Embryo Research Sub-Committee of the National Reproductive Technologies Commission.

and that

270. The Prenatal Diagnosis and Genetics Sub-Committee of the National Reproductive Technologies Commission have as part of its guidelines for centres licensed to provide PND and genetics services that no genetic alteration of a human zygote be permitted.

NON-THERAPEUTIC GENETIC ALTERATION

[The Commission identifies three major kinds of risks associated with so-called "genetic enhancement": social risks, which centre on treating humans as objects, discrimination against certain types of people, inequitable access to the technology and unclarity of the aims of using such a technology; medical risks, such as disrupting a tumor suppressor or activating a cancer gene; and opportunity costs, which means that the technology would take resources away from "real medical problems." The Commission then continues:]

It is extremely doubtful that any use of this technology for individual enhancement would ever be proposed by a genetics centre; but, if this ever did occur, the National Reproductive Technologies Commission would be able to turn down any such proposal.

It is important to remain vigilant about the possible misuse of technology that can change DNA, and it is important for the general public to become more aware of the issues it raises. Although these areas are outside our mandate, and the uses of genetic technology in general (for example, to "improve" individuals) are outside the span of new reproductive technologies and the

Proceed With Care: Final Report of the Royal Commission on New Reproductive Technologies (Ottawa: Minister of Supply and Services, 1993), 943-45.

National Reproductive Technologies Commission, we believe that a mechanism for keeping a watching brief on this area is desirable. Hence, we conclude that the National Council on Bioethics in Human Research (NCBHR) should consider this to be an area that warrants continued attention. The Commission recommends that

271. No research involving the alteration of DNA for enhancement purposes be

permitted or funded in Canada. Proposals for any such project should be refused by the Medical Research Council national review committee on gene therapy.

and that

272. The National Council on Bioethics in Human Research address the question of non-therapeutic genetic alteration and monitor developments in this field.

FURTHER READINGS

American Fertility Society. "Ethical Considerations of the New Reproductive Technologies." *Fertility and Sterility* 46: 3 (Sept., 1986) Supplement, H.B.

Anderson, W.F. "Genetic Therapy" in *The New Genetics and the Future of Man*. Ed. Hamilton, M.P., Grand Rapids, Mich.: William B. Erdmans Pub., 1972: 109-118.

European Medical Research Council. *Draft Guidelines for the Application of Gene Therapy to Human Beings* (Strasbourg: undated).

Fletcher, Joseph. *The Ethics of Genetic Control*. New York: Doubleday, 1974.

Fowler, Gregory, Eric T. Juengst and Burke K. Zimmerman. "Germ-Line Gene Therapy and the Clinical Ethos of Medical Genetics." *Theoretical Medicine* 10: 2 (June 1989) 151-165.

Holmes, B., B. Hoskins and M. Gross, eds. *The Custom-Made Child? Women-Centered Perspsectives*. Clifton, N.J.: Humana Press, 1981.

Knoppers, B.M. *Human Dignity and Genetic Heritage*. Study Paper for the Law Reform Commission of Canada. Ottawa: Law Reform Commission of Canada, 1991.

Lappé, M. "Ethical Issues in Manipulating the Human Germ Line." *Journal of Medicine and Philosophy* 16 (1991) 621-639.

Law Reform Commission of Ontario. *Report on Artificial Human Reproduction and Related Matter*. Toronto: Ministry of the Attorney General, 1985.

Milunsky, A. and G.J. Annas, eds. *Genetics and the Law*. New York: Plenum Press, 1976.

Perry, Clifton. "Wrongful Life and Comparison of Harms." *Westminster Institute Review* 1: 4 (1982), 7-9.

Ramsey, Paul. *Fabricated Man: The Ethics of Genetic Control*. New Haven and London: Yale University Press, 1970.

Sacred Congregation for the Doctrine of the Faith. *Instruction on Respect for Human Life in Its Origin and Dignity of Procreation*. Rome: Vatican, 1987, 14H.

Society of Obstetricians and Gynecologists of Canada. *Submission to the Royal Commission on New Reproductive Technologies*. "Genetic Manipulation." SOGC: Toronto, 1990.

Suzuki, D. and P. Knudtson. *Genethics: The Clash Between the New Genetics and Human Values*. Cambridge, Mass.: Harvard University Press, 1989.

Walters, L. "The Ethics of Gene Therapy," *Nature* 320 (1986) 225-227.

Wertz, D.C. and J.C. Fletcher. "Moral Reasoning Among Medical Geneticists in Eighteen Nations." *Theoretical Medicine* 10: 2 (June 1989), 123-138.

World Council of Churches, Working Group Sub-Unit on Church and Society. "Manipulating Life." *Church and Society* 1982 (Sept./Oct.).

Zimmerman, B. "Human Germ-line Therapy: The Case for Its Development and Use." *Journal of Medicine and Philosophy* 16 (1991) 593-612.

CHAPTER 19
CODES OF ETHICS FOR CANADIAN HEALTH CARE PROFESSIONALS

INTRODUCTION

The standards we expect of professionals in their actions are higher than what we expect from ordinary people. This is true whether we consider their actions as professionals or as moral agents. For example, if a parent gives acetylsalicylic acid (aspirin) to an asthmatic child who is running a temperature and the child has an adverse reaction, we will not condemn the parent for not knowing that aspirin is contraindicated for asthmatics. But if a physician were to give aspirin to that same child, we would hold the physician responsible. We expect physicians to know these things. That is part of their training. Similarly, we would not condemn a patient for failing to report a physician whose breath smelled of alcohol during office hours, whereas we would condemn the physician's colleague for not taking appropriate steps.

There are several reasons we expect such higher standards from medicine. The first reason is simply the fact that medicine is a profession. This means that, like all professions, it is self-regulating: it has the right to set the standards that someone must meet in his or her role as physician.

However, with that right goes the duty to make sure that these standards are met in actual practice. That is why in each province there is a regulatory body whose function it is to oversee the licensure of new physicians, to check the credentials of physicians who move into the province and want to set up a practice, and to enforce the requirements that the profession itself has set. In most provinces, it is the College of Physicians and Surgeons. In Quebec, it is the Corporation Professionelle des Médecins du Québec; in Newfoundland, the

Newfoundland Medical Association; in the Yukon, the Yukon Medical Council; and in the Northwest Territories, the Licensing Department of the Department of Justice and Public Service.

The second reason is that medicine is a legally entrenched service monopoly. This means that by law, only someone who meets the requirements set by the profession itself may practise medicine. This puts the profession into a uniquely privileged position because, in effect, it allows the profession to control health care at the delivery level. Such control imposes a tremendous obligation on the profession in a material as well as in an ethical sense. It must ensure that health care is provided appropriately, adequately, equitably and universally.

A third reason we expect more from medicine is that it is a fiduciary profession. This means that the physician-patient relationship is characterized by an ineluctable element of trust. In order for a physician to be able to exercise his/her profession, s/he must know the patient's medical history and current medical condition. This involves knowing details of the patient's personal life which the patient normally would not reveal to anyone — or at least not to someone with whom the patient did not have a close and intimate personal relationship. That imposes certain ethical constraints on the physician. Confidentiality is clearly central here. Unless there are overwhelming ethical reasons that derive from a higher obligation that the physician owes to other patients or to other members of society, the physician may not divulge what is told to him/her in confidence.

A fourth reason for expecting higher standards from physicians is that usually a patient comes to the physician when the patient is ill. However, the fact that the patient is in a position of need, that s/he must divulge extremely personal details to the physician, that s/he is dependent on the physician — even the simple fact of illness itself — all exert a powerful compromising effect on the abilities of the average person to make decisions. Sometimes even their ability to understand is interfered with. Therefore, when the patient comes to see his/her physician, the physician is in a position of psychological power. Physicians have a special duty not to take advantage of this.

Finally, physicians are incomparably more knowledgeable about health, illness and appropriate treatments than the ordinary person. Such knowledge is the physician's stock-in-trade. Knowledge, however, is power — certainly when it comes to decision making. What decision is made frequently depends on what information is given and how it is divulged. The physician must be very careful not to abuse that power.

All of these considerations find reflection in the Code of Ethics of the Canadian Medical Association, reprinted below. For instance, the obligation to be properly prepared finds its expression in the clauses that enjoin physicians to "teach and be taught," and the injunction to consult with their colleagues in matters that fall outside of their own area of expertise. The obligations that derive from the fact of monopoly find expression in the obligation not to refuse service in emergency circumstances, not to engage in unethical discrimination, to be responsible in setting fee schedules, and so on. The obligations that are entailed by the fiduciary nature of the physician-patient relationship are expressed in the various clauses governing confidentiality and related matters, and the duties that derive from the unique power position in which physicians find themselves by virtue of the compromised position of the patient are reflected in the clauses that deal with informed consent.

However, the Code and the clauses that it contains are not mere expressions of how the profession would like its members to behave. Although the various clauses that the Code contains are not laws — they have not been passed by any parliamentary legislative body — they do have the force of law. The reason is that in Canada, the practice of medicine is regulated by provincial legislation specific to medicine. Included in this legislation is usually some reference to the standards of the profession as accepted either by the relevant provincial College of Physicians and Surgeons or the appropriate provincial Medical Association. These bodies have the legal power to enforce their rulings on members who have been found guilty of an infraction against them, by striking them from the roles of individuals allowed to practise, or by levying a fine or exacting some other form of punishment. The Code of Ethics of the Canadian Medical Association should therefore be considered carefully from this perspective. Is what it enjoins really ethically appropriate?

The reason for including the Code of Ethics of the Canadian Nurses Association is that physicians do not practise in isolation. Physicians depend on nurses in their everyday practice. It is therefore important to have some idea of how nurses see their ethical position. Comparing and contrasting the two Codes may help to bring out areas of strength and weakness that might not be apparent when we look at the Code of the CMA in isolation.

One of the things that should become clear is that the two professions approach the relationship with patients from somewhat different perspectives. While nursing tends to approach the relationship with the patient more in the sense of co-adventuring in order to maximize the health potential of the patient, medicine tends to be much more concerned with the physician as professional and with the actions of the physician as independent agent. The mutuality of action that is characteristic of nursing seems to recede into the background. This of course has important implications for the way in which the ethical relationship between nurses and patients, as opposed to physicians and patients, is ethically perceived.

Code of Ethics of the Canadian Medical Association

Canadian Medical Association

PREFACE

The Canadian Medical Association accepts the responsibility for delineating the standard of ethical behaviour expected of Canadian physicians and has developed and approved this Code of Ethics as a guide for physicians.

The Code is an ethical document. Its sources are the traditional codes of medical ethics such as the Hippocratic Oath, as well as developments in human rights and recent bioethical discussion.

Legislation and court decisions may also influence medical ethics. Physicians should be aware of the legal and regulatory requirements for medical practice in their jurisdiction. However, the Code may set out different standards of behaviour than does the law.

The Code has been prepared by physicians for physicians. It is based on the fundamental ethical principles of medicine, especially compassion, beneficence, non-maleficence, respect for persons and justice. It interprets these principles with respect to the responsibilities of physicians to individual patients, family and significant others, colleagues, other health professionals, and society.

The Code is not, and cannot be, exhaustive. Its statements are general in nature, to be interpreted and applied in particular situations. Specific ethical issues such as abortion, transplantation and euthanasia are not mentioned; they are treated in appropriate detail in CMA policy statements.

Physicians may experience conflict between different ethical principles, between ethical and legal or regulatory requirements, or between their own ethical convictions and the demands of patients, proxy decision makers, other health professionals, employers or other involved parties.

Training in ethical analysis and decision making during undergraduate, postgraduate and continuing medical education is recommended for physicians to develop the knowledge, skills and attitudes needed to deal with these conflicts. Consultation with colleagues, licensing authorities, ethicists, ethics committees or others who have expertise in these matters is also recommended.

The Code applies to physicians, including residents, and medical students.

GENERAL RESPONSIBILITIES

1. Consider first the well-being of the patient.

2. Treat all patients with respect; do not exploit them for personal advantage.

3. Provide for appropriate care for your patient, including physical comfort and spiritual and psychosocial support even when cure is no longer possible.

4. Practise the art and science of medicine competently and without impairment.

5. Engage in lifelong learning to main-

"Code of Ethics of the Canadian Medical Association (Approved by CMA General Council, August 1996)" — Reprinted from, by permission of the publisher, *CMAJ*, 1996; 155 (8), pp. 1176A.

tain and improve your professional knowledge, skills and attitudes.

6. Recognize your limitations and the competence of others and when indicated, recommend that additional opinions and services be sought.

RESPONSIBILITIES TO THE PATIENT

Initiating and Dissolving a Patient-Physician Relationship

7. In providing medical service, do not discriminate against any patient on such grounds as age, gender, marital status, medical condition, national or ethnic origin, physical or mental disability, political affiliation, race, religion, sexual orientation, or socioeconomic status. This does not abrogate the physician's right to refuse to accept a patient for legitimate reasons.

8. Inform your patient when your personal morality would influence the recommendation or practice of any medical procedure that the patient needs or wants.

9. Provide whatever appropriate assistance you can to any person with an urgent need for medical care.

10. Having accepted professional responsibility for a patient, continue to provide services until they are no longer required or wanted; until another suitable physician has assumed responsibility for the patient; or until the patient has been given adequate notice that you intend to terminate the relationship.

11. Limit treatment of yourself or members of your immediate family to minor or emergency services and only when another physician is not readily available; there should be no fee for such treatment.

Communication, Decision Making and Consent

12. Provide your patients with the information they need to make informed decisions about their medical care, and answer their questions to the best of your ability.

13. Make every reasonable effort to communicate with your patients in such a way that information exchanged is understood.

14. Recommend only those diagnostic and therapeutic procedures that you consider to be beneficial to your patient or to others. If a procedure is recommended for the benefit of others, as for example in matters of public health, inform your patient of this fact and proceed only with explicit informed consent or where required by law.

15. Respect the right of a competent patient to accept or reject any medical care recommended.

16. Recognize the need to balance the developing competency of children and the role of families in medical decision making.

17. Respect your patient's reasonable request for a second opinion from a physician of the patient's choice.

18. Ascertain wherever possible and recognize your patient's wishes about the initiation, continuation or cessation of life-sustaining treatment.

19. Respect the intentions of an incompetent patient as they were expressed (e.g., through an advance directive or

proxy designation) before the patient became incompetent.

20. When the intentions of an incompetent patient are unknown and when no appropriate proxy is available, render such treatment as you believe to be in accordance with the patient's values or, if these are unknown, the patient's best interests.

21. Be considerate of the patient's family and significant others and cooperate with them in the patient's interest.

Confidentiality

22. Respect the patient's right to confidentiality except when this right conflicts with your responsibility to the law, or when the maintenance of confidentiality would result in a significant risk of substantial harm to others or to the patient if the patient is incompetent; in such cases, take all reasonable steps to inform the patient that confidentiality will be breached.

23. When acting on behalf of a third party, take reasonable steps to ensure that the patient understands the nature and extent of your responsibility to the third party.

24. Upon a patient's request, provide the patient or a third party with a copy of his or her medical record, unless there is a compelling reason to believe that information contained in the record will result in substantial harm to the patient or others.

Clinical Research

25. Ensure that any research in which you participate is evaluated both scientifically and ethically, is approved by a responsible committee and is sufficiently planned and supervised that research subjects are unlikely to suffer disproportionate harm.

26. Inform the potential research subject, or proxy, about the purpose of the study, its source of funding, the nature and relative probability of harms and benefits, and the nature of your participation.

27. Before proceeding with the study, obtain the informed consent of the subject, or proxy, and advise prospective subjects that they have the right to decline or withdraw from the study at any time, without prejudice to their ongoing care.

Professional Fees

28. In determining professional fees to patients, consider both the nature of the service provided and the ability of the patient to pay, and be prepared to discuss the fee with the patient.

RESPONSIBILITIES TO SOCIETY

29. Recognize that community, society and the environment are important factors in the health of individual patients.

30. Accept a share of the profession's responsibility to society in matters relating to public health, health education, environmental protection, legislation affecting the health or well-being of the community, and the need for testimony at judicial proceedings.

31. Recognize the responsibility of physicians to promote fair access to health care resources.

32. Use health care resources prudently.

33. Refuse to participate in or support practices that violate basic human rights.

34. Recognize a responsibility to give the generally held opinions of the profession when interpreting scientific knowledge to the public; when presenting an opinion that is contrary to the generally held opinion of the profession, so indicate.

RESPONSIBILITIES TO THE PROFESSION

35. Recognize that the self-regulation of the profession is a privilege and that each physician has a continuing responsibility to merit this privilege.

36. Teach and be taught.

37. Avoid impugning the reputation of colleagues for personal motives; however, report to the appropriate authority any unprofessional conduct by colleagues.

38. Be willing to participate in peer review of other physicians and to undergo review by your peers.

39. Enter into associations only if you can maintain your professional integrity.

40. Avoid promoting, as a member of the medical profession, any service (except your own) or product for personal gain.

41. Do not keep secret from colleagues the diagnostic or therapeutic agents and procedures that you employ.

42. Collaborate with other physicians and health professionals in the care of patients and the functioning and improvement of health services.

RESPONSIBILITIES TO ONESELF

43. Seek help from colleagues and appropriately qualified professionals for personal problems that adversely affect your service to patients, society or the profession.

Code of Ethics for Registered Nurses

Canadian Nurses Association

PREAMBLE

The Code of Ethics for Registered Nurses gives guidance for decision making concerning ethical matters, serves as a means for self-evaluation and reflection regarding ethical nursing practice, and provides a basis for peer review initiatives. The code not only educates nurses about their ethical responsibilities, but also informs other health care professionals and members of the public about the moral commitments expected of nurses.

The Canadian Nurses Association (CNA) periodically revises its code to address changing societal needs, values, and conditions that challenge the ability of nurses to practise ethically. Examples of such factors are: the consequences of economic constraints; increasing use of technology in

Code of Ethics for Registered Nurses (Ottawa: Canadian Nurses Association, 1997).

health care; and changing ways of delivering nursing services, such as the move to care outside the institutional setting. This revised Code of Ethics for Registered Nurses provides nurses with direction for ethical decision making and practice in everyday situations as they are influenced by current trends and conditions. It applies to nurses in all practice settings, whatever their position and area of responsibility.

Ethical problems and concerns, as well as ethical distress at the individual level, can be the result of decisions made at the institutional, regional, provincial and federal levels. Differing responsibilities, capabilities and ways of working toward change also exist at the client,[1] institutional and societal levels. For all contexts the code offers guidance on providing care that conforms with ethical practice, and on actively influencing and participating in policy development, review and revision.

The complex issues in nursing practice have both legal and ethical dimensions. The laws and ethics of health care overlap, as both are concerned that the conduct of health professionals show respect for the well-being, dignity and liberty of clients. An ideal system of law would be compatible with ethics, in that adherence to the law ought never require the violation of ethics. Still, the domains of law and ethics remain distinct, and the code addresses ethical responsibilities only.

ELEMENTS OF THE CODE

A value is something that is prized or held dear; something that is deeply cared about. This code is organized around seven primary values that are central to ethical nursing practice:

- Health and well-being
- Choice
- Dignity
- Confidentiality
- Fairness
- Accountability
- Practice environments that are conducive to safe, competent and ethical care

Each value is articulated by responsibility statements that clarify its application and provide more direct guidance. Where it is clear that an action or inaction would involve an ethical violation (i.e., the neglect of a moral obligation), the level of guidance is prescriptive. The statement is intended to tell the nurse and others what is ethically acceptable and what is not. Where the situation involves an ethical problem[2] or dilemma, guidance is advisory. No ready-made answers can be offered and thoughtful consideration is required to increase the quality of decision making. Where the situation provokes feelings of guilt, concern, or distaste, it is a situation of ethical distress. In instances of ethical distress the level of guidance is more limited but there remains a responsibility for the nurse to examine the situation in light of the provisions of the code. Decisions will be influenced by the particular circumstances of the situation. Ethical reflection and judgement are required to determine how a particular value or responsibility applies in a particular nursing context.

There is room within the profession for disagreement among nurses about the relative weight of different ethical values and principles. More than one proposed intervention may be ethical and reflective of good practice. Discussion is extremely helpful in the resolution of ethical issues. As appropriate, clients, colleagues in nursing and other disciplines, professional nurses associations and other experts are included in discussions about ethical problems. In addition to this code, legislation, and the standards of practice, policies, and guidelines of professional nurses associations may also assist in problem solving.[3]

The values articulated in this code are grounded in the professional nursing relationship with clients and indicate what nurses care about in that relationship. For example, to identify health and well-being as a value is to say that nurses care for and about the health and well-being of their clients. The nurse-client relationship presupposes a certain measure of trust on the part of the client. Care and trust complement one another in professional nursing relationships. Both hinge on the values identified in the code. By upholding these values in practice, nurses earn and maintain the trust of those in their care. For each of the values, the scope of responsibilities identified extends beyond individuals to include families, communities and society.

VALUES

Health and Well-being

Nurses value health and well-being and assist persons to achieve their optimum level of health in situations of normal health, illness, injury or in the process of dying.

Choice

Nurses respect and promote the autonomy of clients and help them to express their health needs and values, and to obtain appropriate information and services.

Dignity

Nurses value and advocate the dignity and self-respect of human beings.

Confidentiality

Nurses safeguard the trust of clients that information learned in the context of a pro-fessional relationship is shared outside the health care team only with the client's permission or as legally required.

Fairness

Nurses apply and promote principles of equity and fairness to assist clients in receiving unbiased treatment and a share of health services and resources proportionate to their needs.

Accountability

Nurses act in a manner consistent with their professional responsibilities and standards of practice.

Practice Environments Conducive to Safe, Competent and Ethical Care

Nurses advocate practice environments that have the organizational and human support systems, and the resource allocations necessary for safe, competent and ethical nursing care.

HEALTH AND WELL-BEING

Nurses value health and well-being and assist persons to achieve their optimum level of health in situations of normal health, illness, injury, or in the process of dying.

1. Nurses provide care directed first and foremost toward the health and well-being of the client.

2. Nurses recognize that health is more than the absence of disease or infirmity and assist clients to achieve the maximum level of health and well-being possible.

3. Nurses recognize that health status is influenced by a variety of factors. In ways that are consistent with their professional role and responsibilities, nurses are accountable for addressing institutional, social, and political factors influencing health and health care.

4. Nurses support and advocate a full continuum of health services including health promotion and disease prevention initiatives, as well as diagnostic, restorative, rehabilitative and palliative care services.

5. Nurses respect and value the knowledge and skills other health care providers bring to the health care team and actively seek to support and collaborate with others so that maximum benefits to clients can be realized.

6. Nurses foster well-being when life can no longer be sustained, by alleviating suffering and supporting a dignified and peaceful death.

7. Nurses provide the best care circumstances permit even when the need arises in an emergency outside an employment situation.

8. Nurses participate, to the best of their abilities, in research and other activities that contribute to the ongoing development of nursing knowledge. Nurses participating in research observe the nursing profession's guidelines, as well as other guidelines, for ethical research.

CHOICE

Nurses respect and promote the autonomy of clients and help them to express their health needs and values, and to obtain appropriate information and services.

1. Nurses seek to involve clients in health planning and health care decision making.

2. Nurses provide the information and support required so that clients, to the best of their ability, are able to act on their own behalf in meeting their health and health care needs. Information given is complete, accurate, truthful, and understandable. When they are unable to provide the required information, nurses assist clients in obtaining it from other appropriate sources.

3. Nurses demonstrate sensitivity to the willingness/readiness of clients to receive information about their health condition and care options. Nurses respect the wishes of those who refuse, or are not ready, to receive information about their health condition.

4. Nurses practise within relevant legislation governing consent or choice. Nurses seek to ensure that nursing care is authorized by informed choice, and are guided by this ideal when participating in the consent process in cooperation with other members of the health team.

5. Nurses respect the informed decisions of competent persons to refuse treatment and to choose to live at risk. However, nurses are not obliged to comply with clients' wishes when doing so would require action contrary to the law. If the care requested is contrary to the nurse's moral beliefs, appropriate care is provided until alternative care arrangements are in place to meet the client's needs.

6. Nurses are sensitive to their position of relative power in professional relationships with clients and take care to foster self-determination on the part of their clients. Nurses are sufficiently clear about personal values to recognize and deal appropriately with potential value conflicts.

7. Nurses respect decisions and lawful

directives, written or verbal, about present and future health care choices affirmed by a client prior to becoming incompetent.

8. Nurses seek to involve clients of diminished competence in decision making to the extent that those clients are capable. Nurses continue to value autonomy when illness or other factors reduce the capacity for self-determination, such as by providing opportunities for clients to make choices about aspects of their lives for which they maintain the capacity to make decisions.

9. Nurses seek to obtain consent for nursing care from a substitute decision-maker when clients lack the capacity to make decisions about their care, did not make their wishes known prior to becoming incompetent, or for any reason it is unclear what the client would have wanted in a particular circumstance. When prior wishes of an incompetent client are not known or are unclear, care decisions must be in the best interest of the client and based on what the client would want, as far as is known.

DIGNITY

Nurses value and advocate the dignity and self-respect of human beings.

1. Nurses relate to all persons receiving care as persons worthy of respect and endeavour in all their actions to preserve and demonstrate respect for each individual.

2. Nurses exhibit sensitivity to the client's individual needs, values, and choices. Nursing care is designed to accommodate the biological, psychological, social, cultural, and spiritual needs of clients. Nurses do not exploit clients' vulnerabilities for their own

interests or gain, whether this be sexual, emotional, social, political, or financial.

3. Nurses respect the privacy of clients when care is given.

4. Nurses treat human life as precious and worthy of respect. Respect includes seeking out and honouring clients' wishes regarding quality of life. Decision making about life-sustaining treatment carefully balances these considerations.

5. Nurses intervene if others fail to respect the dignity of clients.

6. Nurses advocate the dignity of clients in the use of technology in the health care setting.

7. Nurses advocate health and social conditions that allow persons to live with dignity throughout their lives and in the process of dying. They do so in ways that are consistent with their professional role and responsibilities.

CONFIDENTIALITY

Nurses safeguard the trust of clients that information learned in the context of a professional relationship is shared outside the health care team only with the client's permission or as legally required.

1. Nurses observe practices that protect the confidentiality of each client's health and health care information.

2. Nurses intervene if other participants in the health care delivery system fail to respect client confidentiality.

3. Nurses disclose confidential information only as authorized by the client, unless there is substantial risk of serious harm to the client or other persons, or a legal obligation to disclose. Where disclosure is warranted, both the amount of information disclosed

and the number of people informed is restricted to the minimum necessary.

4. Nurses, whenever possible, inform their clients about the boundaries of professional confidentiality at the onset of care, including the circumstances under which confidential information might be disclosed without consent. If feasible, when disclosure becomes necessary, nurses inform clients what information will be disclosed, to whom, and for what reasons.

5. Nurses advocate policies and safeguards to protect and preserve client confidentiality and intervene if the security of confidential information is jeopardized because of a weakness in the provisions of the system, e.g., inadequate safeguarding guidelines and procedures for the use of computer databases.

FAIRNESS

Nurses apply and promote principles of equity and fairness to assist clients in receiving unbiased treatment and a share of health services and resources proportionate to their needs.

1. Nurses provide care in response to need regardless of such factors as race, ethnicity, culture, spiritual beliefs, social or marital status, gender, sexual orientation, age, health status, lifestyle or the physical attributes of the client.

2. Nurses are justified in using reasonable means to protect against violence when they anticipate acts of violence toward themselves, others or property with good reason.

3. Nurses strive to be fair in making decisions about the allocation of services and goods that they provide, when the distribution of these is within their control.

4. Nurses put forward, and advocate, the interests of all persons in their care. This includes helping individuals and groups gain access to appropriate health care that is of their choosing.

5. Nurses promote appropriate and ethical care at the institutional/agency and community levels by participating, to the extent possible, in the development, implementation, and ongoing review of policies and procedures designed to make the best use of available resources and of current knowledge and research.

6. Nurses advocate, in ways that are consistent with their role and responsibilities, health policies and decision-making procedures that are fair and comprehensive, and that promote fairness and inclusiveness in health resource allocation.

ACCOUNTABILITY

Nurses act in a manner consistent with their professional responsibilities and standards of practice.

1. Nurses comply with the values and responsibilities in this Code of Ethics for Registered Nurses as well as with the professional standards and laws pertaining to their practice.

2. Nurses conduct themselves with honesty and integrity.

3. Nurses, when they are engaged in clinical, administrative, research or educational endeavours, have professional responsibilities and accountabilities toward safeguarding the quality of nursing care clients receive. These responsibilities vary but are all oriented to the expected outcome of safe, competent and ethical nursing practice.

4. Nurses, individually or in partnership with others, take preventive as well as corrective action to protect clients from unsafe, incompetent or unethical care.

5. Nurses base their practice on relevant knowledge, and acquire new skills and knowledge in their area of practice on a continuing basis, as necessary for the provision of safe, competent and ethical nursing care.

6. Nurses, whether engaged in clinical practice, administration, research or education, provide timely and accurate feedback to other nurses about their practice, so as to support safe and competent care and contribute to ongoing learning. By so doing, they also acknowledge excellence in practice.

7. Nurses practise within their own level of competence. They seek additional information or knowledge; seek the help, and/or supervision and help, of a competent practitioner; and/or request a different work assignment, when aspects of the care required are beyond their level of competence. In the meantime, nurses provide care within the level of their skill and experience.

8. Nurses give primary consideration to the welfare of clients and any possibility of harm in future care situations when they suspect unethical conduct or incompetent or unsafe care. When nurses have reasonable grounds for concern about the behaviour of colleagues in this regard, or about the safety of conditions in the care setting, they carefully review the situation and take steps, individually or in partnership with others, to resolve the problem.

9. Nurses support other nurses who act in good faith to protect clients from incompetent, unethical or unsafe care, and advocate work environments in which nurses are treated with respect when they intervene.

10. Nurses speaking on nursing and health-related matters in a public forum or a court provide accurate and relevant information.

PRACTICE ENVIRONMENTS CONDUCIVE TO SAFE, COMPETENT AND ETHICAL CARE

Nurses advocate practice environments that have the organizational and human support systems, and the resource allocations necessary for safe, competent and ethical nursing care.

1. Nurses collaborate with nursing colleagues and other members of the health team to advocate health care environments that are conducive to ethical practice and to the health and well-being of clients and others in the setting. They do this in ways that are consistent with their professional role and responsibilities.

2. Nurses share their nursing knowledge with other members of the health team for the benefit of clients. To the best of their abilities, nurses provide mentorship and guidance for the professional development of students of nursing and other nurses.

3. Nurses seeking professional employment accurately state their area(s) of competence and seek reasonable assurance that employment conditions will permit care consistent with the values and responsibilities of the code, as well as with their personal ethical beliefs.

4. Nurses practise ethically by striving for the best care achievable in the circumstances. They also make the effort, individually or in partnership with others, to improve practice environments by advocating on behalf of their clients as possible.

NOTES

1. In this document client means the individual persons and groups of persons such as families and communities with whom the nurse is engaged in a professional relationship.

2. Ethical problems arise when ethical reasons both for and against one or more courses of action are present and choices must be made. Disagreement about the type and amount of information needed to reach an ethically acceptable decision may further complicate efforts to reach agreement on the appropriate course(s) of action.

3. The CNA and its member associations publish policy statements and guidelines on a variety of issues, e.g., advance directives, resuscitative interventions, boundary violations, the use of technology in health care, quality of nurses' worklife, support for safe nursing care, etc.

REFERENCES

Canadian Health Care Association/Canadian Medical Association/Canadian Nurses Association/Catholic Health Association of Canada/in association with the Canadian Bar Association (1995). *Joint statement on resuscitative interventions.* Authors: Ottawa.

Canadian Home Care Association/Canadian Hospital Association/Canadian Long Term Care Association/Canadian Nurses Association/Canadian Public Health Association/ Home Support Canada (1994). *Joint statement on advance directives.* Authors: Ottawa.

Canadian Nurses Association (1992). *The role of the nurse in the use of health care technology.* CNA: Ottawa.

Canadian Nurses Association (1994). *A question of respect: Nurses and end of life treatment dilemmas.* CNA: Ottawa.

Canadian Nurses Association (1994). *Ethical guidelines for nurses in research involving human participants,* 2nd revised edition. CNA: Ottawa.

Canadian Nurses Association (1996). *Necessary support for safe nursing care.* CNA: Ottawa.

Canadian Nurses Protective Society (1993). *Confidentiality of health information: Your clients' rights;* Info Law, Vol. 1, 2 (September). CNPS: Ottawa.

Canadian Nurses Protective Society (1994). *Consent to treatment: The role of the nurse;* Info Law, Vol. 3, 2 (December). CNPS: Ottawa.

FURTHER READINGS

Bandman, E.L., and B. Bandman. "Moral Implications in Codes of Nursing." In Bandman and Bandman, *Nursing Ethics Through the Life Span*. Norwalk, Conn.: Appleton and Lange, 1990, 23-39.

Beauchamp, T.L., and L.B. McCullough. *Medical Ethics: The Moral Responsibility of Physicians*. Englewood Cliffs, N.J.: Prentice Hall, 1984.

Bonds, Curley. "The Hippocratic Oath: A Basis for Modern Ethical Standards." *Journal of the American Medical Association* 264:17 (Nov.7, 1990) 2311.

Engelhardt, Jr., H.T. *The Foundations of Bioethics*. New York: Oxford University Press, 1986.

Feinberg, Joel. *Social Philosophy*. Englewood Cliffs, N.J.: Prentice Hall, 1973.

Flaherty, J., and L. Curtin. *Nursing Ethics*. Bowen Maryland: Bradey, 1982.

Glick, S. "Comparison of the Oaths of Hippocrates and Asaph." *Koroth: A Bulletin Devoted to the History of Medicine and Science* 9:3-4 (Spring, 1986) 297-302.

Jacob, J.M. *Doctors and Rules: A Sociology of Professional Values*. New York: Routledge, 1988.

Jameton, A. *Nursing Practice*. Englewood Cliffs, N.J.: Prentice Hall, 1984.

Jecker, N.S. "Integrating Medical Ethics with Normative Theory: Patient Advocacy and Social Responsibility." *Theoretical Medicine* 11:2 (1990) 125-139.

Khan, M.I. "The Oath of Hippocrates Updated by Muslim Physicians." *Plastic and Reconstructive Surgery* 83:3 (1989) 579.

May, R. "Code and Covenant or Philanthropy and Contract?" In S.J. Reiser, A.J. Dyck and W.J. Curran, eds., *Ethics in Medicine: Historical Perspectives and Contemporary Concerns*. MIT Press: Cambridge, Mass., 1977, 65-76.

Muyskens, J. *Moral Problems in Nursing: A Philosophical Investigation*. Towanda: Rowman & Littlefield, 1982.

Pence, Terry, and K. J. Cantrall, eds. *Ethics in Nursing: An Anthology*. New York: National League for Nursing, 1990.

Sawyer, L. "Nursing Codes of Ethics: An International Comparison." *International Nursing Review* 36:5 (1989) 145-148.

Thompson, J.E., and H.O. Thompson, eds. *Professional Ethics in Nursing*. Malabar, Fla.: Krieger, 1990.

World Medical Association. "An International Code of Medical Ethics." *World Medical Association Bulletin* 1: 3 (1949).

References

PART I: HEALTH CARE AND ETHICS

CHAPTER 1. Ethical Theory

Eike-Henner W. Kluge: Brief discussion of ethical approaches and theories.

CHAPTER 2. Health As an Ethical Issue

1. Preamble: Constitution of the World Health Organization, reproduced by permission of WHO from *Basic Documents: Thirty-Ninth Edition* (Geneva: World Health Organization, 1992) pp. 1-2.
2. Daniel Callahan, "The WHO Definition of Health," *Hastings Center Report* 1:3 (1973).
3. Caroline Whitbeck, "A Theory of Health," in A.L. Caplan, H.T. Engelhardt, Jr., and J.J. McCartney, eds., *Concepts in Health and Disease: Interdisciplinary Perspective* (Reading, Mass.: Addison-Wesley Publishing Co., 1981), 661-626.

CHAPTER 3. The Right to Health Care

1. Canada Health Act.
2. Benjamin Freedman and Françoise Baylis, "Purpose and Function in Government-Funded Health Coverage," *Journal of Health Policy, Politics and Law* 12:1 (Spring 1987), 97-112.
3. John K. Iglehart, "Canada's Health Care System Faces Its Problems," *New England Journal of Medicine* 1990; 322:8, 562-71.

CHAPTER 4. Allocation of Resources

a) Macro-allocation:
1. R.M. Nelson and T. Drought, "Justice and the Moral Acceptability of Rationing Health Care: The Oregon Experiment," *Journal of Medicine and Philosophy* 1992; 17/1: 97-117.
2. Benjamin Freedman and the McGill/Boston Research Group, "Nonvalidated Therapies and HIV Disease," *Hastings Center Report* 19:3 (June 1989), 14-20.
b) Micro-allocation:
3. Alvin H. Moss and Mark Siegler, "Should Alcoholics Compete Equally for Liver Transplantation?" *JAMA* 265 (March 13, 1991), 1295-1298.
4. M.F. McKneally, B.M. Dickens, E.M. Meslin, P.A. Singer, "Bioethics for clinicians: 13. Resource allocation" — Reprinted from, by permission of the publisher, *CMAJ* 157:2 (1997), 163-167.

Fertilization," 553-54; "The Retrieval and Use of Human Ova," 592-94; "Preconception Arrangement," 683-84.

4. Canadian Medical Association, "Surrogate and Gestational Motherhood" — Reprinted from *The New Reproductive Technologies: A Preliminary Perspective of the Canadian Medical Association*, by permission of the publisher, Canadian Medical Association, 1991.

5. Nancy Jecker, "Conceiving a Child to Save a Child: Reproductive and Filial Ethics," *The Journal of Clinical Ethics* 1:2 (Summer 1990), 99-107.

PART VII. THE GENETIC BASIS OF HUMAN LIFE

CHAPTER 17. Genetic Knowledge

1. Royal Commission on New Reproductive Technologies, "Prenatal Diagnosis, Genetic Disease and Genetic Alteration," from *Proceed With Care: Final Report of the Royal Commission on New Reproductive Technologies* (Ottawa: Minister of Supply and Services, 1993).

2. David DeGrazia, "The Ethical Justification for Minimal Paternalism in the Use of Predictive Tests for Huntington's Disease," *Journal of Clinical Ethics* 2:4 (1991), 219-28.

3. L.M. Purdy, "Genetic Diseases: Can Having Children Be Immoral?" in *Genetics Now: Ethical Issues in Genetic Research,* ed. by J.J. Buckley, Jr. (Washington, D.C.: University Press of America, 1978).

CHAPTER 18. Genetic Engineering

1. Medical Research Council of Canada, *Guidelines for Research on Somatic Cell Gene Therapy in Humans*, Chapter 2, "Ethical Issues" (Ottawa: Minister of Supply and Services, 1990), 24-33.

2. Royal Commission on New Reproductive Technologies, "Regulating Germ-Line Genetic Alteration" from *Proceed With Care: Final Report of the Royal Commission on New Reproductive Technologies* (Ottawa: Minister of Supply and Services, 1993).

PART VIII. CODES OF ETHICS

CHAPTER 19. Codes of Ethics for Canadian Health Care Professionals

1. "Code of Ethics of the Canadian Medical Association" (Approved by General Council, August 1996) — Reprinted from, by permission of the publisher, *CMAJ*, 1996; 155 (8): 1176A.

2. "Code of Ethics for Registered Nurses" (Ottawa: Canadian Nurses Association, 1997).